Mathematics to Sixteen Plus

P. J. Holt *B.A., B.Sc., Ph.D.*

Head of Mathematics, Wimbledon College

HODDER AND STOUGHTON
LONDON SYDNEY AUCKLAND TORONTO

British Library Cataloguing in Publication Data
Holt, P. J.
 Mathematics to sixteen plus.
 1. Mathematics—1961–
 I. Title
 510   QA39.2

 ISBN 0–340–33560–2

First printed 1985

Typeset in 10/12pt Univers by D P Press Ltd
Printed in Great Britain for
Hodder and Stoughton Educational,
a division of Hodder and Stoughton Ltd.,
Mill Road, Dunton Green, Sevenoaks, Kent TN13 2YD,
by Richard Clay (The Chaucer Press) Ltd, Bungay, Suffolk.

Contents

Geometry

Trigonometry

Mensuration

Statistics and Probability

Matrices, Vectors, Transformation Geometry

Calculus

Preface

This book is suitable for candidates expecting to achieve the first four grades in the new GCSE examinations and is also appropriate for the latest O-level syllabuses. The book is probably best used to provide a two-year course, but the layout should also enable it to be used easily by final-year students who need a quick revision of some topics and a more thorough study of others. A large supply of worked examples and practice questions is provided, particularly on the 'modern' topics such as Sets, Matrices, Probability and Transformations. Very little prior knowledge is assumed, although the topics which most students will have met before, such as elementary arithmetic and algebra, are covered more rapidly than the more difficult or advanced topics.

The subject matter is grouped under the usual headings *Arithmetic, Set Theory, Algebra, Geometry,* etc. I have deliberately not tried to 'integrate' the material and exercises, partly because I believe that it is only possible to appreciate mathematics as a unified subject *after* its individual topics and skills have been mastered, and partly because, as a teacher, I have found integrated exercises to be of little practical use. During a single lesson a very limited amount of material can be taught, and normally an exercise is required for homework which provides practice in just the techniques taught in that lesson and recent lessons. When an exercise attempts to integrate a number of different topics, the difficulty usually arises that some students have forgotten most of the topics and others have never met them at all!

In a book of this kind the order in which the material is studied must obviously be left to students and teachers. One point should however be mentioned. When a topic requires knowledge from another area, the material needed is normally elementary and has been covered at an earlier stage in the book. For example, transformation geometry requires an elementary knowledge of graphs, and graphs are included in the Algebra section, which precedes the Geometry section.

Inexact answers in both the worked examples and exercises are normally given to 3 significant figures. The use of calculators is assumed, and in numerical examples the working is therefore given only up to the expressions which would in practice be evaluated by calculator. When the use of a calculator would be inappropriate, as for example in most of the exercises on fractions and decimals, this is stated.

I would like to thank all the friends and colleagues who have given me encouragement and advice, and in particular Mr George McPartlin for his specialised help with the sections of the book.

PJH

General Information

Some common mathematical terms

Natural number

A natural number is one of the infinite set of numbers 1, 2, 3, ... Note that zero and negative numbers are not included. The set of natural numbers is denoted by $\mathbf{N}$.

Integer

An integer is one of the infinite set of numbers 0, ± 1, ± 2 . . . . The set is denoted by $\mathbf{Z}$.

Prime number

A prime number is a natural number other than 1 which is exactly divisible only by itself and 1. The first few primes are 2, 3, 5, 7, 11.

Square number or perfect square

This is a number which is obtained by squaring a natural number. The first few square numbers are 1, 4, 9, 16, 25.

Factor

A factor of a natural number is a natural number which divides into it exactly. Thus the factors of 20 are 1, 2, 4, 5, 10 and 20. To *fully factorise* a natural number is to express it as a product of its *prime* factors. Thus 12, fully factorised, is $2 \times 2 \times 3$ or $2^2 \times 3$. The factor 2 in this expression is called a *repeated* factor.

Mutiple

A multiple of a number is obtained when the number is *multiplied* by an integer. Thus the multiples of 3 are ± 3, ± 6, ± 9 . . . .

Reciprocal

The reciprocal of a number x is $1/x$. Thus the reciprocal of 3 is $\frac{1}{3}$ and the reciprocal of $4\frac{1}{2}$ is $\frac{2}{9}$. The reciprocal of a fraction is obtained by inverting the fraction.

Modulus

The modulus of a number is its *numerical* value or *magnitude,* the sign of the number being ignored. Thus the modulus of a positive number is equal to the number itself, and the modulus of a negative number is obtained by removing the minus. The modulus of a number is denoted by placing a pair of vertical lines around the number. For example $|4| = 4$ and $|-7| = 7$.

Number-line

A number-line is an infinitely long graduated line, each point of which represents a positive or negative number. E.g:

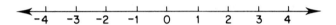

The arrows indicate that the line stretches to infinity in both directions.

Rational number

A rational number is a number which can be expressed as a fraction of the form p/q, where p and q are integers. All integers and mixed numbers (integers and fractions) are rational numbers; e.g. -6, $2\frac{1}{2}$, $-5\frac{1}{3}$. Rational numbers can also be expressed as integers together with terminating or recurring decimals. Thus, for example, $8\frac{1}{2} = 8.5$ and $2\frac{1}{3} = 2.333 \ldots$ or $2.\dot{3}$. The set of rational numbers is denoted by $\mathbf{Q}$.

Irrational number

An irrational number is one which cannot be expressed in the form p/q. There is an infinite number of points on a number-line corresponding to numbers of this kind. Some examples of irrational numbers are π, and roots such as $\sqrt{2}$, $\sqrt[3]{5}$, etc. which are called *surds.* When irrational numbers are expressed in decimal form, the decimals neither terminate nor recur.

Real number

A real number is any number which can be represented by a point on a number-line, that is any rational or irrational number. All the numbers considered in this book will be real. Real numbers are given this name in contrast to *imaginary* numbers, which are square roots of negative numbers. The set of real numbers is denoted by $\mathbf{R}$.

Some common mathematical symbols

$=$ equals
$\equiv$ identical to or congruent to
$\approx$ approximately equal to
$<$ less than
$\leq$ less than or equal to
$>$ greater than
$\geq$ greater than or equal to
$\therefore$ therefore
$\Rightarrow$ implies (usually $\therefore$ and $\Rightarrow$ are alternatives.)
$\Leftarrow$ is implied by
$\Leftrightarrow$ implies and is implied by

Note that a stroke through a symbol always has the effect of negating it. For example, $\neq$ means 'is not equal to' and $\not<$ means 'is not less than'.

Units

Prefixes

The names of units in the metric system are built up by the addition of prefixes to the names of basic units such as the metre and the gram. The most commonly used prefixes, and the only ones we shall use in this book, are the following:

kilo- (k) Placed in front of a unit this makes the unit 1000 times as large. Thus the kilogram is 1000 grams.
mega- (M) This prefix multiplies a unit by 10^6 or 1 million.
centi- (c) This divides a unit by 100. For example the centimetre is one hundredth of a metre.
milli- (m) This divides a unit by 1000.

Units of length

The following are the most commonly used units of length, with their symbols:

millimetre, mm	metre, m
centimetre, cm	kilometre, km

Clearly 1000 mm = 100 cm = 1 m, and 1000 m = 1 km.

Units of area and volume

The main units are the following:

Area	Volume
square metre, m^2	cubic metre, m^3
square centimetre, cm^2	cubic centimetre, cm^3
hectare ($= 10^4\,m^2$)	litre (l) $= 1000\,cm^3$

Units of mass

Mass is *quantity of matter,* and should not be confused with weight, which is the force on a body due to gravity. In everyday life, weight is used as a measurement of mass and the same units tend to be used, incorrectly, for both quantities.

The principal units of mass are the *gram* (g), the *kilogram* (kg), and the *megagram* (Mg), which is also called the *tonne* (t). The *milligram* (mg) is often used in scientific work, but is too small a unit to be used very much in everyday life.

Units of time

The main units of time are the familiar *second* (s), *minute* (min) and *hour* (h). Students should also be familiar with the *twenty-four hour clock,* which is best explained by examples:
07.00 h = 7 a.m., 09.25 h = 9.25 a.m., 15.47 h = 3.47 p.m.,
23.00 h = 11 p.m.

1 Revision of Some Elementary Topics

Note: **Calculators should not be used in any of the exercises in this chapter.**

The topics considered in this chapter will be familiar to most students, and they will therefore be dealt with mainly by worked examples.

Positive and negative numbers

▷ **Example 1**

(a) Subtract 4 from −7. (b) Subtract −9 from −12. (c) Evaluate −12 + 5 − (−7) − 4 + 2.

(a) Subtract 4 can be considered to mean *go down 4*, and going down 4 from −7 gives −11.

(b) Subtracting −9 is equivalent to adding 9, and adding 9 to −12 gives −3.

(c) Two minuses together are equivalent to a plus; hence − (−7) = +7. Now all the positive terms in the given expression add up to 14 and all the negative numbers add up to −16. The final answer is therefore 14 − 16 = −2.   ◁

Multiplication and division can be dealt with by the rule that *an even number of minuses gives a positive answer and an odd number of minuses gives a negative answer.* Thus for example (−5) (−6) = +30, and (−3) (−4) (−5) = −60.

The same rule can be used to deal with powers. E.g. $(-2)^3 = -8$, and $(-3)^4 = 81$. It should be noted, incidentally, that $(-3)^4$ is different from -3^4. *A power applies only to the number immediately preceding it,* unless brackets are used. Hence $-3^4 = -81$. In general, when brackets are used the rule is to *carry out operations inside the brackets before those outside the brackets.*

▷ **Example 2**

Evaluate (a) $(-3)^3 - (2-7)^2$, *(b)* $\dfrac{-2^4 - 3(-2)^3}{(-3-5)(-1+3)}$.

(a) The given expression is equal to $-27 - (-5)^2 = -27 - 25 = -52$.

(b) The given expression is equal to $\dfrac{-16 - 3(-8)}{(-8)(2)} = \dfrac{8}{-16} = -\dfrac{1}{2}$.   ◁

EXERCISE 1a

1 Add -17 to 6.   **2** Subtract 8 from -9.   **3** Add -5 to -8.
4 Subtract -2 from 7.   **5** $(-5)(-9)$.   **6** $(-4)^3$.   **7** $(-2)(-3)(-4)$.
8 Subtract -4 from $(-2)^4$.   **9** $-39 \div -3$.   **10** $\dfrac{56}{-7}$ **11** -2^6.
12 Subtract -2 from -3, then subtract -4 from the result.   **13** $(-3)(-2)^3$.
14 $(-5 + 2)(-3 + 7)$.   **15** $14 - (-5) - 3^2$.   **16** $-18 - (-7) - (-2)^4 - (-9)$.
17 $\dfrac{(-3)(-4)}{-6}$.   **18** What must be subtracted from -6 to give -17?
19 What must be added to $(-2)^3$ to give $(-3)^2$?   **20** $(-3)^2(-2) - [3-(-4)]$
21 $-7 - (2-5)^2$.   **22** $\dfrac{-9^2}{-2^4 - 11}$.   **23** $\dfrac{(-2)^7}{-5-(-13)}$.
24 What must be subtracted from -3^4 to give -2^6?
25 $(1-5)^3 - (1-3)^5$.   **26** $\dfrac{(-5-1)^3}{-2(-3)^2}$.
27 $\dfrac{-5^4 + (-5)^3}{-(-10)^3}$.   **28** $\dfrac{(2-5)^2(5-1)^3}{(-2)(-6) - 4(-3)}$.

Fractions

Equal fractions

The value of a fraction is not altered if the numerator and denominator are multiplied or divided by the same number. For example,

$$\frac{1}{2} = \frac{2}{4} = \frac{3}{6}, \text{etc., and } \frac{350}{450} = \frac{35}{45} = \frac{7}{9}.$$

Dividing top and bottom as in the second of these examples is of course called *cancelling,* and cancelling as far as possible is called *reducing a fraction to its lowest terms.* It should be noted that we cannot perform other operations on numerator and denominator, such as squaring them both, or adding the same number to both, without altering the value of the fraction. If for example we add 1 to the numerator and denominator of $\frac{1}{2}$ we get $\frac{2}{3}$, and if we square both we get $\frac{1}{4}$.

It is sometimes possible to simplify a fraction by *multiplying* numerator and denominator by the same number. For example $2\frac{1}{2}/3\frac{1}{4}$ can be simplified to 10/13 by multiplying the numerator and denominator by 4.

Addition and subtraction of fractions

It is only when we have *quantities of the same kind* that the numbers of the quantities can be added or subtracted. For example 7 apples + 8 apples = 15 apples, but 7 apples + 8 pencils is not equal to 15 of either quantity. Hence to add, for example, thirds and quarters we change both to the same quantities *twelfths,* and to add thirds and sixths we express both as sixths. In general we add fractions by obtaining the *lowest common multiple* (LCM) of the denominators. Suppose for example that the denominators are 6 and 8. The multiples of 6 are 6, 12, 18, 24, 30, etc., and the multiples of 8 are 8, 16, 24, 32, etc. *Common* multiples are those which belong to both of these sets (24, 48, etc.), and the *lowest* common multiple is 24. It is this number which is most conveniently used as the new denominator when we add or subtract the fractions.

▷**Example 3**

Evaluate (a) $7\frac{1}{5} - 2\frac{9}{10}$, *(b)* $3\frac{5}{6} - 8\frac{1}{3}$.

When adding or subtracting mixed numbers it is best to *deal with the whole numbers first:*

(a) $7\frac{1}{5} - 2\frac{9}{10} = 5 + \frac{2}{10} - \frac{9}{10} = 5 - \frac{7}{10} = 4\frac{3}{10}$. (The last step is perhaps easier to follow if 5 is expressed as $4 + \frac{10}{10}$.)

(b) $3\frac{5}{6} - 8\frac{1}{3} = -5 + \frac{5}{6} - \frac{2}{6} = -5 + \frac{3}{6} = -4\frac{1}{2}$.   ◁

EXERCISE 1b

Express the following fractions in their lowest terms:

1 $\frac{16}{20}$ **2** $\frac{21}{49}$ **3** $\frac{64}{72}$ **4** $\frac{48}{66}$ **5** $\frac{33}{121}$

6 $\frac{60}{132}$ **7** $\frac{108}{144}$ **8** $\frac{38}{190}$ **9** $\frac{51}{119}$ **10** $\frac{323}{437}$.

Express the following as mixed numbers, with the fractions in their lowest terms:

11 $\frac{30}{9}$ **12** $\frac{78}{5}$ **13** $\frac{81}{6}$ **14** $\frac{98}{8}$ **15** $\frac{95}{13}$

16 $\frac{153}{12}$ **17** $\frac{145}{15}$ **18** $\frac{188}{24}$.

Simplify the following fractions by multiplying numerator and denominator by an appropriate number:

19 $\frac{2\frac{1}{2}}{3\frac{1}{2}}$ **20** $\frac{2\frac{1}{3}}{4}$ **21** $\frac{1}{2\frac{1}{4}}$ **22** $\frac{9/10}{1/5}$ **23** $\frac{5/6}{2\frac{1}{2}}$.

Write down the lowest common multiples of the following sets of numbers:
24 4 and 6   **25** 8 and 16   **26** 7 and 9   **27** 3, 6 and 9   **28** 12 and 16
29 5, 10 and 15   **30** 4, 5 and 6   **31** 6, 7 and 8.

Evaluate, expressing the answers as simply as possible:

32 $\frac{3}{4} + \frac{5}{8}$ **33** $\frac{1}{6} + \frac{5}{9}$ **34** $\frac{1}{2} - \frac{1}{8}$ **35** $\frac{3}{5} - \frac{1}{10}$ **36** $\frac{2}{3} - \frac{5}{6}$

37 $\frac{7}{12} - \frac{15}{16}$ **38** $\frac{1}{3} + \frac{5}{9} - \frac{5}{6}$ **39** $\frac{1}{4} - \frac{7}{8} - \frac{11}{12}$ **40** $-\frac{2}{3} - \frac{7}{8} + \frac{1}{6}$ **41** $4 - \frac{2}{3}$

42 $10 - \frac{5}{7}$ **43** $2\frac{1}{2} + 3\frac{1}{8} + 6\frac{1}{4}$ **44** $8\frac{1}{5} - 2\frac{7}{10}$

45 $3\frac{11}{12} - 5\frac{3}{4} + 4\frac{2}{3}$ **46** $5\frac{1}{7} - 2\frac{11}{14}$ **47** $4\frac{1}{6} - 7\frac{2}{3}$

48 $10\frac{1}{2} - 4\frac{9}{10} + 3\frac{1}{5}$ **49** $3\frac{31}{36} - 8\frac{2}{9} - 2\frac{1}{12}$ **50** $-12\frac{2}{15} + 7\frac{29}{30} + 4\frac{9}{10}$.

Multiplication of fractions

To multiply fractions we first change mixed numbers to improper ('top-heavy') fractions and then simply *multiply the numerators and multiply the denominators.*

▷**Example 4**

$$1\frac{1}{4} \times \frac{3}{7} = \frac{5}{4} \times \frac{3}{7} = \frac{15}{28}.$$ ◁

Cancelling

Cancelling means *dividing the numerator and the denominator of a fraction by the same number,* and this is possible when the numerator and denominator consist of single terms or *factorised* expressions (products). Thus cancelling *is* possible in such cases as

$$\frac{5 \times 3}{7 \times 6} \text{ or } \frac{3}{4} \times \frac{8}{11} \text{ (since this equals } \frac{3 \times 8}{4 \times 11} \text{)},$$

but it is *not* possible in such cases as

$$\frac{5+3}{7+6} \text{ or } \frac{2}{3} - \frac{6}{7}.$$

▷ Example 5

Evaluate $3\frac{3}{4} \times \frac{2}{3} \times \frac{1}{5}$.
We change mixed numbers to improper fractions and then cancel where possible. The cancelling should be done neatly, so that numbers crossed out are still readable:

$$\frac{\overset{1}{\cancel{15}}}{\underset{2}{\cancel{4}}} \times \frac{\overset{1}{\cancel{2}}}{\underset{1}{\cancel{3}}} \times \frac{1}{\underset{1}{\cancel{5}}} = \frac{1}{2}. \qquad \blacktriangleleft$$

Note: Multiplication questions are sometimes given by means of the word 'of' (as in $\frac{1}{3}$ of 7). When used in this way the word 'of' can simply be replaced by a multiplication sign.

Division of fractions

To divide by a fraction the rule is to *invert the fraction we are dividing by, and then multiply.* Another way of putting this is: multiply by the *reciprocal* of the divisor.

▷ Example 6

$$2\frac{5}{8} \div 4\frac{2}{3} = \frac{21}{8} \div \frac{14}{3} = \frac{21}{8} \times \frac{\overset{3}{3}}{\underset{2}{\cancel{14}}} = \frac{9}{16}. \qquad \blacktriangleleft$$

A more complicated example is the following.

▷ Example 7

Evaluate $\quad \dfrac{2\frac{5}{6} - 1\frac{3}{8}}{2\frac{1}{4} - \frac{5}{6}}$.

Numerator $= 1 + \frac{20}{24} - \frac{9}{24} = 1 + \frac{11}{24} = \frac{35}{24}$.

Denominator $= 2 + \frac{3}{12} - \frac{10}{12} = 2 - \frac{7}{12} = \frac{17}{12}$.

Now since any fraction is equal to its numerator divided by its denominator, the whole expression is equal to

The use of mental arithmetic

Multiplication and division of a fraction by a *whole number* can always be performed mentally, without the use of the standard rules given above. Consider for example the question $3 \times \frac{2}{7}$. If we think of this as 3×2 *sevenths*, it is obvious that the answer is 6 sevenths (just as 3×2 pencils is 6 pencils). Again if the question $\frac{8}{9} \div 2$ is thought of as 8 *ninths* $\div 2$, it is clear that the answer is $\frac{4}{9}$.

In a case such as $\frac{3}{5} \div 2$, in which the 2 does not divide exactly into the numerator, the division can be performed mentally by multiplying the denominator by 2. The answer is therefore $\frac{3}{10}$.

EXERCISE 1c

Work out the following by mental arithmetic:

1 $2 \times \frac{3}{7}$ **2** $5 \times \frac{4}{9}$ **3** $6 \times \frac{2}{5}$ **4** $\frac{4}{11} \div 2$ **5** $\frac{15}{17} \div 5$ **6** $\frac{3}{7} \div 2$ **7** $\frac{5}{12} \div 4$

8 $\frac{1}{2} \div 6$ **9** $\frac{1}{3}$ of $\frac{9}{11}$ **10** $\frac{1}{4}$ of $\frac{8}{13}$ **11** $\frac{1}{2}$ of $1\frac{3}{5}$ **12** $1\frac{5}{7} \div 4$ **13** $\frac{1}{3}$ of $1\frac{1}{4}$.

Work out the following by using the standard rules:

14 $\frac{2}{3} \times \frac{5}{7}$ **15** $\frac{3}{4} \times \frac{2}{9}$ **16** $2\frac{1}{2} \times \frac{4}{5}$ **17** $2\frac{3}{4} \times \frac{2}{33}$ **18** $(\frac{1}{2})^3$ **19** $(1\frac{1}{2})^2$

20 $1\frac{1}{3} \times \frac{5}{6} \times \frac{6}{7}$ **21** $(\frac{2}{3})^2 \times \frac{3}{8}$ **22** $2\frac{2}{5} \times (1\frac{1}{4})^2$ **23** $(2\frac{1}{3})^2 \times \frac{6}{7} \times (1\frac{1}{2})^3$

24 $2 \div \frac{3}{5}$ **25** $\frac{1}{2} \div \frac{3}{4}$ **26** $1\frac{1}{4} \div \frac{3}{8}$ **27** $8 \div 3\frac{1}{3}$ **28** $1\frac{1}{14} \div 4\frac{2}{7}$ **29** $3\frac{8}{9} \div 2\frac{1}{12}$

30 $7\frac{4}{5} \div 1\frac{11}{15}$ **31** $(1\frac{1}{2})^2 \div 1\frac{7}{8}$ **32** $5\frac{5}{6} \div (1\frac{2}{3})^2$ **33** $(\frac{1}{2})^3 \div (\frac{1}{4})^2$

34 $\frac{4}{5}(3\frac{1}{4} + 5\frac{1}{2})$

35 $\dfrac{8\frac{2}{3} - 3\frac{1}{4}}{2\frac{1}{6}}$ **36** $\dfrac{1\frac{1}{2} + \frac{3}{4}}{3\frac{1}{6} + 4\frac{1}{3}}$

37 $(1\frac{1}{3} - 2\frac{1}{4})(6\frac{1}{3} - 1\frac{8}{15})$ **38** $\dfrac{(\frac{2}{3})^2 + \frac{1}{9}}{5}$

39 $\dfrac{2}{1\frac{1}{2}(1\frac{1}{4} - 1\frac{1}{2})}$ **40** $(1\frac{1}{3})^2(2\frac{2}{5} - 1\frac{1}{20})$.

Problems involving fractions

▷ Example 8

A lawn takes up $\frac{3}{7}$ of the area of a garden. If the area of the rest is $26\ m^2$ what is the area of the whole garden?

$$1 - \tfrac{3}{7} = \tfrac{4}{7} \text{ of the garden is not lawn,}$$

$$\therefore\ \tfrac{4}{7} \text{ of garden} = 26\ m^2$$

$$\therefore\ \tfrac{1}{7} \text{ of garden} = 6\tfrac{1}{2}\ m^2$$

$$\therefore\ \text{total area of garden} = 7 \times 6\tfrac{1}{2} = 45\tfrac{1}{2}\ m^2. \qquad \triangleleft$$

▷**Example 9**

A man puts $\frac{1}{5}$ of his monthly income in the bank, spends $\frac{3}{4}$ of the rest on living expenses and keeps the remainder as spending money. If he keeps £120, what is his monthly income?

After $\frac{1}{5}$ of the income is banked, $\frac{4}{5}$ of it is left.
Hence living expenses use up $\frac{3}{4} \times \frac{4}{5} = \frac{3}{5}$ of the income.
Hence the bank and living expenses together take up $\frac{1}{5} + \frac{3}{5} = \frac{4}{5}$ of the income.
Hence $1 - \frac{4}{5} = \frac{1}{5}$ of it is left for spending money.
But the man has £120 as spending money; hence £120 is $\frac{1}{5}$ of the income.
The income is therefore £600 a month.   ◁

EXERCISE 1d

1 A man spends $\frac{3}{5}$ of a sum of money and saves the rest. If he saves £32 what is the original sum?
2 A journey is $\frac{4}{7}$ covered by train and the rest by bus. If the bus travels 75 miles how long is the whole journey?
3 Two sevenths of the area of a wall is painted. If $2\frac{1}{2}$ m² is not painted what area is painted?
4 A man spends $\frac{3}{4}$ of his life, that is 54 years, working. How long is spent not working?
5 Ann puts half of her salary into the building society and spends $\frac{1}{3}$ of the rest. If she spends £150 what is her salary?
6 Fares account for $\frac{1}{4}$ of the cost of a holiday and another $\frac{2}{3}$ of the total cost is spent on the hotel bill. If the remaining cost is £40 how much is spent (a) on fares, (b) on the hotel bill?
7 A girl uses $\frac{2}{5}$ of an exercise book and tears out $\frac{3}{4}$ of the remaining pages. If 4 pages are left how many pages did the book have originally?
8 A sum of money is divided among Tom, Dick and Harry. Tom gets $\frac{1}{4}$ of it, and Dick gets twice as much as Harry. If Dick gets £5, what does Tom get?
9 Peter is given $\frac{1}{4}$ of a sum of money, and Paul gets the rest. If Peter gets £200 less than Paul, what is the sum of money?
10 A man spends $\frac{2}{7}$ of an evening gardening, and the rest of the time reading. If he spends $1\frac{1}{2}$ hours longer on reading than on gardening, how long does he spend gardening?
11 A mother leaves $\frac{1}{3}$ of her money to her first child, $\frac{1}{4}$ to her second child, and gives $\frac{2}{5}$ of the rest to charity. How much is left if the first child gets £400 more than the second?
12 Peter gets $\frac{1}{4}$ of a sum of money, Penelope gets $\frac{1}{5}$, and Paul the rest. If Peter gets £18 less than Paul, what does Penelope get?
13 Every year a car loses $\frac{1}{3}$ of the value it has at the beginning of the year. In the second year it loses £160. What did it cost originally?
14 A journey is $\frac{2}{3}$ covered by car, $\frac{4}{5}$ of the rest is cycled, and the remainder is walked. The distance travelled by car exceeds the distance walked by 36 miles. How long is the journey?
15 A line *AE* is divided into 4 parts by the points *A, B, C, D, E. AB = BC* $= \frac{1}{6}$ of the whole line, and *CD = DE*. If *DE* exceeds *AB* by $2\frac{1}{2}$ cm, how long is the line?

Decimals

A decimal is a fraction whose denominator is a power of 10. E.g.

$$0.3 = \frac{3}{10}, \quad 0.07 = \frac{7}{100}, \quad 0.23 = \frac{2}{10} + \frac{3}{100} = \frac{23}{100}.$$

These examples illustrate the general procedure for converting a decimal to a fraction. The rule is that *the number of decimal places is equal to the number of zeros in the denominator.*

▷ **Example 10**

$$0.075 = \frac{75}{1000} = \frac{3}{40}.$$ ◁

To do the reverse procedure, and convert a fraction to a decimal, we simply use the fact that *any fraction is equal to its numerator divided by its denominator.*

▷ **Example 11**

$\frac{3}{7} = 3 \div 7 = 0.428\,57\ldots = 0.429$ to 3 decimal places (3 d.p.). ◁

Decimal places

The last example illustrates the following rule for giving an answer to a certain number of decimal places. **Add 1 to the final figure required if the figure following it is 5 or more; otherwise leave the final figure required unchanged.**

▷ **Example 12**

Express 2.0452 (a) to 2 d.p., (b) to 1 d.p.
(a) Since the third decimal place contains a 5, we increase the 4 (the final figure required) by 1, obtaining 2.05.
(b) Since the second decimal place contains a number less than 5 (namely 4), we leave the zero unchanged, obtaining 2.0.
(Note that in (b) we considered the *original* number, 2.0452, and *not the already approximated version.* Had we adopted the latter procedure, and used the answer to (a) to do (b), we should have obtained the incorrect answer 2.1.) ◁

▷ **Example 13**

Express 0.2896 to 3 d.p.
In this case we want to increase the third figure by 1 but cannot. We therefore increase the second figure by 1 and change the third to zero, obtaining 0.290. ◁

Significant figures

The number of significant figures in an answer is a measurement of the *accuracy* with which it is being given. A significant figure is one whose value we are prepared to guarantee; thus if we give an answer as '2700, correct to 2 s.f.' we are saying that the second figure is certainly nearer to 7 than to 6 or 8. If we give the answer as '2700, correct to 3 s.f.' we are saying that the third figure is certainly zero but we cannot guarantee the fourth. The function of the fourth figure, and of zeros which are not significant in general, is merely to locate the decimal point.

The following rules regarding significant figures may be helpful.

(1) The first non-zero digit, working from the left, is the first significant figure.

(2) Non-zero digits, and zeros between non-zero digits, are always significant.

(3) Zeros on the right of a number may or may not be significant: they are significant if they give accurate values; they are not significant if they merely locate the decimal point.

▷**Example 14**

Express (a) 49.51 to 2 s.f., (b) 0.001 37 to 2 s.f., (c) 0.030 24 to 3 s.f., (d) 25 036 to 3 s.f.

The answers are (a) 50, (b) 0.0014, (c) 0.0302, (d) 25 000. ◁

Standard form

Very large and very small numbers, such as 25 000 000 and 0.000 005, take up an inconveniently large amount of space if written in the usual way. Consequently it is customary to use a more economical method of writing numbers of this kind, called expressing the numbers in *standard form*.

The general procedure for expressing a number in standard form is to place the decimal point after the first non-zero digit and multiply by an appropriate power of 10. For example,

$$7358 = 7.358 \times 10^3, \quad 85\,000 = 8.5 \times 10^4, \quad 400\,\text{million} = 4 \times 10^8.$$

In these examples we have used the fact that a number can be multiplied by 10 by moving the point 1 place to the right, multiplied by 10^2 by moving the point 2 places to the right, and so on. Now it will also be shown in chapter 6 that

$$10^{-1} = \frac{1}{10}, \quad 10^{-2} = \frac{1}{10^2}, \quad 10^{-3} = \frac{1}{10^3}, \text{etc.,}$$

and thus *multiplication by 10^{-n} moves a decimal point n places to the left.* Hence we have, for example,

$$0.007 = 7 \times 10^{-3}, \quad 0.000\,053 = 5.3 \times 10^{-5}, \quad 0.000\,000\,357 = 3.57 \times 10^{-7}.$$

In general, a number written in standard form is expressed as $a \times 10^b$, where a is a number between 1 and 10, and b is a positive or negative integer.

EXERCISE 1e

Convert the following to fractions in their lowest terms:

1 0.4 **2** 0.06 **3** 0.05 **4** 0.24 **5** 0.008 **6** 0.78
7 0.016 **8** 0.804 **9** 0.1025 **10** 0.0234 **11** 0.000 05 **12** 0.060 25.

Convert the following fractions to decimals, giving the answers to 3 d.p. where appropriate:

13 $\frac{4}{5}$ **14** $\frac{5}{8}$ **15** $\frac{1}{6}$ **16** $\frac{5}{7}$ **17** $\frac{11}{20}$ (multiply top and bottom by 5)

18 $\frac{21}{25}$ **19** $\frac{4}{11}$ **20** $\frac{7}{13}$ **21** $\frac{33}{500}$ **22** $\frac{2}{15}$.

Express each of the following (a) to 3 d.p., (b) to 2 d.p.
23 2.5473 **24** 5.1349 **25** 0.0504 **26** 0.9098 **27** 3.0251 **28** 0.124 53
29 0.2951 **30** 0.0076.

Express each of the following (a) to 3 s.f., (b) to 1 s.f.
31 2457 **32** 0.003 928 **33** 78.02 **34** 5.054 **35** 2 501 010 **36** 0.7498
37 90 667 **38** 0.008 035 01.

Express the following numbers in standard form:
39 247 **40** 5000 **41** 82.64 **42** 538 400 000 **43** 83 million
44 764 million **45** 0.0029 **46** 0.000 043 8 **47** 25×10^4
48 0.5×10^7 **49** 34×10^{-3} **50** 278×10^{-8} **51** 0.0008×10^9
52 0.0062×10^{-5}.

Operations with decimals

Addition and subtraction of decimals present no problems; it is only necessary to remember to place the decimal points in a straight line.

▷**Example 15**

$$
\begin{array}{r}
23.06 \\
1.274 \\
\hline
21.786
\end{array}\ ^{-}
$$

◁

To *multiply* decimals (other than by powers of 10) we first ignore the decimal points and carry out the multiplication. Then we count the total number of figures on the right of the decimal points in the numbers being multiplied, and put the same number of figures on the right of the point in the answer.

▷**Example 16**

Work out (a) 0.3 × 0.2 × 0.8, (b) 42.3 × 0.27, (c) 0.04³.

(a) $3 \times 2 \times 8 = 48$; hence $0.3 \times 0.2 \times 0.8 = 0.048$.

(b) By long multiplication we have $423 \times 27 = 11\,421$;
hence $42.3 \times 0.27 = 11.421$.

(c) $4^3 = 64$, and there are 6 figures to the right of the point if 0.04^3 is written out in full. Hence $0.04^3 = 0.000\,064$.   ◁

To *divide* decimals we begin by making the divisor (the number we are dividing *by*) into a whole number. This is done by multiplying both numbers by the same power of 10, which moves both decimal points the same number of places in the same direction.

▷**Example 17**

Divide (a) 0.046 by 0.000 02, (b) 0.254 by 0.07, giving the answer to 2 d.p.

(a) Moving both points 5 places to the right we have $4600 \div 2$, and the answer is therefore 2300.

(b) Moving both points 2 places to the right gives $25.4 \div 7$, and this equals $3.628\ldots$ Hence the answer to 2 d.p. is 3.63.   ◁

EXERCISE 1f

In the following questions give exact answers.

1 $0.025 + 3.9 - 1.47$ **2** $0.5 \times 0.3 \times 0.6$ **3** Subtract 0.907 from 4.28
4 0.8×0.04 **5** $2.3 \times 0.07 \times 0.1$ **6** 12.8×4.9 **7** 0.2^4 **8** 0.5^2 **9** 0.03^2
10 1.4^2 **11** 0.6^3 **12** 0.002^2 **13** $0.3^3 - 0.2^5$ **14** $0.02^3 \times 12$
15 $1.5^2 + 0.9^2 - 1.3^2$ **16** 25×0.4^3 **17** $1.82 \div 0.2$ **18** $0.4 \div 0.05$
19 $0.169 \div 1.3$ **20** $18 \div 0.12$ **21** $0.0051 \div 0.017$ **22** $0.0406 \div 0.14$
23 $7 \div 0.025$ **24** $0.02^2 \div 0.4^2$ **25** $0.09^2 \div 0.3^2$
26 $(0.4)\,(0.3) \div (0.6)\,(0.2)^2$ **27** $0.3^3 \div (0.9)\,(0.2)$.

In the following questions give the answers to 2 d.p.

28 $0.29 \div 0.3$ **29** $3.8 \div 0.7$ **30** $0.532 \div 1.2$ **31** $0.538 \div 0.13$
32 $0.5^2 \div 0.3^2$ **33** $2.5^2 \div 0.4^2$.

2 Ratio

A ratio is a comparison of the magnitudes of quantities. To say that two quantities are in the ratio 2:3 (read '2 to 3') is to say that for every two parts of the first there are three of the second. The ratio does not give us the actual sizes of the two quantities. These could be 20 and 30, or 100 and 150, or any of an infinite number of other possibilities. In every case however the second quantity is $\frac{3}{2}$ or $1\frac{1}{2}$ times the first, and the first is $\frac{2}{3}$ of the second. The quantities being compared must of course be quantities of the same kind, and measured in the same units. If for example we are comparing lengths of 20 cm and $1\frac{1}{2}$ m, we must either express both quantities in centimetres or both in metres. In either case the ratio in its simplest form is 2:15.

It is clear that, like a fraction, any ratio can be expressed in an infinite number of equivalent ways, e.g.

$$3:4 \ = \ 6:8 \ = \ 9:12 \ = \ 30:40 \ = \ 300:400, \text{etc.}$$

This example shows that, again like a fraction, a ratio is unchanged if each of its numbers is multiplied or divided by the same amount. An important difference between a ratio and a fraction, however, is that a ratio can contain any number of quantities whereas a fraction always contains two. An example of equivalent ratios containing three quantities is the following:

$$2:4:7 \ = \ 4:8:14 \ = \ 20:40:70, \text{etc.}$$

Like a fraction, a ratio is usually expressed in terms of the smallest possible whole numbers.

▷ Example 1

Simplify the ratios (a) 15:21:33 (b) $1\frac{1}{4}:2\frac{1}{2}:3\frac{1}{8}$.

(a) Dividing each number by 3, we have 5:7:11.
(b) First we express the three numbers as improper fractions:

$$\frac{5}{4}:\frac{5}{2}:\frac{25}{8}.$$

Next we multiply each number by the lowest common multiple of the denominators, namely 8:

$$10:20:25.$$

Finally we divide throughout by 5:

$$2:4:5.$$

(The last two steps can be performed in either order.) ◀

▷ Example 2

Express as simply as possible (a) a ratio of 400 cm³ to 1.4 litres (b) a ratio of 500 cm² to 0.25 m² (c) a ratio of 80 cm/s to $1\frac{1}{2}$ m/s.

(a) Here we are comparing volumes. Since 1 litre $= 1000$ cm³ the ratio is

$$400:1400, \text{ that is } 2:7.$$

(b) This is a ratio of areas. Since 100 cm $= 1$ m, it follows that 100×100 cm² $= 1$ m², and hence that 0.25 m² $= 2500$ cm². Hence the ratio is

$$500:2500, \text{ that is } 1:5.$$

(c) In this case speeds are being compared. Since 100 cm $= 1$ m the ratio is

$$80:150, \text{ that is } 8:15. \qquad ◀$$

▷ Example 3

Given that x:y = 3:4 and y:z = 6:5, express x:y:z as simply as possible.

Here we require the lowest common multiple (LCM) of the two numbers representing y, namely 4 and 6. The LCM is 12, and we therefore multiply the numbers of the first ratio by 3 and those of the second by 2:

$$x:y \ = \ 9:12 \text{ and } y:z \ = \ 12:10.$$

It follows that $x:y:z = 9:12:10$. ◀

EXERCISE 2a

Express the following ratios as simply as possible:

1 18:27 **2** 48:56 **3** $1\frac{1}{2}$:2 **4** $\frac{1}{5}$:$\frac{1}{10}$ **5** 14:28:42 **6** $2\frac{1}{2}$:$3\frac{1}{4}$
7 33:77:121 **8** 49:63:70 **9** $2\frac{1}{3}$:$1\frac{2}{3}$ **10** $1\frac{1}{2}$:$2\frac{1}{4}$:$4\frac{1}{2}$
11 $2\frac{2}{3}$:4:$6\frac{2}{3}$ **12** 27:45:81 **13** $2\frac{2}{5}$:6:$8\frac{2}{5}$
14 $2\frac{1}{2}$:$4\frac{1}{6}$ **15** $2\frac{5}{8}$:$3\frac{1}{2}$:$5\frac{1}{4}$ **16** 75 cm to $1\frac{1}{4}$ m **17** 500 g to $\frac{3}{4}$ kg
18 2 m/s to 450 cm/s **19** 800 cm³ to 1.2 litres **20** 900 m to $1\frac{1}{2}$ km
21 2 m² to 5000 cm²

Obtain the ratio $x:y:z$ as simply as possible:

22 $x:y = 1:2$, $y:z = 4:5$ **23** $x:y = 7:9$, $y:z = 3:4$
24 $x:y = 2:3$, $y:z = 4:5$ **25** $x:y = 1:2\frac{1}{2}$, $y:z = 1\frac{1}{2}:2$
26 $x:y = 5:6$, $y:z = 4\frac{1}{2}:5\frac{1}{2}$

Division in a given ratio

Problems involving the division of a quantity in a given ratio can normally be solved in one of two ways, as the following examples show.

▷ **Example 4**

Divide 72 in the ratio 2:3:4.

Method (a) Let the actual sizes of the three shares be $2x$, $3x$ and $4x$.

$$\text{Then } 2x + 3x + 4x = 72$$
$$\therefore \quad 9x = 72$$
$$\therefore \quad x = 8.$$

The shares are therefore 16, 24 and 32.

Method (b) The procedure here is based on method (a), but we do not introduce x.
   First we add up the three numbers 2, 3 and 4, obtaining 9. This tells us that each share will be a certain number of *ninths* of the total; in fact the first will be $\frac{2}{9}$, the second $\frac{3}{9}$ and the third $\frac{4}{9}$ of the total. The next step is therefore to divide 9 into 72, obtaining 8, and then it follows immediately that the shares are 16, 24 and 32.   ◁

(*Note:* This question can be quite easily done mentally, using method (b); but method (a) is simpler to set out in writing, and therefore more appropriate when an explanation is required.)

▷ **Example 5**

A line is divided in the ratio $1\frac{1}{2}:2\frac{1}{4}:3\frac{3}{4}$. If the length of the longest section is 30 cm, how long are the other sections?
Whichever method is used, we begin by simplifying the ratio:

$$1\frac{1}{2} : 2\frac{1}{4} : 3\frac{3}{4} = \frac{6}{4} : \frac{9}{4} : \frac{15}{4} = 2:3:5.$$

Method (a) Let the actual lengths, in centimetres, be $2x$, $3x$ and $5x$.

$$\text{Then } 5x = 30$$
$$\therefore \quad x = 6.$$

The other sections are therefore 12 cm and 18 cm.

Method (b) Adding up 2, 3 and 5 we obtain 10, and hence each section is a certain number of *tenths* of the whole line. In fact we are told that the longest section is 30 cm; hence $\frac{5}{10}$ of the line $= 30$ cm, so $\frac{1}{10} = 6$ cm and the other sections are 12 cm and 18 cm.   ◁

▷**Example 6**

A sum of money is divided among three people, A, B and C, in the ratio 1:2:5. If C gets £60 more than A, how much does B get?

Let the amounts the people get be £x, £2x and £5x.

$$\text{Then } 5x - x = 60$$
$$\therefore \quad 4x = 60$$
$$\therefore \quad x = 15.$$

Hence B gets £30.   ◀

EXERCISE 2b

In questions 1–8, divide the given number in the given ratio mentally.
1 12 in ratio 1:2   **2** 14 in ratio 2:5   **3** 50 in ratio 3:2   **4** 24 in ratio 3:5
5 120 in ratio 1:5   **6** 18 in ratio 2:7   **7** 35 in ratio 4:1
8 42 in ratio 3:4

In the following questions, show the working fully.
9 A line is divided in the ratio 4:7. If the shorter length is 36 cm what is the longer length?
10 Divide 33 in the ratio $1\frac{1}{2}:1\frac{1}{4}$.
11 A man divides £2000 among his three children in the ratio $1:1\frac{1}{2}:2\frac{1}{2}$. How much does each receive?
12 The ratio of three people's ages is $3:3\frac{1}{2}:5$. If the middle one is 28, how old are the others?
13 £630 is divided in the ratio 1:3:5. What is the largest share?
14 A sum of money is divided in the ratio $2\frac{1}{3}:3\frac{2}{3}$. If the larger share is £187, what is the smaller?
15 A line is divided in the ratio $1\frac{1}{2}:2\frac{1}{4}$. If the difference between the lengths is 7 cm, what is the longer length?
16 A sum of money is divided in the ratio 2:3:7. If the largest share is £720 more than the smallest, what is the total sum of money?
17 Divide 174 in the ratio $1\frac{1}{4}:2\frac{3}{8}$.
18 Two children differ in age by 6 years. If the ratio of their ages is 5:17, how old is the elder?
19 A sum of money is divided in the ratio 2:3:9 and the largest share is £4.90 more than the smallest. What is the middle share?
20 A, B, C, D are four points on a line such that $AB:BD = 1:3$ and $BC:CD = 4:5$. If $BC = 42$ cm, how long is AD?

3 Percentage

A percentage is simply a fraction in which the denominator is 100. The advantage of expressing a fraction in this way is that it makes the size of the fraction clear and enables us to compare different fractions easily. Most people would be unable to tell immediately which is the greater of $\frac{7}{9}$ and $\frac{13}{16}$, but if we express these fractions as 78% and 81%, it becomes obvious which is the greater, and by how much.

Conversion to percentage

The method for converting a fraction to a percentage can be derived by elementary algebra. Suppose we want to convert $\frac{3}{4}$ to a percentage. We let $\frac{3}{4} = x\%$ and thus obtain the equation

$$\frac{x}{100} = \frac{3}{4}$$

Now multiplying both sides by 100 gives $x = \frac{3}{4} \times 100 = 75$, and we thus have $\frac{3}{4} = 75\%$. This example illustrates the following general rule.

To convert a fraction to a percentage, multiply it by 100.

▷ **Example 1**

Convert (a) $\frac{4}{7}$, (b) $\frac{11}{25}$, (c) 0.058 to percentages.

(a) $\frac{4}{7} \times 100 = \frac{400}{7} = 57\frac{1}{7}$.

Hence $\frac{4}{7} = 57\frac{1}{7}\%$.

(b) $\frac{11}{25} \times 100 = 11 \times 4$ (cancelling by 25)
$\qquad = 44$.

Hence $\frac{11}{25} = 44\%$.

(c) $0.058 \times 100 = 5.8$.
Hence $0.058 = 5.8\%$. ◀

The percentage equivalents of certain simple fractions should be learned by heart. The following are the main standard cases:

$$5\% = \frac{1}{20} \quad 10\% = \frac{1}{10} \quad 12\tfrac{1}{2}\% = \frac{1}{8} \quad 20\% = \frac{1}{5} \text{ (and } 40\% = \frac{2}{5}\text{, etc.)}$$

$$25\% = \frac{1}{4} \quad 33\tfrac{1}{3}\% = \frac{1}{3} \quad 50\% = \frac{1}{2} \quad 66\tfrac{2}{3}\% = \frac{2}{3} \quad 75\% = \frac{3}{4}.$$

Expressing one quantity as a percentage of another

This is merely an exercise in the conversion of a fraction to a percentage.

▶ Example 2

Express (a) 47 as a percentage of 75 (b) £2.40 as a percentage of £12.

(a) Putting 47 as a *fraction* of 75 we have simply $\frac{47}{75}$. To convert this fraction to a percentage we multiply by 100, as before:

$$\frac{47}{75} \times 100 = \frac{47}{3} \times 4 \text{ (cancelling by 25)}$$
$$= 62\frac{2}{3}.$$

Hence 47 is $62\frac{2}{3}$ % of 75.

(b) Here we express both quantities in pence and proceed as in (a):

$$\frac{240}{1200} \times 100 = \frac{240}{12} = 20.$$

Hence £2.40 is 20% of £12.   ◀

EXERCISE 3a

Convert the following to percentages:

1 $\frac{4}{5}$ **2** 0.69 **3** $\frac{1}{6}$ **4** 0.037 **5** $\frac{4}{25}$ **6** 0.837 **7** $\frac{2}{9}$ **8** $\frac{17}{500}$ **9** $\frac{7}{11}$ **10** $\frac{43}{200}$
11 0.003 **12** $\frac{9}{16}$ **13** $\frac{7}{500}$ **14** $\frac{11}{12}$ **15** $\frac{5}{24}$

What percentage is:

16 14 of 16? **17** 75 p of £3? **18** 39 of 750? **19** 24 cm of 1.5 m?
20 30 g of 2 kg? **21** 600 m of 1.25 km? **22** 2.5 mm of 4 cm?
23 550 kg of 2.5 Mg? **24** 27 cm/s of 1.5 m/s?

Percentages of quantities

Since a percentage is a particular kind of fraction, and 'of' in work on fractions indicates multiplication, finding a percentage of a quantity is just an exercise in the multiplication of fractions.

▶ Example 3

Find (a) 18% of 280, (b) $7\frac{1}{2}$% of £4.80, (c) $12\frac{1}{2}$ % of 42.

(a) 18% of 280 $= \frac{18}{100} \times 280 = \frac{504}{10} = 50.4.$

(b) $7\frac{1}{2}$% of £4.80 $= \frac{7\frac{1}{2}}{100} \times 480\,\text{p} = \frac{15}{200} \times 480\,\text{p} = 36\,\text{p}.$

(c) Since $12\frac{1}{2}\% = \frac{1}{8}$, we simply divide 42 by 8, obtaining $5\frac{1}{4}$.   ◀

EXERCISE 3b

Find:

1 8% of 40	**2** $12\frac{1}{2}$% of 648	**3** 5% of 16	**4** 37% of 400
5 $3\frac{1}{2}$% of 360	**6** 40% of 95	**7** $66\frac{2}{3}$% of 48	**8** $5\frac{1}{4}$% of 200
9 $3\frac{2}{3}$% of 420	**10** 14% of £30	**11** 8% of £3.25	**12** 75% of £1.28
13 15% of £2540	**14** 4% of $2\frac{1}{2}$ m	**15** 23% of $1\frac{1}{2}$kg	**16** $12\frac{1}{2}$% of 1.2 m
17 $\frac{3}{4}$% of 2 Mg	**18** $37\frac{1}{2}$% of 4 cm	**19** 73% of 5 litres	**20** $\frac{1}{2}$% of $2\frac{1}{2}$ litres.

Percentage increase and decrease

To increase a quantity by 20% is to add 20% of the quantity to the quantity itself. This means that if we regard the original quantity as consisting of 100 parts, there will be 120 parts after the increase. So to increase a quantity by 20% we multiply it by $\frac{120}{100}$. Similarly, to decrease a quantity by 20%, we multiply it by $\frac{80}{100}$.

This is worth treating as a standard rule and learning by heart. Putting it more briefly, we have

20% more than x = 120% of x.
20% less than x = 80% of x.

▷ **Example 4**

Find (a) 16% more than 275, (b) 15% less than £430.

(a) 16% more than $275 = 275 \times \dfrac{116}{100} = 319.$

(b) 15% less than $£430 = £430 \times \dfrac{85}{100} = £365.50.$ ◁

Particular care must be taken when the *result* of a percentage change is given, and we have to find the original quantity. One of the best methods here is to let x be the original quantity, obtain an equation involving x by using one of the above rules, and then make x the subject by elementary algebra.

▷ **Example 5**

After receiving a rise of 20% a man has a salary of £10 200. What was his original salary?
Let the original salary be £x. Then we have

$$x \times \frac{120}{100} = 10\ 200.$$

Multiplying both sides by 100 and dividing by 120, we obtain

$$x = 10\ 200 \times \frac{100}{120} = 8500.$$

Hence the man's original salary was £8500. ◁

Note that an increase of 20% is not cancelled out by a decrease of 20%! If we increase 100 by 20% we get 120, and if we then decrease 120 by 20% we get not 100 but 96. The reason of course is that *a percentage change is always calculated as a percentage of the original quantity*, and in the example just given the original quantity is 100 for the first change and 120 for the second.

EXERCISE 3c

Calculate:

1 10% more than 140	**2** 5% less than 480	**3** 15% more than 125
4 24% less than 15	**5** 7% more than £12	**6** 12% less than £3.50
7 35% more than £278	**8** 42% less than £729	**9** $12\frac{1}{2}$% less than 96 p
10 $6\frac{3}{4}$% more than £2800	**11** 2% more than £2.50	**12** 75% less than 32 p.

Find the value of x given that:

13 30% more than x is 780.   **14** 14% less than x is $21\frac{1}{2}$
15 20% more than x is 66   **16** $12\frac{1}{2}$% more than x is 189
17 35% less than x is 156   **18** $2\frac{1}{2}$% less than x is 1365
19 40% more than x is 161   **20** 24% less than x is 57.

21 After appreciating (i.e. gaining in value) by 20%, a house is worth £5040. What was it worth originally?

22 A car costing £3400 depreciates at 15% per year. What is it worth when a year old?

23 V.A.T. is charged at 15%. What is the original price of an article which costs £253 after V.A.T. is added?

24 After 5% cut in salary a woman earns £9690. What did she earn before the cut?

25 5% of the wallpaper bought for a house is wasted. (a) If £160 is spent, what is the value of the paper used? (b) if $28\frac{1}{2}$ m^2 is needed for a certain room, how much paper has to be set aside for this room?

26 A shopkeeper offers a 12% discount on articles paid for in cash. (a) What does a cash customer pay for an article marked at £1.75? (b) If a cash customer pays £5.72 for an article, what was its original price?

27 If V.A.T. is charged at 8%, what is the original cost of something that costs £132.30 after V.A.T. is added?

28 A woman earning £10 000 gets a 10% rise for two successive years. What is her final salary?

29 A man buys a car for £800, improves it, and sells it to a friend for 25% more. The friend later sells it himself at a loss of 25%. How much does he get for it?

30 A man's weight increases by 20% in one year, then in the next year he diets and loses 10% of his weight. If his weight is 180 pounds after the first year, what is it (a) at the beginning of this two-year period, (b) at the end of the period?

4 Applications of Percentage

Profit and loss

The principles involved in this topic have all been dealt with in the last chapter, but we are considering it separately because it is one of the most important and frequently occurring applications of percentage.

When an article is bought and then sold at a profit or loss there are three quantities to consider: the cost price (C.P.), the selling price (S.P.) and the *percentage* profit or loss. It is important to see that the percentage profit or loss is a much better measurement of the success of a financial transaction than the actual profit or loss. The latter quantity on its own tells us very little. Clearly to make a profit of £2 on an article which originally cost £3 is a very successful piece of business: the same profit of £2 on something which originally cost £1000, on the other hand, amounts to a very small gain. This indicates that we get a valid measurement of the real success of a transaction by expressing the actual gain or loss as a *fraction of the cost price.* The fraction is put in percentage form simply because, as explained in the last chapter, percentages are generally easier to deal with than other fractions.

Since a fraction is converted to a percentage by multiplying it by 100, we have the following formula for percentage profit or loss.

$$\text{Percentage profit or loss} = \frac{\text{actual profit or loss}}{\text{cost price}} \times 100$$

Problems involving profit and loss are of essentially three kinds: we can be given any two of the three quantities cost price, selling price and percentage profit or loss, and asked to find the third. As already pointed out, particular care is required with questions in which we are given the *result* of a percentage change, which here means that we are given the selling price and have to find the cost price.

▷ Example 1

A car is bought for £3500 and sold a year later for £3220. Find (a) the percentage loss. If it continues to depreciate at the same annual rate, find (b) its value after a further year.

(a)   Actual loss = £3500 − £3220 = £280.

Hence % loss = $\dfrac{280}{3500} \times 100 = 8\%$.

(b)   Value after another year = £3220 × $\frac{92}{100}$

$$= £2962.40.$$ ◀

▷ Example 2

A grocer buys a crate of 75 oranges and sells them at 8 p each, thereby making a 20% profit. What did the crate cost?
The total S.P. is 75 × 8 p = 600 p. Now let the total C.P. be x pence; then since the S.P. is 20% more than x, we have

$$x \times \frac{120}{100} = 600$$

$$\therefore \ x = 600 \times \frac{100}{120} = 500.$$

Hence the crate cost 500 p or £5. ◀

▷ Example 3

John sells an article to Harry at a 10% profit, and Harry then sells it to Katherine at a 20% loss. If Katherine pays £132, what did John pay?

Let John's cost price be £x. Then we have

$$\text{C.P. for Harry} = £x \times \frac{110}{100} \ .$$

$$\text{C.P. for Katherine} = £x \times \frac{110}{100} \times \frac{80}{100} \ .$$

$$\text{Hence } x \times \frac{110}{100} \times \frac{80}{100} = 132,$$

$$\text{and } x = 132 \times \frac{100}{80} \times \frac{100}{110}$$

$$= 150.$$

John therefore paid £150. ◀

Absolute and percentage error

The principles governing the measurement of error are very similar to those just explained for profit and loss. Suppose a length is measured and we are told that it is *correct to within 2 cm.* Is this an accurate or an inaccurate measurement? Clearly we cannot answer this question until we know what length is being measured. If the length is 500 km an error of 2 cm is very small, while if it is 10 cm an error of 2 cm is very large. In order to get a valid measurement of accuracy we therefore need to express the actual (or *absolute*) error as a percentage of the true value of the quantity being measured. This is called the *percentage error,* and it is clearly a very similar kind of quantity to percentage profit or loss.

▷ Example 4

A length is given as 2.37 cm, correct to 3 s.f. (a) Express this statement in the form of an inequality. (b) Find the maximum possible absolute error. (c) Find the maximum possible percentage error (approximately).

(a) The length lies between 2.365 cm and 2.375 cm, possibly being equal to the former since we then round *up* to 2.37. Letting the true length be *x* cm, we can express this as

$$2.365 \leqslant x < 2.375.$$

(b) From what has just been said the maximum possible absolute error is 0.005 cm.

(c) We do not know the true value of *x*, but a sufficiently accurate measurement of the percentage error is obtained by taking this to be at the centre of the range of possible values, namely the stated value of 2.37. We then have

$$\text{Maximum percentage error} = \frac{0.005}{2.37} \times 100$$

$$= 0.2\% \text{ approximately.} \qquad \triangleleft$$

EXERCISE 4a

In questions 1–6, find the percentage profit or loss.

1 C.P. £4, S.P. £5.50   **2** C.P. 80 p, S.P. 85 p   **3** C.P. £2.50, S.P. £2.25
4 C.P. £2500, S.P. £5000   **5** C.P. 12 p, S.P. 7 p   **6** C.P. £2.40, S.P. £2.80.

In questions 7–12, find, to 1 s.f., the maximum percentage error in the quantities stated.

7 A length of 6.3 cm, correct to 2 s.f.   **8** A mass of 92 kg, correct to the nearest kg.   **9** A height of 35.4 cm, correct to the nearest mm.   **10** 4870, correct to the nearest 10   **11** 1.94, correct to 2 d.p.   **12** A volume of 2.35 litres, correct to the nearest 10 cm^3.

13 C.P. = £8, profit = 4%; find S.P.
14 C.P. = £12.60, loss = 5%; find S.P.
15 S.P. = 54p, profit = 20%; find C.P.
16 S.P. = £9.30, loss = 25%; find C.P.
17 C.P. = 48 p, profit = $37\frac{1}{2}$%; find S.P.
18 S.P. = £3.74, loss = 12%; find C.P.
19 A man buys a car for £2200 and sells it at a loss of 5%. How much does he get for it?
20 A shopkeeper sells an article for 78 p, making a 20% profit. What did he pay for it?
21 A grocer buys a crate of 150 apples for £10, and sells them for 7 p each. Find the percentage profit.
22 A shop sells portable radios for £5.40 each, making a 20% profit. What did the shop pay for a batch of 10 radios?
23 A shop buys 5 articles at 45 p each and another 7 at the discount price of 25 p each. If all the articles are sold at 50 p, what overall percentage profit does the shop make?
24 An article is sold for £708.50 at a profit of 9% What did it cost?

25 Helen sells an article to Alison at a profit of 5%, and Alison later sells it to Judy at a loss of 20%. If Judy pays £357, what did Helen pay?

26 The true length and breadth of a rectangle are 20 cm and 15 cm. If the length is measured as 20.5 cm and the breadth as 15.4 cm, what are (a) the absolute error in the area, (b) the percentage error in the area, to the nearest 1%?

27 A car is bought when new, then sold at a loss of 20%, and then sold again at a loss of 25% for £2400. What did it cost when new?

28 A square has a true area of 625 m². If the side-length is incorrectly measured as 24.7 m, what are the percentage errors, to 2 s.f., in (a) the side-length, (b) the area?

29 A car is sold at a loss of 10%, and then sold again at a loss of 20%. What is its total loss as a percentage of its original price?

30 The lengths of the edges of a cube are estimated at 20 cm. If the true volume is 7750 cm³, what is the percentage error, to 2 s.f., in the estimate of the volume?

Simple and compound interest

The following terms and abbreviations are used in calculations involving interest.

p.a. = per annum (per year).
Principal (P) = sum deposited.
Amount (A) = final sum.

Simple interest

Under the simple interest system a saver or investor receives from the bank or building society *the same interest every year.* Thus for example an interest rate of 8% p.a. simply means that after 2 years the saver's total interest is 16% of the principal, after 3 years it is 24%, and so on. To obtain the total percentage interest paid, we just multiply the rate per year by the number of years. Then any problem that has to be solved reduces to one of the types already considered.

▷**Example 5**

A man deposits £750 and receives $6\frac{1}{2}$% p.a. simple interest. How much does he have altogether after 5 years?

$$\text{Total percentage interest} = 5 \times 6\tfrac{1}{2} = 32\tfrac{1}{2}\%.$$

$$\text{Hence final amount} = £750 \times \frac{132\tfrac{1}{2}}{100} = £993.75.$$ ◁

▷**Example 6**

A man deposits a certain sum at 9% p.a. simple interest and after 3 years it has grown to £9525. Find the sum deposited.

$$\text{Total percentage interest} = 3 \times 9 = 27\%.$$

Hence $P \times \dfrac{127}{100} = 9525$, where £$P$ is the sum deposited (principal).

Hence $P = 9525 \times \dfrac{100}{127} = 7500$.

The sum deposited was therefore £7500.   ◁

Compound interest

Under this system the interest is added on to the principal at regular intervals, and then the next interest is paid on the total amount that has accumulated. Suppose, for example, that the rate of interest paid is 8% p.a.. If the interest is added on every year (the simplest compound interest system), the amount will grow as follows:

Initially: $A = P$.

After 1 year: $A = P \times \dfrac{108}{100} = P \times 1.08$.

After 2 years: $A = P \times 1.08^2$.

After 3 years: $A = P \times 1.08^3$,

etc.

Clearly the amount after n years will be £$P \times 1.08^n$, and in general we have the formula

$$A = P(1 + \frac{r}{100})^n,$$

where r is the annual rate of interest. It is not necessary to learn this formula, however, provided that the reasoning by which it was derived is understood.

▷ Example 7

After 3 years at 10% p.a. compound interest, a sum of money has grown to £598.95. How much interest has been paid?

Letting the principal be £P, we have

$$P \times 1.1^3 = 598.95$$
$$\therefore P = \frac{598.95}{1.1^3} = 450.$$

Hence the interest paid is £598.95 − £450 = £148.95.   ◁

EXERCISE 4b

Find the simple interest on:
1 £200 at 5% p.a. for 3 years   2 £750 at 8% p.a. for $3\frac{1}{2}$ years
3 £40 at $7\frac{1}{2}$% p.a. for 2 years   4 £5250 at 6% p.a. for 5 years.

Compound interest is paid on the following sums of money. Find the *amount* to the nearest penny:

5 £600 at 4% p.a. for 5 years   **6** £250 at 6% p.a. for 2 years
7 £2400 at 10% p.a. for 3 years   **8** £20 at $8\frac{1}{2}$% p.a. for 6 years

9 A certain sum, invested at 5% p.a. simple interest for 4 years, grows to £336. What is the sum?
10 What sum of money, invested at 4% p.a. compound interest, grows to £270.40 in two years?
11 £5000 is invested at 8% p.a. simple interest. After how long will it grow to £8000?
12 £350 is invested at 6% p.a. simple interest for $3\frac{1}{2}$ years. Find the amount it grows to.
13 £250 gains £100 simple interest in 5 years. What rate per annum is being paid?
14 Find to the nearest pound the compound interest on £5000 at 12% p.a. for 5 years.
15 After 3 years at 20% p.a. compound interest, a sum of money grows to £6912. How much interest has been paid?
16 What sum of money, invested at 7% p.a. simple interest for 5 years, grows to £324?
17 £2500 is invested at 4% p.a. simple interest. In how long will it grow to £3100?
18 £6400 grows to £8800 in 5 years. What simple interest rate per annum is being paid?

Rates

Every piece of property, such as a house or a factory, is given a *rateable value* on which *rates* are charged at so much in the pound. Now a rate of so much in the pound is nothing more than a percentage; so if, for example, the rates in a particular borough are 80 p in the pound, a person whose house has a rateable value of £300 pays 80% of £300, that is £240, every year.

▷Example 8

The rateable value of the whole of a borough is £2 500 000. (a) If the borough needs to obtain £1 800 000, what rate must it charge? (b) If a certain householder pays £252 per year, what is the rateable value of his house?

(a) To obtain the rate in the pound we simply express the amount the borough requires as a percentage of the rateable value:

$$\frac{1\ 800\ 000}{2\ 500\ 000} \times 100 = 72.$$

Hence the rate charged must be 72 p in the pound.
(b) £252 is 72% of the house's rateable value. Hence, letting the rateable value be £x, we have

$$252 = \frac{72x}{100}, \quad \therefore x = \frac{252 \times 100}{72} = 350.$$

The rateable value of the house is therefore £350.   ◀

Income tax

The total amount of money someone earns in a year is called his or her *gross income*. Part of this is known as *allowances* and is untaxed, and the remainder is called *taxable income*. On this, tax is paid at rates in the pound which are set by the government. The standard rate is usually around 30 p in the pound, but when earnings rise above a certain level the rate increases and continues to do so, in a step-by-step way, as income rises. In addition to tax, contributions to National Insurance, superannuation and, possibly, a trade union are deducted from an employee's earnings. The final amount, which is actually received, is called his or her *net income*.

▷Example 9

Your gross income is £15 500, and your allowances total £2300. You pay tax at 30 p in the pound on the first £11 000 of your taxable income, and at 40 p in the pound on the next £3000. Your other deductions total £1200. What is your net income?

> Taxable income = £15 500 − £2300 = £13 200.
> Tax on first £11 000 = 30% of £11 000 = £3300.
> Tax on remaining £2200 = 40% of £2200 = £880.
> Hence total tax = £4180.

Since your other deductions are £1200, your net income is £15 500 − £4180 − £1200 = £10 120.   ◁

▷Example 10

A woman's allowances total £800. She pays tax on the rest of her salary at 33 p in the pound, thus paying £132 per month in tax. Calculate her annual salary.

The annual tax paid is £132 × 12, that is £1584. This is 33% of the woman's taxable income, so, letting the latter be £x, we have

$$\frac{33x}{100} = 1584, \quad \therefore \ x = \frac{1584 \times 100}{33} = 4800.$$

Her taxable income is thus £4800, and since her allowances total £800 her gross salary is £5600.   ◁

EXERCISE 4c

In questions 1 and 2, calculate the tax paid.
1 Gross income £8000, allowances £1500, tax rate 30 p in the pound.
2 Gross income £12 400, allowances £2600, tax rate 32 p in the pound.

3 The rateable value of a house is £350. How much does the owner pay per year in rates if the rates are (a) 70 p in the pound, (b) 64 p in the pound?
4 The rateable value of a borough is £450 000. If the borough needs to obtain £270 000 through the rates, what rate in the pound must it charge?

In questions 5 and 6 calculate the net income, given that tax is charged at 30 p in the pound on the first £11 250 of taxable income, 40 p on the next £2000 and 45 p on the next £3000.

5 Gross income £18 500, allowances £2250, other deductions £1450.

6 Gross income £15 750, allowances £1300, other deductions £725.

7 The rateable value of a borough is £600 000. How much extra does the borough get by raising its rate by (a) 2 p in the pound, (b) $3\frac{1}{2}$ p in the pound?

8 A man with a gross income of £7000 has allowances of £1500 and pays £1815 in tax. At what rate in the pound is the tax being charged?

9 The rateable value of a house is £300. What rate is being charged if the owner pays (a) £225, (b) £240, (c) £189?

10 A woman's salary is £12 000 per year. Her allowances amount to 20% of this and she pays tax on the rest at 32 p in the pound. What are her other deductions if her net salary is £7980?

11 In a certain borough the rates are 110 p in the pound, and a householder pays 12 monthly instalments of £38.50. What is the rateable value of his or her house?

12 The net income of certain employees is £7300. They pay tax at 30 p in the pound, their allowances are £1500 and their other deductions total £1200. Calculate their gross income.

13 The rateable value of a property is £400, and the owners pay rates of £240. Owing to a rise in the rate they have to pay 5% more. What is the rise in the rate?

14 The rateable value of a property is £300, and the owner pays £210. What cut in the rate would result in the rate bill being reduced by 10%?

15 An employee's allowances amount to £500 plus 20% of her gross income, and she pays tax on the rest at 32 p in the pound. Find (a) the tax paid when her gross income is £10 000. If her gross income rises from this amount by 20%, find (b) the increase in the tax paid, (c) the percentage increase, to 1 d.p., in her earnings after tax.

16 A borough obtains £455 000 in rates. This is £26 000 less than it needs, and it has to raise the rate by 4 p in the pound to secure the extra revenue. Find (a) the rateable value of the borough, (b) the new rate in the pound being charged.

17 Your allowances are 25% of your gross salary, you pay tax at 30 p in the pound, and your other deductions are £1200. If your net salary is £5620 what is your gross salary?

18 One year a borough charges a rate of 80 p in the pound and spends 5% of the revenue on its nursery schools. Given that it spends £240 000 on this, calculate (a) the total rateable value of the borough, (b) the money spent on other services. The following year only £50 000 is allocated to nursery schools and the rate is increased to 85 p in the pound. Find (c) the percentage increase in the money available for other services, to 2 d.p.

19 A man pays tax at 30 p in the pound on the first £12 000 of his taxable income and at 40 p in the pound on the rest. His allowances are £4500 and the tax he pays at the higher rate is $\frac{1}{9}$ of that payed at the lower rate. Calculate his gross salary.

20 One year a certain authority charges a rate of 65 p in the pound, of which five pence is allocated to social services. The following year the same sum is allocated to social services, but there is a 10% rise in the authority's other expenses. Find (a) the new rate in the pound that has to be charged. Given that the increase in the money spent is £120 000, find (b) the rateable value of the whole district, (c) the sum allocated to social services in each of the two years.

Miscellaneous exercises

In view of the importance of percentage as a topic, some further exercises are provided, of gradually increasing difficulty.

EXERCISE 4d (easy)

Convert to percentage:

1 $\frac{1}{4}$ **2** $\frac{2}{5}$ **3** $\frac{5}{12}$ **4** 0.57 **5** $\frac{17}{20}$ **6** 0.035 **7** $\frac{1}{50}$ **8** $\frac{7}{8}$ **9** $\frac{9}{16}$ **10** $\frac{2}{3}$

11 0.07 **12** $\frac{11}{25}$ **13** $\frac{19}{200}$ **14** $\frac{13}{500}$.

Calculate:
15 7% of 400 **16** 3% of 50 **17** 5% of 460 **18** 45% of 1250 **19** 8% of £3.50 **20** $7\frac{1}{2}$% of £200 **21** $12\frac{1}{2}$% of £7.20 **22** $33\frac{1}{3}$% of £54.30.

What is:
23 18% more than 750 **24** 8% less than 35 **25** 45% more than 80 **26** 3% less than 2500 **27** $7\frac{1}{2}$% more than 16 **28** $2\frac{1}{2}$% less than 3400?

Find the value of x given that:
29 10% more than x is 484 **30** 8% less than x is 69 **31** 5% more than x is 672 **32** $3\frac{1}{2}$% more than x is 621 **33** $7\frac{1}{2}$% less than x is 37.

EXERCISE 4e

1 A car is bought for £1200 and sold for £700. Find the percentage loss.
2 A house is bought for £15 000 and sold for £17 500. Find the percentage gain.
3 A woman buys 25 articles for 5 p each and sells the whole batch for £1.90. Find her percentage profit.
4 A car is bought for £2000 and after 1 year is worth £1500. If it suffers the same percentage depreciation in the next year, what will it be worth when two years old?
5 Find the simple interest on £320 at 5% p.a. for 4 years.
6 Each year a worker gets an 8% rise. If he earns £3000 in 1977, what does he earn in 1979, to the nearest pound?
7 What percentage of $7\frac{1}{2}$ is $4\frac{1}{2}$?
8 After a reduction of $8\frac{1}{3}$%, an article is worth £2.20. What was it worth originally?
9 £210 grows to £252 in 4 years. What annual simple interest rate is being paid?
10 A house appreciates by 20% in one year and 25% in the next. Express the total gain as a percentage of the original price.
11 The number 476 is mistakenly written 467. What is the percentage error, to 2 s.f.?
12 The side of a square of area 196 cm^2 is measured as 15 cm. What is the percentage error in the side-length, to the nearest whole number?
13 x% of 25 is 18. What is x?
14 What is the compound interest on £2000, at 10% p.a. for 2 years?
15 A shopkeeper buys 5 articles, breaks one, but makes an overall profit of 20% by selling the others at £30 each. What did she pay for each article?
16 Find x if (a) 16% of x is 56, (b) x% of 25 is 20.

17 A man invests a certain sum at 6% p.a. simple interest. After 5 years it has increased by £120. What sum did he invest?

18 4 articles are bought for a total of 25 p and sold for 7 p each. Find the percentage profit.

19 Find x if (a) x is $12\frac{1}{2}$% of 52, (b) 40% less than x is 19.2.

20 A grocer buys a crate of 100 oranges for £3 and a crate of 00 apples for £2. If the oranges are sold at 5 p and the apples at 4 p what is the overall percentage profit?

21 A batch of 50 pens costs £32.50. What must each pen be sold for to give a 20% profit?

22 £1200 grows to £1776 in 8 years. Find the simple interest rate per annum.

EXERCISE 4f (harder)

1 After giving away 25% of a sum of money, then spending 15% of the remainder, I am left with £255. What did I start with?

2 A rectangular lawn has length 20 m and breadth 15 m. How much does it cost to spray the lawn if spray costs 4 p for an amount which will deal with 5 m², and 20% of what is bought is wasted?

3 A is 50% more than B, and B is 25% more than C. If A exceeds C by 14, what is B?

4 I start with £1000, and every year for three years give away 10% of what I have. What is my total loss as a percentage of my original amount?

5 20% of x is 25% more than y. What percentage is y of x?

6 By saving 3% of my annual salary for 10 years, I accumulate a sum of money which is £1400 less than my salary itself. What is my salary?

7 After investing a certain sum at 5% p.a. simple interest for 4 years, a man draws his money out, spends 30% of it, and gives away half of the remainder. He is left with £294. What was the original sum invested?

8 A shopkeeper buys 20 oranges at 4 p each, 15 apples at 3 p, and 10 bananas at 5 p. If he sells the oranges for 5 p each and the apples for 4 p, what must he charge for the bananas to make an overall profit of 40%?

9 16% less than x is 12% more than y. What percentage is y of x?

10 A clinic needs 1225 pints of milk, and estimates that 2% of the milk in each bottle it buys is left in the bottle and wasted. How many pints must it buy?

11 40% of the pupils in a school study French and 20% study Spanish. If the number studying Spanish decreases by 25% and those giving up Spanish take up French, what is the percentage increase in the number studying French?

12 £2000 is invested at 4% p.a. compound interest. In how many years does it grow to more than £2500?

13 50% of the people in a certain country drive cars and 20% of the rest ride bicycles. If the number driving cars increases by 8% and the number riding bicycles increases by 20%, what is the percentage decrease in the number who do neither? (Assume that the total number of people in the country remains constant.)

14 The true length and breadth of a rectangle are 50 cm and 20 cm, but owing to faulty instruments both are measured as being less than these values. If the length is measured as 48 cm and the error in the area is 11.2%, what is the percentage error in the breadth?

15 If Mr Smith has a 20% increase in salary and Mrs Brown has a 20% decrease, they will both earn the same amount. In fact Mrs Brown earns £3500 more than Mr Smith. How much does Mrs Brown earn?

5 Speed, Distance, Time; Travel Graphs

Standard formulae

Suppose that a car which is travelling at constant speed covers a distance of 45 m in a time of 3 s. Since the speed is constant the car must travel 15 m in each second and therefore have a speed of 15 metres per second. This example illustrates the following simple formula for the speed of any body moving at constant (or *uniform*) speed.

$$\text{Speed} = \frac{\text{distance}}{\text{time}}.$$

From this we can immediately derive formulae for distance and for time:

$$\text{Distance} = \text{speed} \times \text{time}. \qquad \text{Time} = \frac{\text{distance}}{\text{speed}}.$$

When a body is not moving with constant speed the first of the above formulae gives its *average* speed:

$$\text{Average speed} = \frac{\text{total distance}}{\text{total time}}.$$

Units of speed; conversion of units

The unit *metre per second* used in the above example can be written more shortly in two ways, namely m/s and m s^{-1}. The latter form is preferred in advanced work, and we shall use it in this book; but both forms are acceptable.

In problems the information is often given in mixed units. For example, a distance might be given in metres and a speed in km h^{-1}. In this case we should need to convert either the metres to kilometres or the km h^{-1} to m h^{-1} before using one of the above forumlae. Conversion of pure distance or pure time units presents little difficulty, but units of speed are a little more complicated. To illustrate the conversion procedure we shall show how the unit km h^{-1} is converted to m s^{-1}. Two steps are needed, one for the conversion of the unit of distance and one for the conversion of the unit of time:

$$1 \text{ km h}^{-1} = 1000 \text{ m h}^{-1} = \frac{1000}{60 \times 60} \text{ m s}^{-1} = \frac{5}{18} \text{ m s}^{-1}.$$

(This result can, if desired, be learned by heart.)

▷ **Example 1**

How long does a car travelling at 20 m s⁻¹ take to travel 50 km?

First we deal with the units, which are mixed. The unit of distance is more simply converted than that of speed, so we start by writing

$$50 \text{ km} = 50\,000 \text{ m}.$$

Now we use the standard formula in which *time* is the subject.

$$\text{Time taken} = \frac{\text{distance}}{\text{speed}} = \frac{50\,000}{20}$$

$$= 2500 \text{ s or } 41 \text{ min } 40 \text{ s.} \quad ◁$$

▷ **Example 2**

A man walks at 2 m s⁻¹ for 10 minutes then cycles at 6 m s⁻¹ for 5 minutes. Find his average speed.

We need the total distance and the total time. To find the total distance we find the distance travelled during each stage and add the two answers. Working in metres and seconds we have:

Stage 1   Distance = speed × time = 2 × 600 = 1200 m.
Stage 2   Distance = speed × time = 6 × 300 = 1800 m.

Now we proceed as follows.

$$\text{Average speed} = \frac{\text{total distance}}{\text{total time}} = \frac{1200 + 1800}{600 + 300}$$

$$= \frac{3000}{900} = 3\tfrac{1}{3} \text{ m s}^{-1}. \quad ◁$$

▷ **Example 3**

The average speed of a 50 km journey is 20 km h⁻¹. If the first 5 km takes 30 minutes what is the average speed of the second stage?

Consider the whole journey. We have:

$$\text{Total time} = \frac{\text{total distance}}{\text{average speed}} = \frac{50}{20} = 2\tfrac{1}{2} \text{ h.}$$

Now since the time for the first stage is 30 minutes it follows that the time for the second stage is 2 h. The distance of the second stage is clearly 50 km − 5 km = 45 km, so we have finally:

$$\text{Average speed for second stage} = \frac{\text{distance}}{\text{time}} = \frac{45}{2} = 22\tfrac{1}{2} \text{ km h}^{-1}. \quad ◁$$

EXERCISE 5a

Convert:

1 2 m min⁻¹ to m s⁻¹   **2** 54 km h⁻¹ to m s⁻¹   **3** 5 m s⁻¹ to cm s⁻¹
4 2½ m s⁻¹ to km h⁻¹   **5** 45 km h⁻¹ to m min⁻¹.

6 A man walks 750 m in 12 min. Find his average speed (a) in m min^{-1}, (b) in km h^{-1}.

7 How long does a car take to travel 405 km at an average speed of 90 km h^{-1}?

8 A man walks for $2\frac{1}{2}$ h at an average speed of 7 km h^{-1}. How far does he travel?

9 An aeroplane flies at 150 m s^{-1}. How long does it take to fly 60 km?

10 A car travels 45 km at an average speed of 10 m s^{-1}. How long does the journey take in minutes?

11 What is the average speed in m s^{-1} of a body which travels 7.2 km in 2 minutes?

12 A snail travels at 50 cm min^{-1}. (a) How far does it travel in $1\frac{1}{2}$ h? (b) How long does it take to travel 0.1 km?

13 A man walks at 6 km h^{-1} for 30 minutes then cycles at 16 km h^{-1} for $1\frac{1}{2}$ h. Find (a) the total distance he covers, (b) his average speed.

14 I travel 40 km by bus at an average speed of 20 km h^{-1}, and then walk 10 km at a speed of 4 km h^{-1}. Find (a) how long my journey takes, (b) my average speed.

15 How long is a journey which takes 2 h 15 min at an average speed of 68 km h^{-1}?

16 The first 60 km of a 90 km journey takes 3 h, and the rest is covered at a speed of 15 km h^{-1}. Find the average speed of the whole journey.

17 The first 50 km of a 200 km journey is covered at 25 km h^{-1}, and the rest at 50 km h^{-1}. Find the average speed of the whole journey.

18 A man walks at 2 m s^{-1} for 8 s, then runs at 5 m s^{-1} for 12 s. What is his average speed?

19 A journey of 180 km is covered in 3 stages whose lengths are in the ratio 2:3:4. The speed is $2\frac{1}{2}$ km h^{-1} throughout. Find the time taken for each stage.

20 A man walks 20 km at 5 km h^{-1}, then cycles for the same time at 3 times the speed. Find his average speed.

21 An aeroplane flies at 50 m s^{-1} for 30 minutes, lands and is stationary for a time, then flies 80 km at 200 km h^{-1}. If it averages 60 km h^{-1} for the whole journey, for how long is it stationary?

22 A car does a 20 km journey in two stages: 12 km at 60 km h^{-1} and 8 km at another speed. If the average speed for the whole journey is 40 km h^{-1}, what is the speed for the second stage?

23 A journey is covered in three stages, the times for which are in the ratio 1:3:4. The speed is constant, the length of the second stage is 30 km, and the time of the third is 2 h. Find (a) the length of the journey, (b) the speed.

24 A 200 m runner covers the first 100 m in 12 s. If he averages 27 km h^{-1} for the whole run, what is his time for the second 100 m to the nearest tenth of a second?

25 A body travels 600 m in three stages of 200 m each, taking 35 s altogether. The speeds for the three stages are in the ratio 2:4:1. Find the time of the first stage.

26 A man does the first 80 km of a 96 km journey by train, rests for a while, then does the rest of the journey by bus at an average speed of 20 km h^{-1}. The overall average speed is 48 km h^{-1} and the resting time is half the time spent on the train. Find the average speed of the train.

27 A two-stage journey takes 20 s and the average speed is 9 m s^{-1}. The lengths of the stages are in the ratio 1:2 and the speeds are in the ratio 1:3. Find the speed of the first stage.

28 A body travels from A to B at 2 m s^{-1}, from B to C at 4 m s^{-1} and finally from C to D, taking 20 s altogether and averaging $2\frac{1}{4}$ m s^{-1}. $CD = 15$ m, and $AB = 2BC$. Find the average speed (a) from A to C, (b) from B to D.

Travel graphs

It is possible to display journeys in graphical form by representing the time taken on a horizontal axis and the distance travelled on a vertical axis. A graph of this kind is called a *distance–time graph* or a *travel graph*. To see how the form of a travel graph indicates the nature of the motion it represents, consider the motion of a car travelling at a constant speed of 15 m s^{-1}. The following table gives the total distance travelled against the total time taken:

Total time (s)	0	1	2	3	4
Total distance (m)	0	15	30	45	60

From this table a *straight line* graph (Fig. 5.1) can be constructed:

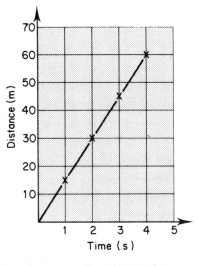

Fig. 5.1

(Journeys at constant speed, to which we shall limit our attention in this chapter, are always represented by straight line graphs. When acceleration or deceleration occurs the graphs become curved.)

Compare the above graph with those in Fig. 5.2, representing bodies moving at 5 m s^{-1} and 20 m s^{-1}.

It can be seen from these examples that the *steeper* a graph is, the greater is the speed of the motion it represents. The speed is in fact given by the *gradient* of the graph, whose meaning is illustrated by Fig. 5.3.

When a body moves from the point represented by A to the point represented by B, the distance it travels is given by BP and the time it takes is represented by AP. Hence the speed is given by $\dfrac{BP}{AP}$. This quantity is clearly a measurement of the steepness of the graph, and it is known as the graph's *gradient*. It follows that *the speed of a moving body is given by the gradient of its travel graph.*

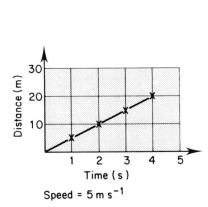

Speed = 5 m s^{-1}

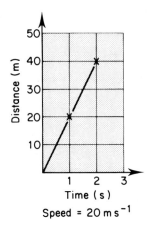

Speed = 20 m s^{-1}

Fig. 5.2

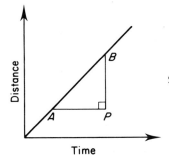

Speed = $\dfrac{BP}{AP}$ = gradient of graph

Fig. 5.3

When a body is moving *towards* the point from which distance is measured, the graph slopes *downwards*. Also when the body is stationary the distance remains constant while the time changes, and the graph is therefore *horizontal*. Fig. 5.4 represents a journey in which a man walks at $1\frac{1}{2}$ m s^{-1} for 4 s, stops for 3 s, and then returns to his starting point at 2 m s^{-1}.

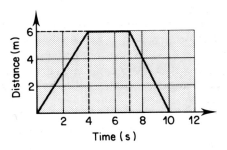

Fig. 5.4

Problems requiring the use of travel graphs often involve the simultaneous movement of two objects which *meet* at some point. The meeting point is given by the point at which the two travel graphs cross (Fig. 5.5).

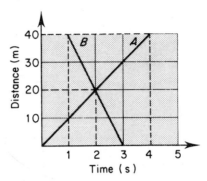

Fig. 5.5

Fig. 5.5 represents the motion of two bodies *A* and *B*. Body *A* starts when the time is taken to be zero and moves with a speed of 10 m s^{-1}. Body *B* starts 1 s after *A*, from a point 40 m away, and moves towards *A* at 20 m s^{-1}. The graph shows that they meet when the time is 2 s, at a point midway between their starting points.

▷ Example 4

At 10.00 h a fast train leaves a town P for a town Q which is 100 km away. The train is intended to travel at a steady 120 km h^{-1}, but after covering 30 km it is forced to stop for 15 minutes. After the delay the train increases its speed and arrives at Q at 11.00 h. At 10.10 h a slow train leaves Q and travels to P at a steady 80 km h^{-1}. Represent this information in a travel graph and use the graph to find (a) the speed of the fast train after the delay and its average speed for the whole journey, (b) how late the fast train is in arriving, (c) the time at which the trains cross, (d) how much nearer to P they cross owing to the delay, (e) the distance apart of the trains at 10.50 h.

The dotted line in Fig. 5.6 represents the journey which the fast train would have made if it had not been delayed.

(a) After the delay the fast train travels 70 km in half an hour, and its speed is therefore 140 km h^{-1}. The average speed is given by the total distance covered divided by the total time taken, and since the train covers a total of 100 km in 1 hour, its average speed is 100 km h^{-1}.

(b) The dotted line shows that the fast train was scheduled to arrive at 10.50 h. Since its actual time of arrival is 11.00 h it is ten minutes late.

(c) The point at which the trains cross is represented by the point *A* at which the graphs intersect. This is at a time of 10.42 h.

(d) If the delay had not occurred the trains would have crossed at the point represented by *B*. Now at *A* the distance from *P* is about 57.5 km (according to the graph), while at *B* this distance is 68 km. Hence to the accuracy available from the graph the difference in these distances is 10.5 km. This is the amount by which the crossing point is nearer to *P* owing to the delay.

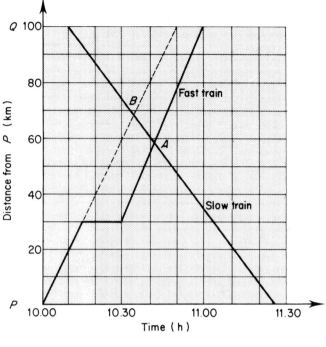

Fig. 5.6

(e) At 10.50 h it appears from the graph that the slow train is about 47 km from
P and the fast train is about 77 km from this point. Hence the trains are 30 km
apart to the nearest kilometre.   ◁

EXERCISE 5b

Use travel graphs to solve the following problems and give the answers as
accurately as your graphs allow.

1 A cyclist starts at a point 20 km from home at 08.00 h, rides directly away
from home at a steady speed until 09.50 h, then returns home at a different
steady speed. If he passes a point 30 km from home at 08.40 h and at 10.45 h,
find his two speeds and his maximum distance from home.

2 At 15.00 h a man starts walking at 6 km h^{-1}. After 15 minutes a cyclist
follows him at 20 km h^{-1}. At what time does the cyclist overtake the walker and
how far ahead is he after a further 25 minutes?

3 A car and a coach both start at 11.00 h and drive towards each other from
two towns 65 km apart. If the car travels at 80 km h^{-1} and the coach at 60 km h^{-1} find (a) the time at which they cross, (b) their distance apart at 11.10 h, (c)
the first time at which they are 20 km apart.

4 A cyclist plans to make a 30 km journey at a steady speed of 25 km h^{-1}, but
after completing part of his journey is forced to reduce his speed to 15 km h^{-1}.
If he arrives at his destination 20 minutes later than he intended, find (a) the
distance he travels before reducing speed, (b) his average speed.

5 A car starts a journey at 12.00 h, travels 80 km at a steady speed, stops for a time and then returns at a different speed. If it passes a point 50 km from its starting point at 12.20 h and at 13.05 h, and takes $1\frac{1}{2}$ h altogether, find the two speeds and the time for which the car is stationary.

6 A train leaves London at 14.00 h and, travelling at a steady speed, reaches Brighton, 95 km away, at 15.10 h. Another train leaves Brighton at 14.30 h and travels to London at 100 km h^{-1}. Find (a) the time at which the two trains cross, (b) their distance from London at this time, (c) their distance apart when the first train reaches Brighton.

7 Two men, A and B, start 3 km apart and walk towards each other at steady speeds. They cross after 20 minutes, and after a further 25 minutes A reaches B's starting point. Find (a) the two speeds, (b) the two times at which A and B are $1\frac{1}{2}$ km apart.

8 A coach and a cyclist start down the same road in the same direction at the same time, the cyclist being initially 40 km ahead of the coach. The cyclist maintains a steady speed of 30 km h^{-1}, but the coach travels at 60 km h^{-1} for 2 hours, then stops for $1\frac{1}{2}$ hours, and then resumes its journey at the same speed as before. Find the three times at which they overtake each other and the average speed of the coach between the start of its journey and the third overtaking.

9 A train leaves London at 11.00 h and travels at a steady speed to Birmingham, 180 km away, arriving at 12.15 h. Another train leaves Birmingham at 11.10 h, stops for 10 minutes at a station S after travelling 70 km, then resumes its journey to London at the same speed. If the two trains reach S at the same time, find (a) the speed of the second train, (b) the time of its arrival at London, (c) its distance from London when the first train arrives at Birmingham.

10 A train starts at P at 09.00 h, travels 200 km to Q at 100 km h^{-1}, waits for 10 minutes and then returns at the same speed. Another train starts at Q at 09.00 h, travels at a steady speed to P, waits for a certain time and then returns to Q at a different steady speed. If the trains cross at 09.50 h and 12.15 h, and the second train arrives back at Q at 13.10 h, find the time for which this train waits at P and its speeds on the two journeys.

6 Indices

Note: **Calculators should not be used in either of the exercises in this chapter.**

Consider the quantity 2^4. The number 4 in this quantity is called a *power* or *exponent* or *index* (plural *indices*) and here it is a positive integer. There are three index laws which are easily shown by examples to hold for indices of this kind:

$$(1) \quad x^a \times x^b = x^{a+b}$$

$$(2) \quad \frac{x^a}{x^b} = x^{a-b}$$

$$(3) \quad (x^a)^b = x^{ab}.$$

As an illustration of law (1) consider $2^4 \times 2^3$. The law states that this is equal to 2^7, which is easily seen to be true since

$$2^4 \times 2^3 = (2 \times 2 \times 2 \times 2) \times (2 \times 2 \times 2) = 2^7.$$

It is important to become familiar with the index laws, and the following worked examples show how they can be used to simplify expressions involving indices.

▷**Example 1**

Express as powers of 3 : (a) $9^3 \times 3^5$, *(b)* $(27^4)^5$, *(c)* $\dfrac{3^7 \times 9^4}{27^3}$

(a) Using law (3), we have $9^3 = (3^2)^3 = 3^6$.
Then by law (1), $3^6 \times 3^5 = 3^{11}$.

(b) By law (3), $27^4 = (3^3)^4 = 3^{12}$.
Applying the same law again, $(3^{12})^5 = 3^{60}$.

(c) Here all the laws are used:

$$\frac{3^7 \times 9^4}{27^3} = \frac{3^7 \times (3^2)^4}{(3^3)^3} = \frac{3^7 \times 3^8}{3^9} = \frac{3^{15}}{3^9} = 3^6.$$

◁

▷ **Example 2**

Express $\dfrac{125^{x+y}}{25^{x-y}}$ *as a power of 5.*

First we must notice that $125 = 5^3$ and $25 = 5^2$. Then, applying law (3), we have

$$125^{x+y} = (5^3)^{x+y} = 5^{3x+3y},$$
$$25^{x-y} = (5^2)^{x-y} = 5^{2x-2y}.$$

Now applying law (2), we obtain

$$\frac{5^{3x+3y}}{5^{2x-2y}} = 5^{x+5y}.$$

◁

EXERCISE 6a

Express as powers of 2:

1 $2^5 \times 2^7$ **2** $\dfrac{2^{10}}{2^4}$ **3** $(2^3)^5$ **4** 4^3 **5** 8^4 **6** 16^{12} **7** $4^5 \times 8^6$

8 $\dfrac{32}{2^3}$ **9** $\dfrac{16^3}{4^4}$ **10** $\dfrac{64 \times 4^5}{8^4}$ **11** $(2^x)^7$ **12** $2^{3x} \times 2^{5x}$

13 $2^{p+1} \times 2^{p-4}$ **14** $\dfrac{2^{a+b}}{2^{a-b}}$ **15** $(2^6)^x \times (2^x)^3$ **16** $4^{3y} \times 8^{1-2y}$

17 $\dfrac{32^{x+2}}{4^{5-x}}$ **18** $16^{w-1} \times 8^{2w+1}$ **19** $\dfrac{8^{4x-3}}{4^{3x-5}}$ **20** $\dfrac{(2^{a-2b})^4}{(2^{b-a})^2}$.

Express as powers of 5:

21 $25 \times 125 \times 625$ **22** $\dfrac{625^2}{25^3}$ **23** $\dfrac{5^3 \times 25^4}{625}$

24 $\dfrac{(125^3)^2}{625^4}$ **25** 125^{3x+2} **26** $25^{4-x} \times 5^{2x-3}$ **27** $\dfrac{25^{y-1}}{5^{y-2}}$

28 $625^{a-b} \times 125^{a+b}$ **29** $\dfrac{125^x \times 25^{1+x}}{625^{x+2}}$ **30** $\dfrac{(25^{2y})^3}{(125^3)^y}$.

Simplify:

31 $(x^3)^4 \div (x^2)^3$ **32** $(p^{2w} \times p^{3w})^4$ **33** $\dfrac{y}{y^{1-x}}$ **34** $(m \times m^x) \div m^{3-x}$

35 $(y \times y^a)^2 \div (y^3)^{a-1}$.

Zero, negative and fractional indices

Quantities such as 3^0 and $5^{-1/2}$ have no meanings until we define them, and the most useful definitions are ones which make these new quantities obey the three index laws. So let us apply law (1) to the new quantities and see what definitions are indicated.

The definition of x^0

By law (1) we have $x^0 \times x^a = x^a$, and this indicates that x^0 *must be defined to equal 1* if law (1) is to continue to hold.

The definition of negative powers

By law (1) we have $x^{-a} \times x^a = x^0$, and since $x^0 = 1$ this indicates that x^{-a} *must be defined to equal* $\dfrac{1}{x^a}$. Alternatively, we could say that x^{-a} is equal to the *reciprocal* of x^a.

The definition of fractional powers

Consider the quantity $x^{1/3}$. By law (1) we have $x^{1/3} \times x^{1/3} \times x^{1/3} = x^1$, and this indicates that $x^{1/3}$ must be defined as the *cube root* of x. Now consider $x^{2/3}$. Law (1) gives $x^{2/3} = x^{1/3} \times x^{1/3}$; hence $x^{2/3}$ must be defined as the *cube root of x, squared.*

Summing up, we have the following three new definitions.

$$x^0 = 1$$
$$x^{-a} = \frac{1}{x^a}$$
$$x^{a/b} = (b\text{th root of } x)^a.$$

It can easily be shown that, with these definitions, the new quantities obey all three index laws.

▷ Example 3

Evaluate (a) $(\tfrac{1}{2})^{-5}$, (b) $16^{3/4}$, (c) $(2\tfrac{1}{4})^{-3/2}$.

(a) $(\tfrac{1}{2})^{-5} = 2^5 = 32$.

(b) $16^{3/4} = (16^{1/4})^3 = 2^3 = 8$.

(c) $(2\tfrac{1}{4})^{-3/2} = (\dfrac{9}{4})^{-3/2} = (\dfrac{4}{9})^{3/2} = (\dfrac{2}{3})^3 = \dfrac{8}{27}$. ◁

Note: Indices of $\tfrac{1}{2}$, $\tfrac{1}{4}$, etc., like the signs $\sqrt{}$ and $\sqrt[4]{}$, denote the *positive* values of the roots only. To denote *both* square roots of, say, 25, we write either $\pm\sqrt{25}$ or $\pm 25^{1/2}$.

EXERCISE 6b

Evaluate:

1 3^{-2} **2** 4^0 **3** 2^{-1} **4** $(\tfrac{1}{2})^{-3}$ **5** $(2\tfrac{1}{2})^0$ **6** $(1\tfrac{1}{2})^{-1}$ **7** $(\tfrac{2}{3})^{-2}$ **8** $(3\tfrac{1}{4})^{-2}$

9 $(0.5)^{-4}$ **10** $(0.4)^{-1}$ **11** $(0.25)^{-3}$ **12** $36^{1/2}$ **13** $125^{1/3}$ **14** $64^{1/6}$

15 $2401^{1/4}$ **16** $(-32)^{1/5}$ **17** $(-216)^{1/3}$ **18** $27^{2/3}$ **19** $4^{1\frac{1}{2}}$ **20** $64^{5/6}$

21 $343^{1\frac{1}{3}}$ **22** $(3\frac{3}{8})^{2/3}$ **23** $(6\frac{1}{4})^{1\frac{1}{2}}$ **24** $(\frac{1}{9})^{-1/2}$ **25** $(\frac{1}{64})^{-1/3}$ **26** $(0.25)^{-1/2}$

27 1^0 **28** $4^{-2\frac{1}{2}}$ **29** $32^{0.4}$ **30** $(11\frac{1}{9})^{-1/2}$ **31** $(5\frac{4}{9})^{-1/2}$

32 $(\frac{8}{27})^{-1\frac{1}{3}}$ **33** $(-512)^{1/3}$ **34** $(0.125)^{-1/3}$ **35** $81^{-0.75}$ **36** $(6.25)^{-1\frac{1}{2}}$

37 $(3^0 - 3^{-1})^{-2}$ **38** $\dfrac{4^{1/2} - 4^{-1/2}}{4^{-1\frac{1}{2}}}$ **39** $\dfrac{9^{-1/2} - 9^{-1}}{9^{-2}}$ **40** $(\dfrac{2^0 - 2^{-1}}{2^3})^{-3/4}$.

7 Number Bases

Our ordinary number system contains *ten* different symbols. These are 0, 1, 2, 3, 4, 5, 6, 7, 8, 9.

When we are writing the whole numbers in ascending order, starting at 1 and working up, we use a different symbol for each number until the symbols run out, which happens after the number *nine*. To carry on, we use *combinations* of symbols, starting 10, 11, 12.

Now if we only had, say, *four* different symbols, namely 0, 1, 2, 3, we would use the same procedure, but then '10', '11', '12', etc. would stand for smaller numbers. We would have, in fact,

one	two	three	four	five	six	seven	eight	nine	ten
1	2	3	10	11	12	13	20	21	22,

and so on. This is called a *base 4* number system, and numbers in it are called *numbers to base 4*. They are written, for example, 13_4 (which has just been shown to mean *seven*), 22_4 (which means *ten*), and so on.

There is clearly a variety of different number systems, the nature of each one depending on how many symbols it uses. The most common are the ordinary base ten or *denary* system, and the *binary* or base two system. The latter uses only the two symbols 0 and 1, and it is important because of its use in computing. The first few numbers in the binary system are

one	two	three	four	five	six	seven	eight	nine	ten
1	10	11	100	101	110	111	1000	1001	1010

Conversion to ordinary (base ten) numbers

Consider any base ten number, say 4107. In the base ten system the digits in this number — the 4, 1, 0 and 7 — are to be interpreted according to the following table.

1000's	100's	10's	1's
4	1	0	7

In other words, the number can be regarded as

$$(4 \times 1000) + (1 \times 100) + (0 \times 10) + (7 \times 1)$$

Now the numbers 10, 100, 1000, etc. are, of course, all powers of 10. We have, in fact, $10 = 10^1$, $100 = 10^2$, $1000 = 10^3$, and so on. It is easy to see, therefore, that in, for example, the base 3 system the digits must be interpreted as follows:

81's	27's	9's	3's	1's

Again in the base 6 sytem we have

216's	36's	6's	1's

It follows that the method for converting a number in an unusual system to one in base 10 is as illustrated in the following examples.

$$2012_3 = (2 \times 27) + (0 \times 9) + (1 \times 3) + (2 \times 1)$$
$$= 54 + 0 + 3 + 2$$
$$= 59_{10}.$$

$$4103_5 = (4 \times 125) + (1 \times 25) + (0 \times 5) + (3 \times 1)$$
$$= 500 + 25 + 0 + 3$$
$$= 528_{10}.$$

Conversion from base 10 to other bases

Suppose we want to convert 137_{10} to the base 5 system. In one method we start by writing down all the powers of 5 (including 5^0, which is 1) up to just below 137:

$$1, 5, 25, 125.$$

Now we express 137 in terms of multiples of these:

$$137 = (1 \times 125) + (0 \times 25) + (2 \times 5) + (2 \times 1).$$

And now it follows immediately that

$$137_{10} = 1022_5.$$

Here is another example. We require 235_{10} in base 4. First we write down all the powers of 4 which are less than 235:

$$1, 4, 16, 64.$$

Now we have

$$235 = (3 \times 64) + (2 \times 16) + (2 \times 4) + (3 \times 1)$$

and hence

$$235_{10} = 3223_4.$$

The procedure just given should make the reasoning clear, but it is not the quickest way to obtain the answer. The reader may realise that the numbers 1, 0, 2, 2 in the first example, and 3, 2, 2, 3 in the second are simply the remainders obtained when we start with 137 and keep dividing by 5, or start with 235 and keep dividing by 4. It should be noted that the order in which the remainders appear is the reverse of the order of the digits in the final answer.

Using this idea we can obtain the first answer more rapidly as follows:

5)137 remainder 2
  27

5)27 remainder 2
  5

5)5 remainder 0
  1

5)1 remainder 1
  0

Hence $137_{10} = 1022_5.$

EXERCISE 7a

Express in base 10:
1 25_7 **2** 2102_3 **3** 523_6 **4** 306_8 **5** 1011_2 **6** 11202_3 **7** 88_9
8 10110_2 **9** 3401_5 **10** 1032_4.

Convert the following base 10 numbers to base 6:
11 39 **12** 18 **13** 195 **14** 200 **15** 1400 **16** 2739.

Convert the following base 10 numbers to binary numbers:
17 15 **18** 32 **19** 37 **20** 117 **21** 196.

By converting to base 10 first, express the following numbers in base 5:
22 36_7 **23** 1101_2 **24** 302_4 **25** 634_8.

Addition

Consider the addition of the three base 10 numbers 49, 78 and 26:

$$
\begin{array}{r}
49 \\
78 \\
26 \\
\hline
153
\end{array}
$$

Let us examine this procedure in detail. We begin by adding 6, 8 and 9, which gives 23. What we actually write is 3, which is *the amount by which 23 exceeds an exact multiple of 10.* We carry 2 into the next column — the 10's column — because 23 contains two 10's in addition to the 3 we have written. More briefly, we are regarding 23 as (2 × 10) + 3, and putting the 3 and the 2 in the units and 10's columns, respectively.

Now let us apply the same procedure to the following addition in base 6:

$$
\begin{array}{r}
24 \\
15 \\
44 \\
\hline
131
\end{array}
$$

Here we begin by adding 4, 5 and 4, obtaining *thirteen.* This is (2 × 6) + 1, so we put 1 in the units column and carry 2 into the 6's column. Adding the numbers in this column gives *nine,* and since this is (1 × 6) + 3, we write down 3 and carry 1 into the next column.

Here are two more examples. The first is in base 8 and the second in base 2.

$$
\begin{array}{r}
27 \\
54 \\
\hline
103
\end{array}
\qquad\qquad
\begin{array}{r}
1011 \\
1001 \\
\hline
10100
\end{array}
$$

Multiplication

The procedure here is very similar to that used in addition. Consider the following multiplication in base 8:

$$
\begin{array}{r}
736 \\
7 \\
\hline
6422
\end{array}
$$

First we multiply 7 by 6, obtaining *forty-two.* (Multiplication tables still work, but we should not write *42* if we are in base 8.) This is (5 × 8) + 2, so we put down 2 and carry 5 into the next column. Then we have 7 × 3 = twenty-one; adding 5 gives twenty-six, and this is (3 × 8) + 2. We put down 2 and carry 3 to the next column. And so on.

Here are two more examples, the first being in base 7 and the second in base 2.

$$
\begin{array}{r}
2453 \\
6 \\
\hline
22044
\end{array}
\qquad\qquad
\begin{array}{r}
1011 \\
11 \\
\hline
10110 \\
1011 \\
\hline
100001
\end{array}
$$

EXERCISE 7b

In each case leave the answer in the same base as the original numbers.
1 $21_3 + 12_3 + 11_3$ **2** $635_7 + 546_7$ **3** $11001_2 + 1001_2$ **4** $40_5 + 23_5 + 304_5$
5 $623_8 + 155_8$ **6** $1010_2 + 111_2 + 11011_2$ **7** $878_9 + 6886_9 + 2678_9$
8 $312_4 \times 3$ **9** $67_8 \times 4$ **10** $1101_2 \times 11_2$ **11** $35_6 \times 3$ **12** $624_7 \times 5$
13 $32_4 \times 23_4$ **14** $506_8 \times 35_8$ **15** $5435_6 \times 415_6$.

Subtraction

Consider the following subtraction in base 10:

$$
\begin{array}{r}
44 \\
28 \\
\hline
16
\end{array}
$$

Since we cannot take 8 from 4, *we take it from 10 more than 4*. This means that we have 'borrowed' 1 from the 10's column, and we pay it back by either adding 1 to the bottom number in this column, or subtracting 1 from the top number.

A similar procedure is adopted in, say, the base 8 system. When we have to subtract a larger number from a smaller we subtract it from *eight* more than the number and pay back the 1 borrowed in the next column.

The following two examples are in the base 8 and base 4 systems, respectively.

$$
\begin{array}{r}
73 \\
26 \\
\hline
45
\end{array}
\qquad\qquad
\begin{array}{r}
3102 \\
1212 \\
\hline
1230
\end{array}
$$

Division

This operation is the most difficult to perform in bases other than 10, and can be omitted by weaker students. Consider the following division in base 5:

$$
\begin{array}{r}
4)\overline{2411} \\
\hline
324
\end{array}
$$

First we need to divide 24_5 by 4. In order to do this we must recognise 24_5 as the number *fourteen.* Now fourteen divided by 4 is 3, with remainder 2; so we put down 3 and then have to divide 4 into 21_5. Since 21_5 is *eleven*, we obtain 2 with remainder 3. Finally we divide 4 into 31_5, which gives 4 exactly.

EXERCISE 7c

(All divisions come out exactly.)
1 $62_8 - 25_8$ **2** $31_5 - 14_5$ **3** $100_4 - 32_4$ **4** $10100_2 - 1011_2$
5 $1023_6 - 545_6$ **6** $1021_3 - 222_3$ **7** $121_3 \div 2$ **8** $212_5 \div 3$ **9** $4154_6 \div 2$
10 $1302_4 \div 3$ **11** $453_7 \div 6$ **12** $2070_8 \div 6$.

8 Introduction to Sets

Definitions and terminology

A set is a well-defined collection of objects called *elements* or *members*. The term 'well-defined' means that there must be a way of deciding, for any object at all, whether or not it is a member of a given set. Thus for example the description 'tall men' does not define a set since 'tall' has only a rough meaning. The description 'men over six feet tall', on the other hand, does define a set.

Sets are denoted by capital letters and their elements are listed within 'braces' (curly brackets). Each element is listed once only, the order of listing being of no significance. Thus for example the set of letters in the word *DETESTED* is $\{D, E, T, S\}$, or $\{T, E, S, D\}$ or $\{S, T, E, D\}$, etc.

The most common method of defining a set is by stating a common property of its members. Consider the following sets:

$$A = \{5, 9, 14, 23\} \quad B = \{2, 3, 5, 7, 11\} \quad V = \{a, e, i, o, u\}$$

The elements of set A have no common property, and therefore the only way of defining this set is by listing its elements. However B could be described as {prime numbers under 12}, and V could be described as {vowels}. This method is essential when the number of elements is infinite or very large, as in the case of {prime numbers}, or {people with blue eyes}. Note that a description such as {vowels} means the set of *all* vowels, and that it would therefore be incorrect to describe, say, $\{e, o, u\}$ as {vowels}.

In mathematical work we often describe sets in the following way:

$$\{x : x \text{ is an integer}\} \quad \{x : x < 3\} \quad \{x : x^2 = 7\}$$

These are read, respectively, 'the set of all numbers x such that x is an integer', 'the set of all numbers x such that x is less than 3', 'the set of all numbers x such that $x^2 = 7$'. The colon (:) stands for 'such that'. This method might seem rather pointless in the first case, since we could simply write {all integers}, but in the second and third examples the alternative descriptions {numbers less than 3} and {solutions of the equation $x^2 = 7$} are longer and more cumbersome.

The *empty* (or *null*) set, denoted by $\emptyset$ or $\{\}$, is any set with no members. Examples are {people over 50 feet tall}, and {odd multiples of 2}.

The symbol $\in$ means *is an element of* and $\notin$ means *is not an element of*. (A stroke through a symbol always has the effect of negating it.) For example, referring to the sets defined above, we have $i \in V$ and $7 \notin A$.

The symbol $\in$ must be carefully distinguished from $\subset$. The latter means *is a subset of* and it relates sets and not elements. A subset of a set S is a set containing no elements which are not elements of S. Again referring to the sets defined above, we have $\{e, i, o\} \subset V$, but $\{2, 3, 4\} \not\subset B$. Note that it is completely wrong to write, say, $i \subset V$ or $\{i, o\} \in V$ or even $p \not\subset V$. The correct form is $p \notin V$.

All sets are considered to be subsets of themselves, and $\emptyset$ is regarded as a subset of all sets; but these are not *proper* subsets. A proper subset is defined to be one other than the set itself or $\emptyset$.

The symbol $\supset$ means *contains as a subset*. So the statement $P \supset Q$ is equivalent to $Q \subset P$. Relations such as $P \supset Q$ and $Q \subset P$ are called *inclusion relations*.

Sets are said to be *equal* if they have exactly the same elements. For example the sets {odd numbers between 16 and 20} and {prime numbers between 14 and 22} are equal since both contain the elements 17 and 19 only. Sets with *the same number* of elements are said to be *equivalent*.

The *number of elements* in a set P is denoted by $n(P)$ or $n\{...\}$. For example $n(A) = 4$ (where A is the set defined above), $n(V) = 5$ and $n\{x:x^2 = 9\} = 2$ since $x^2 = 9$ when $x = 3$ and when $x = -3$.

EXERCISE 8a

In this exercise the following standard symbols are used: $\mathbf{N} = $ {natural numbers}, $\mathbf{Z} = $ {integers}, $\mathbf{Q} = $ {rational numbers}, $\mathbf{R} = $ {real numbers}. See the *General Information* section for explanations of these terms.

1 List in pairs of braces the elements of the following sets: (a) letters of the word *PEPPER*, (b) digits in the number two thousand and twenty, (c) primes between 30 and 50, (d) multiples of 7 between 40 and 65, (e) square numbers between 40 and 130, (f) factors of 30, (g) solutions of the equation $x^2 = 25$.

2 Describe as simply as possible the elements of the following sets: (a) {1, 3, 5, 7}, (b) {b, c, d, f}, (c) {1, 4, 9}, (d) {45, 54, 63, 72}, (e) {clubs, spades}, (f) {September, April, June, November}, (g) {83, 89, 97}, (h) {Tuesday, Thursday}.

3 Say whether or not each of the following sets is equal to $\emptyset$: (a) {5-sided quadrilaterals}, (b) {even prime numbers}, (c) {triangles with 2 obtuse angles}, (d) {negative natural numbers}, (e) {days of the week whose names have 9 letters}, (f) {square numbers between 260 and 290}, (g) {odd multiples of 6}, (h) {primes between 116 and 126}, (i) {parallelograms whose angles are all different}, (j) {prime square numbers}, (k) {real solutions of $x^2 = -9$}.

4 Say whether or not each of the following pairs of sets are equal: (a) {Monday, Friday} and {days of the week whose names have 6 letters}, (b) {primes between 85 and 95} and $\{x:2x - 44 = x + 45\}$, (c) {right-angled isosceles triangles} and {triangles with two angles of 45°}, (d) $\{x:x^2 = 36\}$ and $(x:3x = 18)$, (e) {letters of the word *DINE*} and {letters of the word *INDEED*}, (f) {non-negative integers} and {natural numbers}, (g) {Bach, Beethoven} and {composers whose names begin with B}, (h) {20 mm, 50 cm} and {0.5 m, 2 cm} (i) $\{x:x^3 = 216\}$ and $\{x:2x - 5 = 7\}$.

5 Find the values of (a) n\{multiples of 6 between 40 and 80\}, (b) n\{months with 31 days\}, (c) n\{primes between 20 and 40\}, (d) n\{square numbers below 80\}, (e) n\{faces of a cube\}, (f) $n\{x:x^2 = 5\}$, (g) n\{factors of 12\}, (h) n\{primes between 114 and 130\}, (i) n\{diagonals of a 5-sided figure\}, (j) n\{prime factors of 252\}.

6 Say which of the symbols $\in$, $\notin$, $\subset$, $\not\subset$ should be placed in the following spaces:
(a) 29 . . . {primes} (b) {49, 63, 84} . . . multiples of 7 (c) -3 . . . **N**
(d) $\sqrt{2}$ . . . **Q** (e) **N** . . . **Z** (f) { 37, 79, 143} . . . {primes}
(g) {$x : x^2 = -4$} . . . **R** (h) 0.6 . . . **Q** (i) (57 ÷ 19) . . . **N**
(j) {rectangles} . . . {squares} (k) **Q** . . . **Z**.

7 Say whether the following statements are true (T) or false (F): (a) {1, 2, 3, 7} = {primes below 10} (b) 225 $\in$ {square numbers} (c) {books} $\subset$ {novels} (d) {3, 4, 8, 12} $\subset$ {factors of 108} (e) 221 $\in$ {primes} (f) {vowels in *EARLIER*} $\subset$ {letters in *NEARLY*} (g) n {primes below 12} = n {square numbers below 30} (h) {primes} $\not\subset$ **Q** (i) {letters in *APPEARED*} = {letters in *DRAPED*} (j) {regular polygons} $\supset$ {squares}.

8 List all the proper subsets of {a, b, c}.

9 Find (a) the number of subsets with 2 members possessed by a set with 4 members, (b) the number of subsets with 4 members possessed by a set with 5 members.

In questions 10–12, find an element which is common to the given sets.
10 {square numbers below 100} and {multiples of 27}.

11 {$x:x - 2$ is a square number} and {primes between 20 and 100}.

12 {$x: \frac{x}{2}$ is prime and $x < 80$} and {$x:x - 2$ is a multiple of 7}.

Universal set, complement of a set

A universal set, denoted by $\mathscr{E}$, is a *background* set, or a set containing *all the elements under consideration* when we are carrying out a piece of work or trying to solve a problem. Suppose for example that we are doing a survey to find out how people's jobs affect their health. The background set might be {working people in England}, and all the sets we would be likely to consider would be subsets of this, e.g. {people who work in offices}, {people who are overweight}, {people who work in offices and are overweight}, and so on. If, on the other hand, we are working on a mathematical problem, such as how to solve the quadratic equation $x^2 - x = 2$, our background set will usually be some set of numbers. If x is a number of men, or molecules, then x will have to be a member of the set of natural numbers, **N**, and this could appropriately be regarded as the background set within which we are looking for solutions. But if we are simply solving the equation as an exercise in school, then our universal set, by implication, is likely to be the set of all real numbers. Sometimes the universal set is not specified precisely, and sometimes there is more than one possible universal set; but the universal set always contains as subsets all other sets that are likely to arise.

When a universal set has been defined we can define the *complement* of any set A as *the set of all elements which are in the universal set but not in A*. The complement of a set A is denoted by A'. Thus if $\mathscr{E}$ is {positive even numbers under 11}, and $A = \{2, 4\}$, then $A' = \{6, 8, 10\}$. Again if $\mathscr{E}$ is {all integers} and $A = \{$odd numbers$\}$, then $A' = \{$even numbers and zero$\}$. Clearly the complement of $\mathscr{E}$ itself is $\varnothing$ and the complement of $\varnothing$ is $\mathscr{E}$.

Union and intersection, disjoint sets

Suppose we have two sets $A = \{1, 2, 3, 4\}$ and $B = \{3, 4, 5, 6\}$. The *union* of the two sets, denoted by $A \cup B$, is defined to be the set of *all the elements in A or B or both*. Clearly in this case $A \cup B = \{1, 2, 3, 4, 5, 6\}$. The *intersection* of the sets, denoted by $A \cap B$, is defined to be the set of elements in *both* A and B, that is the set of elements *common* to the two sets. In this case $A \cap B = \{3, 4\}$. *Disjoint* sets are defined to be ones with no common elements; so if A and B are disjoint sets we have $A \cap B = \emptyset$.

The definitions of union and intersection are not limited to the case of two sets. $A \cup B \cup C$ means the set of all the elements in A or B or C, and $A \cap B \cap C$ denotes the set of elements common to A, B and C.

Brackets

Brackets are not needed in the expressions $A \cup B \cup C$ and $A \cap B \cap C$ because these expressions have unambiguous meanings. A little thought will show that $(A \cup B) \cup C = A \cup (B \cup C)$, so each expression can be denoted by $A \cup B \cup C$ without danger of confusion. But $A \cup (B \cap C)$, in which $B \cap C$ is worked out first, does not in general mean the same as $(A \cup B) \cap C$, in which $A \cup B$ is worked out first. So $A \cup B \cap C$ is meaningless and brackets are essential. Similarly, brackets are essential in all other expressions in which both $\cup$ and $\cap$ occur.

▷ Example 1

$A = \{1, 2, 3, 4\}$, $B = \{2, 3, 4, 5, 6\}$, $C = \{3, 6, 8\}$. *List the elements in the sets (a)* $A \cup B \cup C$ *(b)* $A \cap B \cap C$ *(c)* $A \cup (B \cap C)$ *(d)* $(A \cup B) \cap C$.

(a) $A \cup B \cup C$ is the set of all elements in A or B or C, i.e. $\{1, 2, 3, 4, 5, 6, 8\}$.
(b) $A \cap B \cap C$ is the set of elements common to A, B and C, i.e. $\{3\}$.
(c) $B \cap C = \{3, 6\}$, so $A \cup (B \cap C) = \{1, 2, 3, 4, 6\}$.
(d) $A \cup B = \{1, 2, 3, 4, 5, 6\}$, so $(A \cup B) \cap C = \{3, 6\}$. ◁

Venn diagrams

Venn diagrams provide a convenient pictorial way of showing the relationships between sets. The universal set (if one is defined) is represented by a rectangle, and other sets are represented by ovals or circles within this rectangle. The elements of the sets can be represented as dots within the rectangles, though these are not always shown individually.

The meanings of union and intersection could be demonstrated by the following Venn diagrams (Fig. 8.1).

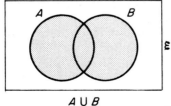

$A \cup B$

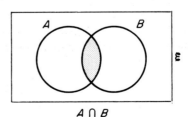

$A \cap B$

Fig. 8.1

▷ **Example 2**

The small letters in the Venn diagram shown in Fig. 8.2 represent elements.
List the elements in the sets (a) A ∩ B (b) (A ∪ B)' (c) A' ∪ B (d) A' ∪ B' (e) A ∩ B'.

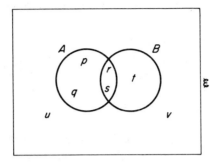

Fig. 8.2

(a) $A \cap B$ is clearly the set $\{r, s\}$.
(b) $A \cup B = \{p, q, r, s, t\}$, and $(A \cup B)'$ is the set of elements in $\mathscr{E}$ but not in
$A \cup B$. Hence $(A \cup B)' = \{u, v\}$.
(c) $A' = \{t, u, v\}$, and $B = \{r, s, t\}$. Hence $A' \cup B = \{r, s, t, u, v\}$.
(d) $A' = \{t, u, v\}$, and $B' = \{p, q, u, v\}$. Hence $A' \cup B' = \{t, u, v, p, q\}$.
(e) $A = \{p, q, r, s\}$, and $B' = \{p, q, u, v\}$. Hence $A \cap B' = \{p, q\}$.   ◁

It is important to realise that regions shown in Venn diagrams do not
necessarily contain elements. Consider the Venn diagram shown in Fig.
8.3.

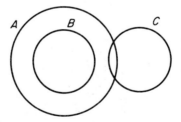

Fig. 8.3

We can certainly deduce from this that all members of B, if any exist, are
members of A, and thus that $B \subset A$. Also we can deduce that B and C are
disjoint sets and thus that $B \cap C = \varnothing$. But the diagram does not tell us the
exact relationship between A and C. It is drawn so as to allow the
possibilities that C lies entirely inside A, or entirely outside A, or partially
inside and partially outside. All these possibilities occur if appropriate
regions in the diagram represent empty sets. Venn diagrams showing
pairs of sets should always be drawn in this way when the exact
relationship between the sets is not known.

If we want to show that a set represented by a region in a Venn diagram
definitely does contain some elements, we can either place a number in
the region — representing the number of elements it contains — or, if the

number is unknown, shade the region and state that shading indicates the presence of elements.

When we are dealing with three or more related sets, Venn diagrams are virtually essential to display the relationship in a simple way. Just three sets can be related in many different ways, some of which are shown in Fig. 8.4.

Fig. 8.4

Sometimes regions in Venn diagrams are denoted by letters placed within them, the actual elements in the regions being unspecified. It is important to learn to describe any such region in set terminology, as well as to identify any regions so described. The following example illustrates the procedure.

▷ Example 3

Describe in set terminology the regions in the Venn diagram (Fig. 8.5) labelled (a) x (b) w (c) r. State also which regions represent (d) $(A \cup B) \cap C$ (e) $A \cap (B' \cup C)$.

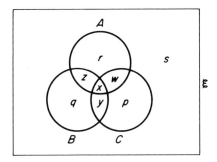

Fig. 8.5

(a) The elements in region x are those which are common to A, B and C. Hence x represents $A \cap B \cap C$.
(b) The elements in w belong to A and C, but not to B. Hence w represents $A \cap B' \cap C$.
(c) The elements in r belong to A, but not to B or C. Hence r represents $A \cap B' \cap C'$.
(d) $A \cup B$ is represented by the sum of the regions r, w, x, z, y, q, and C is represented by w, x, y, p. We require the regions common to $A \cup B$ and C, which are w, x and y.
(e) B' is represented by the regions outside B, namely s, r, w, p. Hence $B' \cup C$ is represented by s, r, w, p, x, y. A is represented by r, w, x, z, and we require the regions common to $B' \cup C$ and A. These are r, w and x. ◀

EXERCISE 8b

1 $A = \{a, b, e, f, g\}$ and $B = \{b, c, d, g, h\}$. List the sets (a) $A \cup B$ (b) $A \cap B$.
2 $A = \{$primes below 12$\}$ and $B = \{$odd numbers between 2 and 10$\}$. List the sets (a) $A \cup B$ (b) $A \cap B$.
3 The small letters in the Venn diagram (Fig. 8.6) represent elements. List the sets (a) $A \cup B$ (b) $A \cap B$ (c) A' (d) $(A \cup B)'$ (e) $(A \cap B)'$ (f) $A' \cap B$.

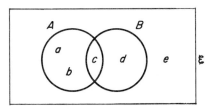

Fig. 8.6

4 A is any set. Express in a simpler way (a) $A \cup A$ (b) $A \cup A'$ (c) $A \cap A$ (d) $A \cap A'$ (e) $A \cup \varnothing$ (f) $A \cap \varnothing$ (g) $A \cup \mathscr{E}$ (h) $A \cap \mathscr{E}$.
5 Use set notation to name the shaded areas in the Venn diagrams of Fig. 8.7:

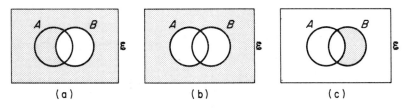

(a)   (b)   (c)

Fig. 8.7

6 $\mathscr{E} = \{1, 2, 3, 4, 5\}, A = \{2, 5\},\ B = \{1, 2, 3\}$. List (a) A' (b) $A' \cup B'$ (c) $A \cap B'$ (d) $(A \cup B)'$.
7 $\mathscr{E} = \{$natural numbers below 12$\}, P = \{$primes$\},\ Q = \{1, 3, 5, 7, 9\}$. List (a) P' (b) $P \cap Q'$ (c) $P' \cup Q$ (d) $(P \cup Q)'$ (e) $(P \cap Q)'$.
8 $A = \{x : x^2 = 4\}, B = \{-3, -2, -1, 0\}, C = \{-2, -1, 0, 1\}$. List (a) $A \cup B \cup C$, (b) $A \cap B \cap C$, (c) $(A \cup B) \cap C$, (d) $A \cup (B \cap C)$.

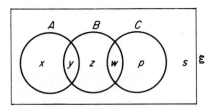

Fig. 8.8

9 The small letters in the Venn diagram (Fig. 8.8) denote regions. Use set notation to name the regions (a) y (b) p (c) s. State also which regions represent (d) $A' \cap B$ (e) $A \cup B'$ (f) $B \cap (A \cup C)$.
10 $\mathscr{E} = \{2, 4, 6, 8, 10, 12\}, A = \{4, 8, 12\},\ B = \{2, 4, 10\}$. List (a) $(A \cup B)'$, (b) $(A \cap B)'$, (c) $(A \cup B) \cap B'$.
11 Simplify (a) $\varnothing \cap \mathscr{E}$, (b) $\varnothing \cup \mathscr{E}$, (c) $(A \cup A') \cap A$, (d) $A \cap (A' \cup \varnothing)$, (e) $A \cup \varnothing \cup A'$, (f) $A \cap \varnothing \cap A'$.

12 Assuming that each separate region in the Venn diagram (Fig. 8.9) contains elements, say whether the following are true (T) or false (F):
(a) $A \supset C'$, (b) $A \cap C = \varnothing$, (c) $B \cap C \subset A'$, (d) $A' \cup C' = \mathscr{E}$, (e) $(A \cap C) \cup B = \varnothing$, (f) $A \cap (B \cup C) = A \cap B$.

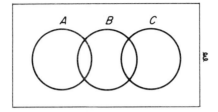

Fig. 8.9

13 $\mathscr{E} = \{$integers from 3 to 17 inclusive$\}$, $A = \{$odd numbers$\}$, $B = \{x : x^2 \in \mathscr{E}\}$.
Find (a) $n(A')$, (b) $n(B')$, (c) $nA \cup B)$, (d) $n(A \cap B')$.
14 Assuming that each separate region in the Venn diagram (Fig. 8.10) contains elements, say whether the following are true (T) or false (F):
(a) $A \cup B$ and C are disjoint, (b) $B \cap C \subset A$, (c) $A \cup B' = A' \cup B$,
(d) $A \cup (B \cup C) = \varnothing$, (e) $C \supset A' \cap B'$, (f) $A' \cup C' = B' \cup C' = \mathscr{E}$.

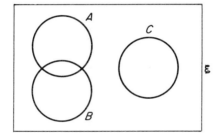

Fig. 8.10

15 Simplify (a) $A \cup (A \cap B)$, (b) $A \cap (A \cup B)$, (c) $B \cap (A \cup A')$, (d) $A \cup (B \cap B')$.
16 $\mathscr{E} = \{$natural numbers below 10$\}$, $A = \{x : x > 5\}$, $B = \{3, 4, 5, 6\}$,
$C = \{$multiples of 3$\}$. List (a) $A \cap B \cap C$, (b) $A' \cap C'$, (c) $A \cap (B' \cup C)$,
(d) $(A \cup B) \cap C'$.
17 The small letters in the Venn diagram (Fig. 8.11) denote regions. Use set notation to name the regions (a) s, (b) t, (c) q. State also which regions represent (d) $A' \cup C$, (e) $C' \cap A$, (f) $B' \cap (A \cup C)$.

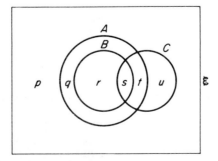

Fig. 8.11

9 Venn Diagrams and Simple Logical Problems

Note: **This is a difficult chapter. Some students should omit it and proceed straight to chapter 10.**

The techniques explained in the last chapter can be used to simplify expressions in set notation, to prove statements, and to investigate the logical relations between statements. The methods will be illustrated by examples.

▷ Example 1

Simplify the expression $(A' \cup B')'$.

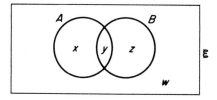

Fig. 9.1

The Venn diagram in Fig. 9.1 is drawn in the most general way and allows all possible relations between the two sets. (The small letters denote regions and not elements.)

A' is represented by the regions w, z, and B' is represented by w, x. Hence $A' \cup B'$ is represented by w, z, x. The complement of this is represented by y, that is the region representing $A \cap B$. Hence $(A' \cup B')' = A \cap B$. ◁

▷ Example 2

Prove that $P' \cup (Q' \cap P) = (P \cap Q)'$.

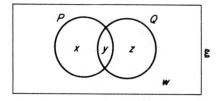

Fig. 9.2

Once again we draw the most general Venn diagram (Fig. 9.2) for two sets. We begin by working out which regions represent the left-hand side of the statement to be proved. Q' is represented by w, x, and P by x, y. Hence $Q' \cap P$ is represented by x. Also P' is represented by w, z; hence the left-hand side is represented by x, w, z.

Next we consider the right-hand side. $P \cap Q$ is represented by y, and the complement of this set is represented by all the regions other than y, that is x, w, z. Hence the statement is proved.   ◁

Implication

To say that a statement p *implies* a statement q means that if p is true, q *has* to be true. We write this $p \Rightarrow q$. It is important to realise that if p implies q it does not follow that q implies p. To illustrate this consider the statements *John is a normal human being (p)* and *John has two eyes (q)*. Here p implies q but q does not imply p. This is because, on the basis of q, John could be a dog, cat, or any other animal with two eyes. We can sum up the relationship between the two statements by writing $p \Rightarrow q$, $q \not\Rightarrow p$.

When the implication works both ways, that is $p \Rightarrow q$ and $q \Rightarrow p$, we say that p and q are *equivalent* statements, and write $p \Leftrightarrow q$. This can be read, 'p implies and is implied by q'. The symbol $\Leftarrow$ means *is implied by*.

A simple mathematical example of equivalent statements is the pair of statements $x = 2$, $3x = 6$. The implication clearly works both ways here. Contrast this case with the two statements $x = 2$, $x^2 = 4$. Here the first statement does imply the second, but $x^2 = 4$ implies that *either $x = 2$ or $x = -2$*. So the second statement does not *compel* the first to be true, and therefore does not imply it. This is a case in which $p \Rightarrow q$, but $q \not\Rightarrow p$.

The examples given so far show that when one statement fails to imply another, it does not necessarily prove the second statement to be false. $x^2 = 4$ does not make it certain that $x = 2$, but it does not make this impossible. On the other hand $x^2 = 4$ does make it impossible that $x = 7$. In this latter kind of case, when the two statements are *incompatible*, we say that each *denies* the other. There is no standard symbol for denies.

To sum up, if we are given a statement p, which we are taking to be true, there are three possibilities for another statement q, namely: q *must be true*, q *must be false*, and q *may be either true or false*.

When the statements we are concerned with involve sets, drawing Venn diagrams often helps us to discover the relationships between them. The following examples illustrate some cases of this kind.

▷ **Example 3**

In each of the following cases assume that statement (1) is true, and say whether statement (2) is definitely true, definitely false, or possibly true and possibly false. If the statements are equivalent, say so.

(a) (1) $A \cap B = A$ (2) $A \subset B$

(1) states that all elements which are common to the two sets are members of A. Hence we have one of the two possibilities shown in Fig. 9.3.

In either case $A \subset B$, since any set is a subset of itself. Hence (2) is *definitely true*. Also, if we assume (2) to be true, it is easily seen that (1) has to be true, so the implication works both ways and the statements are *equivalent*.

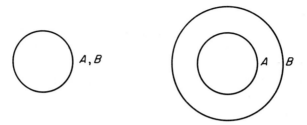

Fig. 9.3

(b) (1) $A \cup B \neq A$ *(2)* $A' \cap B = \emptyset$

(1) states that not all the elements of $A \cup B$ are members of A. Hence some of the elements of B are outside A, and we have the Venn diagram shown in Fig. 9.4. Shading indicates the presence of elements.

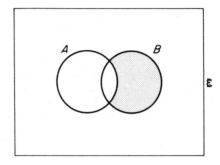

Fig. 9.4

Now consider statement (2). $A' \cap B$ is the set of elements which are in B but outside A, and that is just the set represented by the shading in the Venn diagram. Since statement (2) says that this set is empty, this statement is *definitely false*.

(c) (1) $A \cap B \cap C = \emptyset$ *(2)* $A \cap C = \emptyset$

(1) states that there are no elements common to all three sets, and (2) states that there are no elements common to A and C. In this case (2) can be *either true or false*, for on the basis of (1) either of the Venn diagrams shown in Fig. 9.5 is possible:

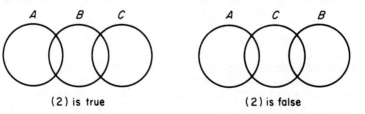

Fig. 9.5

▷**Example 4**

Say whether the following statement is true or false, and consider whether the answer remains the same when the implication sign is reversed:
$A \cap B = A \cap C \Rightarrow A \cap B' \cap C = \emptyset$.

Here we draw the most general Venn diagram (Fig. 9.6) for three sets. The small letters denote regions.

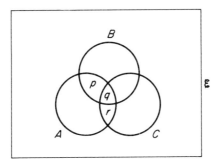

Fig. 9.6

The equation on the left of the implication sign states that all elements which are common to A and B are also common to A and C and vice-versa. This is only possible if regions p and r represent empty sets. The equation on the right states that there are no elements common to A, B' and C, that is that region r represents an empty set. This does follow from the first equation, so the whole statement is true.

When the implication sign is reversed the statement clearly becomes false since it then effectively states: 'r represents an empty set $\Rightarrow$ both r and p represent empty sets'. ◁

EXERCISE 9a

In questions 1–9, say whether the statements are true (T) or false (F).
1 $A \cup B = \emptyset \Leftrightarrow A = B = \emptyset$. **2** $A \cap B = \emptyset \Leftarrow A \cup B = \mathscr{E}$.
3 $A \cup B = \mathscr{E} \Rightarrow A = B'$.
4 $A \cup B = \mathscr{E} \Leftarrow A = B'$. **5** $P \subset Q$ and $P \subset R \Rightarrow Q \subset R$. **6** $R \subset S$ and $S \subset T \Rightarrow R \subset T$.
7 $A \cap B = A \cap C \Rightarrow B = C$. **8** $A \cap B = A \cap C \Leftarrow B = C$. **9** $A = B' \Leftrightarrow A' = B$.

Simplify the expressions in questions 10–12:
10 $(A' \cap B')'$ **11** $(A' \cap B) \cup (A \cap B)$ **12** $A \cap (B \cup A')$

13 Prove that $(A' \cap B)' = A \cup B'$ **14** Prove that $A' \cap B' \cap C' = (A \cup B \cup C)'$.

In questions 15–22 assume that statement (a) is true and say whether statement (b) is definitely true (T), definitely false (F), or possibly true and possibly false (T or F).
15 (a) $A \cap B = \emptyset$ (b) $B \subset A'$ **16** (a) $A \cup B = A \cup C$ (b) $B = C$
17 (a) $A \cap B \neq \emptyset$ (b) $A' \cap B = B$ **18** (a) $A \subset B$ (b) $A \cap B' = \emptyset$
19 (a) $A \subset B$ and $P \subset A'$ (b) $P \cap B = \emptyset$ **20** (a) $A \cap B$ is a proper subset of A
(b) $A \cup B = A$ **21** (a) $A \cap B = B$ and $A \subset C$ (b) $B \not\subset C$ **22** (a) $A \cap B = A \cup B$
(b) $A \cap B' = \emptyset$

In questions 23–30, say whether the statements are true or false.
23 $A \cap B \neq \varnothing \Rightarrow A \cup B \neq A$ **24** $A \cap B \cap C = A \cap C \Leftarrow A \cup C \subset B$
25 $A \cup B \cup C = \mathscr{E} \Leftrightarrow A' \cap B' \cap C' = \varnothing$ **26** $A' \cup B = \mathscr{E} \Leftrightarrow A \subset B$
27 $A \subset B \Leftrightarrow B' \subset A'$ **28** $A = B \Leftarrow A \cup B' = \mathscr{E}$ **29** $A = B \Rightarrow A \cup B' = \mathscr{E}$
30 A is a proper subset of $B \Rightarrow A' \cap B \neq \varnothing$.

Simplify the expressions in questions 31–33.
31 $(A' \cap B') \cup (A' \cap B)$ **32** $A \cup (A' \cap B)$ **33** $(A \cap B) \cup (B \cap C) \cup (A' \cap B \cap C')$

34 Prove that $(A \cup B) \cap (A' \cup B') = (A \cap B') \cup (A' \cap B)$
35 Prove that $(A \cap B) \cup (B \cap C) \cup (C \cap A) = (A \cup B) \cap (B \cup C) \cap (C \cup A)$.

In questions 36–41, say whether the statements are true (T) or false (F).
36 $A' \cup B = \mathscr{E} \Rightarrow A \cap B' = \varnothing$ **37** $A' \cup B = \mathscr{E} \Leftarrow A \cap B' = \varnothing$
38 $A \subset B$ and $A' \cap B = \varnothing \rightarrow A$ is a proper subset of B.
39 $A \cap B \neq \varnothing$ and $A' \cap B = \varnothing \Rightarrow B$ is a proper subset of A.
40 $A \subset A \cap B' \Rightarrow A \cap B = \varnothing$ **41** $A \subset A \cap B' \Leftarrow A \cap B = \varnothing$

Statements involving the terms 'some', 'all'

Venn diagrams are particularly useful in illustrating what is meant by statements such as *some men are tall*, *all lions are fierce*, etc. To illustrate the first statement we might have a universal set consisting of all human beings, and within the rectangle representing this show the set of men overlapping with the set of tall people (Fig. 9.7).

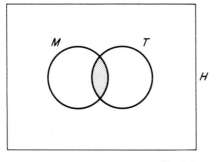

H = humans,

M = men,

T = tall people.

Shading indicates the existence of elements.

Fig. 9.7

Expressed in set language, the statement that some men are tall is $M \cap T \neq \varnothing$. It should be noted that the word 'some' does not exclude the possibility of all, and the Venn diagram allows for this since the region representing $M \cap T'$ does not necessarily contain elements.

The universal set for the statement that *all lions are fierce* could be {all animals}, and within the rectangle representing this we could show the set of lions as a subset of the set of fierce animals (Fig. 9.8). In set terminology, the statement that all lions are fierce is $L \subset F$.

Consider next statements such as *no lions are tame*. Statements such as these are equivalent to ones involving the term 'all'; in this case the statement could be re-expressed *all lions are not tame* and represented in a Venn diagram as in Fig. 9.9. Expressed in set language, this statement is $L \cap T = \varnothing$ (or $L \subset T'$ or $T \subset L'$).

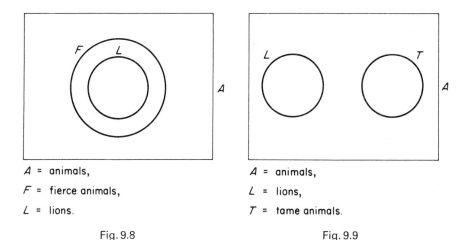

A = animals,

F = fierce animals,

L = lions.

Fig. 9.8

A = animals,

L = lions,

T = tame animals.

Fig. 9.9

Note that the word 'some' implies that elements definitely exist, while the word 'all' does not. It is true that all men over 50 feet tall are over 40 feet tall, even though no men of either type (presumably) exist.

When we have to deal with more complicated statements involving the terms 'some' and 'all', Venn diagrams are useful in helping us to sort out the logical relationships involved. The following example illustrates the method.

▷ **Example 5**

Some of the children in a class like English, some like Maths and some like French. All those who like French like English, and none of those who like French dislike Maths. Display this information in a Venn diagram, calling the sets E, M and F, and, assuming that all the information is correct, say whether each of the following statements is definitely true, definitely false, or possibly true and possibly false. (a) F ⊂ M, (b) E ⊂ M, (c) all children who like French like both Maths and English, (d) some who dislike English and French like Maths, (e) not all who like Maths like French, (f) all who dislike English dislike French.

We must notice first that *none who like French dislike Maths* is equivalent to *all who like French like Maths*. Then the Venn diagram can be constructed, as follows (Fig. 9.10):

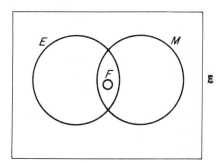

$\mathscr{E}$ = all children in the class,

E = those who like English,

M = those who like Maths,

F = those who like French.

Fig. 9.10

(a) Clearly $F \subset M$ is *definitely true*. (b) $E \subset M$ is not definitely true, but since the regions in the Venn diagram do not all necessarily contain elements, it is not definitely false. Hence the statement is *possibly true and possibly false*. (c) This statement is *definitely true* since F is a subset of both E and M. (d) This statement is *possibly true and possibly false* since the part of M outside E and F may or may not contain elements. (e) This statement is *possibly true and possibly false* since M may or may not be equal to F. (f) This statement is *definitely true* since all elements which are outside E are certainly outside F. ◁

EXERCISE 9b

1 $\mathscr{E} = $ {natural numbers}, $P = $ {primes}, $E = $ {even numbers}, $M = $ {multiples of 4}. Express in set terminology (a) all multiples of 4 are even, (b) no even numbers are prime, (c) some even numbers are multiples of 4, (d) some non-primes are even.

2 $\mathscr{E} = $ {men}, $F = $ {footballers}, $T = $ {men over six feet}, $H = $ {men over thirteen stone}. Express in set terminology (a) no men of six feet or under weigh over thirteen stone, (b) some footballers who do not weigh over thirteen stone are over six feet, (c) all footballers are either over six feet or over thirteen stone or both, (d) some men over six feet are not footballers.

3 The sets of children who like apples, oranges, pears and dates are represented by A, O, P and D, respectively. Express the following in set terminology: (a) all children who like apples also like oranges or pears or both, (b) all children who like dates like both apples and pears, (c) every child who likes oranges dislikes pears, (d) no child likes both dates and pears, (e) some of the children who like pears like both oranges and apples, (f) no child who likes apples dislikes dates, (g) some of the children who like both oranges and dates dislike pears.

In the following questions draw a Venn diagram to illustrate the information given at the beginning, then say whether statements (a), (b), (c), etc. are definitely true (T), definitely false (F), or possibly true and possibly false (T or F). (Assume that the information given is correct.)

4 All boys who play football are healthy, and some healthy boys play cricket.
(a) Some boys play both cricket and football. (b) No unhealthy boys play football. (c) Boys who are both healthy and play cricket are not all footballers.

5 A survey shows that some working women are married and some have children. None of the unmarried women in the survey have children.
(a) All the married women with no children work. (b) None of the women who do not work have children. (c) A married woman who works definitely has no children. (d) All the unmarried working women are childless.

6 All healthy children like games and all clever children dislike games.
(a) All healthy children are not clever. (b) No children who dislike games are healthy. (c) If a child is unhealthy and likes games he may or may not be clever.

7 All pigs who like potatoes are fat, but no pigs are fat who are not greedy.
(a) A pig who is greedy may not be fat. (b) Fat pigs all like potatoes. (c) No pigs who are not greedy are fat. (d) Some, possibly all, greedy pigs like potatoes. (e) The pigs who are neither greedy nor fat all dislike potatoes.

8 Children who like French all dislike Maths, but all those who like Maths like Latin.
(a) Any child who dislikes French and Latin dislikes Maths. (b) If a child likes Maths he cannot also like French. (c) No child likes more than two of the three subjects. (d) Some, possibly all, children who like Latin like French.

10 Venn Diagrams and Numerical Problems

In the last chapter we used the terms 'some', 'all', etc., but never dealt with cases in which we knew or had to find the exact numbers of elements in the various sets. Consider now the following simple problem.

▷ **Example 1**

In a class of 25 children, 17 study Physics, 15 study Chemistry and 10 study both. How many study neither subject?
This question can quite easily be answered without a Venn diagram, but the diagrammatic method illustrates the general procedure which is needed in more complicated problems.

Let $\mathscr{E}$ = {all the children in the class}, P = {children who study Physics} and C = {children who study Chemistry}. We draw a diagram (Fig. 10.1) showing the two sets overlapping since some children study both subjects. When we know the number of elements in any particular region of the diagram we write that number straight into the region, and when we know the number of elements in a whole set we write that number in brackets after the name of the set. Here the given information is shown in diagram (i).

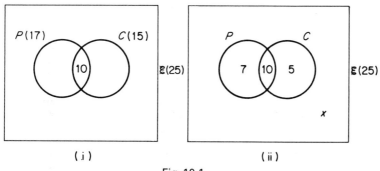

Fig. 10.1

From diagram (i) we can deduce that the numbers of elements in the remaining parts of sets P and C are 7 and 5; and if we let the number we have to find be x, we have the information shown in diagram (ii). Since the total number of elements is 25, an equation involving x can be obtained:

$$x + 7 + 10 + 5 = 25$$
$$\therefore \ x = 3.$$

◁

Before turning to problems involving three sets we consider a somewhat less common type of problem in which the answer is a range of values rather than one definite value.

▷ Example 2

Given that n(A ∪ B) = 10 and n(A ∩ B) = 6, find the possible values of n(B).

The information given is shown in the following Venn diagram (Fig. 10.2), in which the set $A \cup B$ is indicated by shading:

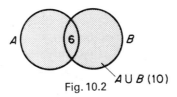

Fig. 10.2   A ∪ B (10)

Now since the whole shaded region contains 10 elements, there are 4 to be placed in the regions other than that representing $A \cap B$. Clearly the set B can contain either 0, 1, 2, 3 or 4 of these; hence the possible values of $n(B)$ are 6, 7, 8, 9 and 10.   ◁

The next examples involve three sets and here it is essential to draw Venn diagrams. The general procedure in the more complicated cases is to put as many numbers into the Venn diagram as possible, expressing unknowns in terms of letters. Equations relating the unknowns should then follow from the information given. When the number of elements in the central region (the region of maximum overlap) is given, it is generally best to start at the centre and work outwards. The next example illustrates this procedure.

▷ Example 3

All of a group of 30 people play at least one of the games chess, bridge and draughts. Four people play all three games, 3 play just bridge and chess, 6 play both chess and draughts, 10 play only chess, 5 play only bridge and 3 play only draughts. How many play both bridge and draughts?

Since all the people play at least one of the three games we do not require a separate universal set. The Venn diagram (Fig. 10.3) is drawn in the most general possible way for three sets, with each set overlapping with both of the others:

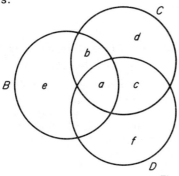

C = { chess players }
B = { bridge players }
D = { draughts players }

Fig. 10.3

Starting at the centre and working outwards, we proceed as follows.

$n(C \cap B \cap D) = 4$, so we place a 4 in region a.

$n(B \cap C \cap D') = 3$, so we place a 3 in region b.

$n(C \cap D) = 6$, so there are 6 elements in regions a and c combined. Since there are 4 in a, we place a 2 in region c.

$n(C \cap B' \cap D') = 10$, so we place a 10 in region d.

$n(B \cap C' \cap D') = 5$, so we place a 5 in region e.

$n(D \cap B' \cap C') = 3$, so we place a 3 in region f.

We now have a diagram (Fig. 10.4) in which the only missing number is denoted by x:

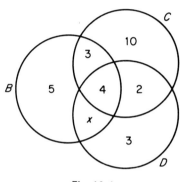

Fig. 10.4

Since there are 30 people altogether, the following equation is obtained:

$$x + 10 + 3 + 4 + 2 + 5 + 3 = 30$$
$$\therefore \ x = 3.$$

It follows that 7 people play both bridge and draughts.   ◁

▷ Example 4

An investigation is made into the popularity of football, cricket and tennis among schoolboys. It is found that all like at least one of the three games, that 60% like football, 32% like football and cricket, 22% like football and tennis, 20% like cricket and tennis, 15% like cricket only and 10% like tennis only. What percentage like football only?

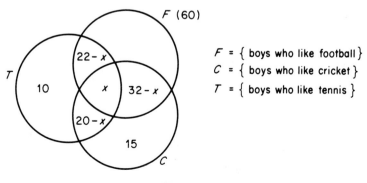

F = { boys who like football }
C = { boys who like cricket }
T = { boys who like tennis }

Fig. 10.5

In this case we do not know the number who like all three games, so we cannot employ the procedure used in the last example. The method is to let one of the unknown numbers be x, and express the other unknowns in terms of x. Taking a typical sample of 100 boys, and letting the number who like all three games be x, we obtain the Venn diagram shown in Fig. 10.5.

Now we look for some way of obtaining an equation involving x. In fact since the total number of boys is 100 and $n(F) = 60$, we have $n(F') = 40$ and hence

$$10 + 15 + 20 - x = 40$$
$$\therefore x = 5.$$

The percentage who like football only is $60 - (22 - x) - x - (32 - x)$, that is 11%. ◁

▷ Example 5

In a class of 28 children, 5 study both Chemistry and Physics, 7 study both Chemistry and Biology and none study both Physics and Biology. Equal numbers study Physics and Biology, 16 study Chemistry and 2 study none of the three subjects. How many study Biology only?

Putting in as much information as possible and introducing letters where necessary we have the Venn diagram shown in Fig. 10.6.

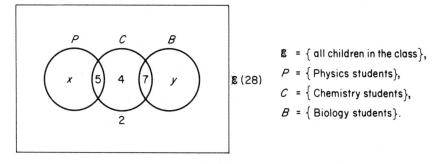

$\mathscr{E}$ = { all children in the class },
P = { Physics students },
C = { Chemistry students },
B = { Biology students }.

Fig. 10.6

We can obtain two equations in x and y by using the facts (a) that the total number is 28, (b) that equal numbers study Physics and Biology:

$$x + 5 + 4 + 7 + y + 2 = 28$$
$$\therefore x + y = 10 \tag{1}$$
$$x + 5 = y + 7$$
$$\therefore x - y = 2 \tag{2}$$

Solving the simultaneous equations (1) and (2) gives $x = 6$, $y = 4$; hence the number of children who study Biology only is 4. ◁

EXERCISE 10

1 $n(A) = 20, n(B) = 15$ and $n(A \cap B) = 7$. Find $n(A \cup B)$.

2 $n(A) = 12, n(B) = 14$ and $n(A \cup B) = 18$. Find $n(A \cap B)$.

3 $n(A) = 40, n(A \cup B) = 60$ and $n(A \cap B) = 10$. Find $n(B)$.

4 $n(A \cup B) = 10$ and $n(A) = 4$. Find the possible values of $n(B)$.

5 $n(\mathscr{E}) = 18, n(A \cap B) = 2$ and $n(B) = 10$. Find the maximum and minimum possible values of $n(A)$.

6 $A \subset B$ and $B \cap C = \varnothing$. If $n(\mathscr{E}) = 12, n(A) = 5$ and $n(C) = 3$, what are the possible values of $n(B)$?

7 $n(\mathscr{E}) = 20, n(A \cap B) = 3$ and $n(A' \cap B') = 15$. Find the possible values of $n(A)$.

8 In a group of 26 children, 14 like apples, 16 like oranges and 10 like both. How many like neither?

9 10 of a group of 15 men drink beer, 7 smoke and 5 do both. How many do neither?

10 All of a group of 20 people play bridge or chess or both. 12 play chess only and 3 play both. How many play bridge?

11 All of a group of 30 people own a car or a motorcycle or both. 20 of them are car owners and 5 of these have a motorcycle also. How many have motorcycles only?

12 25 out of a class of 33 children study French or German or both. 16 study French but not German and 4 study German but not French. How many (a) study both, (b) do not study French?

13 In a class of 30 children equal numbers study Geography and History. If 3 study both and 25 study at least one of the two subjects, how many do not study Geography?

14 14 of a group of 20 children have blond hair, 8 have brown eyes and 3 have neither. How many have both?

15 70% of families have televisions, 50% have record players and 15% have neither. What percentage have both?

16 In a group of 26 children, twice as many like sweets as like apples, 2 like neither and 3 like both. How many like apples?

17 In a group of 50 people, 2 have neither televisions nor cars, 12 have cars but not televisions, and the number who have either or both is 3 times the number who have both. How many have televisions only?

18 All of a class of 30 girls like at least one of the activities swimming, athletics and hockey. Four girls like all three activities, 7 like both swimming and hockey, 9 like athletics and hockey, 6 like swimming and athletics but not hockey, 5 like only swimming and 3 like only athletics. How many like (a) hockey, (b) exactly one of the activities?

19 In a class of 32 children, 18 study Geography, 3 study Geography and History but not French, 7 study Geography and French, 6 study History and French, 3 study French only and 2 study all three subjects. If all study at least one of the three, how many (a) study exactly one subject, (b) do not study History?

20 In a sixth-form class of 16 students, 7 study Physics, 12 study Chemistry, 5 study Biology and Chemistry and 2 study all three subjects. If all study at least one of the three subjects, and all the Physics students study Chemistry, how many study (a) Chemistry only, (b) Biology only?

21 There are 32 boys in a certain class, 2 of whom like neither cricket, football nor tennis. 20 like cricket, 12 like cricket and tennis, 4 like cricket and football but not tennis, 3 like tennis only, 5 like football only and 7 like all three sports. How many like exactly two of the three?

22 The number of elements belonging to at least one of the sets A, B and C is 70. Given that $n(A) = 47, n(B) = 46, n(A \cap B) = 27, n(B \cap C) = 18,$

$n(A \cap B \cap C) = 12$ and n$(A \cap B' \cap C') = 0$, find $n(C)$ and $n(A' \cap B \cap C')$.

23 18 children are asked whether they like apples, pears and oranges. Eight children like apples, 4 like only apples, 6 like oranges, 2 like only apples and pears, 2 like only apples and oranges, 3 like only pears and 3 like oranges and pears. How many like (a) all of the fruits, (b) none of them?

24 The sets P, Q and R are such that $Q \subset P$ and $R \subset P$. Given that $n(P) = 65$, $n(Q) = 42, n(R) = 40$ and $n(P \cap Q' \cap R') = 8$, find $n(Q \cap R)$.

25 Forty people are asked which newspapers they read. Eight read the Times only, 6 the Mail only, 5 the Guardian only, 7 the Times and the Mail, 5 the Times and the Guardian, 7 the Mail and the Guardian, and 12 read none of the three papers. Let x be the number who read all three papers, obtain an equation in x and solve it, and hence find the number of people who (a) read exactly two of the papers, (b) do not read the Times.

26 A survey shows that 19% of the people questioned like neither driving, cycling nor walking, 6% like all three, 8% like driving and cycling only, 16% like both driving and walking, 40% like walking, 44% like driving and 35% like cycling. Let x be the percentage who like walking and cycling only, obtain an equation in x and solve it. Hence find the percentage who like walking only.

27 A survey of 60 men shows that all have tried either cigarettes, cigars or a pipe. 11 have tried cigarettes only, 12 cigars only and 9 a pipe only; 10 have tried both cigarettes and cigars, 14 both cigars and a pipe, and 12 both cigarettes and a pipe. How many have tried all three?

28 A, B and C are three sets, and $B \subset A$. Given that $n(A) = 30, n(B) = 20$, $n(C) = 22, n(A \cup B \cup C) = 40$ and $n(A \cap B' \cap C') = 6$, find $n(B \cap C)$.

29 A bookshelf contains 20 books, all of which are textbooks, paperbacks or both. There are 4 books with over 300 pages, all of which are textbooks. No paperbacks have over 300 pages. There are 8 textbooks in paperback, and the total number of textbooks is equal to the total number of paperbacks. Find (a) the number of textbooks with 300 pages or fewer, (b) the number of paperbacks.

30 A survey of men shows that 35% like whisky, 50% like beer, 15% like gin but not beer, and 5% like none of the three drinks. If gin and whisky are equally popular, but no men like both, what percentage of men like beer only?

31 Of 70 people questioned, 6 like neither fishing nor bird-watching nor sailing, 34 like sailing, 12 like fishing and bird-watching, 12 like fishing and sailing, 10 like bird-watching and sailing, 14 like only fishing and 10 like only bird-watching. How many like only sailing?

32 A survey is made of people, all of whom enjoy at least one of the activities music, painting and sculpture. 34% enjoy painting only, 9% sculpture only, 18% both sculpture and painting, 24% both painting and music, and 16% both sculpture and music. If twice as many enjoy painting as enjoy sculpture, what percentage enjoy (a) all three, (b) just one of the three?

33 A survey of people shows that 37% like opera, 40% like jazz, 42% like orchestral music and 25% like none of the three types of music. 18% like opera and jazz, 19% like orchestral music and jazz, and 17% like opera and orchestral music. What percentage like more than one of the three types of music in the survey?

34 A, B and C are sets which together form a universal set, and $A \cap C = \emptyset$. Given that $n(A) = 8, n(B \cap C) = 6, n(B \cap C') = 7, n(B \cup C) = 15$ and $n(A \cup B \cup C) = 20$, find $n(A \cap B)$ and $n(B')$.

35 In the fifth year at a certain school all the pupils study at least one of the subjects French, German and Latin. 100 study French, 40 both French and German, 36 both French and Latin, 10 Latin and German only, and 20 Latin only. If the number studying French only is twice the number studying all three subjects, and there are 6 more studying Latin than German, find (a) the number studying all three subjects, (b) the number in the whole year.

36 A medical survey is made of 100 people, 44 of whom smoke. There are 12 unhealthy non-smokers and 40 people who exercise regularly, all of whom are healthy. Of the healthy smokers, twice as many exercise regularly as do not, and the number of healthy non-exercisers exceeds the number of unhealthy smokers by 8. Find the number who (a) both smoke and exercise regularly, (b) both smoke and are unhealthy.

11 Some Elementary Algebra

Substitution of values into algebraic expressions

Practice in applying the elementary rules of algebra can be obtained by substituting numbers into algebraic expressions and calculating the values of the expressions. The following example illustrates the procedure.

▷ **Example 1**

Given that $x = -2$, $y = 3$ *and* $w = -1$, *find the values of (a)* wxy^2,
(b) $-(w - x + y)$, *(c)* $-\dfrac{y - w}{x}$, *(d)* $x(w + y)^3$, *(e)* $\dfrac{x}{x + y + w}$.

(a) Only y is raised to the power 2, and we have

$$wxy^2 = (-1)(-2)(3^2) = 18.$$

(b) Here we can either calculate the value of the expression inside the brackets and then change its sign, or begin by changing the sign of each term inside the brackets. Adopting the latter procedure we have

$$-(w - x + y) = -w + x - y = 1 - 2 - 3 = -4.$$

(c) Fraction lines work in a similar way to brackets, and the minus outside the fraction can thus be used to change the signs of *both* terms on the top line. We have

$$-\frac{y - w}{x} = \frac{w - y}{x} = \frac{-1 - 3}{-2} = \frac{-4}{-2} = 2.$$

(d) Only the bracketed expression is raised to the power 3, and we have

$$x(w + y)^3 = -2(-1 + 3)^3 = (-2)(2^3) = -16.$$

(e) In this case we obtain a fraction in which the denominator is zero:

$$\frac{x}{x + y + w} = \frac{-2}{-2 + 3 - 1} = \frac{-2}{0}.$$

Now division by zero is impossible, so this expression is meaningless or *indeterminate*. (Note that division *into* zero is perfectly legitimate; the fraction $\frac{0}{3}$, for example, simply has the value zero.) ◁

EXERCISE 11a

(In the case of a fraction whose denominator is zero, write 'indeterminate'.)

Given that $a = 2, b = 3$ and $c = 1$, evaluate the following expressions.

1 abc　**2** $ab - c$　**3** $2a^2 b$　**4** $2ab^2$　**5** $(3ac)^2$　**6** $a(b - c)^2$　**7** $a^2 - c^2$

8 $(c - a)^3$　**9** $-\dfrac{c - b}{a}$　**10** $\dfrac{a}{a - b + c}$.

Given that $x = -1, y = -2, w = 3$, evaluate the following expressions.

11 $y - 2x$　**12** $-(2x + y)$　**13** $\frac{1}{2}(x^2 + y)$　**14** $\dfrac{w}{x + y}$　**15** $-\dfrac{y - w}{w}$　**16** $\dfrac{x}{1 + x}$

17 $-\dfrac{w + x - y}{y}$　**18** $\dfrac{x + y + w}{y}$.

Given that $r = 4, s = -2, t = 0$, evaluate the following expressions.

19 $rs - st$　**20** $-r(s - t)^3$　**21** $\dfrac{t + s}{t}$　**22** $\dfrac{r - s}{r + s}$　**23** $rs^2 - r^2 s$

24 $-\dfrac{t - s}{s - r}$　**25** $2rst - s^3$　**26** $-\dfrac{2s}{2s - r}$　**27** $-\dfrac{t - r + s}{t + r - s}$　**28** $\dfrac{r}{r - s^2}$

29 $\dfrac{2s + r}{r + t}$　**30** $\dfrac{2st}{s + 2}$

Like and unlike terms

We have already mentioned in the Arithmetic section the principle that *only quantities of the same kind can be added and subtracted.* For example, 3 pencils + 5 pencils = 8 pencils but 3 pencils + 5 oranges is not 8 of anything (unless we allow '8 objects', in which case we are regarding the pencils and oranges as quantities of the same kind). The same principle applies in algebra. We can add $3p$ and $5p$ to obtain $8p$, but $3p + 5s$ is not 8 of any quantity. Now $3p$ and $5p$ are examples of *like terms*, and $3p$ and $5s$ are examples of *unlike terms.* We therefore have the algebraic principle that *only like terms can be added and subtracted to give single terms of the same kind.*

▷ **Example 2**

Simplify (a) $3x - 5y - 7x + 6y$, *(b)* $3 - \dfrac{x}{2} - \dfrac{3x}{4}$,

(c) $2x^2 - xy - 3x^2 y + 4xy$, *(d)* $(3p)^2 - 2p^2 - (2p^2)^2$, *(e)* $\dfrac{2}{x} + \dfrac{3}{x}$.

(a) $3x - 5y - 7x + 6y = y - 4x.$

(b) Here there are two kinds of terms: 3 is a *pure number* and the other terms are terms *in x.* We can add or subtract the latter terms but the 3 must be left as it is:

$$3 - \dfrac{x}{2} - \dfrac{3x}{4} = 3 - \dfrac{2x}{4} - \dfrac{3x}{4} = 3 - \dfrac{5x}{4} .$$

(c) Here only the terms in xy are like terms. The expressions x^2, x^2y and xy are unlike and cannot be combined.
We have

$$2x^2 - xy - 3x^2y + 4xy = 2x^2 + 3xy - 3x^2y.$$

(d) $(3p)^2 - 2p^2 - (2p^2)^2 = 9p^2 - 2p^2 - 4p^4 = 7p^2 - 4p^4.$

(e) The two terms here can both be regarded as terms in $\dfrac{1}{x}$ (or in x^{-1}).

We have

$$\frac{2}{x} + \frac{3}{x} = 2\left(\frac{1}{x}\right) + 3\left(\frac{1}{x}\right) = 5\left(\frac{1}{x}\right) = \frac{5}{x}. \qquad \triangleleft$$

Particular care must be taken with terms such as x^2 and x^3. It is a very common mistake to think that $x^2 + x^3 = x^5$ or x^6, or to think, for example, that $2x^2 + 3x^3 = 5x^5$. It must be stressed that x^2 and x^3 are *unlike terms*, and that there are therefore no simpler forms for expressions such as $x^2 + x^3$ or $2x^2 + 3x^3$.

When quantities of the same kind are added the result is *another quantity of the same kind*. Thus 3 pencils + 5 pencils = 8 *pencils* and $3x + 5x = 8x$. A mistake sometimes made is to think that $3x + 5x = 8x^2$ or, more commonly, that $2x^2 + 3x^2 = 5x^4$ (for example). The correct statement is of course $2x^2 + 3x^2 = 5x^2$.

Algebraic quantities of different kinds *can* be multiplied and divided. The kind of quantity resulting is given by the index laws which were considered in chapter 6. For example $4x^3 \times 5x^6 = 20x^9$ and $8a^5 \div 2a^3 = 4a^2$.

EXERCISE 11b

Simplify the following expressions:

1 $a - 2b - 3a + 5b$ **2** $2\frac{1}{2}x + 1\frac{1}{4}x$ **3** $5 - p - 7 + 3p$ **4** $\dfrac{3}{a} + \dfrac{4}{a}$

5 $\dfrac{a}{4} - 3b - \dfrac{3a}{4} + b$ **6** $1 - k - \dfrac{k}{6}$ **7** $\dfrac{8}{x} - \dfrac{2}{x} + \dfrac{3}{x}$ **8** $x^2 - x - 2x^2 + x^3$

9 $\dfrac{2}{x} - x - \dfrac{1}{x} + 2x$ **10** $4x^2 + 3x^2$ **11** $4x^2 \times 3x^2$ **12** $x - \dfrac{x^2}{3} - \dfrac{x}{2} + x^2$

13 $\dfrac{3}{x^2} - 1 - \dfrac{1}{x^2} + 2$ **14** $a^2 \times a \times 2a^3 \times \dfrac{a}{4}$ **15** $2xy - 3wx - 5yx - wy$

16 $3a^4b^2 \div 6ab$ **17** $2x^2 - (2x)^2$ **18** $(ab)^2 - ab^2 + a^2b^2 - b^2a$

19 $\left(\dfrac{p}{2}\right)^4 \div 2p^2$ **20** $\left(\dfrac{2p}{3}\right)^2 - \dfrac{1}{p^2} + p^2 + \left(\dfrac{1}{2p}\right)^2.$

Removal of brackets

The general rules for the removal of brackets will be familiar to most students. The simplest type of case is that in which there is a single term outside the brackets, as in the following example.

▷Example 3

(a) $2(a + b) = 2a + 2b$.

(b) $x(x + y) = x^2 + xy$.

(c) $-2x^2y(3xy^2 - 4xy - 1) = -6x^3y^3 + 8x^3y^2 + 2x^2y$.

(d) $\dfrac{2}{x}(3x - \dfrac{x^2}{4}) = 6 - \dfrac{x}{2}$.   ◁

When two expressions consisting of two or more terms are to be multiplied together, each should initially be placed in brackets. The brackets can be removed by multiplying each term in the first pair of brackets by each term in the second. After the multiplication has been performed like terms should be added or subtracted.

▷Example 4

(a) $(x + y)(p + q) = xp + xq + yp + yq$.

(b) $(2 - x)(3 - x) = 6 - 2x - 3x + x^2 = 6 - 5x + x^2$.

(c) $(3x^2 - x + 1)(2x - 3) = 6x^3 - 9x^2 - 2x^2 + 3x + 2x - 3 = 6x^3 - 11x + 5x - 3$.

Note: In an expression such as $3 - x$, it is useful to think of the two terms as $(+3)$ and $(-x)$, the minus being regarded as part of the second term. Then the rules for multiplying positive and negative numbers can be applied.   ◁

Squaring two-term expressions

Consider $(x + y)^2$. If we remove the brackets in the usual way we obtain

$$(x + y)(x + y) = x^2 + xy + yx + y^2$$
$$= x^2 + 2xy + y^2.$$

This is worth treating as a standard result and learning by heart. In words it can be expressed as follows:

To square a two-term expression, square the first term, square the second term, and add twice the product.

When one of the terms is negative the rule still works, but while the two squared terms remain positive (since a minus squared gives a plus), the product term becomes negative.

▷Example 5

(a) $(x + 3)^2 = x^2 + 6x + 9$.

(b) $(a - 5)^2 = a^2 - 10a + 25$.

(c) $(3p - 4s)^2 = 9p^2 - 24ps + 16s^2$.   ◁

EXERCISE 11c

Remove the brackets:

1 $a(a - b)$ **2** $2x(x - 3y)$ **3** $-xy(y - x)$ **4** $\dfrac{x}{2}(4 - 6x)$ **5** $-2ab(4a^2 + 2b^2)$

6 $\frac{1}{3}(12p - 9r)$ **7** $\frac{1}{x}(x - x^2)$ **8** $5pq(1 - 2p - 3q)$ **9** $\frac{2}{y}(xy - \frac{1}{4})$

10 $4x^2y^3w(3x^3yw^2 + 2y^2w^3)$ **11** $\frac{x}{2y}(\frac{4y^2}{x} - xy)$ **12** $-\frac{3}{x}(\frac{x^2}{6} - \frac{x}{3})$.

Remove the brackets and simplify if possible:
13 $(p + q)(2p + q)$ **14** $(x + 2)(x + 3)$ **15** $(x + 5)(x - 7)$
16 $(a - 6)(a - 3)$ **17** $(2 - k)(5 + k)$ **18** $(3y - 1)(4y - 3)$ **19** $(7x - 8)(x - 2)$
20 $(a + 4b)(2a - b)$ **21** $(2p - 3)(2p + 3)$ **22** $(2x^2 + x - 1)(x - 1)$
23 $(r^2s - t)(r^2s + t)$ **24** $(2 + s)(2 - s - s^2)$ **25** $(p - 1)(p^2 + p + 1)$
26 $(2x + 1)(4x^2 - 2x + 1)$ **27** $(2a + c)(3ab - bc)$ **28** $(a + b - c)(a - b + c)$.

Use the squaring rule (see above) to remove the brackets immediately:
29 $(a + 4)^2$ **30** $(p - 3)^2$ **31** $(6 + y)^2$ **32** $(3 - w)^2$ **33** $(2x - 1)^2$
34 $(3a + 2b)^2$ **35** $(5x + 4y)^2$ **36** $(7p - 4s)^2$ **37** $(1 - 3xy)^2$
38 $(2ab - bc)^2$ **39** $(y - \frac{1}{y})^2$ **40** $(\frac{2}{x} + \frac{x}{2})^2$ **41** $(\frac{3}{a} - \frac{a}{6})^2$.

Simplify:
42 $(x - 2)^2 - (x + 2)^2$ **43** $4x^2 - (1 + 2x)(1 - 2x)$ **44** $3x(2 + 3x) - (1 + 3x)^2$
45 $(a^2 + b^2)^2 - (a^2 - b^2)^2$.

12 Simple Equations and Inequalities

It is convenient to consider an equation to consist of a 'left-hand side' (LHS) and a 'right-hand side' (RHS) which are separated by the 'equals' sign. The general principle governing the manipulation of all equations is that *we can do whatever we like to one side, provided that we do the same to the other.* The justification for this is obvious: if the two sides are initially equal, and we do the same to both, they will remain equal.

The values which make an equation true are said to *satisfy* the equation and they are called its *solutions* or *roots.*

Linear equations

The simplest equations to solve are *linear* equations or *equations of degree 1.* These are defined to be equations which contain no terms other than pure numbers (terms of degree zero) and terms of degree 1; for example $4 - 7x = 3 + x$.

▷ **Example 1**

Solve the equation $2 - 8x = 7 - 4x$
It is generally best to place the terms in x on the side which initially contains the larger coefficient of x, so that the resulting term in x is positive. Here since -4 is greater than -8 we move the terms in x to the right. Adding $8x$ to both sides and subtracting 7 from both sides, we have

$$2 - 7 = 8x - 4x$$
$$\therefore \quad -5 = 4x.$$

Now we divide both sides by 4:

$$x = -\frac{5}{4} = -1\frac{1}{4}.$$

◁

▷ **Example 2**

Solve the equation $\dfrac{2x + 1}{3} - \dfrac{1 - x}{6} = \dfrac{1}{2}.$

73

We can remove all the fractions by multiplying throughout (that is, each term) by the lowest common multiple of all the denominators, namely 6:

$$2(2x + 1) - (1 - x) = 3$$
$$\therefore\ 4x + 2 - 1 + x = 3$$
$$\therefore\ 5x = 2$$
$$\therefore\ x = \frac{2}{5}.$$

Note: When the second fraction line is removed it is replaced by a pair of brackets. The brackets are needed because there is a minus preceding the fraction, and this affects *each term* of the numerator of the fraction. The brackets would not be needed if the fraction were preceded by a plus.   ◀

▷ **Example 3**

Solve the equation $2(\frac{x}{4} + 1) - 3(2 - \frac{x}{2}) = 1 + \frac{3x}{4}$.

Here it is best to remove the fractions and brackets in separate steps, and not to try to remove both in one step. Removing the brackets we have

$$\frac{x}{2} + 2 - 6 + \frac{3x}{2} = 1 + \frac{3x}{4}.$$

Now we remove the fractions by multiplying throughout by 4:

$$2x + 8 - 24 + 6x = 4 + 3x$$
$$\therefore\ 5x = 20$$
$$\therefore\ \ x = 4.$$

Note: Suppose we had decided to remove the fractions first and wanted to multiply $2(\frac{x}{4} + 1)$ by 4. It is important to realise that we do *not* multiply *both* the 2 and the expression in brackets by 4. This would have the effect of multiplying the whole expression by 16.   ◀

EXERCISE 12a

Solve the following equations:

1 $5x - 3 = 17$ **2** $2 - 4x = -6$ **3** $7 = -x + 3$ **4** $-3 + 6x = -5$
5 $8x + 1 = 3x + 11$ **6** $7x - 2 = x + 8$ **7** $2x + 5 = 5x + 3$
8 $x - 2 = 9x + 4$ **9** $2 - 3x = x - 9$ **10** $7 - x - 3 = 4 + 2x$

11 $3(x - 1) - 5(2 - x) = 0$ **12** $\frac{x - 2}{2} - 1\frac{1}{2} = \frac{x - 3}{4}$

13 $\frac{1}{3}(x + 1) - \frac{5}{6}(x - 1) = 1\frac{2}{3}$ **14** $\frac{5 - x}{5} - \frac{2 - x}{10} = \frac{7}{10}$

15 $1\frac{1}{4}(3x - 4) - 2\frac{1}{2}(x + 1) = 1\frac{3}{4}$ **16** $3(\frac{x}{2} - 1) - 2(\frac{x}{3} - 2) = \frac{1}{3} - x$

17 $2 - 1\frac{1}{2}x = \frac{2}{3}(3x - 6)$ **18** $2(1 - \frac{x}{4}) - 5(1 - \frac{x}{2}) = 2\frac{1}{4}$

19 $\frac{2(1 - x)}{3} - \frac{3(2 - x)}{4} = \frac{5(x - 1)}{12}$ **20** $\frac{1\frac{1}{2}(2 - x)}{6} = \frac{2\frac{1}{2}(3 - x)}{5}$.

Other types of simple equation

▷ Example 4

Solve the equation $\dfrac{4x-1}{1-3x} = -\dfrac{2}{3}$.

This equation reduces to a linear equation when we remove the fractions.
Multiply both sides by $1 - 3x$ and by 3 [or by $3(1 - 3x)$]:

$$3(4x - 1) = -2(1 - 3x).$$

(Note that we are regarding $-\dfrac{2}{3}$ as $\dfrac{-2}{3}$.)

$$\therefore\ 12x - 3 = -2 + 6x$$
$$\therefore\ 6x = 1$$
$$\therefore\ x = \frac{1}{6}.$$

◁

▷ Example 5

Solve the equation $5x^2 - 3 = 2x^2 + 5$.
This equation can be regarded as a *linear equation in* x^2. We treat it just like
an ordinary linear equation until x^2 has been found; then take the square root
of both sides:

$$3x^2 = 8$$
$$\therefore x^2 = \frac{8}{3}.$$

It follows that $x = \pm\sqrt{\tfrac{8}{3}}$ or ± 1.63 to 3 s.f.

◁

EXERCISE 12b

Solve the following equations:

1 $\dfrac{2}{x} = \dfrac{3}{4}$ **2** $\dfrac{1}{1-x} = \dfrac{1}{2}$ **3** $2x^2 - 1 = 7$ **4** $\dfrac{3-x}{x} = \dfrac{2}{3}$ **5** $3 - x^2 = 4 - 2x^2$

6 $\dfrac{2x-1}{2x+1} = -\dfrac{1}{2}$ **7** $5x^2 - 7 = 9 + 3x^2$ **8** $-\dfrac{3}{4} = \dfrac{1-2x}{2x}$ **9** $2\dfrac{2}{3} = -\dfrac{3x}{1-x}$

10 $x^2 - 4 = 5 - 3x^2$ **11** $\dfrac{1}{2x} = \dfrac{x}{8}$ **12** $\dfrac{3}{5x-2} = -\dfrac{2}{2x-1}$

13 $\dfrac{1}{x^2+1} = \dfrac{2}{3x^2}$ **14** $\dfrac{1-2x^2}{1+2x^2} = -\dfrac{3}{4}$ **15** $\dfrac{2x}{27} = \dfrac{3}{8x}$.

Linear inequalities (or 'inequations')

A simple example of a linear inequality is $x + 3 > 5$, which states that the
value of $x + 3$ is greater than 5. The solution of this inequality is $x > 2$, and
it will be noticed that this is a different kind of solution to that of a typical
equation. In general, the solution of an inequality consists of a *range* of
values, while that of an equation consists of a finite number of definite
values.

In order to find general methods of solving inequalities the first task is to decide what we can and cannot do to both sides. Here again inequalities differ in a significant way from equations, since it is certainly not the case that we can do whatever we like to both sides. To find out what we can and cannot do, we shall look at some examples.

Consider the inequality $7 > 3$, which states, correctly, that 7 is greater than 3. If we add or subtract the same number to both sides it is clear that the left-hand side will remain greater than the right-hand side. For example, if we add 2 to both sides we get $9 > 5$, and if we subtract 4 we get $3 > -1$.

Now consider multiplication and division. If we multiply both sides by a *positive* number, say 5, the inequality does remain true: we get $35 > 15$. But if we multiply by a *negative* number the inequality becomes false. For example, multiplying both sides by -2 gives $-14 > -6$. It is easy to verify by other examples that this always happens. E.g. $2 > -5$ is true, but if we multiply both sides by -10 we get $-20 > 50$, which is false.

The examples given illustrate the following rules for inequalities, which should be learned by heart:

(1) **Any number can be added to both sides of an inequality, or subtracted from both sides.**

(2) **Both sides of an inequality can be multiplied (or divided) by any positive number.**

(3) **If both sides of an inequality are multiplied (or divided) by a negative number, the inequality sign must be reversed.**

Other operations, such as raising to a power, taking the reciprocal, etc., should be treated with caution; in general it is best to assume that they are not allowed unless we can prove otherwise.

It is worth noting that the more complicated rule for multiplication and division makes many inequalities considerably more difficult to solve than the corresponding equations. For example, to solve the equation $\dfrac{1}{1-x}$ $= 2$ we would simply multiply both sides by $1 - x$ and then solve the resulting linear equation. But the inequality $\dfrac{1}{1-x} < 2$ cannot be solved in this way because we do not know until we have the solution whether $1 - x$ is positive, negative, or sometimes positive and sometimes negative.

We shall now apply the above rules to the solution of linear inequalities. The method is very similar to that used for linear equations, and will be illustrated by an example.

▷ Example 6

Solve the inequality 5x − 1 < 2x − 7.
As with equations, it is best to start by putting the x terms on the side which initially contains the larger number of x's; here the left. However, to demonstrate how the procedure differs when we put the x terms on the other side, we shall give both methods.

Method (a) Subtract $2x$ from both sides and add 1 to both sides:

$$3x < -6.$$

Now divide both sides by 3, which is positive:

$$x < -2.$$

Method (b) Subtract $5x$ from both sides and add 7 to both sides:

$$6 < -3x.$$

Now divide both sides by -3. This is negative, so we reverse the inequality sign:

$$-2 > x, \text{ or } x < -2, \text{ as before.} \qquad \triangleleft$$

Representation of a range of values on a number-line

The range of values satisfying the inequality $x > 2$ can be represented on a number-line as follows:

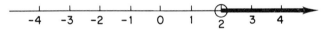

The arrow indicates that the range extends to infinity, and the *open* circle indicates that the value at the end of the line, namely 2, is *not* included in the range.

When we do want the end-value to be included, as for example in the case of $x \leq 1$ (x is less than or equal to 1), a filled-in circle is used:

When quadratic inequalities come to be considered we shall meet solutions such as 'x is between -2 and 3'. This is written $-2 < x < 3$ and represented on a number-line as follows:

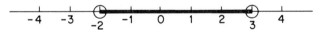

This kind of solution can also arise from *simultaneous linear inequalities*. Suppose that the inequalities $2x < 5$ and $x + 3 > 4$ are both true at the same time (*simultaneously* true). The two individual solution ranges are $x < 2\frac{1}{2}$ and $x > 1$, and the inequalities are therefore both true together for the range $1 < x < 2\frac{1}{2}$.

EXERCISE 12c

Represent the following statements (a) in symbols, (b) on a number-line.
1 x is greater than -3. 2 x is less than or equal to 4.
3 x is between -1 and 2. 4 x is either equal to 4 or between 1 and 4.

Solve the following inequalities.
5 $2x - 1 < 5$ 6 $2 - x > 4 + 3x$ 7 $5x - 2 < 3 - 2x$ 8 $\frac{x}{2} + 3 > 1$

9 $3(2x - 1) > 2(1 + x)$ **10** $4 - \frac{2x}{3} > 1 - \frac{x}{6}$ **11** $\frac{1 - 3x}{4} < \frac{2x - 1}{2}$

12 $\frac{1}{3}(6x - 2) > \frac{1}{2}(x - 4)$.

Find the ranges for which the following pairs of inequalities are simultaneously true.

13 $2x > -4$, $4x < 12$ **14** $x + 1 < 5$, $x - 1 > -4$

15 $x > 5$, $x > 3$ **16** $x > 0$, $2x - 1 < x + 2$

17 $2x < 4$, $3x < -6$ **18** $\frac{x}{2} - 3 < -4$, $2x - 1 < 2 + 3x$.

Solution sets, universal sets other than $\mathbf{R}$

The solutions of any equation or inequality can be considered to constitute a set of values called a *solution set*. For example the solution set of the equation $x^2 = 4$ is $\{-2, 2\}$, and that of the inequality $x + 3 < 5$ is $\{x : x < 2\}$. Now in the section dealing with set theory we explained that problems concerning sets usually involve a background set, or universal set, within which all elements and sets under discussion must lie. Does such a background set exist when we are seeking solutions to an equation or inequality?

In all the examples considered so far it has been assumed without being stated that x (or the unknown quantity) can take any real value. The technical way of expressing this is 'x is a variable *on* $\mathbf{R}$', and it amounts to the same thing as saying that $\mathbf{R}$ (the set of all real numbers) is the universal set for our problem. All acceptable solutions must be elements of $\mathbf{R}$ and all solution sets must be subsets of $\mathbf{R}$. This is the usual assumption when equations and inequalities are being solved as exercises.

In real problems, however, the background set is often quite different. Sometimes, for example, x represents a number of physical objects which cannot be fractional or negative, and then any acceptable solutions must be elements of $\mathbf{N}$, the set of natural numbers. Again if x represents a length, area or volume, negative solutions will be unacceptable and the universal set will be the set of positive real numbers. It is important to get used to the idea that unknown quantities cannot always take all real values, and we shall therefore consider some examples of inequalities with universal sets other than $\mathbf{R}$.

▷ Example 7

Find the solution set of the inequality $3x - 1 \leqslant 11$, given that x is a variable on (a) $\mathbf{N}$ (b) $\mathbf{Z}$.

Solving the inequality in the usual way without setting any limits on x, we have

$$3x \leqslant 12 \text{ and hence } x \leqslant 4.$$

(a) If $x \in \mathbf{N}$ the only allowed values are positive integers; hence the solution set is $\{1, 2, 3, 4\}$.

(b) if $x \in \mathbf{Z}$ all integers are allowed, so the solution set is $\{4, 3, 2, 1, 0, -1 \ldots\}$.

(A series of dots at the end of a sequence of numbers means 'and so on'.)   ◁

▷ Example 8

Find the solution set of the inequality $8 - x > x - 12$, given that x is a variable on the set of (a) positive multiples of 3, (b) square numbers, (c) primes.

Solving in the usual way we have $20 > 2x$ and hence $x < 10$. The solution sets in cases *(a)*, *(b)* and *(c)* are therefore $\{3, 6, 9\}$, $\{1, 4, 9\}$ and $\{2, 3, 5, 7\}$, respectively.   ◁

EXERCISE 12d

Find the solution sets of the following inequalities within the universal sets stated:

1 $4x - 1 < 11$, where x is a variable on the set (a) $\{1, 2, 3, 4, 5\}$,
(b) $\{-6, -3, 0, 3, 6\}$.
2 $3x - 2 > 7$, where x is a variable on the set of (a) positive multiples of 2,
(b) primes between 0 and 10.

3 $\frac{x}{3} - 2 < 7$, where x is a variable on the set of (a) odd square numbers,

(b) positive multiples of 7.

4 $\frac{x}{4} < 50$, where x is a variable on the set of square numbers over 100.

5 $5x - 9 < -3 + 8x$, where x is a variable on **Z**.
6 $2 - x \leqslant 10 - 2x$, where x is a variable on the set of (a) positive even numbers,
(b) non-prime natural numbers.
7 $\frac{2}{3}x - 5 < 15$, where (a) x is a multiple of both 3 and 4, (b) x is a variable on the set of primes over 20.

8 $\frac{x}{5} < 20$, where x is a variable on the set of primes over 85.

9 $2x < 12$, where x is a variable on the set $\{x : x \geqslant 4\}$.
10 $3x - 6 > 2 - x$, where x is a variable on the set $\{x : x \leqslant 10\}$.
11 $3x > 6$, where x is a variable on the set $\{x : x \in \mathbf{N} \text{ and } x^2 < 30\}$.
12 $\frac{1}{2}(3x - 5) \leqslant \frac{1}{3}(2x + 10)$, where x is a variable on the set $\{x : x^2 < 100\}$.

Find the solution sets of the following pairs of simultaneous inequalities within the universal sets stated:

13 $x < 7$, $2x > 6$, where x is a variable on **N**.
14 $2x < 5$, $3x + 2 > -3$, where x is a variable on **Z**.
15 $3x > 7$, $x - 1 < 1$, where x is a variable on **R**.
16 $5x < 100$, $x + 9 < 3x - 5$, where x is a variable on the set of primes.
17 $2x - 1 < 7$, $3x + 1 < 14$, where x is a variable on **N**.

13 Factorisation and Some Applications

Definitions

To factorise a number or an algebraic expression is to *express it as a product*. For example, 10 when factorised is 5×2 and 12 is $2 \times 2 \times 3$ or $2^2 \times 3$. In the latter case the 2 is called a *repeated* factor.

Similarly, abc and x^2y^3 are examples of algebraic factorised expressions. A somewhat more complicated example is $2x(x + y)(x + y + z)$. This expression, complicated though it looks, is in fact not essentially different from $2abc$; the factors $(x + y)$ and $(x + y + z)$ simply stand for unknown numbers and they could just as easily be denoted by single letters. It is important to see that $(x + y)$ and $(x + y + z)$ are not related in any interesting way; $(x + y)$ is not for example a factor of $(x + y + z)$ and therefore $2x(x + y)(x + y + z)$ does not contain any repeated factors. The expression $2x(x + y)^2$, on the other hand, has $(x + y)$ as a repeated factor.

Some examples of unfactorised expressions are $abc - d$ and $x(x + y) + z$. Both of these are *two-term* expressions, the factorised parts, namely abc and $x(x + y)$, each counting as single terms.

Methods of factorising

Common factor

An expression such as $ab + bc$ is said to have a *common factor* of b; the b is a factor of both terms and thus is *common* to the two terms. ('Common' means belonging to two or more things at the same time.) When we factorise the expression it becomes $b(a + c)$, and this procedure is called *taking out the common factor*. Similarly, the expression $2x^2y^2 - 4x^3y$ has a common factor of $2x^2y$. This *whole* common factor, and not just x^2 or 2 or $2xy$, should be taken out when the expression is factorised; otherwise it will not be fully factorised. The expression when fully factorised is $2x^2y(y - 2x)$.

▷ **Example 1**

(a) $3x - 6xy - 9x^2y = 3x(1 - 2y - 3xy)$.
(b) $2a^4 + 4a^7 = 2a^4(1 + 2a^3)$.
(c) $8x^5y^3z^4 - 12x^4y^6z^3 = 4x^4y^3z^3(2xz - 3y^3)$. ◁

Sometimes the common factor is itself an expression containing more than one term. Consider for example the expression

$$a(x + y) + 2(x + y)$$

This expression really has the same form as $ab + 2b$; we can regard $(x + y)$ as a single quantity. Since $ab + 2b$ is simply equal to $b(a + 2)$, the above expression factorises to $(x + y)(a + 2)$. Here are some more examples of the same kind.

▷ **Example 2**

(a) $x(a + b) - 2y(a + b) = (a + b)(x - 2y)$.

(b) $p - 1 + p(p - 1)$.
Here we regard $p - 1$ as a single quantity and obtain $(p - 1)(1 + p)$.

(c) $(2 - x)(x + 3) + 4x(2 - x)$.
In this case like terms occur after the common factor $2 - x$ has been taken out:

$$(2 - x)(x + 3 + 4x) = (2 - x)(5x + 3).$$

(d) (*slightly harder*)
$$\begin{aligned}
(3x - 1)^2 - (3x - 1)(x - 1) \\
= (3x - 1)[3x - 1 - (x - 1)] \\
= (3x - 1)(3x - 1 - x + 1) \\
= 2x(3x - 1).
\end{aligned}$$
◁

It should be noted that *the expressions $a - b$ and $b - a$ are negatives of each other*. This can be illustrated with a numerical example: $6 - 4 = 2$ and $4 - 6 = -2$. The statement can be proved in a more general way as follows:

$$\begin{aligned}
-(a - b) &= -a + b \\
&= b - a.
\end{aligned}$$

On the other hand, $a + b$ and $a - b$ are unrelated expressions; like x and y they simply stand for two unknown and in general unrelated quantities.

When two of the terms in an expression to be factorised contain $a - b$ and $b - a$ (or other expressions of this form), either $a - b$ or $b - a$ can be treated as a common factor. The following example illustrates the procedure.

▷ **Example 3**

(a) $2(a - b) + x(b - a) = 2(a - b) - x(a - b)$
$$= (a - b)(2 - x).$$

(b) $2x(1 - x) - (1 + x)(x - 1) = 2x(1 - x) + (1 + x)(1 - x)$
$$\begin{aligned}
&= (1 - x)(2x + 1 + x) \\
&= (1 - x)(3x + 1).
\end{aligned}$$
◁

EXERCISE 13a

Factorise the following expressions:
1 $2x - 4y$ **2** $xy + x^2$ **3** $2 - 4x + 6y$ **4** $x^2 - x$ **5** $2p + 4p^3$
6 $5a - 10ab + 15a^3$ **7** $pqr - qrs$ **8** $ab - bc - abc$ **9** $a^7 - a^6$
10 $3x^3y^4 - 6x^2y^5$ **11** $4p^5r^2 - 2p^4r$ **12** $4a^2bc^3 - 6ab^2c + 8a^3b^3c^2$.

Factorise the following expressions and collect like terms where appropriate:
13 $2(x - y) + x(x - y)$ **14** $a(b - c) - b(b - c)$
15 $2x(2x + 1) - 3(2x + 1)$ **16** $a(b - 2c) + b - 2c$
17 $x + 2y + x(x + 2y)$ **18** $x(1 - x) + (y + 2)(1 - x)$
19 $p(q + r) + 2p(q + r)$ **20** $x(w - y) + (2x - w)(w - y)$
21 $(x + 2)^2 + 2x(x + 2)$ **22** $(2 - x)^2 + 2 - x$ **23** $(k + 3)^2 + (k - 2)(k + 3)$
24 $(2p + 3)(r + 2) - (r + 2)(p - 1)$ **25** $(3a + 2)(a - 1) - (a - 1)^2$.

Factorise the following expressions using the fact that $a - b = -(b - a)$:
26 $2(x - 1) - x(1 - x)$ **27** $4p(r - s) + p(s - r)$
28 $(k - 1)(k + 2) + (1 - k)(2k - 1)$ **29** $1 - 2ab - b(2ab - 1)$
30 $(2x - 5)^2 - (x - 1)(5 - 2x)$.

Difference of two squares

Consider the expression $(x + y)(x - y)$. If we remove the brackets we obtain

$$(x + y)(x - y) = x^2 - xy + xy - y^2$$
$$= x^2 - y^2.$$

Now any expression of the form $x^2 - y^2$ is called a *difference of two squares*, and the result just obtained shows that it can be factorised by using the rule

$$x^2 - y^2 = (x + y)(x - y).$$

Note: A *sum* of two squares, that is an expression of the form $x^2 + y^2$, cannot be factorised. $x^2 + y^2$ is *not* equal to $(x + y)^2$.

▷ **Example 4**

(a) $p^2 - 4q^2 = (p + 2q)(p - 2q)$.

(b) $25 - 16a^4b^2 = (5 + 4a^2b)(5 - 4a^2b)$.

(c) $y^{12} - 1 = (y^6 + 1)(y^6 - 1) = (y^6 + 1)(y^3 + 1)(y^3 - 1)$.

(d) $1 - (x - 3)^2 = [1 + (x - 3)][1 - (x - 3)]$
$\qquad\qquad\quad = (x - 2)(4 - x)$. ◁

The first step in the factorisation of any expression is to take out any common factors that are present, and sometimes a common factor has to be taken out before a difference of squares is obtained. The next example deals with expressions of this kind.

▷ **Example 5**

(a) $8 - 2a^2 = 2(4 - a^2)$
$\quad\quad\quad = 2(2 + a)(2 - a).$
(b) $x^3 - x = x(x^2 - 1)$
$\quad\quad\quad = x(x + 1)(x - 1).$ ◁

EXERCISE 13b

Factorise the following expressions:
1 $x^2 - 9$ **2** $16 - a^2$ **3** $4y^2 - 49$ **4** $p^2 - 100q^2$ **5** $1 - 9x^2y^2$
6 $a^{10} - 81$ **7** $25r^6s^4 - 1$ **8** $(x + 5)^2 - 4$ **9** $(y - 7)^2 - 9$
10 $16 - (3 - k)^2$ **11** $4x^2 - (x + 1)^2$ **12** $(p - 3)^2 - 25p^2.$

Factorise the following expressions, starting by taking out common factors:
13 $3 - 3x^2$ **14** $2k^2 - 32$ **15** $y^3 - 9y$ **16** $2a^3 - 50a$ **17** $p^3q - 36pq$
18 $y^5 - y$ **19** $8a^3b^2 - 18ab^2$ **20** $(x - 3)^3 - 4(x - 3)$
21 $9(y + 1) - (y + 1)^3$ **22** $(a - b)^5 - a^2(a - b)^3.$

Expression requiring grouping of terms

Consider the expression

$$2x - 4 + xy - 2y.$$

There is no common factor of all four terms, but if we split the expression into two groups of two terms we can factorise each group:

$$2(x - 2) + y(x - 2).$$

Now this expression has only two terms, and since these terms contain a common factor of $(x - 2)$ we can complete the factorisation:

$$(x - 2)(2 + y).$$

Here are some similar examples.

▷ **Example 6**

(a) $x^2 - 5x + xy - 5y = x(x - 5) + y(x - 5)$
$\quad\quad\quad\quad\quad\quad\quad\quad = (x - 5)(x + y).$
(b) $2 - y + 4x - 2xy = (2 - y) + 2x(2 - y)$
$\quad\quad\quad\quad\quad\quad\quad\quad = (2 - y)(1 + 2x)$ ◁

Sometimes an expression can only be factorised if its terms are re-grouped. Consider the expression

$$x^2 + xy - 3y - 9.$$

Trying the obvious grouping we get

$$x(x + y) - 3(y + 3).$$

There is no common factor here so we must go back and try re-grouping. (Note that it is a complete mistake to proceed to $(x + y)(y + 3)(x - 3)$!) Since there is a difference of two squares in the original expression we try a grouping which enables this to be used:

$$x^2 - 9 + xy - 3y.$$

Now factorising the two groups leads to a two-term expression with a common factor of $(x - 3)$:

$$(x + 3)(x - 3) + y(x - 3)$$
$$= (x - 3)(x + 3 + y).$$

EXERCISE 13c

Factorise the following expressions:

1 $3x - 6y + ax - 2ay$ **2** $p^2 + 2p + ps + 2s$ **3** $2a - 8b + a^2 - 4ab$
4 $x^2 + xy - 2x - 2y$ **5** $2rs + s - 2r^2 - r$ **6** $a + 1 + ab + b$
7 $p - pr + 1 - r$ **8** $x^2 - 2x + y(2 - x)$ [Remember that $2 - x = -(x - 2)$]
9 $6w - 4y + w(2y - 3w)$ **10** $4a - 2b + b^2 - 2ab$ **11** $p - r + r^2 - rp$
12 $x^2 - y^2 + 2x - 2y$ **13** $k^2 - 1 + kt - t$ **14** $a^2 - 4b^2 + 2bx - ax$
15 $y - x + y^2 - x^2$ **16** $a^2 + 2b - 2a - b^2$ **17** $y^2 + 3y - w^2 + 3w$
18 $4x^2 + 2xy - 1 + y$ **19** $x^2 - 9y^2 + xy^2 - 9x$ **20** $9a^2 - 3ab^2 + b^3 - b^2$
21 $4 - a^2x^2 + 2x - 2a^2x$ **22** $4 - 9a^2x^2 + 3ax^2 - 2x$
23 $p^3 - p^2 + pr - r$ **24** $p^3 - p + pr - r$ **25** $p^3 - p^2 - pr^2 + r^2$.

Quadratics

A quadratic *in x* is an expression of the form $ax^2 + bx + c$, where a is not zero. A quadratic *in x and y* has the general form $ax^2 + bxy + cy^2$. Another name for a quadratic is an *expression of degree 2*; that is an expression in which the term of highest degree has degree 2.

Quadratics in general factorise into products of linear expressions, and the procedure in factorising quadratics is the reverse of that of multiplying two linear expressions together. E.g.

$$(x + 3)(x + 4) = x^2 + 4x + 3x + 12$$
$$= x^2 + 7x + 12.$$

Hence $x^2 + 7x + 12$ factorises to $(x + 3)(x + 4)$.

The general method of factorising quadratics will be demonstrated by examples of gradually increasing difficulty. The easiest type is that in which the coefficient of x^2 is 1.

▷ Example 7

Factorise $x^2 + 12x + 20$.
We look for two numbers which give 20 when multiplied and 12 when added
or subtracted. These are 10 and 2. Since there are only pluses in the original
expression there can only be pluses in the answer:

$$(x + 10)(x + 2).$$ ◁

▷ Example 8

Factorise $x^2 - 3x - 10$.
We look for two numbers which give 10 when multiplied and 3 when added
or subtracted. These are 5 and 2 and we therefore have

$$(x \quad 5)(x \quad 2)$$

Now in order to insert the signs *we look at the x-term in the original
expression*. This is obtained from the following two products:

$$(x \quad 5)(x \quad 2)$$

There is only one way to get $-3x$ from $5x$ and $2x$, and that is to have $-5x$ and
$+2x$. Hence the signs must be as follows:

$$(x - 5)(x + 2)$$

Now we check to see if the sign of the constant term 10 is correct. Since
$-5 \times 2 = -10$ this is so and the above factors are therefore correct.   ◁

▷ Example 9

Factorise $x^2 - 5x - 6$.
Here there is a choice of numbers; we can try either 3 and 2 or 6 and 1. Using
3 and 2, and putting in the signs which give $-5x$, we have

$$(x - 3)(x - 2)$$

Now we look at the constant term, and find that since $-3 \times -2 = +6$, the
factors are not in fact correct. *At this point it is no use trying different signs.*
This is because there is only one combination of signs which gives $-5x$ with
the numbers 3 and 2. We must try a different pair of numbers. Using 6 and 1
we obtain the following factors which give both $-5x$ and -6 when multiplied
out:

$$(x - 6)(x + 1)$$ ◁

▷ Example 10

Factorise $4x^2 - 4x + 1$.
Here the pair of numbers must be 1 and 1 but to obtain $4x^2$ we can try $4x$ and
x or $2x$ and $2x$. The latter combination is required to give the correct x-term:

$$(2x - 1)(2x - 1).$$

Since the two factors happen to be equal the answer can be expressed as a perfect square:

$$(2x - 1)^2. \qquad \triangleleft$$

▷Example 11

Factorise $12 - x - x^2$.
When the terms of a quadratic are in reverse order (that is, in ascending rather than descending powers), it is usually best to leave the order as it is. The *first* term, whether a constant or an x^2 term, should if possible be positive. Note that it is a complete mistake to change the sign of each term! This mistake, which is very common, no doubt arises because we *can* change the signs in quadratic *equations*. But to alter the signs in a quadratic *expression* is simply to alter the value of the expression.

The factors in this kind of case should be written with the constants on the left and the x-terms on the right. Using the same method as before to obtain the signs we have

$$(4 + x)(3 - x). \qquad \triangleleft$$

▷Example 12

Factorise $2x^2 - 6x - 8$.
Here we should notice the common factor 2 and begin by taking this out. Then we proceed as before:

$$2(x^2 - 3x - 4)$$
$$= 2(x - 4)(x + 1). \qquad \triangleleft$$

▷Example 13

Factorise $4x^2 - 13x - 12$.
Here we begin by tabulating all the pairs of numbers which give 4 when multiplied and all the pairs which give 12. One of these sets is tabulated in both orders:

$$4 \quad ① \quad 2 \qquad\qquad 1 \quad 2 \quad ③$$
$$1 \quad ④ \quad 2 \qquad\qquad 12 \quad 6 \quad ④$$

The ringed numbers are the ones which give 13 when multiplied as shown and then added or subtracted. The final answer is

$$(x - 4)(4x + 3). \qquad \triangleleft$$

▷Example 14

Factorise $12x^2 - 17xy + 6y^2$.
This is a quadratic in x and y. It factorises into two linear expressions, each of which contains both x and y. We begin by tabulating the factors of 12 and 6, as in the last example:

$$1 \quad 2 \quad ③ \qquad\qquad 1 \quad 6 \quad ③ \quad 2$$
$$12 \quad 6 \quad ④ \qquad\qquad 6 \quad 1 \quad ② \quad 3$$

Using the numbers ringed we obtain

$$(3x - 2y)(4x - 3y). \qquad \triangleleft$$

EXERCISE 13d

(Note: Remember to start by looking for a common factor.)

Factorise the following expressions:
1 $x^2 + 8x + 12$ **2** $x^2 + 11x + 24$ **3** $2x^2 + 6x + 4$ **4** $x^2 - 2x - 8$
5 $x^2 + x - 20$ **6** $x^2 - 13x + 36$ **7** $5x^2 - 25x + 20$ **8** $12x^2 - 11x - 1$
9 $9x^2 - 6x + 1$ **10** $90 - 21x - 3x^2$ **11** $60 - 11x - x^2$ **12** $60 - 17x + x^2$
13 $2x^2 - 10x - 12$ **14** $18 - 3x - 3x^2$ **15** $5x^2 + 10x + 5$ **16** $2x^2 + 7x + 3$
17 $5x^2 + 9x + 4$ **18** $3x^2 - 11x - 4$ **19** $4x^2 - 12x + 5$ **20** $9x^2 + 6x - 8$
21 $8x^2 - 60x + 72$ **22** $5x^2 - 6xy - 8y^2$ **23** $10x^2 - 21xy + 9y^2$
24 $8 - 2x - 15x^2$ **25** $15 + 11x - 12x^2$ **26** $16x^2 + 20x + 6$
27 $28y^2 + 11xy - 24x^2$ **28** $15x^2 - 26xy + 8y^2$.

The next exercise gives a miscellaneous selection of expressions to factorise.

EXERCISE 13e (miscellaneous)

Factorise the following expressions:
1 $9 - a^2b^2$ **2** $4a^2b^2 - 6ab^3$ **3** $1 - 7x - 18x^2$ **4** $a - 5b + ac - 5bc$
5 $2y^2 - 10y + 12$ **6** $25x^4 - 1$ **7** $25 + 5x - y^2 - xy$ **8** $32y^3 - 2y$
9 $x^2 - 14x - 51$ **10** $76 - 15p - p^2$ **11** $3(x - 1) + (x - 1)^2$ **12** $2a^5 - 8a^3$
13 $2a - 6b + b(3b - a)$ **14** $6x^3y^2 - 9xy^3$ **15** $10r^2 - 9r - 9$
16 $4x + 4x^2 + 6y - 9y^2$ **17** $16a^2 - 30ab + 9b^2$ **18** $(x - 5)^2 + 10x - 2x^2$
19 $20 - 13p - 15p^2$ **20** $x^2 - 4y^2 + x^2y - 4y^3$.

Some applications of factorisation

Cancelling fractions

The factors of a number or expression give us its *divisors*, that is the quantities which divide into it exactly. The divisors are simply the factors themselves and the products of the factors. For example, the divisors of $3a^2b$ are 3, a, b, $3a$, $3b$, etc. To perform the division, we simply cross out the factors we are dividing by. For example $5abc \div 5b = ac$, and $2x(y + 3)^2 \div 2(y + 3) = x(y + 3)$. If all the factors are removed the result is of course 1 and not zero.

Now cancelling a fraction means *dividing numerator and denominator by the same quantity*, and we therefore have the following rule for cancelling an algebraic fraction.

To cancel an algebraic fraction, factorise the numerator and denominator and then cross out any factors which are common to the numerator and denominator.

▷**Example 15**

Simplify the following expressions by cancelling:

(a) $\dfrac{2x - 4y}{x^2 - 4y^2}$,   (b) $\dfrac{2 - 2x}{2 + 2x - 4x^2}$,   (c) $\dfrac{3 - a}{a^2 - 9}$.

(a) $\dfrac{2x - 4y}{x^2 - 4y^2} = \dfrac{2(x - 2y)}{(x + 2y)(x - 2y)} = \dfrac{2}{x + 2y}$.

(b) $\dfrac{2 - 2x}{2 + 2x - 4x^2} = \dfrac{2(1 - x)}{2(1 + x - 2x^2)} = \dfrac{2(1 - x)}{2(1 + 2x)(1 - x)} = \dfrac{1}{1 + 2x}$

(c) $\dfrac{3 - a}{a^2 - 9} = \dfrac{3 - a}{(a + 3)(a - 3)} = -\dfrac{(a - 3)}{(a + 3)(a - 3)} = -\dfrac{1}{a + 3}$

◁

Finding the lowest common multiple (LCM)

If we have two or more expressions in factorised form we can immediately write down their LCM. For example the LCM of abc and bcd is $abcd$ and that of $4x^3y$ and $6x^2y^2$ is $12x^3y^2$. The set of factors in the LCM is the *union* of the sets of factors in the original expressions.

▷**Example 16**

Find the LCM of $3x^2 + 3x - 18$ and $2x^2 - 8x + 8$.
Factorising the two expressions we have

$$3x^2 + 3x - 18 \qquad\qquad 2x^2 - 8x + 8$$
$$= 3(x^2 + x - 6) \qquad\qquad = 2(x^2 - 4x + 4)$$
$$= 3(x + 3)(x - 2). \qquad\qquad = 2(x - 2)^2.$$

It follows that the LCM is $6(x + 3)(x - 2)^2$.

◁

EXERCISE 13f

Simplify by cancelling:

1 $\dfrac{4x - 8}{x^2 - 2x}$ **2** $\dfrac{xy}{y^2 + 3y}$ **3** $\dfrac{2 - 10x}{1 - 25x^2}$ **4** $\dfrac{1 - a}{1 + a - 2a^2}$

5 $\dfrac{3 - 3x^2}{6 - 6x}$ **6** $\dfrac{y^2 - 7y + 12}{xy - 4x}$ **7** $\dfrac{9 - x^2}{x - 3}$ **8** $\dfrac{3x^2y - 9xy^2}{3y - x}$

9 $\dfrac{2p^2 - 50}{5 + 4p - p^2}$ **10** $\dfrac{6x^2 - 5xy - y^2}{y^2 + 6xy}$.

Find the LCM's of the following expressions:
11 $2ab$ and $4a^2$ **12** $2x^2, 3xy$ and $6y^2$ **13** $8a^3b^2c, 12a^2bc^2$ and $6a^4$
14 $3 - 9x$ and $x - 3x^2$ **15** $3k^2$ and $k + k^2$ **16** $1 - x^2$ and $1 - 2x + x^2$
17 $2a, 2a - 1$, and $4a^2 - 1$ **18** $3x^2 - 12, 2x - 4$ and $6x^2 + 12x$
19 $a^2b - b$ and $b - ab$ **20** $2xy, 2y - xy$ and $2x - 4$.

14 Quadratic Equations

All quadratic equations can be expressed in the form $ax^2 + bx + c = 0$, where a is not equal to zero. They can be divided into two types: those in which the left-hand side can be factorised (by one of the methods explained in the last chapter), and those in which it cannot. We shall deal with the former type first.

Quadratic equations which can be solved by the factor method

The method is based on the fact that *if a product of two quantities equals zero, one of those quantities must itself be zero.* The first example illustrates the procedure.

▷**Example 1**

Solve the equation $x^2 - 10 = 3x$.
First we move all the terms to one side, preferably making the x^2 term positive. As in the case of quadratic expressions, the terms should normally be arranged in descending powers.

$$x^2 - 3x - 10 = 0.$$

Now we factorise the left-hand side:

$$(x - 5)(x + 2) = 0.$$

Now since the two quantities $x - 5$ and $x + 2$ give zero when multiplied, *one of these quantities must itself equal zero.* Hence we proceed as follows:

$$\text{Either } x - 5 = 0$$
$$\therefore \ x = 5$$
$$\text{or } x + 2 = 0$$
$$\therefore \ x = -2.$$

The solutions (or roots) are therefore 5 and -2. ◁

The next two examples are slightly more complicated, but the method is essentially the same.

▷Example 2

Solve the equation $4 - 9x^2 = 16x$.
First we move all the terms to one side, making the x^2 term positive:

$$9x^2 + 16x - 4 = 0$$

$$\begin{array}{cc} ⑨ & 3 \\ ① & 3 \end{array} \qquad \begin{array}{ccc} 4 & 1 & ② \\ 1 & 4 & ② \end{array}$$

$$(9x - 2)(x + 2) = 0.$$

Hence either $9x - 2 = 0$
$$\therefore\ 9x = 2$$
$$\therefore\ \ x = \tfrac{2}{9}$$
or $\quad x + 2 = 0$
$$\therefore\ \ x = -2.$$

The solutions are therefore $\tfrac{2}{9}$ and -2.

▷Example 3

Solve the equation $(2x - 1)(x + 3) = 4$.
It is no help that the left-hand side is factorised, because we do not have zero on the right. Hence we simply remove the brackets and then proceed as before:

$$2x^2 + 6x - x - 3 = 4$$
$$\therefore\ 2x^2 + 5x - 7 = 0$$
$$\therefore\ (2x + 7)(x - 1) = 0.$$

Hence either $\quad 2x + 7 = 0$
$$\therefore\ 2x = -7$$
$$\therefore\ x = -3\tfrac{1}{2},$$
or $\quad x - 1 = 0$
$$\therefore\ x = 1.$$

The solutions are therefore $-3\tfrac{1}{2}$ and 1. ◁

On further point should be noted: if the left-hand side of a quadratic equation is a *perfect square (such as $x^2 + 2x + 1$)*, the factors will be equal and the equation will have only one distinct root instead of the usual two. Even so, since quadratic equations *in general* have two roots, mathematicians find it convenient to say that such an equation has *two equal* roots.

EXERCISE 14a

Note: Always look to see if the equation can be simplified by dividing each term by the same number.

Solve the following quadratic equations:
1 $x^2 + 4x + 3 = 0$ **2** $x^2 + 8x + 12 = 0$ **3** $x^2 + 5x - 14 = 0$ **4** $x^2 - 7x - 18 = 0$
5 $3x^2 - 6x - 9 = 0$ (Divide throughout by 3 before factorising)

6 $x^2 - 9x + 20 = 0$ **7** $x^2 + 10x + 24 = 0$ **8** $4x^2 - 4x - 24 = 0$
9 $x^2 - 12x + 36 = 0$ **10** $x^2 + 6x = 16$ **11** $x^2 - x = 42$ **12** $x^2 + 30 = 13x$
13 $x^2 - 36 = 5x$ **14** $5x^2 + 125 = 50x$ **15** $20x - x^2 = 36$ **16** $48 - x^2 = 13x$
17 $6x^2 - x = 1$ **18** $12x^2 + 1 = 7x$ **19** $8x^2 - 8x + 2 = 0$ **20** $2x^2 - x = 3$
21 $3x^2 + 5 + 8x = 0$ **22** $5x^2 - x = 4$ **23** $4x^2 - 12x = 7$ **24** $6x^2 + 5x = 6$
25 $8x^2 - 9 - 6x = 0$ **26** $12x - 9x^2 = 4$ **27** $12 - x = 6x^2$ **28** $5 + 19x + 18x^2 = 0$
29 $x(x - 1) = 30$ **30** $(x - 1)(x + 5) = 7$ **31** $2x(x - 3) = 80$
32 $3x^2 - 600 = 30x$ **33** $2x(2x + 1) = 5(6 - x)$ **34** $8x^2 + 15 = 43x$
35 $6x - x(x - 8) = 24$ **36** $3x(4x - 1) = 10(2x - 1)$ **37** $2x^2 + 8000 = 260x$
38 $36x^2 - 33x = 20$ **39** $3x(3x - 8) - 5(x - 4) = 0$ **40** $43x - 18 = 24x^2$.

Special cases

All quadratic equations must have terms in x^2, but some do not have terms in x and some do not have constant terms. The next examples deal with these special cases.

▷ Example 4

Solve the equation $10x = 15x^2$.
In this case it happens that we can simplify the equation by dividing both sides by 5:

$$2x = 3x^2.$$

Now we put all the terms on one side, as before:

$$3x^2 - 2x = 0.$$

Since there is no constant term, the two remaining terms must have a common factor of x:

$$x(3x - 2) = 0.$$

It now follows as before that one of the two factors must be zero.

$$\text{Either } x = 0$$
$$\text{or } 3x - 2 = 0$$
$$\therefore \quad 3x = 2$$
$$\therefore \quad x = \tfrac{2}{3}.$$

The solutions are therefore 0 and $\tfrac{2}{3}$. ◁

Note: If a quadratic equation has no constant term, the two remaining terms will always have a common factor of x, and therefore this type of equation will always have a root of zero.

▷**Example 5**

Solve the equation $3x^2 = 75$.
We begin by dividing both sides by 3:

$$x^2 = 25.$$

Now there are two alternative procedures. The simpler is just to take the square root of both sides:

$$x = \pm 5.$$

Alternatively we can proceed as before, placing the two terms on one side and factorising. If factorisation is to be possible at all in this kind of equation the two terms must form a difference of two squares:

$$x^2 - 25 = 0$$
$$\therefore \ (x + 5)(x - 5) = 0,$$

from which we obtain $x = \pm 5$, as before.   ◁

The first of the following two exercises deals entirely with the special quadratic equations in which either the term in x or the constant term is missing, and the second exercise gives a miscellaneous selection of quadratic equations.

EXERCISE 14b

Solve the following quadratic equations:
1 $x^2 = 3x$ **2** $3x^2 = 5x$ **3** $x^2 = 16$ **4** $2x^2 = 8$ **5** $2x + 6x^2 = 0$
6 $12x = 16x^2$ **7** $x^2 - 64 = 0$ **8** $5x^2 = 5$ **9** $8x^2 - 14x = 0$ **10** $98 = 2x^2$
11 $1\frac{1}{2}x = 3\frac{1}{2}x^2$ (multiply both sides by 2.)   **12** $9x^2 - 4 = 0$ **13** $-10x = 25x^2$
14 $1\frac{1}{4}x^2 = 45$ **15** $2x^2 = 12\frac{1}{2}$ **16** $x(x - 2) = 2x(x - 3)$ **17** $25x^2 = 1$
18 $\dfrac{1 - x}{2} = \dfrac{x^2 + 2}{4}$ **19** $40x = 88x^2$ **20** $288 = 50x^2$ **21** $(1 - 2x)^2 = 1 - 5x$
22 $6(x^2 - 4) = 2(x^2 + 6)$ **23** $(4 - x)(1 + 2x) = (2 - x)^2$
24 $2(50 - 3x) = 3x(3x - 2)$ **25** $4x(x + 3) - 3x(2 - x) = 0$ **26** $7\frac{1}{2}x = 6\frac{1}{4}x^2$
27 $12x^2 = 16\frac{1}{3}$ **28** $(2x - 3)^2 = (x - 6)^2$ **29** $(3x - 1)^2 = (1 - 5x)^2$
30 $4 - x(10 - x) = -5(2x - 17)$ **31** $x(x - 3) - 3(2 - x) = 250$
32 $25 - (3 - 5x)^2 = (4 - x)^2$.

EXERCISE 14c (Miscellaneous quadratic equations)

1 $x^2 - 3x - 4 = 0$ **2** $x^2 + x = 12$ **3** $2x^2 - 2x - 4 = 0$ **4** $x^2 + 8 = 6x$
5 $1 - x^2 = 0$ **6** $x^2 + 24 = 14x$ **7** $2x^2 = 4x$ **8** $1 - x = 2x^2$ **9** $x = 3x^2$
10 $1 - 36x^2 = 5x$ **11** $5x^2 - 20 = 0$ **12** $6x^2 = 54$ **13** $2x^2 + 19x + 9 = 0$
14 $4x^2 = 49$ **15** $x(x + 8) = 65$ **16** $2x(x - 5) = 12$ **17** $2x^2 + 18 = 12x$
18 $4 - 5x^2 = 8x$ **19** $12x = 9x^2$ **20** $x(x - 4) = 2(x + 8)$ **21** $18x^2 = 32$
22 $19x - x^2 = 48$ **23** $10x + 15 = 5x^2$ **24** $108 = 3x^2$ **25** $(x - 5)(x + 3) = 9$
26 $7x = 9x^2$ **27** $18 - 13x - 21x^2 = 0$ **28** $7x - 18x^2 = -8$ **29** $5 - 7x^2 = -34x$
30 $54 = 24x^2$ **31** $(3x - 2)(5x - 6) = (5x - 4)(2x - 3)$ **32** $2x^2 - 1000 = 10x$
33 $3x^2 - 165x + 1800 = 0$ **34** $35x - 12 = 8x^2$ **35** $20 - 24x^2 = 17x$.

Quadratic equations which cannot be solved by the factor method

There are two methods of solving this type of equation. The first is based on a technique called 'completion of the square', and the second involves the use of a formula which gives the solutions directly.

The 'completion of the square' method

Consider the quadratic expressions $x^2 + 2x + 1, x^2 - 6x + 9, x^2 + 10x + 25$. All of these are *perfect squares*: they are equal to $(x + 1)^2$, $(x - 3)^2$ and $(x + 5)^2$, respectively. Now do these expressions have any feature which makes them easily recognisable as perfect squares? In fact examination shows that in each case *the constant term can be obtained by taking half the coefficient of x and squaring it*. This gives us a method of making a perfect square when we have the first two terms of a quadratic expression. Provided that the coefficient of x^2 is 1, the procedure is:

Take half the coefficient of x, square it, and add.

This procedure is called 'completing the square'. The following examples show how it can be used to solve quadratic equations.

▷ Example 6

Solve the equation $x^2 + 6x - 4 = 0$, giving the roots to 3 s.f.

We want only the x^2 and x terms on the left, so 4 is added to both sides:

$$x^2 + 6x = 4.$$

Now we complete the square by adding 9 to both sides:

$$x^2 + 6x + 9 = 13,$$
$$\text{i.e.}\quad (x + 3)^2 = 13.$$

Taking the square root of both sides:

$$x + 3 = \pm 3.6056.$$

Finally, taking the plus sign we obtain $x = 0.6056$ and taking the minus sign $x = -6.6056$.
Hence the solutions are 0.606 and -6.61 to 3 s.f.   ◁

It must be noted that the completion of the square technique only works if the coefficient of x^2 is 1. If the coefficient is a different number we begin by dividing through by that number.

▷**Example 7**

Solve the equation $2x^2 - 3x - 6 = 0$, giving the roots to 2 d.p.

Adding 6 to both sides and dividing through by 2 we have

$$x^2 - \frac{3x}{2} = 3.$$

Now half the coefficient of x is $-\frac{3}{4}$ and the square of this is $\frac{9}{16}$. We add this quantity to both sides to complete the square:

$$x^2 - \frac{3x}{2} + \frac{9}{16} = 3\frac{9}{16}$$

i.e. $(x - \frac{3}{4})^2 = 3.5625$

∴ $x - \frac{3}{4} = \pm 1.8875.$

Taking the plus sign we have $x = 2.6375$ and taking the minus sign $x = -1.1375$.

Hence the roots are 2.64 and -1.14 to 2 d.p. ◀

Note: If we require an answer to 3 s.f. or 2 d.p. *we work to a greater accuracy than this until the final stage.* This is a principle which holds in all calculations in which the answer is not given exactly.

The quadratic formula

By applying the completion of the square procedure to the general quadratic equation $ax^2 + bx + c = 0$, it can be shown that the roots are always given by the following formula:

$$x = \frac{-b \pm \sqrt{b^2 - 4ac}}{2a}.$$

▷**Example 8**

Solve to 2 d.p. the equation $2x^2 + 7x + 4 = 0$.
We have $a = 2, b = 7, c = 4$.
Hence

$$x = \frac{-7 \pm \sqrt{49 - 32}}{4} = \frac{-7 \pm 4.123}{4}.$$

Taking the plus sign $x = \frac{-2.877}{4} = -0.719$, and taking the minus sign $x = \frac{-11.123}{4} = -2.781$.

Hence the roots are -0.72 and -2.78 to 2 d.p. ◀

▷ **Example 9**

Solve to 3 s.f. the equation $3x^2 - 5x - 7 = 0$.
We have $a = 3, b = -5, c = -7$.
Hence

$$x = \frac{5 \pm \sqrt{25 - (4)(3)(-7)}}{6} = \frac{5 \pm \sqrt{25 + 84}}{6}$$

$$= \frac{5 \pm 10.4403}{6}.$$

Taking the plus sign $x = \dfrac{15.4403}{6} = 2.573$, and taking the minus sign $x = \dfrac{-5.4403}{6} = -0.9067$.

Hence the roots are 2.57 and -0.907 to 3 s.f.   ◁

Note: If the quantity under the square root sign is negative, the equation has *no real roots* because there are no real square roots of a negative number. It is also worth noting that if this quantity is a perfect square the equation can be solved by the factor method and has *rational* roots. That is, the roots are expressible either in terms of fractions or decimals which terminate or recur. In examples 6–9 above the roots are irrational.

EXERCISE 14d

Say what number must be added to the following expressions to complete the square:
1 $x^2 + 12x$ **2** $x^2 + 8x$ **3** $x^2 - 20x$ **4** $x^2 - 16x$ **5** $x^2 + 5x$ **6** $x^2 - x$
7 $x^2 - 3x$ **8** $x^2 + x/2$ **9** $x^2 - \frac{2}{3}x$ **10** $x^2 + \frac{3}{4}x$ **10** $x^2 - \frac{4}{5}x$ **12** $x^2 - \frac{7}{4}x$

Solve the following equations to 2 d.p. by the completion of the square method:
13 $x^2 + 4x = 1$ **14** $x^2 - 6x = 5$ **15** $x^2 + 8x = -11$ **16** $x^2 - 2x - 6 = 0$
17 $x^2 + x - 1 = 0$ **18** $x^2 + 3x = -\dfrac{1}{4}$ **19** $2x^2 - 8x = 13$ **20** $3x^2 + 6x = 2$
21 $2x^2 + 6x = 3$ **22** $4x^2 + 6x + 1 = 0$ **23** $3x^2 - 5x + 1 = 0$
24 $5x^2 - 4x - 7 = 0$.

Solve the following equations to 2 d.p. by using the quadratic formula:
25 $x^2 + 2x = 5$ **26** $x^2 - 2x = 5$ **27** $x^2 - 10x + 15 = 0$ **28** $2x^2 + 11x + 3 = 0$
29 $5x^2 + x - 1 = 0$ **30** $2 - 4x = 3x^2$ **31** $x^2 + \frac{3}{2}x = 2$ (Multiply throughout by 2 first.) **32** $10 - 3x^2 = 12x$ **33** $2 + 9x = 4x^2$
34 $11x - 3 - 2x^2 = 0$ **35** $x^2 - \frac{3}{4} = \frac{3}{2}x$ **36** $4x - 1 = 3\frac{1}{2}x^2$.

15 Simultaneous Equations

Simultaneous equations are equations which are *true at the same time*. If we require the values of two unknown quantities it is normally necessary to have two simultaneous equations relating them, if we require three quantities three equations are needed, and so on. In general, *n* simultaneous equations are needed to find *n* quantities.

For example, the equation $x + y = 10$ is satisfied by an infinite number of pairs of values, some of which are shown in the following table:

x	0	1	2 . . .
y	10	9	8 . . .

Similarly, the equation $x - y = 2$ is satisfied by the following infinite set:

x	10	9	8 . . .
y	8	7	6 . . .

If, however, the two equations are *both true at the same time*, there is only one possible pair of values, namely $x = 6$, $y = 4$. This is said to be the solution of the pair of simultaneous equations.

The simplest simultaneous equations to solve are pairs of *linear* equations. This is an elementary topic and most students will be familiar with at least one method of solving simultaneous equations of this kind. Slightly more difficult is the type in which one equation is linear and one quadratic. When both equations are non-linear or there are more than two equations the difficulty of solution can be quite considerable and we shall not deal with such types in this book.

Both equations linear

The usual method of solution is that called *equalising the coefficients*. The method will be illustrated by an example which will also show a simple method of setting out this type of question. The way in which each equation is clearly numbered should be particularly noted.

▷ Example 1

Solve the simultaneous equations 5x = 2y + 4, y − 4x = − 1.
First we re-arrange the equations as follows:

$$5x - 2y = 4 \quad (1)$$
$$4x - y = 1 \quad (2)$$

Now we equalise the coefficients of y:

$$(1) \times 1: \quad 5x - 2y = 4 \quad (3)$$
$$(2) \times 2: \quad 8x - 2y = 2 \quad (4)$$

Next y is eliminated by subtracting either (3) from (4) or (4) from (3):

$$(4) - (3): \quad 3x = -2$$
$$\therefore \ x = -\frac{2}{3}.$$

Having found x we find y by substituting the value of x into either equation (1) or equation (2).
Substituting in (2):

$$-\frac{8}{3} - y = 1$$
$$\therefore \ y = -3\frac{2}{3}.$$

The solutions are therefore $x = -\frac{2}{3}, y = -3\frac{2}{3}.$

(If a check is required, these values can be substituted into the equation which was *not* used to find the second unknown.) ◁

When one of the coefficients of x or y is 1 or −1, the *method of substitution* is usually as quick or quicker than the method of equalising the coefficients.

▷ Example 2

Solve the following pair of simultaneous equations by the method of substitution:

$$8x - 2y = 5 \quad (1)$$
$$2x - y = -1 \quad (2)$$

The coefficient of y in equation (2) is −1, so we begin by making y the subject of this equation:

$$y = 2x + 1 \quad (3)$$

Now we substitute $2x + 1$ for y in equation (1):

$$8x - 2(2x + 1) = 5$$
$$\therefore \ 8x - 4x - 2 = 5$$
$$\therefore \ 4x = 7$$
$$\therefore \ x = 1\frac{3}{4}$$

To find y the best equation to use is that in which y is the subject, namely (3). Substituting $1\frac{3}{4}$ for y in (3), we have

$$y = 2(1\tfrac{3}{4}) + 1$$
$$= 4\tfrac{1}{2}.$$

The solutions are therefore $x = 1\frac{3}{4}, y = 4\frac{1}{2}$.   ◁

Note: The methods of equalising the coefficients and substitution are really ways of doing the same thing, namely *eliminating one of the unknowns*. When this has been done a single equation in one unknown is obtained.

The next example appears more complicated, but is easily reduced to the type just considered.

▷**Example 3**

Solve the following simultaneous equations:

$$\frac{4}{x} - \frac{1}{y} = 3$$
$$\frac{5}{x} - \frac{2}{y} = 1$$

If we regard the unknowns as $\frac{1}{x}$ and $\frac{1}{y}$, the equations are of the same kind as before. This is more obvious if we let $\frac{1}{x} = a$ and $\frac{1}{y} = b$:

$$4a - b = 3$$
$$5a - 2b = 1$$

Proceeding now as previously we obtain $a = \frac{5}{3}, b = \frac{11}{3}$. It follows that $x = \frac{3}{5}$ and $y = \frac{3}{11}$.   ◁

Sometimes the equations are given in a more complicated way. For example,

$$2x - y - 1 = 2(2x + y - 1) = x + 5y - 2.$$

This statement is equivalent to *two* independent equations. If, for example, we equate the first expression to the second and the first to the third, it is implied that the second equals the third and there is no point in writing this down as a third equation.

Proceeding in this way and removing the brackets we obtain

$$2x - y - 1 = 4x + 2y - 2$$
$$\text{and} \quad 2x - y - 1 = x + 5y - 2.$$

Now collecting like terms and arranging the equations as before, we have

$$2x + 3y = 1$$
$$x - 6y = -1.$$

After this we can use either the method of equalising the coefficients or that of substitution.

EXERCISE 15a

Solve the following pairs of simultaneous equations:

1 $2x - y = 5$
  $x + x = 4$

2 $x + y = 3$
  $x + 2y = 4$

3 $3x - 2y = 6$
  $2x - y = 5$

4 $2x + 5y = 9$
  $3x - y = 5$

5 $2x - y = 4$
  $3x - 2y = 5$

6 $5x - 3y = 13$
  $3x + 4y = 2$

7 $2x = 5y$
  $4x - 3y = 7$

8 $y = 2x - 11$
  $x + 3y + 5 = 0$

9 $y = 2x - 1 = 3x - 4$

10 $3x - 8y = 18$
  $5x - 9y = 17$

11 $2y = 1 - 3x = 5y + 3x$

12 $2\frac{1}{2}y - 3x = 4$
  $2y - 1\frac{1}{2}x = 5$

13 $x = 2y - 1 = 5y - 3$

14 $3x + 9 = -7y$
  $2y + 22 = 4x$

15 $\dfrac{2}{x} - \dfrac{5}{y} = 3$
  $\dfrac{3}{x} - \dfrac{7}{y} = 3$

16 $3x - 7y = -6$
  $1\frac{1}{2}x = 2\frac{1}{2}y$

17 $\dfrac{3}{x} - 4y = 7$
  $\dfrac{5}{x} - 2y = 14$

18 $1\frac{2}{3}x = 1 + \dfrac{y}{3}$
  $3x - 2y = -8$

19 $8(1 - x) = 3y$
  $3(1 - 3y) = 10x$

20 $x = \dfrac{1}{4}(1 + y)$
  $y = \dfrac{2}{3}(x - 2)$

21 $\dfrac{2}{x} + \dfrac{5}{y} = 1$
  $\dfrac{3}{x} + \dfrac{4}{y} = 2$

22 $3x - \dfrac{2}{y} = 6$
  $7x + \dfrac{12}{y} = 4$

23 $\dfrac{x}{2} = 2 - y = 1\frac{1}{2}y + 1$

24 $\dfrac{1}{x} - \dfrac{3}{y} = 1$
  $\dfrac{3}{x} - \dfrac{5}{y} = 6$

25 $16x + 7y = 5$
  $11x + 5y = 3\frac{1}{2}$

26 $2x - 3y - 1 = 3x - 4y - 2 = x + 2y - 4$

27 $2x + 3y + 3 = 2\frac{1}{2}y - 1\frac{1}{2}x = 3y - 2x - 1$

28 $3x + y + 2 = 6x - y - 2 = 5 - 3x$

29 $2x + y - 1 = \frac{1}{2}(2x - y + 9) = 3x + 2y - 2$

30 $2(x - 2y) - 3 = x + 2y - 1 = 10y + 3(1 - x).$

One equation linear, one quadratic

In this type of question the standard method used is substitution. We start by making x or y the subject of the *linear* equation, and then substitute into the quadratic. There are normally two solutions for x and two for y, and it should always be made clear which value of x goes with which value of y when the final answer is stated.

▶**Example 4**

Solve the simultaneous equations

$$x^2 - 2y^2 = -14 \quad (1)$$
$$2x - y = 1 \qquad (2)$$

Here the linear equation is (2), and it is easier to make y than x the subject. From (2) we have

$$y = 2x - 1 \qquad (3)$$

Now we substitute $2x - 1$ for y in equation (1):

$$x^2 - 2(2x - 1)^2 = -14$$
$$\therefore \ x^2 - 2(4x^2 - 4x + 1) = -14$$
$$\therefore \ x^2 - 8x^2 + 8x - 2 = -14$$
$$\therefore \ 7x^2 - 8x - 12 = 0$$
$$\therefore \ (7x + 6)(x - 2) = 0$$

Hence either $7x + 6 = 0$

from which $x = -\dfrac{6}{7}$,

or $x - 2 = 0$
and $x = 2$.

Now we return to equation (3) to find y.

When $x = -\dfrac{6}{7}, y = 2(-\dfrac{6}{7}) - 1 = -2\dfrac{5}{7}$.

When $x = 2, y = 2(2) - 1 = 3$.

The solutions are therefore $x = -\dfrac{6}{7}, y = -2\dfrac{5}{7}$ and $x = 2, y = 3$. ◁

EXERCISE 15b

Solve the following pairs of simultaneous equations:

1 $x + y = 2$
   $x^2 + y^2 = 10$

2 $x - 2y = 1$
   $xy - y^2 = 6$

3 $x^2 - y = 1$
   $x + y = 5$

4 $x - 2y = 5$
   $xy = -2$

5 $x^2 + y^2 = 13$
   $x - y = 1$

6 $y - 3x = -7$
   $x^2 - y = 5$

7 $xy = 1$
   $x - 2y = 1$

8 $y - x = -2$
   $x^2 + 2y = -1$

9 $x - y = -3$
   $x^2 + y = 5$

10 $x^2 - y = 0$
    $y - 3x = -2$

11 $x - 2y = 1$
    $2x - y^2 = 6$

12 $x^2 + 2y = 7$
    $2x + y = 1$

13 $x + y = 1$
    $y^2 + 2x = 5$

14 $x - 3y = 1$
    $xy = 4$

15 $x^2 = 5 - y^2$
    $x - y = 1$

16 $xy = 1$
    $3y + x = 4$

17 $2x - y = 2$
    $xy = 12$

18 $y = 3x^2 - 6$
    $y = 2 - 2x$

19 $2x^2 - y = -1$
    $x + y = 4$

20 $y - 2x = 7$
    $xy + y = -3$

21 $3x + y = 5$
    $xy = 2$

22 $xy - x^2 = -10$
    $2x + y = -1$

23 $4x - y = 1$
    $2y - xy = 3$

24 $3xy = 6$
    $6x - 2y = -5$

25 $2x^2 - y^2 = -1$ **26** $y^2 - xy = 3$ **27** $x - 2y = 4$ **28** $x^2 - 3y^2 = -18$
    $5 - y = x$ $x - 2y = -4$ $x^2 + xy = 2$ $x - 3y = 12$

29 $x(x - 2y) = -3$ **30** $2x^2 - y^2 = 2$ **31** $2(x + y) = 3x(x - y)$
    $x + y + 3 = 0$ $2x - y = 2$ $2x - y = 3$

32 $x^2 - y^2 = 1 + xy$ **33** $3x - y = 1$ **34** $3x - y = 3$
    $3x + 1 = -y + 4$ $y^2 - xy = 12$ $9x^2 - y^2 = y - 1$

35 $y^2 - xy = 35$
    $4x + y = -3.$

EXERCISE 15c (miscellaneous simultaneous equations)

Solve the following pairs of simultaneous equations:

1 $x - 2y = -6$ **2** $x^2 + y^2 = 5$ **3** $y = 5 - 7x = 3x - 15$ **4** $\dfrac{2}{x} + \dfrac{3}{y} = 7$
    $x + 4y = -3$ $3x - y = 1$

   $\dfrac{5}{x} - \dfrac{2}{y} = 8$

5 $x^2 - 2xy = 16$ **6** $\dfrac{1}{2}(x - y) = \dfrac{5}{6}$ **7** $y - 2x = xy = 1$ **8** $x^2 + 2y^2 = 6$
    $x + y = -1$ $x - y = 1$
                        $3x + 4y = -2$

9 $\dfrac{1}{x} + 3y = 4$ **10** $\dfrac{x}{2} - \dfrac{y}{3} = -2$ **11** $y(x + 1) = x^2 - 4$
                                                                 $2y - x = -8$
   $\dfrac{4}{x} + 2y = 11$ $\dfrac{x}{3} + \dfrac{y}{2} = \dfrac{5}{6}$

12 $3(x - 1) = 5y$ **13** $x + xy = y^2 - 1$
    $4(x - 2y - 1) = 1 - y$ $2x - y = 3$

14 $2x - 3y - 6 = 3x + y + 7 = x - 2y + 1$

15 $2y^2 - 3x^2 = 5$ **16** $2xy - x^2 = -3y^2$
    $x + y = 1$ $x - \dfrac{y}{2} = 2\dfrac{1}{2}$

16 Problems

A mathematical problem arises when we have information which leads to an equation or set of equations, but the equations are not given directly. This usually means that we have to introduce letters to stand for unknown quantities, and then use the information given to construct for ourselves equations from which they can be found. With regard to these procedures, the following points should be noted.

(1) Any letters introduced must be clearly defined.

(2) Letters normally stand for pure numbers and not for numbers of things: thus, for example, we might let unknown times or weights be t *seconds* or w *grams,* but we should not let them be merely t or w.

(3) It is generally best to introduce as few unknowns as possible. For example, if we are told that two quantities have a sum of 15, it is usually better to call them x and $15 - x$ rather than to denote them by x and y. In the first case the information given is 'built into' the symbols used, whereas in the second the equation $x + y = 15$ has to be brought in at some point in order to use the information given.

(4) The units of the quantities involved in a problem must be consistent. For example, if a question concerns speed, distance and time, and the speed is in m s^{-1}, then the distance must be in metres and the time in seconds.

(5) Sometimes the solutions of an equation are not acceptable solutions to the problem which led to the equation. Suppose, for example, that x cm is the length of a box and we have a quadratic equation in x whose solutions are -3 and 5. The -3 is physically impossible and should be *discarded* (i.e. rejected, or thrown away) with a brief explanation such as 'negative solution impossible'. The equation should however be properly solved, with both solutions shown, before the unacceptable solution is discarded.

Problems leading to simultaneous equations

▷Example 1

The area of a rectangle is 14 cm^2 and its perimeter is 15 cm. Find its length and breadth.

Let the lengths of the sides be x cm and y cm. Then

$$xy = 14 \qquad (1)$$
$$\text{and} \quad 2x + 2y = 15 \quad (2)$$

From (1) $y = \dfrac{14}{x}$.

Substituting in (2):

$$2x + \frac{28}{x} = 15$$
$$\therefore\ 2x^2 - 15x + 28 = 0$$
$$\therefore\ (2x - 7)(x - 4) = 0$$
$$\therefore\ x = 3\tfrac{1}{2} \text{ or } x = 4.$$

Since x can stand for either the length or the breadth of the rectangle these two alternative solutions for x in fact give us both x and y. The equations (1) and (2) are said to be *symmetrical in x and y,* that is, they are unaltered if x and y are interchanged. It follows from this that if one pair of solutions is $x = 3\tfrac{1}{2}, y = 4$, then $x = 4, y = 3\tfrac{1}{2}$ must be another.

The lengths of the sides are 4 cm and $3\tfrac{1}{2}$ cm. ◁

▷ Example 2

Four years ago a man was 5 times his son's age, and in 2 years' time he will be 3 times his son's age. Find the present ages of the father and son.

Let the present ages of the man and his son be x years and y years, respectively. Then 4 years ago the ages were $x - 4$ and $y - 4$, and in 2 years time they will be $x + 2$ and $y + 2$. Hence we have

$$x - 4 = 5(y - 4)$$
$$\text{and} \quad x + 2 = 3(y + 2).$$

Removing brackets and re-arranging:

$$x - 5y = -16 \quad (1)$$
$$x - 3y = 4 \qquad (2)$$
$$(2) - (1): \qquad 2y = 20$$
$$\therefore\ y = 10.$$

Substituting 10 for y in (2):

$$x - 30 = 4$$
$$\therefore\ x = 34$$

The present ages are therefore 34 years and 10 years. ◁

▷ Example 3

The value of a 2-digit number is 4 times the sum of its digits and it exceeds the sum of the squares of its digits by 4. Find the number.

Let the 10's digit be x and the units digit be y. Then the value of the number is $10x + y$ and we have

$$10x + y = 4(x + y) \quad (1)$$
$$\text{and } 10x + y = x^2 + y^2 + 4 \quad (2)$$

Removing the brackets in (1) and simplifying, we obtain

$$6x = 3y$$
$$\therefore 2x = y \quad (3)$$

Substituting $2x$ for y in (2):

$$10x + 2x = x^2 + 4x^2 + 4$$
$$\therefore 3x^2 - 8x + 4 = 0$$
$$\therefore (3x - 2)(x - 2) = 0$$
$$\therefore x = \frac{2}{3} \text{ or } x = 2.$$

Since x must be a whole number $\frac{2}{3}$ is clearly impossible. When $x = 2$ equation (3) gives $y = 4$ and the number is therefore 24.   ◀

▷ Example 4

The sides of a rectangle are $(x + y)$ cm and $(x - y)$ cm. Find the two sides, given that the area of the rectangle is 15 cm^2 and that of the square on its diagonal is 34 cm^2.
The area of the rectangle, in cm^2, can be expressed as $(x + y)(x - y)$ or $x^2 - y^2$.
Hence

$$x^2 - y^2 = 15 \quad (1)$$

By Pythagoras' theorem, the area of the square on the diagonal of the rectangle is the sum of the squares on its two sides.
Hence

$$(x + y)^2 + (x - y)^2 = 34$$
$$\therefore x^2 + 2xy + y^2 + x^2 - 2xy + y^2 = 34$$
$$\therefore 2x^2 + 2y^2 = 34$$
$$\therefore x^2 + y^2 = 17 \quad (2)$$
$$(1) + (2): \quad 2x^2 = 32$$
$$\therefore x^2 = 16$$
$$\therefore x = \pm 4$$

Substituting 16 for x^2 in (2):

$$y^2 = 1$$
$$\therefore y = \pm 1$$

The solutions which make both sides of the rectangle positive are $x = 4$, $y = \pm 1$, and whether we use the plus or the minus sign for y the sides are 5 cm and 3 cm.   ◀

EXERCISE 16a

Note: Some of the problems in this exercise can be treated either as involving two unknowns and leading to simultaneous equations, or as involving only one unknown and leading to a single equation. Point (3) at the beginning of the chapter explains this.

1 3 apples and 2 oranges cost 34 p, while 5 apples and 1 orange cost 38 p. Find the cost of an apple and the cost of an orange.

2 The sides of an equilateral triangle are $(x + y)$ cm, $(2x - y - 2)$ cm and $(x - y + 4)$ cm. Find the length of each side.

3 A man is now twice the age of his son, and in 20 years time he will be $1\frac{1}{2}$ times his son's age. What is his present age?

4 The length of a rectangle exceeds its breadth by $1\frac{1}{2}$ cm, and the area is 22 cm². Find the length.

5 Two numbers are such that 5 times the first is 3 more than 6 times the second, and 4 times the second is 5 more than the first. Find the numbers.

6 Jane has 65 p in her pocket, made up entirely of 10 p and 5 p pieces. If the numbers of the two types of coin were interchanged, she would only have 55 p. How many of each coin does she have?

7 The value of a 2-digit number is 7 times the sum of its digits, and the 10's digit is 2 more than the units digit. What is the number?

8 The denominator of a fraction exceeds the numerator by 3, and if 1 is added to both numerator and denominator the value of the fraction becomes $\frac{1}{2}$. What is the fraction?

9 For £1 it is possible to buy 6 rulers and 2 pencils or 2 rulers and 9 pencils. Find the cost of a ruler and the cost of a pencil.

10 The length and breadth of a rectangle are $(2x - y + 4)$ cm and $(2y - x - 4)$ cm, respectively. If the length exceeds the breadth by 2 cm and the perimeter is 16 cm, what are x and y?

11 A man has 13 coins in his pocket, all 1 p's and 5 p's, of total value 49 p. How many has he of each?

12 A firm calculates that if it employs 4 men and 3 boys its total weekly wage bill will be £410, while if it employs 2 men and 7 boys its total bill will be £370. What are the wages of a man and of a boy?

13 Two numbers differ by 6, and the square of the larger number exceeds that of the smaller by 24. What are the numbers?

14 The sum of the digits in a two-digit number is 9, and if the digits are reversed the number decreases by 45. What is the number?

15 The sum of two numbers is 6, and their product is 36 less than the larger number. What are the numbers?

16 When a man cycles for half an hour and walks for an hour he covers 13 km, while he covers $18\frac{1}{2}$ km when he cycles for an hour and walks for half an hour. Find the speeds at which he walks and cycles.

17 A batch of 100 rulers and 50 compasses weighs 1.8 kg, while another batch of 200 rulers and 25 compasses weighs 2.1 kg. Find the weight of a ruler and the weight of a compass.

18 When one positive number is divided by another the result is 5, while if the two numbers are multiplied the result is 245. Find the numbers.

19 The perimeter of a rectangle is 18 cm, and the area of the square on its diagonal is 45 cm². Find the lengths of the rectangle's sides.

20 On a certain journey the fare for an adult is £3.50 and that of a child is £2. If the total cost for a party of 22 is £62, how many adults does the party contain?

21 A certain fraction becomes equal to 1 when 6 is added to its numerator, and becomes equal to $\frac{1}{2}$ when 1 is subtracted from its denominator. What is the fraction?

22 Two numbers are such that the sum of their squares added to their product is 13, and the difference between them is 7. What are the numbers?

23 The length and breadth of a rectangle are $(2x + y)$ cm and $(x + 1)$ cm, and the sides of a square are all $(x + 2y)$ cm. If the two figures have equal perimeters, and the length of the rectangle exceeds its breadth by 2 cm, what are x and y?

24 If a man were a year older and his son a year younger the ratio of their ages would be 3:1. In 9 years' time the ratio will be 2:1. How old are they now?

25 The perimeter of a rectangle is 14 cm, and the area of the square on its diagonal exceeds the area of the rectangle itself by 19 cm². What are its length and breadth?

26 A man travels 200 km by car and 600 km by train, taking 7 hours altogether. He calculates that if he had travelled 300 km by car and 480 km by train his journey would have taken the same time. Find the speeds of the car and the train, assuming both to be constant.

27 The two longest sides in a right-angled triangle differ in length by 4 cm, and the area of the square on the shortest side is 80 cm². Find the length of the longest side.

28 The sides of a square of area 9 cm² are all $(x - y)$ cm, and the perimeter is $3xy$ cm. Find x and y.

Problems leading to quadratic equations

Note: It is usual for quadratic equations derived from problems to be solvable by the factor method. Consequently it is advisable to check for a mistake before using the quadratic formula if the equation obtained cannot be solved by factorising.

▷ Example 5

The distance in metres through which a falling body moves in t seconds is given by the formula 2t + 5t². How long does the body take to fall 24 m?

Here we have simply to equate the formula for distance travelled to 24:

$$2t + 5t^2 = 24$$
$$\therefore \ 5t^2 + 2t - 24 = 0$$
$$\therefore \ (5t + 12)(t - 2) = 0$$

$$\therefore \ t = -\frac{12}{5} \text{ or } 2.$$

Since the negative answer is clearly impossible here, the time taken is 2 s. ◁

▷ Example 6

The product of two successive even numbers is 80 less than twice the square of the smaller number. What are the numbers?

Let the numbers be x and $x + 2$. Then we have

$$2x^2 - x(x + 2) = 80$$
$$\therefore\ x^2 - 2x - 80 = 0$$
$$\therefore\ (x - 10)(x + 8) = 0$$
$$\therefore\ x = 10 \text{ or } -8.$$

Both solutions are possible here, and since x is the smaller number, the pair of numbers is either 10, 12 or -8, -6. ◀

▷ Example 7

The sides of a rectangle are $(2x - 1)$ cm and $(x + 1)$ cm. Find x if the area of the square on the diagonal exceeds the area of the rectangle itself by 39 cm².

By Pythagoras' theorem the area of the square on the diagonal is $(2x - 1)^2 + (x + 1)^2$. The area of the rectangle itself is $(2x - 1)(x + 1)$, so we have

$$(2x - 1)^2 + (x + 1)^2 = (2x - 1)(x + 1) + 39$$
$$\therefore\ 4x^2 - 4x + 1 + x^2 + 2x + 1 = 2x^2 + 2x - x - 1 + 39$$
$$\therefore\ 3x^2 - 3x - 36 = 0$$
$$\therefore\ x^2 - x - 12 = 0$$
$$\therefore\ (x - 4)(x + 3) = 0$$
$$\therefore\ x = 4 \text{ or } -3.$$

Discarding the negative solution, which is impossible since it implies that the lengths of the sides are negative, we have $x = 4$. ◀

The next example introduces a particularly important type of problem which can appear in many different guises. It is characterised by the fact that we initially obtain a fractional equation which becomes a quadratic when the fractions are removed. The first example of this type is set in such a way that we are 'led through' the first stages of the problem – a common way of setting examination questions.

▷ Example 8

A group of N people agree to pay equal amounts towards an outing costing £660. 5 people drop out, and the firm running the outing drops the price to the remainder to £600. As a result, each person has to pay £2 more.
(a) Write down an expression in terms of N for the original amount each person agreed to pay.
(b) Write down a similar expression for the new amount each pays.
(c) Form an equation in N and solve it to find the number of people in the original group.

(a) Since N people pay a total of £660, the amount each pays is $£\dfrac{660}{N}$.

(b) After 5 people drop out and the price is reduced, $N - 5$ people pay a total

of £600. Hence each pays $£\dfrac{600}{N - 5}$.

(c) To form an equation in N, we look for a way of relating the two expressions we have just written down. In fact since each person pays £2 more in the second case, the value of the second expression must be 2 more than that of the first. Hence we have

$$\frac{660}{N} + 2 = \frac{600}{N-5}$$

The next step is to remove the fractions. This is done by multiplying throughout (that is, each term) by the lowest common multiple of the denominators, namely $N(N-5)$:

$$660(N-5) + 2N(N-5) = 600N.$$

Dividing through by 2:

$$330(N-5) + N(N-5) = 300N$$
$$\therefore\ 330N - 1650 + N^2 - 5N = 300N$$
$$\therefore\ N^2 + 25N - 1650 = 0$$
$$\therefore\ (N+55)(N-30) = 0$$
$$\therefore\ N = -55 \text{ or } 30.$$

Since N stands for a number of people the negative solution can be discarded and it follows that there were 30 people in the original group.   ◀

▷ Example 9

What is the price of a pencil, if a reduction in price of 2 p would increase the number obtained for £2 by 5?
Here it is important to notice that the money units are mixed. If we decide to work in pence rather than pounds we proceed as follows.
Let the price of a pencil be x pence.

Then the number obtained for £2 is $\frac{200}{x}$.

After the reduction the price of one pencil is $x - 2$ pence, so the number obtained for £2 is $\frac{200}{x-2}$.

We are told, however, that the second number is 5 more than the first, so we can form the equation

$$\frac{200}{x} + 5 = \frac{200}{x-2}.$$

It should be noticed now that each term can be divided by 5:

$$\frac{40}{x} + 1 = \frac{40}{x-2}.$$

Multiplying by $x(x-2)$:

$$40(x-2) + x(x-2) = 40x$$
$$\therefore\ x^2 - 2x - 80 = 0$$
$$\therefore\ (x-10)(x+8) = 0$$
$$\therefore\ x = 10 \text{ or } -8.$$

The negative solution can be discarded and it follows that a pencil costs 10 p.   ◀

▷ **Example 10**

The speed of a boat in still water is x km h⁻¹. It takes $3\frac{1}{2}$ hours to travel 24 km upstream and return to its starting point in a river flowing at 2 km h⁻¹. Obtain an equation in x, solve it, and deduce the time for the journey upstream.

From the basic equation $speed = \dfrac{distance}{time}$ we have $time = \dfrac{distance}{speed}$.

When the boat travels against the flow of the river its net speed is $(x - 2)$ km h⁻¹ and when it travels with the river its net speed is $(x + 2)$ km h⁻¹.

Hence the time for the journey upstream is $\dfrac{24}{x - 2}$ hours and the time for the journey downstream is $\dfrac{24}{x + 2}$ hours.

Since the total time is $3\frac{1}{2}$ hours we can form the following equation:

$$\frac{24}{x - 2} + \frac{24}{x + 2} = \frac{7}{2}.$$

Multiplying throughout by $2(x - 2)(x + 2)$ and proceeding as in the last examples we now obtain

$$7x^2 - 96x - 28 = 0$$
$$\therefore (7x + 2)(x - 14) = 0$$
$$\therefore x = -\frac{2}{7} \text{ or } 14.$$

It follows that the time for the journey upstream is $\dfrac{24}{14 - 2}$ hours $= 2$ hours. ◁

EXERCISE 16b (problems leading to quadratic equations)

1 The sum of the first n terms of a certain series is $n^2 - 3n$. Find the number of terms whose sum is 28.

2 The distance travelled by a moving body in t seconds is $(3t^2 + t)$ metres. How long does the body take to travel 30 m?

3 The product of two consecutive positive odd numbers exceeds 10 times the intermediate even number by 23. Find the even number.

4 The reciprocal of a positive number, added to $\frac{1}{2}$, gives half the number. What is the number?

5 Divide 30 into two parts with a product of 216.

6 If we add twice the square of a certain whole number to the number itself, the result is 253. What is the number?

7 Divide 22 into two parts such that the sum of the squares of those parts is 250.

8 The sides of a right-angled triangle are $(x - 1)$cm, $(x + 1)$ cm and $(x + 3)$ cm. Find the length of the shortest side.

9 The hypotenuse of a right-angled triangle is $(2x + 1)$ cm and one of the other sides is $(x + 2)$ cm. If the area of the square on the third side is 24 cm², what is x?

10 Two whole numbers differ by 3 and the sum of their reciprocals is 0.7. Find the two numbers.

11 A bill of £20 is shared between x people. Write down an expression for the amount that each pays. If 3 of them had no money, and the rest shared the bill, how much would each pay then? If, in fact, each would pay £1.50 more in the second case, form an equation in x and solve it to find the number of people sharing the bill.

12 x radios are obtained for £160. What is the cost of each in terms of x? If slightly more expensive radios are bought, 4 fewer are obtained for the same money. Write down a second expression for the cost of each radio. Find x if, in fact, the second type of radio costs £2 more than the first.

13 Find a number which gives 11 when added to 24 times its own reciprocal.

14 The sum of the two short sides in a right-angled triangle is 11 cm and the area of the square on the hypotenuse is 65 cm^2. Find the shortest side.

15 The first half of a 600 km journey is covered at a speed of x km h^{-1} and the second half at a speed of $(x - 10)$ km h^{-1}. The total time is 11 hours. Form an equation and solve it to find x.

16 One worker makes x articles per hour and another makes 10 more articles per hour than the first. Write down expressions for the times they take, in hours, to make 200 articles. If the second time is in fact 1 hour less than the first, form an equation in x, solve it, and deduce the time the first worker takes to make 1000 articles.

17 The sides of a right-angled triangle are $(x - 2)$cm, $(x + 5)$cm and $(x + 7)$cm. Find the length of the hypotenuse.

18 When a positive number is decreased by 3, its reciprocal increases by $\frac{1}{6}$. Find the number.

19 A train does a 288 km journey at x km h^{-1}. Write down an expression for the time in hours. Another train does the journey 16 km h^{-1} faster. Write down an expression for the time in hours that this train takes. If the second journey in fact takes 54 minutes less than the first, form an equation in x and solve it to find the speed of the first train.

20 (Proceed as in example 9.) What is the price of a pencil if the number obtained for £1 would decrease by 2 if the price were increased by $2\frac{1}{2}$p?

21 Two positive numbers differ by 10, and the sum of their squares is 850. Find the numbers. (Let the numbers by $x - 5$ and $x + 5$.)

22 The sides of a rectangle differ by 3 cm, and the area of the rectangle differs from that of the square on its diagonal by 79 cm^2. Find the lengths of the rectangle's sides.

23 The speed of a boat in still water is 8 m s^{-1}. The boat goes 247 m upstream and returns, taking a total time of 64 s. What is the speed of the water?

24 Two cars race over a 60 km course. The car which wins completes the course in 15 minutes less time and its average speed is 20 km h^{-1} more. Find the two speeds.

25 The hypotenuse of a right-angled triangle is $(3x - 4)$ cm and the other two sides are $(x + 1)$ cm and $(2x + 1)$ cm. Find x.

26 A walker and a cyclist, whose speeds differ by 90 m min^{-1}, both travel 240 m. The cyclist starts 3 minutes after the man and arrives 3 minutes before him. Find the speed of the walker.

27 When a certain article's price is reduced by 10 p, 2 more are obtained for £6. Find the original price of the article.

28 A boat takes 75 s to travel 90 m upstream and back in a river flowing at 0.5 m s^{-1}. Find the speed of the boat in still water.

29 A man buys some articles for a total cost of 72 p. He keeps 4 and sells the rest for 2 p more each, making an overall profit of 28 p. How many articles did he buy?

30 A group of workers with equal wages earn a total of £5000 per week. They win a wage increase of £20, and the company makes 5 of them redundant. Even so, the total wage bill rises by £400. Find the original wage.

31 Two trains cover 400 km in the same time. The first travels at constant speed, while the second takes half an hour longer for the first 200 km, but averages 20 km h^{-1} more for the second 200 km. Find the speed of the first train in km h^{-1}.

32 Two numbers can be represented by $2x - 3$ and $x - 2$. Find x if the first number added to 4 times the reciprocal of the second gives $3\frac{1}{2}$ times the second.

EXERCISE 16c (miscellaneous problems)

1 I think of a number, square it, and add twice the original number. The result is 24. Find the number.

2 Find two consecutive positive odd numbers the sum of whose squares is 394.

3 A moving object travels $(4t + \frac{1}{2}t^2)$ cm in t seconds. How long does it take to travel 120 cm?

4 2 apples and 7 oranges cost 84 p, while 5 apples and 4 oranges cost 75 p. Find the price of an apple and the price of an orange.

5 Two positive numbers differ by 4, and the sum of their squares is 106. What are the numbers?

6 Find three consecutive positive even numbers whose product is 12 times the middle number.

7 The units of the lengths in the diagram (Fig. 16.1) are cm and all the angles are 90°. If the area of the figure is 27 cm^2, what is x?

Fig. 16.1

8 For 80 p x articles are obtained. Write down an expression for the price of each. If the articles cost 1 p more, 4 fewer would be obtained for 80 p. Write down a second expression for the price of each article, obtain an equation in x and solve it to find the number of articles obtained for 80 p.

9 (Proceed as in question 8) For 60 p x articles are obtained. If the articles cost 1 p more, 3 fewer would be obtained. Find x.

10 A man has £4 in 10 p's and 50 p's. If he had twice as many 10 p's and 3 fewer 50 p's he would have £3. How many of each coin does he have?

11 The two shorter sides of a right-angled triangle of area 20 cm^2 differ by 3 cm. What are the lengths of the two sides?

12 The perimeter of a rectangle equals that of a square of area 36 cm^2, and its own area differs from that of the square on its diagonal by 48 cm^2. Find the lengths of its sides.

13 A 12 km journey is covered at x km h^{-1}. The journey takes 2 hours less if the speed is raised to $(x + 1)$ km h^{-1}. Find x.

14 When the speed of a moving body rises by 2 m s^{-1}, it covers 60 m in 5 s less. Find the original speed.

15 The length and breadth of a rectangle are x cm and y cm. Its own area is 0.75 cm^2, and the area of the circle whose radius is its diagonal is $2\frac{1}{2}\pi$ cm^2. Find x and y. (Area of a circle $= \pi r^2$.)

16 A man spends £1.20 on 3 p stamps and 4 p stamps. If instead of the 3 p stamps he had bought 3 times as many 2 p stamps, he would have obtained 9 fewer 4 p stamps for the same total outlay. How many 3 p stamps did he buy?

17 In a right-angled triangle the two shorter sides differ by 1 cm and the hypotenuse is 9 cm longer than the shortest side. Find the three lengths.

18 200 books are distributed equally among x children. 10 children then leave, and their books are shared equally among the remainder. This results in each child receiving 1 extra book. Find x.

19 A rectangle and a square each have an area of 576 cm^2. 24 times the perimeter of the rectangle is equal to 25 times that of the square. Find the length and breadth of the rectangle.

20 A company employs x people on the same salary, paying them £20 000 altogether. Each person gets a rise of £5, but the company then declares 50 of them redundant. As a result its salary bill becomes £20 250. Find x.

21 John runs 1 m in x seconds and Harry runs 1 m in y seconds. Harry takes 0.2 s more than John to run 100 m, but when he is given a 3 m start in a 100 m race he takes 0.1 s less than John. Find x and y.

22 A car travels 260 km at x km h^{-1}, and returns 2 km h^{-1} faster, taking 12 minutes less. Find x.

23 If the price of an article is raised by 2 p, one article fewer is obtained for £8.40. Find the original price.

24 The hypotenuse of a right-angled triangle of area 54 cm^2 is $(x + y)$ cm and the other two sides are x cm and $(x - y)$ cm. Find x and y.

25 One train does a 300 km journey at a steady speed of x km h^{-1}. Another train travels 5 km h^{-1} faster but is held up for 45 minutes during the journey. As a result it takes 30 minutes longer for the whole journey. Find x.

26 The present ages of two people are x years and y years. 8 years ago the ratio of their ages was 4 : 5 and in 8 years time the ratio will be 6 : 7. Find x and y.

27 A 2-digit number, added to the number obtained by reversing the digits, gives 110. Half of the number is 13 more than the number obtained by reversing the digits. What is the number?

28 A car travels 480 km at x km h^{-1}. It returns 5 km h^{-1} faster by a route which is 60 km shorter, and as a result takes 48 minutes less time. Find x.

17 Algebraic Fractions

Simplifying fractions, multiplication and division

In chapter 13 it was explained that the standard way to simplify fractions is by *cancelling,* and that to cancel a fraction we factorise numerator and denominator and then cross out factors common to numerator and denominator. Suppose now that two fractions are multiplied, as in the case of

$$\frac{ax}{2b} \times \frac{b}{x}.$$

Can we cancel the x's and b's before performing the multiplication? If we carry out the multiplication first, we have

$$\frac{axb}{2bx},$$

and since both numerator and denominator are factorised expressions the x's and b's can be cancelled to give $a/2$. The same result would clearly be obtained if we cancelled before multiplying, so it follows that *when fractions are multiplied, factors common to the numerators and denominators can be cancelled before the multiplication is performed.*

▷ **Example 1**

Simplify $\dfrac{ab}{c} \times \dfrac{c^2}{2b}$.

The numerators and denominators are already factorised, so we can cancel immediately to obtain $\dfrac{ac}{2}$. ◁

▷ **Example 2**

Simplify $\dfrac{2a^2 - 8b^2}{3a - b} \div \dfrac{4a - 8b}{3b - 9a}$.

Here we invert the divisor and then multiply, factorising where possible:

$$\frac{2(a + 2b)(a - 2b)}{3a - b} \times \frac{3(b - 3a)}{4(a - 2b)}.$$

Remembering now that $3a - b = -(b - 3a)$, we cancel and obtain

$$- \frac{3(a + 2b)}{2}.$$ ◁

A somewhat different type of simplification is illustrated by the next example.

▷ **Example 3**

Simplify $\dfrac{\dfrac{1}{4x} - x}{\dfrac{1}{4x} - \dfrac{1}{2}}$.

The best method here is to multiply each term by the lowest common multiple of all the individual denominators, namely $4x$. This amounts to multiplying the top and bottom of the whole fraction by $4x$:

$$\frac{1 - 4x^2}{1 - 2x} .$$

Now we proceed in the usual way:

$$\frac{(1 + 2x)(1 - 2x)}{1 - 2x}$$

$$= 1 + 2x. \qquad \qquad ◁$$

EXERCISE 17a

Simplify:

1 $\dfrac{2xy}{w} \times \dfrac{w}{6x}$ **2** $ab \times \dfrac{b}{2a}$ **3** $\dfrac{2}{9a} \times \dfrac{a^2}{4b} \times \dfrac{6b^2}{a^2}$ **4** $\dfrac{9x^2}{y} \times \dfrac{4}{6x^2y} \times \dfrac{y^3}{2x}$

5 $\dfrac{4x}{y^2} \div \dfrac{2x^2}{y}$ **6** $\dfrac{ab}{c} \div b^2$ **7** $8pr \div \dfrac{6pr^2}{s}$ **8** $\dfrac{xy^2}{4w^3} \div \dfrac{x^2y}{6w^2}$

9 $\dfrac{2abc}{d} \div \dfrac{2ab^2c}{d}$ **10** $\dfrac{2x - 2y}{x} \times \dfrac{x^2}{x^2 - y^2}$ **11** $\dfrac{a^2 - 2ab}{2ab - 4b^2} \times \dfrac{b}{a^2}$

12 $\dfrac{rs - 2s^2}{r} \times \dfrac{2r + 4s}{r^2 - 4s^2}$ **13** $\dfrac{4 - x^2}{x} \div \dfrac{4 - 2x}{x^2}$ **14** $\dfrac{x^2 - x - 2}{x} \div \dfrac{3x - 6}{x^2}$

15 $\dfrac{2a}{a - 3b} \div \dfrac{a^2}{6b - 2a}$ **16** $\dfrac{1}{a - 5b} \div \dfrac{1}{5ab - a^2}$

17 $\dfrac{2y^2 - y}{1 + 2y} \div (1 - 4y^2)$ **18** $\dfrac{2x^2 + xy - y^2}{x - y} \div \dfrac{y^2 - 2xy}{y - x}$

19 $\dfrac{\dfrac{1}{x^2} - \dfrac{1}{x}}{\dfrac{1}{x^2} - 1}$ **20** $\dfrac{x + y}{\dfrac{1}{x} + \dfrac{1}{y}}$ **21** $\dfrac{\dfrac{1}{2a} - 1}{\dfrac{1}{4a} - \dfrac{1}{2}}$ **22** $\dfrac{ab - \dfrac{1}{ab}}{\dfrac{1}{ab} - 1}$

23 $\dfrac{\dfrac{1}{2p} - 1}{2p - 1}$ **24** $\dfrac{\dfrac{2}{x} - 1 - 3x}{x - \dfrac{1}{x}}$ **25** $\dfrac{1 - \dfrac{b}{a + b}}{a + b - \dfrac{a^2 + b^2}{a + b}}$ **26** $\dfrac{a + 2 - \dfrac{8a}{a + 2}}{a - \dfrac{5a - 2}{a + 2}}$.

Addition and subtraction

The principles governing this topic have also been considered in earlier chapters. It will be remembered that when we write, for example,

$$\frac{2}{7} + \frac{3}{7} = \frac{5}{7},$$

we are adding the like quantities *sevenths.* In a similar way, when we have

$$\frac{2}{x} + \frac{3}{x},$$

we can add up the $\frac{1}{x}$'s, which are like quantities, to obtain $\frac{5}{x}$. The general principle, which holds for both arithmetical and algebraic cases, is that *fractions can be added or subtracted to give single fractions when they have the same denominators.*

▷ Example 4

(a) $\dfrac{3}{xy} + \dfrac{t}{xy} = \dfrac{3+t}{xy}$.   (b) $\dfrac{x}{w^2} - \dfrac{1}{w^2} + \dfrac{2x}{w^2} = \dfrac{3x-1}{w^2}$.   ◁

When the denominators are different we use the same method as in arithmetical cases, namely find their lowest common multiple (LCM) and express each fraction with this as the new denominator. This is done by multiplying the numerator and denominator of each fraction by an appropriate quantity. The next few examples illustrate the procedure with some easy cases in which the LCM is obvious.

▷ Example 5

(a) $1 - \dfrac{1}{x} = \dfrac{x}{x} - \dfrac{1}{x} = \dfrac{x-1}{x}$.   (b) $\dfrac{2}{x} + \dfrac{3}{y} = \dfrac{2y}{xy} + \dfrac{3x}{xy} = \dfrac{2y+3x}{xy}$.   ◁

Most students will find that after a little practice they can omit the intermediate step in this type and write down the answer immediately.

In the next example the LCM is still obvious but the top line has to be simplified after the addition or subtraction.

▷ Example 6

(a) $1 - \dfrac{p-q}{p+q} = \dfrac{p+q-(p-q)}{p+q} = \dfrac{p+q-p+q}{p+q} = \dfrac{2q}{p+q}$.

(b) $\dfrac{3}{1-3x} + \dfrac{1}{x} = \dfrac{3x+1-3x}{x(1-3x)} = \dfrac{1}{x(1-3x)}$.   ◁

The last of this group of examples gives some cases in which the LCM is not simply the product of the original denominators.

▷**Example 7**

(a) $\dfrac{1}{p^2} - \dfrac{1}{pq} = \dfrac{q}{p^2q} - \dfrac{p}{p^2q} = \dfrac{q-p}{p^2q}$.

(b) $\dfrac{xy-3}{3y} + \dfrac{1}{y} = \dfrac{xy-3+3}{3y} = \dfrac{xy}{3y} = \dfrac{x}{3}$.

(c) $\dfrac{x+2}{x+3} - \dfrac{x-4}{x-3} = \dfrac{(x+2)(x-3)-(x-4)(x+3)}{(x+3)(x-3)}$

$\qquad = \dfrac{x^2 - 3x + 2x - 6 - (x^2 + 3x - 4x - 12)}{(x+3)(x-3)}$

$\qquad = \dfrac{6}{(x+3)(x-3)}$.

◁

EXERCISE 17b

Make into one fraction, giving the answer as simply as possible:

1 $\dfrac{a}{b} - \dfrac{c}{b}$ **2** $\dfrac{3y}{x^2} + \dfrac{1}{x^2} - \dfrac{2y}{x^2}$ **3** $2 - \dfrac{1}{x}$ **4** $\dfrac{3}{r} + \dfrac{r}{s}$

5 $\dfrac{1}{2x} - 1$ **6** $\dfrac{a^2}{b} + b$ **7** $1 - \dfrac{x}{x+y}$ **8** $y - \dfrac{1+xy}{x}$

9 $\dfrac{2a}{a+b} - 2$ **10** $\dfrac{x^2}{x-y} - x$ **11** $1 - \dfrac{a-1}{a}$ **12** $\dfrac{a}{b-c} - \dfrac{a}{b}$

13 $\dfrac{y}{x^2} - \dfrac{1}{2x}$ **14** $\dfrac{3+p}{ps} - \dfrac{1}{s}$ **15** $\dfrac{ax+2}{2x} - \dfrac{1}{x}$ **16** $\dfrac{x+2y}{xy} - \dfrac{2}{x}$

17 $\dfrac{w+2}{5w} - \dfrac{1}{5}$ **18** $\dfrac{1}{x} + \dfrac{x-y}{xy}$ **19** $\dfrac{1-a}{2a} - \dfrac{a+b}{ab} + \dfrac{b+1}{2b}$ **20** $\dfrac{1}{2x} + \dfrac{1-x}{x^2}$

21 $\dfrac{x+y}{xy} + \dfrac{1-x}{2x^2} - \dfrac{1}{y}$ **22** $\dfrac{1+y}{xy} - \dfrac{2+x}{2x}$ **23** $1 + a - \dfrac{2a}{1+a}$

24 $\dfrac{r-s}{s} + \dfrac{s}{r+s}$ **25** $\dfrac{x+1}{(x-1)^2} - \dfrac{1}{x-1}$ **26** $\dfrac{2+x}{2-x} - \dfrac{2-x}{2+x}$.

More complicated examples of addition and subtraction

In the examples considered so far the lowest common multiple has been fairly obvious because the denominators have all been either factorised expressions, such as $2xy$, or expressions which cannot be factorised such as x or $x+3$. The LCM is less obvious if the denominators are unfactorised expressions which it is possible to factorise, and in these cases we use the general technique for obtaining LCMs which was explained in chapter 13.

▷ **Example 8**

Make into one fraction $\dfrac{3}{2a-4} - \dfrac{a-1}{a^2-4}$.

The first step is to factorise the denominators:

$$\frac{3}{2\,(a-2)} - \frac{a-1}{(a+2)\,(a-2)}.$$

Now it is clear that the LCM is $2\,(a+2)\,(a-2)$ and we proceed:

$$\frac{3\,(a+2) - 2\,(a-1)}{2\,(a+2)\,(a-2)} = \frac{3a+6-2a+2}{2\,(a+2)\,(a-2)} = \frac{a+8}{2\,(a+2)\,(a-2)}. \qquad \triangleleft$$

▷ **Example 9**

Make into one fraction $\dfrac{1}{6x-3} + \dfrac{1-x}{1-x-2x^2}$.

Factorising the denominators we have

$$\frac{1}{3\,(2x-1)} + \frac{1-x}{(1-2x)\,(1+x)}.$$

Since $1-2x = -(2x-1)$ and $1-x = -(x-1)$ this can be re-expressed as

$$\frac{1}{3\,(2x-1)} + \frac{x-1}{(2x-1)\,(x+1)}$$

$$= \frac{x+1+3\,(x-1)}{3\,(2x-1)\,(x+1)} = \frac{4x-2}{3\,(2x-1)\,(x+1)} = \frac{2\,(2x-1)}{3\,(2x-1)\,(x+1)} = \frac{2}{3\,(x+1)}. \qquad \triangleleft$$

EXERCISE 17c

Make into one fraction, giving the answer as simply as possible:

1 $\dfrac{1}{x-1} - \dfrac{2}{x^2-1}$

2 $\dfrac{2x-1}{x^2-5x} + \dfrac{3}{x-5}$

3 $\dfrac{3}{a-1} - \dfrac{7-a}{a^2-1}$

4 $\dfrac{3}{2-2y} - \dfrac{2-5y}{1-y^2}$

5 $\dfrac{3}{2-6a} - \dfrac{a-1}{a-3a^2}$

6 $\dfrac{x-3}{x^2-2x} + \dfrac{1}{2x-4}$

7 $\dfrac{7x-5}{x^2-x-2} - \dfrac{3}{x-2}$

8 $\dfrac{2p}{p^2-4} + \dfrac{1}{2-p}$

9 $\dfrac{1}{12x^2-7x+1} - \dfrac{1}{3x^2-x}$

10 $\dfrac{3}{4y-2} - \dfrac{y-2}{1+y-6y^2}$

11 $\dfrac{3}{x^2+x-2} + \dfrac{1}{x-x^2}$

12 $\dfrac{4a-5}{2a^2-2a-4} - \dfrac{1}{2a-4}$.

Equations

Some simple examples of fractional equations have already arisen in chapters 12 and 16. In these examples the lowest common multiple of the denominators was obvious and the fractions could be immediately removed by multiplying throughout by the LCM. The only type which remains to be considered is that in which the LCM has to be found by the factorisation technique used above.

▷ **Example 10**

Solve the equation $\dfrac{2}{3x-6} - \dfrac{x+1}{x^2+x-6} = \dfrac{1}{2x+6}$.

Factorising the denominators we have

$$\frac{2}{3(x-2)} - \frac{x+1}{(x+3)(x-2)} = \frac{1}{2(x+3)}.$$

The LCM is $6(x+3)(x-2)$. Multiplying throughout by this we obtain

$$4(x+3) - 6(x+1) = 3(x-2)$$
$$\therefore \ 4x + 12 - 6x - 6 = 3x - 6$$
$$\therefore \ 5x = 12$$
$$\therefore \ x = 2\tfrac{2}{5}. \qquad \qquad \qquad \triangleleft$$

EXERCISE 17d

Solve the following equations:

1 $\dfrac{x-1}{3x^2} = \dfrac{5}{6x}$

2 $\dfrac{1}{2x} - \dfrac{1-x}{x^2} = \dfrac{1+2x}{4x^2}$

3 $\dfrac{1}{2-4x} = \dfrac{x-1}{x-2x^2}$

4 $\dfrac{x+2}{x^2-9} = \dfrac{3}{2x-6}$

5 $\dfrac{1}{x+1} = \dfrac{x}{x^2-1} + \dfrac{2}{x-1}$

6 $\dfrac{x}{x^2-2x-3} = \dfrac{3}{x-3} + \dfrac{2}{x+1}$

7 $\dfrac{3}{x} = \dfrac{1}{2-2x} + \dfrac{2-x}{x^2-x}$

8 $\dfrac{x+3}{3x+6} + \dfrac{1}{x} + \dfrac{1}{3} = 0$

9 $\dfrac{x}{2-6x} - \dfrac{1-2x}{3-9x} = \dfrac{1}{3}$

10 $\dfrac{x+1}{6x-4} = \dfrac{x+2}{2x} - \dfrac{1}{2}$

11 $\dfrac{1}{1-2x} - \dfrac{1-x}{1-4x^2} = \dfrac{2}{3+6x}$

12 $\dfrac{5}{8x-2} = \dfrac{3x}{1-5x+4x^2} - \dfrac{1}{2}$.

18 Transformation of Equations

Equations and formulae

An equation relating letters is usually called a *formula* when its letters stand for definite quantities. For example, the formula $s = ut$ gives the distance s travelled by a body moving with a speed of u in a time of t. In this chapter, however, the letters have been left undefined, and we shall therefore use the term *equations* throughout.

The subject of an equation

The equation $x = y + 2w$, in which x is expressed entirely in terms of other quantities, is said to have x as its *subject*. On the other hand, x is not considered to be the subject of the equation $x = y + 2xw$, because x also occurs on the right-hand side. We could not find x from this equation by substituting values for w and y and evaluating the right-hand side. So an equation is only said to have a subject when one letter is *isolated* on one side.

Re-arranging equations

The rules for re-arranging (or *transforming,* or *transposing*) equations are just the same as the rules for solving simple equations with one unknown. The procedure is to *do the same to both sides* until the equation is in the required form. It is very important, when re-arranging an equation, always to be aware of the mathematical procedure that is being applied to both sides and not to use rules of thumb such as 'swap sides and change the sign' or 'cross multiply'. These rules only apply in particular circumstances and it is easy to misapply them when the reasons behind them are not understood.

Re-arrangements of equations usually take the form of making some specified letter the subject. The procedure is easiest when the letter in question only occurs once in the equation, and we shall start with some examples of this kind.

▷ Example 1

Make y the subject of the equation w − ay = t.
First the term containing y must be isolated on one side. It is best to place the term on the right-hand side, where it will be positive, so we add *ay* to both sides and subtract *t* from both sides:

$$w - t = ay.$$

Now we divide both sides by *a*:

$$y = \frac{w - t}{a}. \qquad \triangleleft$$

▷ Example 2

Make x the subject of $y = \frac{x + w}{s}$.
Here we begin by removing the fraction. Multiplying both sides by *s* and remembering that fraction lines work like brackets, we have

$$ys = \frac{(x + w)\cancel{s}}{\cancel{s}},$$
$$\text{i.e. } ys = x + w.$$

The cancelling is legitimate here because *s* is a *factor* of the top and bottom of the fraction.
   Finally we subtract *w* from both sides:

$$x = ys - w. \qquad \triangleleft$$

▷ Example 3

Make l the subject of $T = 2\pi \sqrt{\dfrac{l}{g}}$.
First we remove the square root by squaring both sides:

$$T^2 = \frac{4\pi^2 l}{g}$$

Now we simply multiply both sides by *g* and divide both sides by $4\pi^2$:

$$l = \frac{T^2 g}{4\pi^2}. \qquad \triangleleft$$

▷ Example 4

Make w the subject of $\dfrac{p^2}{w^2 - r^2} = s^2$.
The first step is to move the term involving *w* from the bottom line to the top. This can be done by multiplying both sides by the *whole bottom line* $w^2 - r^2$:

$$p^2 = s^2 (w^2 - r^2).$$

Now we remove the brackets and isolate w^2:

$$p^2 = s^2w^2 - s^2r^2$$
$$\therefore s^2w^2 = p^2 + s^2r^2$$

$$\therefore w^2 = \frac{p^2 + s^2r^2}{s^2}.$$

The final step is to take the square root of both sides and this requires some care. The square root of a fraction *is* equal to the square root of the top divided by the square root of the bottom, but the square root of the above top line $p^2 + s^2r^2$ is *not* $p + sr$. This immediately becomes clear if we square $p + sr$; we get not $p^2 + s^2r^2$ but $p^2 + s^2r^2 + 2psr$. In general, *we cannot take square roots term-by-term.* It follows that the simplest expression for w is given by

$$w = \frac{\pm\sqrt{(p^2 + s^2r^2)}}{s}.$$

◁

The procedure adopted in the above examples is summed up in the following general rules:
(1) Remove fractions, brackets and roots.
(2) Isolate the whole term containing the required letter on one side.
(3) Divide both sides by the other factors of that term, and take roots of both sides if necessary.

EXERCISE 18a

Make the letter given in brackets after the equation the subject of the equation.

1 $ax - y = w$ (x) **2** $p = \frac{w - r}{s}$ (w) **3** $\frac{2ab}{c} = d$ (a) **4** $\frac{x}{y} = \frac{w}{r}$ (r)

5 $r^2s + t = w$ (r) **6** $\frac{3xy - 2}{ax} = x$ (y) **7** $3x\sqrt{\frac{w}{r}} = y$ (w) **8** $\frac{x^2y}{t} = \frac{a}{b}$ (x)

9 $\frac{x}{w + y} = 2$ (y) **10** $\sqrt{\left(\frac{a - b}{3c}\right)} = 2a$ (c) **11** $y(w - 2x) = w$ (x)

12 $\frac{2}{ab - c} = \frac{3}{c}$ (b) **13** $2ab\sqrt{(x - 1)} = 1$ (x) **14** $2a(b - a) = a^2 - 2$ (b)

15 $\frac{5x}{2y - 3} = \frac{2}{w}$ (y) **16** $\frac{2\sqrt{(xy - w)}}{3y} = w$ (x) **17** $\sqrt{(y^2 - w^2)} = \frac{2a}{x}$ (w)

18 $4w\sqrt{\left(\frac{x}{1 - y}\right)} = 3$ (y) **19** $\frac{w^2}{2} = \frac{w^2x^2 - 2}{x^2 - y^2}$ (y) **20** $4ps = \frac{p - r}{ps}$ (s).

More complicated examples of making a letter the subject

In the set of examples given above the letter required as subject occurred in one term only. The next examples illustrate the more general procedure which is needed when the required letter occurs in more than one term.

▷**Example 5**

Make x the subject of $\dfrac{ax - y}{xy - a} = -\dfrac{2}{3}.$

As before, we begin by removing the fractions. This is done by multiplying both sides by 3 $(xy - a)$. Note that $-\dfrac{2}{3}$ can be regarded as $\dfrac{-2}{3}$; it is *not* equal to $\dfrac{-2}{-3}.$

$$3ax - 3y = -2\,(xy - a)$$
$$\therefore\ 3ax - 3y = -2xy + 2a.$$

Now we place all the terms containing x on one side, and move other terms to the other side. Adding $2xy$ and $3y$ to both sides:

$$3ax + 2xy = 3y + 2a.$$

Now the side on which we have placed the x terms must contain a common factor of x, so we can factorise by taking out this common factor:

$$x\,(3a + 2y) = 3y + 2a.$$

Finally we divide both sides by $3a + 2y$:

$$x = \frac{3y + 2a}{3a + 2y}.\qquad\qquad ◁$$

▷**Example 6**

Make x the subject of $\dfrac{1}{2y} + \dfrac{1}{x} = \dfrac{1}{4w}.$

It should be noted first that it is a complete mistake to invert each term. We can, if we wish, take the reciprocal of *both sides,* but the reciprocal of the left-hand side is not equal to the sum of the individual reciprocals. This can be most simply seen by a numerical example: since $\frac{1}{4} + \frac{1}{4}$ is equal to $\frac{1}{2}$, its reciprocal is 2; but the sum of the individual reciprocals is $4 + 4 = 8$. The operation of taking the reciprocal, like that of taking the square root, cannot be performed term-by-term.

The simplest method is to remove the fractions by multiplying throughout by the LCM of the denominators, namely $4xyw$:

$$2xw + 4yw = xy.$$

Now we proceed as in the last example, placing all the terms containing x on one side:

$$xy - 2xw = 4yw.$$

The common factor x is now taken out:

$$x\,(y - 2w) = 4yw.$$

And finally we divide both sides by $y - 2w$:

$$x = \frac{4yw}{y - 2w}.$$

The following general rules for making a letter the subject may be helpful:

(1) Remove fractions, brackets and roots.
(2) Place all the terms containing the required letter on one side, and the other terms on the other side.
(3) Take out the required letter as a common factor.
(4) Divide both sides by the other factor obtained, and take roots of both sides if necessary.

EXERCISE 18b

Make the letter given in brackets after the equation the subject of the equation:

1 $ax + y = xy$ (x) **2** $ps + r + s = pr$ (p) **3** $a - ac = 2b - bc$ (c)

4 $3x - 2ab = ax + 5b$ (a) **5** $x(y - w) = 2y(w - 3)$ (y) **6** $\dfrac{2 - xy}{x} = 2$ (x)

7 $\dfrac{p - rs}{r} = \dfrac{2}{3}$ (r) **8** $\dfrac{w}{wx - y} = \dfrac{3}{4}$ (w) **9** $\dfrac{a}{b} = \dfrac{ab - c}{c}$ (a) **10** $\dfrac{2x}{x - y} = \dfrac{y}{3 - y}$ (x)

11 $\dfrac{1}{s} + \dfrac{1}{t} = \dfrac{1}{w}$ (t) **12** $\dfrac{2}{x} - \dfrac{1}{y} = \dfrac{1}{w}$ (x) **13** $\dfrac{a}{r} = \dfrac{2}{s} - \dfrac{1}{t}$ (t) **14** $\dfrac{2}{3x} - \dfrac{1}{6y} = s$ (x)

15 $y = \dfrac{1}{x} - \dfrac{y}{x^2}$ (y) **16** $\dfrac{2ay - 3yc}{ac - y} = \dfrac{1}{2}$ (y) **17** $\dfrac{3 - x}{a - xy} = -\dfrac{3}{4}$ (x)

18 $aT^2 - R^2 = T^2$ (T) **19** $1 - \dfrac{R^2}{p^2} = \dfrac{Q^2}{4}$ (P) **20** $\dfrac{a^2}{a^2 + b^2} = \dfrac{2}{3}$ (a)

21 $\sqrt{\left(\dfrac{A - x}{Ay}\right)} = -\dfrac{1}{2}$ (A) **22** $P = 2r\sqrt{\left(\dfrac{a^2 + b^2}{2rs}\right)}$ (a) **23** $\dfrac{a^3 b - c}{a^2} = \dfrac{a}{b}$ (a)

24 $\dfrac{2}{3x} - \dfrac{1}{y} = \dfrac{1}{w^2}$ (w) **25** $x\sqrt{(P^2 - S^2)} = aS$ (S) **26** $\dfrac{1}{y^2} + \dfrac{w^2}{x^2} = 1$ (x)

27 $\dfrac{T^2 x - r}{T^2 r - x} = -1\tfrac{1}{2}$ (T) **28** $\sqrt{(a^2 b^2 - 2ab)} = a - b$ (b)

29 $\dfrac{m - n}{mn} = \dfrac{1}{m^2} - \dfrac{m}{n}$ (n) **30** $\sqrt{(p^2 s^2 - r^2)} = ps - t$ (s).

19 Variation

Direct variation

Suppose that two quantities x and y vary together in such a way that when one of them is doubled the other becomes doubled, when one is trebled the other becomes trebled, and so on. E.g.

x	1	2	3	4	5
y	5	10	15	20	25

In these circumstances we say that y is *directly proportional to* x, or that y *varies directly as* x. (The word 'directly' is sometimes omitted.) The relationship can be expressed by means of the equation $y = kx$, where k is a constant called a *constant of proportionality*. In the above example $k = 5$.

The following are some examples of direct variation:

(1) The circumference of a circle is directly proportional to its radius, the equation relating the two quantities being $C = 2\pi r$. Here 2π is the constant of proportionality.

(2) The area of a circle is proportional to the square of its radius, the equation relating the quantities being $A = \pi r^2$.

(3) When a body is moving with constant speed, the distance it has travelled (s) is proportional to the time for which it has been moving (t). The equation relating the quantities is $s = ut$, the speed u being the constant of proportionality.

When y is directly proportional to x it clearly follows that x is directly proportional to y, since $y = kx \Rightarrow x = (1/k) \times y$.

x and y need not be quantities of the same kind, and there is no necessary relationship between their units. Even when they are quantities of the same kind, moreover, they can have different units. For example, if both are lengths, y might be in km while x is in cm. The units in the equation $y = kx$ must of course be consistent, which means that k must have the appropriate units.

Inverse variation

Suppose now that when one of two quantities is doubled the other becomes halved, when one is multiplied by 5 the other becomes divided by 5, and so on. E.g.

x	1	2	3	4
y	12	6	4	3

Here we say that y *is inversely proportional to x*, or that y *varies inversely as x*. The equation relating the quantities now has the form $y = \frac{k}{x}$, the constant k having the value 12 in the above example. If y is inversely proportional to x it clearly follows that x is inversely proportional to y. Again the equation $s = ut$ can be used to provide an example of this kind of relationship: since $t = \frac{s}{u}$ the time taken to complete a journey of definite length is inversely proportional to the speed.

▷ Example 1

y is directly proportional to x^2 and $y = 3$ when $x = 2$. Find y when $x = 6$.
We have $y = kx^2$ and since $y = 3$ when $x = 2$, $3 = 4k$ and $k = \frac{3}{4}$. Hence the exact relationship between x and y is given by the equation $y = \frac{3x^2}{4}$. When $x = 6$ we have $y = \frac{3 \times 36}{4} = 27$. ◁

▷ Example 2

y is directly proportional to w^3 and w varies inversely as x^2. Find the relationship between y and x.
When more than one constant of proportionality occurs in a question we must not denote each by k since this implies without justification that the constants are equal. The initial letters of the alphabet are useful symbols for the constants when there are several of them. We therefore have

$$y = Aw^3 \quad \text{and} \quad w = \frac{B}{x^2}.$$

To obtain the relationship between y and x we must eliminate w, and this is easily done by substituting $\frac{B}{x^2}$ for w in the first equation:

$$y = \frac{AB^3}{x^6}.$$

AB^3 is simply an unknown constant, and it is therefore best denoted by a single letter. Hence, letting $AB^3 = C$, we have $y = \frac{C}{x^6}$ and it follows that y is *inversely proportional to x^6*. ◁

▷ Example 3

The area of a circle is directly proportional to the square of its circumference. What happens to the area when the circumference (a) is doubled, (b) is decreased by 10%?
(a) The general relationship between the area and the circumference is given by the equation $A = kC^2$. Let A_1 and C_1 be a particular pair of values of A and

C, and let A_2 be the area when the circumference becomes $2C_1$. Then we have

$$A_1 = kC_1^2 \qquad (1)$$
$$\text{and} \quad A_2 = k(2C_1)^2$$
$$\text{i.e.} \quad A_2 = 4kC_1^2 \qquad (2)$$

Now from equations (1) and (2) it is clear that $A_2 = 4A_1$ and thus that when the circumference is doubled the area is 4 times as great.

(b)   Again let A_1 and C_1 be a particular pair of values of the area and circumference. When the circumference is decreased by 10% its value becomes $90C_1/100$ or $9C_1/10$ and we have

$$A_1 = kC_1^2 \qquad (1)$$
$$\text{and} \quad A_2 = k\frac{(9C_1)^2}{10}$$
$$\text{i.e.} \quad A_2 = \frac{81kC_1^2}{100} \qquad (2)$$

From equations (1) and (2) we see that $A_2 = \dfrac{81A_1}{100}$ and thus that when the circumference is decreased by 10% the area is decreased by 19%.   ◀

Joint variation

Sometimes one variable quantity depends not on just one other variable, as in the above examples, but on two or more others. For example, the formula $V = \pi r^2 h$ gives the volume of a cylinder in terms of its radius and its length. In this case we say that V *varies directly as both* r^2 *and* h. (It can also be said that V is *directly proportional* to both r^2 and h, though this wording is less common.) More generally, if we have an equation of the form

$$w = k\frac{xy\dots}{pq\dots}$$

we say that w varies directly as $x, y \dots$ and inversely as $p, q \dots$.

▷ **Example 4**

y varies directly as x and inversely as w^2, and $y = \frac{1}{3}$ when $x = 3$ and $w = 6$. Find x when $y = 2$ and $w = 3$.

We have $y = \dfrac{kx}{w^2}$ and, substituting the given values, $\dfrac{1}{3} = \dfrac{3k}{36}$. Hence $k = 4$ and the equation giving the exact relationship between the three variables is $y = \dfrac{4x}{w^2}$. When $y = 2$ and $w = 3$ we have $2 = \dfrac{4x}{9}$ and hence $x = 4\frac{1}{2}$.   ◀

Partial variation

Consider the equation $y = Ax^2 + \dfrac{B}{x}$, where x and y are variables and A and B are constants. An exact description of the relationship would be: 'y is equal to the sum of two parts, one of which varies directly as x^2 and one of which varies inversely as *x*.' This kind of relationship is sometimes called *partial variation*, an alternative description of the above example being: '*y* varies partially as x^2 and partially inversely as *x*'. It is important not to confuse partial and joint variation, and therefore the first description, though longer, is probably preferable to the second.

▷ Example 5

The resistance to a moving body is equal to the sum of two parts, one of which varies as the speed and the other as the square of the speed. The resistance is 720 N (newtons) at 80 m s⁻¹ and 1000 N at 100 m s⁻¹. What is the resistance when the speed is 120 m s⁻¹?

Let *R* = resistance in N and *v* = speed in m s⁻¹. Then $R = av + bv^2$, and we can find *a* and *b* by substituting the given values of *v* and *R* and solving the resulting simultaneous equations:

$$720 = 80a + 6400b$$
$$1000 = 100a + 10\,000b$$

Solution of these equations gives $a = 5$, $b = \frac{1}{20}$, and the exact relationship between *R* and *v* is therefore given by the equation $R = 5v + \frac{v^2}{20}$. When $v = 120$ we have $R = 600 + \frac{14\,400}{20} = 1320$, and the resistance is therefore 1320 N.   ◁

EXERCISE 19

1 *y* is directly proportional to x^2, and $y = 16$ when $x = 2$. Find (a) *y* when $x = 3$, (b) *x* when $y = 100$.

2 *y* is inversely proportional to *x*, and $y = 3$ when $x = 2$. Find *y* when *x* is (a) 12, (b) $\frac{1}{2}$.

3 *y* varies directly as x^2, and $y = 8$ when $x = 2$. Find (a) *y* when $x = 3$, (b) *y* when $x = \frac{1}{4}$, (c) *x* when $y = 4\frac{1}{2}$.

4 *y* varies inversely as x^3, and $y = \frac{1}{16}$ when $x = 2$. Find *y* when *x* is (a) -1, (b) $\frac{1}{2}$.

5 *y* is inversely proportional to the positive square root of *x*, and $y = \frac{1}{4}$ when $x = 4$. Find (a) *y* when $x = 9$, (b) *x* when $y = 1$.

6 *x* varies inversely as w^3, and $x = 2$ when $w = \frac{1}{2}$. Find (a) *x* when $w = \frac{1}{4}$, (b) *w* when $x = 54$.

7 *y* is inversely proportional to *x* and *x* is directly proportional to w^2. Obtain in its simplest form an equation relating *y* and *w*.

8 *y* varies inversely as x^2 and *x* varies directly as w^3. Given that $y = \frac{1}{8}$ when $w = 2$, find *y* when $w = 1$.

9 *P* varies inversely as *R* and *R* varies directly as the square of *S*. If $P = 1$ when $S = 2$, what is *P* when $S = 4$?

10 *t* varies directly as r^2 and *r* varies inversely as *s*. If $t = 12$ when $s = \frac{1}{4}$, find (a) *t* when $s = \frac{1}{2}$, (b) *s* when $t = \frac{3}{16}$.

11 *y* is directly proportional to x^2. By what factor is *y* multiplied when *x* is multiplied (a) by 3, (b) by $\frac{1}{2}$?

12 The weight of a body is inversely proportional to the square of its distance from the centre of the Earth. By what factor is the weight of a body multiplied if it is taken 4 times as far from the Earth's centre?

13 *y* is directly proportional to x^2. What is the percentage increase in *y* if *x* is increased (a) by 20%, (b) by 50%?

14 y varies directly as x and inversely as w^2. Given that $y = 6$ when $x = 3$ and $w = 2$, find (a) y when $x = 2$ and $w = 4$, (b) x when $y = 16$ and $w = \frac{1}{2}$.

15 p varies directly as the positive square root of x and inversely as y. Given that $p = 1$ when $x = 9$ and $y = 6$, find (a) p when $x = 4$ and $y = 8$, (b) y when $x = 1$ and $p = 2$.

16 p is directly proportional to r and the square of s. Given that $p = 2$ when $r = s = \frac{1}{2}$, find (a) p when $r = \frac{1}{8}$ and $s = 2$, (b) s when $p = r = 2$.

17 y varies directly as x^2 and inversely as the positive square root of w. Given that $y = 2$ when $x = 3$ and $w = 9$, find (a) y when $x = 6$ and $w = 4$, (b) x when $w = \frac{1}{4}$ and $y = \frac{1}{3}$.

18 The time taken to repair a road is directly proportional to the length of the road and inversely proportional to the number of men working on it. Given that 5 men take 8 days to repair 200 m, calculate (a) the time it will take 6 men to repair 480 m, (b) the length of road which 7 men will repair in 3 days.

19 The mass of a cylindrical piece of metal varies directly as its length and the square of its radius. Given that the mass is 2 kg when the radius is 6 cm and the length 30 cm, find (a) the mass when the radius is 3 cm and the length 40 cm, (b) the length of a cylinder of mass 4 kg and radius 4 cm.

20 y varies directly as x and inversely as w^2. By what factor is y multiplied when (a) x is multiplied by 8 and w by 2, (b) x and w are both divided by 2?

21 P varies directly as R and S. What is the percentage increase in P when R is increased by 50% and S is decreased by 20%?

22 y is equal to the sum of two parts, one of which is constant and one of which varies as the square of x. Given that y has the value 17 when $x = 1$ and the value 32 when $x = 2$, find its value when $x = 3$.

23 x varies partly as r and partly as s. Given that $x = 9$ when $r = s = 2$, and $x = 6$ when $r = 4$ and $s = 1$, find x when $r = 6$ and $s = 3$.

24 y is equal to the sum of two parts, one of which varies as x and one of which varies inversely as x^2. Given that $y = 34$ when $x = \frac{1}{2}$ and $y = 10$ when $x = 2$, find y when $x = 4$.

25 A salesman's monthly salary consists of a fixed sum plus a commission which is proportional to the number of articles he sells. His salary is £325 when he sells 25 articles and £400 when he sells 50 articles. Find (a) his salary when he sells 40 articles, (b) the number of articles he must sell to make his salary £475.

26 The distance travelled by an accelerating body varies partly as the time for which it moves and partly as the square of the time. Given that it travels 48 m in 2 s and 78 m in 3 s find (a) how far it travels in $\frac{1}{2}$s, (b) how long it takes to travel 150 m.

20 Functions

A function (or *mapping*) can be regarded as a rule which transforms or 'maps' one number to another number called its *image*. For example the function 'multiply by 2' maps 3 to 6, 5 to 10, and so on. The set of all the numbers to which the rule applies is called the *domain* of the function, and the set of all the images is called its *range*. The idea of a function is explained pictorially in the following *arrow diagram,* (Fig. 20.1), which illustrates the function 'multiply by 2'.

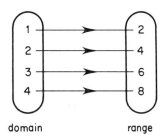

Fig. 20.1

An essential feature of a function is that each element in the domain has a *unique* image, so that an image is *determined* (made definite) once an element of the domain has been specified. Thus in an arrow diagram representing a function, *one and only one arrow* must leave each element of the domain. Any arrow diagram which does not have this feature provides an example of a more general mathematical concept called a *relation*; so a function could be defined as *a relation in which each element of the domain has a unique image.*

Most mathematical functions are defined by means of formulae. Thus if elements in the domain and range are denoted by x and y respectively, the funtion 'multiply by 2' could be defined by the formula $y = 2x$. A formula must, however, give a definite value of y for each value of x if it is to define a function. For example the formula $y = \sqrt{x}$ does define a function because the square root sign denotes the positive square root only; but the formula $y = \pm\sqrt{x}$ defines a relation and not a function because each value of x now has two images.

The domain of a function defined by a formula is usually taken to be $\mathbf{R}$

(the set of all real numbers) or all the values of $\mathbf{R}$ for which the defining formula is meaningful. For example the formula $y = 2x$ is meaningful when x takes any value of $\mathbf{R}$, the formula $y = \sqrt{x}$ is meaningful for all positive values of $\mathbf{R}$, and the formula $y = \dfrac{1}{x - 3}$ is meaningful for all values of $\mathbf{R}$ except 3. When the domain of a function is $\mathbf{R}$ and its range is a subset of $\mathbf{R}$, the function is said to be defined *on* $\mathbf{R}$.

Notation

Functions are normally denoted by the small letters f, g, h, etc. These are used in the following two ways.

$$\textbf{1}\ \ f{:}x \rightarrow 2x.$$

This statement can be read,'the function f which maps x to $2x$', or 'f is the function which maps x to $2x$'.

$$\textbf{2}\ \ f(x) = 2x.$$

In this statement the symbol $f(x)$ is read 'f of x' and it denotes the *image* of x under the function f. The symbol $f(x)$ is thus an alternative to y. Its advantage is that it provides a convenient way of denoting the image of any particular number. For example the image of 5 is denoted by $f(5)$, and if $f(x) = 2x$ we have $f(5) = 10$. The symbol $f(5)$ is also called *the value of the function* when $x = 5$; thus the value of the 'multiply by 2' function is 10 when x is 5 and 14 when x is 7.

▷**Example 1**

The function $f{:}x \rightarrow 2x^2 - 3x$ is defined on $\mathbf{R}$. (a) Calculate $f(-2)$. (b) Find the image of 3 under f. (c) Find the values of x at which the value of the function is 5.
(a) $f(-2) = 2(-2)^2 - 3(-2) = 8 + 6 = 14$.
(b) The image of 3 is simply $f(3)$, that is $2(3)^2 - 3(3) = 18 - 9 = 9$.
(c) When the value of the function is 5 we obtain the quadratic equation $2x^2 - 3x = 5$, which can be solved by the factor method:

$$2x^2 - 3x - 5 = 0$$
$$\therefore\ (2x - 5)(x + 1) = 0$$
$$\therefore\ x = 2\tfrac{1}{2}\text{ or } -1.$$ ◀

▷**Example 2**

A function f defined on $\mathbf{R}$ is such that $f(x) = x^2 - 4$ when x is negative or zero and $f(x) = x + 3$ when x is positive. Find (a) the range of f, (b) the solutions of the equation $f(x) = 3x$.
(a) When x is negative or zero, x^2 is positive or zero and varies between zero and $+\infty$. Hence $x^2 - 4$ varies between -4 and $+\infty$. When x is positive the expression $x + 3$ varies between $+3$ and $+\infty$ and therefore does not extend the range given by $x^2 - 4$. The range of the complete function f is thus $\{x: -4 \leqslant x < \infty\}$.

(b) Solving the equation $x^2 - 4 = 3x$, we have $x^2 - 3x - 4 = 0$; hence $(x - 4)(x + 1) = 0$; hence $x = 4$ or -1. Since however $f(x) = x^2 - 4$ only when x is negative or zero, the solution $x = 4$ must be discarded.

Solving the equation $x + 3 = 3x$, we have $2x = 3$ and $x = 1\frac{1}{2}$. Since $f(x) = x + 3$ when x is positive, this is an acceptable solution.

The final solutions are thus -1 and $1\frac{1}{2}$.   ◀

The following exercise is partly designed to accustom students to function notation, and the terminology is varied from question to question. Thus it must be realised that whether a question asks for, say, $f(2)$, or the image of 2, or the value of the function when $x = 2$, the method and answer will be the same.

EXERCISE 20a

(The functions in the exercises of this chapter are defined on $\mathbf{R}$ unless otherwise stated.)

1 Calculate the images of (a) 0, (b) 2, (c) -1, under the function $x \to 3x - 2$.

2 Given a function $g:x \to 1 - 2x$, find (a) g(1), (b) g(3), (c) g(-2), (d) g($-3\frac{1}{2}$).

3 The function p is defined by the equation $p(x) = x^2 - 2x$. Find the values of the function when x is (a) 3, (b) 6, (c) -4, (d) $\frac{1}{2}$, (e) $-1\frac{1}{2}$.

4 A function is defined by the equation $y = \frac{1}{2}(x - 2)$. Find the values of the function when x is (a) 6, (b) -4, (c) 0, (d) $-6\frac{1}{2}$.

5 Given a function $f:x \to 2x^2 - 5x + 3$, find (a) f(0), (b) f(1), (c) f(-1), (d) f(3), (e) f(-3).

6 Given the mapping $x \to (2x - 1)(3x + 2)$, find the images of (a) 0, (b) 1, (c) 2, (d) $\frac{1}{2}$, (e) -3.

7 Given that $g(x) = x^3 - 3x^2 + 4x - 4$, find (a) g(0), (b) g(1), (c) g(2), g(-2).

8 Given the function $x \to x^3 + 2x^2 - 5x - 6$, find the values of the function when x is (a) 0, (b) 1, (c) -1, (d) 2, (e) -4.

9 A function is defined by the equation $y = 2x^3 + x^2 - 2x + 1$. Find the values of y when x is (a) 2, (b) -1, (c) 3, (d) -3.

10 Given the function $m:x \to 3x^4 - 2x^3 - 5$, calculate (a) m(-1), (b) m(2), (c) m(-2).

11 Given that $f(x) = 4^x$, find (a) f(0), (b) f($\frac{1}{2}$), (c) f(-1), (d) f($2\frac{1}{2}$), (e) f($-1\frac{1}{2}$).

12 Given the mapping $x \to x^{-1/2}$, find the images of (a) 9, (b) 0.25, (c) 0.01, (d) $2\frac{1}{4}$.

13 Given that $g(x) = |x| - 3$, find (a) g(-5), (b) g(6). (*Note:* $|x|$ means the *numerical value* of x — see the *General Information* section.)

14 Given the function $x \to |2x - 8|$, find the values of the function when x is (a) 2, (b) 6, (c) -5.

15 Find the elements whose images under the mapping $x \to 5x - 3$ are (a) 7, (b) -18, (c) 0.

16 Given the function $x \to 2 - \frac{1}{2}x$, find the values of x at which the values of the function are (a) 5, (b) -1, (c) $-\frac{1}{2}$.

17 Given the function $f:x \to x^2 - 4x$, solve the equations (a) $f(x) = 5$, (b) $f(x) = 12$, (c) $f(x) = -3$.

18 Find the elements whose images are (a) 4, (b) -3, under the mapping $x \to 2x^2 + 7x$.

19 A function is defined by the equation $y = 9^x$. Find the values of x for which y is (a) 1, (b) 3, (c) $\frac{1}{81}$ (d) 27.

20 Given the function $g:x \rightarrow 2^{1-x}$, find the values of x whose images under g are (a) 1, (b) 4, (c) $\frac{1}{2}$.

21 Given that $h(x) = |x + 5|$, find the two values of x which have an image under h of 2.

22 The domain of the mapping $f:x \rightarrow x^2$ is the set $\{x: -2 \leqslant x \leqslant 2\}$. What is the range of f?

23 The domain of the function $g:x \rightarrow 2x + 3$ is $\{x: 0 \leqslant x \leqslant 5\}$. What is the range of g?

24 The domain of the function defined by $f(x) = x^2 + 2$ is **R**. What is the range of f.

25 The domain of the function $p:x \rightarrow 2x - 1$ is **N**. What is the range of p?

26 The domain of the function $h:x \rightarrow \frac{1}{2}x$ is {positive even numbers}. What is the range of h?

27 The function $f:x \rightarrow \frac{1}{2}x + 2$ has domain $\{0, 2, 4, 6, 8\}$. Find (a) the range of f, (b) a solution of the equation $f(x) = x$, (c) a value of x for which $x \rightarrow x - 2$.

28 A function g which is defined by the equation $g(x) = x^2 - 3x$ has domain $\{1, 2, 3, 4, 5\}$. Find (a) the range of g, (b) a solution of the equation $g(x) = x$, (c) the values of x which are mapped to $x - 3$ by g.

29 The function f is defined on the set $S = \{$integers from 0 to 10 inclusive$\}$ as follows: $x \rightarrow 2x$ for $0 \leqslant x \leqslant 5$; $x \rightarrow x - 2$ for $6 \leqslant x \leqslant 10$. (a) Which elements of S are not images under f? (b) Which elements of S are images of two elements? (c) Solve the equation $f(x) = 6$.

30 The function $g:x \rightarrow$ *the remainder when x is divided by 7* has domain {integers from 80 to 100 inclusive}. (a) Calculate g(89) and g(93). (b) Solve the equation $g(x) = 6$. (c) How many values of x are mapped to zero by g?

31 A function h is defined on **R** as follows: $h(x) = 2 - x$ when x is negative and $h(x) = x - 1$ when x is positive or zero. Find (a) the range of h, (b) the solution(s) of the equation $h(x) - 5$, (c) the solution(s) of the equation $h(x) = 7 - 3x$.

32 A function f defined on **R** is such that $f(x) = x^2$ when x is negative or zero and $f(x) = 2x - 3$ when x is positive. Find (a) the range of f, (b) the solutions of the equation $f(x) = 9$, (c) the solutions of the equation $f(x) = -2x$.

Composite functions

A composite function is one which is built up from two or more simpler functions. The composite function fg means 'apply g and then apply f'. (Note the order.) For example, if f is the function 'multiply by 2' and g is the function 'add 3', then fg means 'add 3 and then multiply by 2' while gf means 'multiply by 2 and then add 3'. E.g.

$$fg(5) = f(8) = 16,$$
$$gf(5) = g(10) = 13.$$

(This example shows that it is not really illogical to begin by applying the function on the right, because the function on the right is the one next to the number being operated on.)

To obtain the single function which is equivalent to a composite function we simply apply the individual functions, in the correct order, to the general number x. For example, with the above definitions of f and g, we have

$$fg(x) = f(x+3) = 2(x+3),$$
$$gf(x) = g(2x) = 2x + 3.$$

Using the 'mapping' notation, these results could be expressed as $fg:x \to 2(x+3)$ and $gf:x \to 2x + 3$.

A composite function can be built up from any number of functions, as the following example shows.

▷**Example 3**

Given the functions $f:x \to x - 1$, $g:x \to 1 - 2x$ *and* $h:x \to \dfrac{1}{x}$, *find (a) hgf(x),*
(b) fhg(x).

(a) $hgf(x) = hg(x-1) = h[1 - 2(x-1)] = h(3 - 2x) = \dfrac{1}{3 - 2x}$.

(b) $fhg(x) = fh(1 - 2x) = f\left(\dfrac{1}{1-2x}\right) = \dfrac{1}{1-2x} - 1 = \dfrac{1-(1-2x)}{1-2x} = \dfrac{2x}{1-2x}$. ◁

The next examples illustrate some further techniques involving composite functions.

▷**Example 4**

Given the functions $f:x \to x^2$ *and* $g:x \to x + 3$, *express the following in terms of f and g: (a)* $(x+3)^2$, *(b)* $x + 12$, *(c)* $x^2 + 6$.

(a) The function which maps x to $(x+3)^2$ could be expressed as 'add 3 and then square'. This is equivalent to 'apply g and then f'; hence $(x+3)^2 = fg(x)$.
(b) The function which maps x to $x + 12$ could be expressed as 'add 3 four times'. Hence $x + 12 = gggg(x)$.
(c) The function which maps x to $x^2 + 6$ could be expressed as 'square and then add 3 twice'. Hence $x^2 + 6 = ggf(x)$. ◁

▷**Example 5**

(a) Given that $g(x) = 2x$ *and* $fg(x) = 4x^2 - 3$, *find f(x). (b) Given that*
$f(x) = \dfrac{x}{2}$ *and* $fg(x) = x + 3$, *find g(x).*

(a) The information given tells us that the function f can be regarded as a set of rules which turns $2x$ into $4x^2 - 3$. This set of rules could be expressed as 'square and then subtract 3'; hence $f(x) = x^2 - 3$.
(b) f is the function 'divide by 2', and we are told that when this rule is applied to $g(x)$ the result is $x + 3$. Hence $g(x) = 2(x + 3)$ or $2x + 6$. ◁

EXERCISE 20b

1 Apply the function 'multiply by 4' followed by the function 'add 5' to the numbers (a) 2, (b) 7, (c) −3, (d) −6.
2 Apply the function $x \to x + 3$ followed by the function $x \to 2x$ to the numbers (a) 5, (b) −3, (c) −5.
3 f and g are the functions 'multiply by 5' and 'subtract 3', respectively. Find (a) fg(5), (b) gf(5), (c) fg(−2), (d) gf(−2), (e) ff(3), (f) ggg(14).
4 Given the functions $f:x \to x^2$ and $g:x \to x - 2$, find (a) fg(6), (b) gf(6), (c) fg(−4), (d) gf(−4), (e) ff(3), (f) gfg(5).

5 Given that $f(x) = \dfrac{1}{x}$ and $g(x) = x - 1$, find (a) fg(3), (b) gf(3), (c) fg($\frac{1}{2}$), (d) gf($\frac{1}{2}$), (e) ff(4), (f) fgf(2).

6 Given that $f(x) = 2x - 4$ and $g(x) = 1 - 2x$, find (a) fff(2), (b) ggg(1), (c) fgf(3), (d) gfg(-2).

7 Given the functions $f:x \rightarrow 4^x$ and $g: x \rightarrow \dfrac{2}{x}$, find (a) fg(4), (b) ff($-\frac{1}{2}$), (c) fg($1\frac{1}{3}$).

8 Given the functions $f:x \rightarrow x - 8$ and $g:x \rightarrow 5 - x$, find (a) fff(2), (b) ggg(7), (c) fgf(4), (d) fggf(-3).

9 Given the functions $f:x \rightarrow x - 5$ and $g:x \rightarrow 4x$, express as single mappings (a) fg, (b) gf, (c) ff, (d) gg, (e) fgf, (f) gfg.

10 Given the functions $f:x \rightarrow 2x - 1$ and $g:x \rightarrow 3x + 1$, obtain the simplest possible expressions for (a) fg(x), (b) gf(x), (c) ff(x), (d) ggg(x).

11 Given that $f(x) = x^2 - 3$ and $g(x) = x + 2$, obtain the simplest possible expressions for (a) gf(x), (b) fg(x), (c) ff(x).

12 Given the functions $f:x \rightarrow x - 1$ and $g:x \rightarrow \dfrac{1}{x + 1}$, express as single mappings as simply as possible (a) fg, (b) gf, (c) gg, (d) gfg.

13 Given the functions $f:x \rightarrow 1 - x$, $g:x \rightarrow 3x + 2$ and $h:x \rightarrow 2x$, express as single mappings as simply as possible (a) fgh, (b) hgf, (c) gfh.

14 Given that $f(x) = \dfrac{x}{2}$, $g(x) = 2x - 4$ and $h(x) = x + 3$, obtain the simplest possible expressions for (a) hfg(x), (b) fgh(x), (c) ghf(x).

15 Given the functions $f:x \rightarrow 2x + 1$ and $g:x \rightarrow x + 3$, solve the equations (a) fg(x) = g(x), (b) gf(x) = g(x),(c) ff(x) = gg(x).

16 Given that $f(x) = 2x - 1$ and $g(x) = 2 - 3x$, solve the equations (a) fg(x) = f(x), (b) gf(x) = g(x), (c) ff(x) = gg(x).

17 Given the functions $f:x \rightarrow x - 3$ and $g:x \rightarrow x^2$, solve the equations (a) fg(x) = f(x), (b) gf(x) = g(x), (c) fg(x) = gf(x).

18 Given that $f(x) = \dfrac{1}{x}$ and $g(x) = x + 2$, solve the equations (a) fg(x) = g(x), (b) gf(x) = g(x).

19 The functions $f:x \rightarrow x - 1$ and $g:x \rightarrow 2x$ have the domain $\{x:0 \leqslant x \leqslant 5\}$. Find the range of (a) fg, (b) gf.

20 The functions $f:x \rightarrow x^2$ and $g:x \rightarrow x + 3$ have the domain $\{x:0 \leqslant x \leqslant 2\}$. Find the range of (a) fg, (b) gf.

21 The function $f:x \rightarrow x^2$ and $g:x \rightarrow 2x$ have the domain $\{x:-5 \leqslant x \leqslant 5\}$. Find the range of (a) fg, (b) gf.

22 Given the functions $f:x \rightarrow 2x$ and $g:x \rightarrow x + 1$, express the following in terms of f and g: (a) $x \rightarrow 2x + 1$, (b) $x \rightarrow 4x$, (c) $x \rightarrow 2(x + 1)$, (d) $x \rightarrow x + 3$.

23 Given the functions $f:x \rightarrow x^2$ and $g:x \rightarrow x - 2$, express the following in terms of f and g: (a) $x \rightarrow x^8$, (b) $x \rightarrow (x - 2)^2$,(c) $x \rightarrow x^2 - 4$, (d) $x \rightarrow (x - 2)^4$.

24 Given the functions $f:x \rightarrow 2x$, $g:x \rightarrow x + 3$ and $h:x \rightarrow x^2$, express the following in terms of f, g and h: (a) $2(x + 3)^2$, (b) $2(x + 6)$, (c) $2x^4$, (d) $4(x^2 + 3)$, (e) $4x^2 + 12x + 9$.

25 Given that $g(x) = 2x$ and $fg(x) = 6x - 1$, what is $f(x)$?

26 Given that $f(x) = x - 1$ and $gf(x) = x^2$, what is $g(x)$?

27 Given that $h(x) = 2^x$ and $gh(x) = 2^{3x}$ what is $g(x)$?

28 Given that $g(x) = 2x^2$ and $hg(x) = 4x^4 - 2x^2 + 1$, what is $h(x)$?

29 Given that $f(x) = 2x - 3$ and $fg(x) = 6x - 5$, find $g(x)$. (Let $g(x) = ax + b$.)

30 Given that $f(x) = 5 - 2x$ and $fg(x) = 8x - 1$, find $g(x)$.

31 Given that $f(x) = \sqrt{x}$ and $fg(x) = 2x$, find $g(x)$.

32 Given that $f(x) = \dfrac{2}{x}$ and $fg(x) = 4x$, find $g(x)$.

33 Given that $f(x) = 3x + 2$ and $g(x) = 2x + k$, find the value of k such that $fg = gf$.
34 Given the functions $f:x \rightarrow 1 - 2x$ and $g:x \rightarrow 5x - k$, find the value of k such that $fg = gf$.
35 Given that $f(x) = \frac{1}{2}(x + 1)$ and $g(x) = 4x - k$, find the value of k such that $fg = gf$.

Inverse functions

If a function f is regarded as a rule which maps a number x to a number y, then the inverse or 'opposite' function f^{-1} is the rule which maps y to x. For example the inverse of the function 'add 2' is 'subtract 2', and the inverse of the function 'multiply by 5' is 'divide by 5'. The image of a number under an inverse function is called an *inverse image*; so that, for example, the inverse image of 6 under the function 'add 2' is 4.

The simplest method of obtaining inverse functions is to express the original function as a formula giving y in terms of x, and use the 'transformation of equations' technique (see chapter 18) to express x in terms of y. The following example illustrates the technique.

▷ **Example 6**

Obtain the inverse function f^{-1}, given (a) $f:x \rightarrow 2x - 3$, (b) $f:x \rightarrow \frac{x - 2}{x}$.

(a)
$$\text{Let } y = 2x - 3.$$
$$\text{Then } 2x = y + 3$$
$$\therefore x = \frac{y + 3}{2}.$$

The inverse function f^{-1} can now be expressed in any of the following ways:

$$f^{-1}:y \rightarrow \frac{y + 3}{2}, \quad f^{-1}:x \rightarrow \frac{x + 3}{2}, \quad f^{-1}(x) = \frac{x + 3}{2}.$$

(b)
$$\text{Let } y = \frac{x - 2}{x}.$$
$$\text{Then } xy = x - 2$$
$$\therefore x - xy = 2$$
$$\therefore x(1 - y) = 2$$
$$\therefore x = \frac{2}{1 - y}.$$

We can now write either $f^{-1}:y \rightarrow \frac{2}{1 - y}$ or $f^{-1}:x \rightarrow \frac{2}{1 - x}$ or $f^{-1}(x) = \frac{2}{1 - x}$. ◀

Domain and range for inverse functions

The domain of the function f^{-1} is the *range* of the function f, and since a function can only exist if each element of its domain has a *unique* image, it follows that *an inverse function can only exist if there is a one-to-one correspondence between the elements of the domain and the elements of the range.* The following arrow diagrams (Fig. 20.2) illustrate this principle.

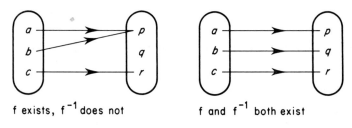

f exists, f^{-1} does not   f and f^{-1} both exist

Fig. 20.2

An inverse function does not exist in the first case because when the arrows are reversed in direction p has two images. The first diagram in fact provides an example of a 'many–one' function, and the inverse of any function of this kind is a *relation* and not a function. For example the inverse of the function $f:x \rightarrow x^2$ (or $y = x^2$) is the relation $f^{-1}:x \rightarrow \pm \sqrt{x}$. Many mathematical formulae define relations rather than functions, and this simply means that for a given value of the variable they are many-valued rather than single-valued.

The inverse of a composite function

The inverse of 'do g and then f' is 'do the inverse of f and then the inverse of g'. The reason for the reversal of order which occurs here is best explained by a practical example. To cancel out the combination of procedures 'put the article in the box and close the lid', a person must do the opposite or inverse procedures *the other way round*; that is 'open the lid and take out the article'. This demonstrates the theorem

$$(fg)^{-1} = g^{-1}f^{-1}$$
$$(fgh)^{-1} = h^{-1}g^{-1}f^{-1},$$
$$\text{etc.}$$

▷**Example 7**

Given $f:x \rightarrow 2x$ and $g:x \rightarrow x - 3$, find $(fg)^{-1}(x)$ by two methods.
Method (a)
We have $f^{-1}:x \rightarrow \dfrac{x}{2}$ and $g^{-1}:x \rightarrow x + 3$. Hence, using the above theorem,

$$(fg)^{-1}(x) = g^{-1}f^{-1}(x) = \frac{x}{2} + 3 \text{ or } \frac{x+6}{2}.$$

Method (b)
We have $fg(x) = 2(x - 3) = 2x - 6$. Now letting $y = 2x - 6$ and making x the subject, we obtain

$$2x = y + 6$$
$$\therefore \quad x = \frac{y + 6}{2}.$$

It follows once more that $(fg)^{-1}(x) = \dfrac{x+6}{2}.$

◁

EXERCISE 20c

1 Write down the inverse mappings of (a) $x \rightarrow x + 2$, (b) $x \rightarrow 3x$, (c) $x \rightarrow \frac{x}{5}$, (d) $x \rightarrow \sqrt{x}$.

2 Given the functions $f:x \rightarrow \frac{x}{3}$ and $g:x \rightarrow x^2$, find (a) $f^{-1}(2)$, (b) $g^{-1}(4)$, (c) $f^{-1}(1\frac{1}{3})$, (d) $g^{-1}(2\frac{1}{4})$.

3 Find the inverse images of (a) 10, (b) -5, under the mapping 'multiply by 3 and then add 4'.

4 Find the inverse images of (a) -4, (b) $2\frac{1}{2}$, under the mapping 'subtract 3 and then divide by 2'.

In questions 5–17 obtain an expression for $f^{-1}(x)$.

5 $f(x) = 2x + 1$ **6** $f(x) = (2x + 1)$ **7** $f(x) = \frac{1}{2}x - 3$ **8** $f(x) = \frac{x-3}{2}$

9 $f(x) = x^2 + 4$ **10** $f(x) = (x + 4)^2$ **11** $f(x) = \frac{1}{x-2}$ **12** $f(x) = \frac{3}{x} - 2$

13 $f(x) = \frac{1}{4-x}$ **14** $f(x) = 2 - \frac{1}{x^2}$ **15** $f(x) = \sqrt{(2x + 3)}$

16 $f(x) = 2 - \sqrt{x}$ **17** $f(x) = \sqrt{(3 - 4x)}$.

18 Which of the inverse relations obtained in the answers to questions 5–17 are not functions?

In questions 19–23 obtain the inverse of the given function in the form $x \rightarrow$.

19 $x \rightarrow \frac{x+1}{x}$ **20** $x \rightarrow \frac{1-2x}{x}$ **21** $x \rightarrow \frac{3x-1}{3x+1}$ **22** $x \rightarrow \frac{x^2}{1-x^2}$

23 $x \rightarrow \sqrt{\left(\frac{1-2x^2}{1-3x^2}\right)}$

24 Given the functions $f:x \rightarrow 2x$ and $g:x \rightarrow x + 1$, obtain an expression for $(fg)^{-1}(x)$ (a) by finding the inverse of fg directly, (b) by finding $g^{-1}f^{-1}$.

25 Repeat question 24 with the functions $f:x \rightarrow x - 3$ and $g:x \rightarrow \frac{x}{2}$.

26 Given the functions $f:x \rightarrow x - 2$, $g:x \rightarrow 3x$ and $h:x \rightarrow x^2$, express as single mappings (a) $(fgh)^{-1}$, (b) $(hgf)^{-1}$, (c) $(fhg)^{-1}$.

27 Given the function $f:x \rightarrow 2 - x$, show that ff is the *identity function,* i.e. the function $x \rightarrow x$. What does this tell us about the inverse of f?

28 Repeat question 27 with the function $x \rightarrow \frac{1}{4x}$.

29 In each of the following cases say whether or not the given function is its own inverse (self-inverse):

(a) $x \rightarrow \frac{2}{x}$ (b) $x \rightarrow 3 + x$ (c) $x \rightarrow x - 5$ (d) $x \rightarrow 9 - x$ (e) $x \rightarrow -\frac{1}{3x}$

(f) $x \rightarrow \frac{x-1}{x+2}$ (g) $x \rightarrow \frac{x+3}{x-1}$ (h) $x \rightarrow \frac{4-x}{1+x}$.

30 Find the value of k for which the function $f(x) = \frac{2x+3}{x+k}$ is self-inverse.

31 Find the value of k for which the function $f(x) = k + \frac{1}{x-3}$ is self-inverse.

32 Given the functions $f:x \rightarrow 2x - 4$, $g:x \rightarrow 2 + \sqrt{x}$, solve the equations (a) $f(x) = f^{-1}(x)$, (b) $f(x) = g^{-1}(x)$, (c) $f^{-1}(x) = g^{-1}(x)$.

21 The Factor Theorem and Related Topics

Brackets and coefficients

In chapter 11 we considered the procedure for removing brackets in some simple cases. For example

$$(2x - 1)(x + 3) = 2x^2 + 6x - x - 3$$
$$= 2x^2 + 5x - 3.$$

We shall now look at some slightly more complicated problems involving similar techniques.

▷ Example 1

Remove the brackets in the expression $(2x - 3)(x + 2)(x - 5)$.

There are two methods for multiplying three or more polynomials together. The first is to take a term from each pair of brackets, multiply them together, and repeat this procedure until every possible combination of terms has been obtained:

$$(2x - 3)(x + 2)(x - 5) = 2x^3 - 10x^2 + 4x^2 \ldots$$

The second method, which is perhaps simpler, is to remove the brackets in stages:

$$(2x - 3)(x + 2)(x - 5) = (2x - 3)(x^2 - 3x - 10)$$
$$= 2x^3 - 6x^2 - 3x^2 - 20x + 9x + 30$$
$$= 2x^3 - 9x^2 - 11x + 30. \qquad \triangleleft$$

▷ Example 2

Find the x^2 term in the expansion of $(2x^2 - x + 3)(x^2 + 4x - 1)$.

The products giving x^2 terms are obtained as follows:

$$(2x^2 - x + 3)(x^2 + 4x - 1)$$

Hence the final x^2 term is $-2x^2 - 4x^2 + 3x^2 = -3x^2$. $\qquad \triangleleft$

▷**Example 3**

The coefficient of x in the expansion of (2x + 5) (4x − k) is 8. Find k.
Taking only the x terms, we have

$$20x - 2kx = 8x$$
$$\therefore\ 20 - 2k = 8$$
$$\therefore\ k = 6.$$
◁

▷**Example 4**

Find the possible values of k if the expression $25x^2 + kx + 9$ is a perfect square.

Since the expression is a perfect square its factors are equal. Only the following two pairs of equal factors give the terms $25x^2$ and 9 when multiplied together:

$$(5x + 3)(5x + 3)$$
$$\text{and}\ \ (5x - 3)(5x - 3).$$

In the first case the x term is $15x + 15x = 30x$, and in the second the x term is $-15x - 15x = -30x$. Hence $k = \pm 30$.
◁

▷**Example 5**

Obtain in its simplest form the quadratic equation whose roots are $-\frac{1}{2}$ and 3.
It is clear from the factor method of solving quadratic equations that the required equation must be expressible as

$$(x + \tfrac{1}{2})(x - 3) = 0.$$

When both sides are multiplied by 2 to remove the fraction, this becomes

$$(2x + 1)(x - 3) = 0,$$
$$\text{that is}\ \ 2x^2 - 5x - 3 = 0.$$
◁

▷**Example 6**

$f(x) = 2x^3 + ax^2 - 3x + b$. *Find a and b if f(2) = 9 and f(−1) = 3.*
Substituting 2 for x we have

$$16 + 4a - 6 + b = 9$$
$$\therefore\ 4a + b = -1 \qquad (1)$$

Substituting −1 for x we have

$$-2 + a + 3 + b = 3$$
$$\therefore\ a + b = 2 \qquad (2)$$

We now solve the simultaneous equations (1) and (2).

$$(1) - (2):\ \ 3a = -3$$
$$\therefore\ \ \ a = -1.$$

Substituting -1 for a in (2):

$$-1 + b = 2$$
$$\therefore\ b = 3. \qquad \triangleleft$$

EXERCISE 21a

In questions 1–6, remove the brackets.

1 $(x + 2)(x^2 + 3x + 4)$ **2** $(x - 1)(x^2 - 2x + 3)$ **3** $(2x - 3)(x^2 + x - 2)$
4 $(x + 1)(x + 2)(x + 3)$ **5** $(2x + 3)(x - 1)(x - 2)$ **6** $(3x - 1)(2x - 1)(x - 3).$

In questions 7–12, find the term in x^2.

7 $(4x - 1)(x^2 - x - 2)$ **8** $(x^2 - 3x)(2 + x - x^2)$ **9** $(1 - 2x + x^2)(3 - x - 5x^2)$
10 $(x - 1)(x + 3)(2x - 5)$ **11** $(2 - x)(4 + x)(3 - 5x)$ **12** $(2x - 1)^3.$

In questions 13–18, find the coefficient of x.

13 $(4x - 1)(3x + 7)$ **14** $(5x - 2)^2$ **15** $(x - 3)(x - 4)(x - 5)$ **16** $(x + 2)^3$
17 $(3x - 1)^2(5x + 1)$ **18** $(4x - 3)^3.$

19 The coefficient of x in $(3x + k)(x + 2)$ is 9. Find k.
20 The coefficient of x^2 in $(x^2 + ax)(1 - 2x)$ is 5. Find a.
21 The coefficient of x in $(px - 2)(px - 3)$ is 15. Find p.
22 The coefficient of x in $(4 - kx)(2 + kx)$ is -8. Find k.
23 The coefficient of x^2 in $(x^2 + cx + 3)(cx^2 - x - 2)$ is -12. Find c.
24 The coefficient of x^2 in $(2x - k)^2(x - k)$ is 6. Find k.
25 Find c if $4x^2 - 12x + c$ is a perfect square.
26 Find the possible values of p if $x^2 + px + 49$ is a perfect square.
27 Find a if $ax^2 - 8x + 1$ is a perfect square.
28 Find the possible values of k if $9x^2 + kx + 16$ is a perfect square.

In questions 29–35, obtain as simply as possible the quadratic equations whose roots have the values given.

29 2 and 3   **30** -1 and 5   **31** -3 and -4 **32** $\frac{1}{2}$ and -4 **33** $-\frac{1}{2}$ and $-\frac{1}{3}$
34 $\frac{2}{3}$ and $-\frac{1}{6}$ **35** $-2\frac{1}{4}$ and $-\frac{1}{2}$

36 $f(x) = x^2 - ax - 3$. If $f(-1) = 2$, what is a?
37 $g(x) = px^2 + 2x - 5p$. If $g(2) = 1$, what is p?
38 $h(x) = px^2 - qx + 1$. Find p and q if $h(2) = 3$ and $h(-1) = 6$.
39 $f(x) = 2x^3 - ax^2 + bx - 3$. Find a and b if $f(3) = 45$ and $f(-2) = -5$.
40 $g(x) = s - 2x - tx^2 - x^3$. Find s and t if $g(-1) = 9$ and 2 is a root of the equation $g(x) = 0$.

The factor theorem

We know that there is a simple relationship between the factors of a quadratic expression and the roots of the equation obtained by equating the expression to zero. Consider for example the quadratic equation $x^2 + x - 12 = 0$. To solve this we begin by factorising the quadratic expression $x^2 + x - 12$:

$$x^2 + x - 12 = 0$$
$$\therefore (x - 3)(x + 4) = 0.$$

Now we reason that if the product of two numbers is zero, one of those numbers must equal zero, and thus proceed as follows:

$$\text{either } x - 3 = 0 \text{ and } x = 3,$$
$$\text{or } x + 4 = 0 \text{ and } x = -4.$$

It is clear then that a factor of $x - 3$ indicates a root of $+3$, while a factor of $x + 4$ indicates a root of -4. This example illustrates the following general principle.

A factor of $x - a$ corresponds to a root of $x = a$.

In practice we always deduce the roots of a quadratic equation from the factors of the quadratic expression, as in the example just given. It would be possible, however, to reverse this procedure. If by trial and error we could discover that $x = 3$ is a root of the equation $x^2 + x - 12 = 0$, we could deduce at once that $x - 3$ is a factor of the expression $x^2 + x - 12$. This of course would be a crude method of factorising quadratics because it is quite easy to find the factors directly. But suppose we have to factorise a cubic or quartic expression. A cubic might have three simple linear factors and a quartic might have four, and it is clear that the difficulty of discovering all these factors by trial and error must be considerable.

It is to deal with this kind of case that we use the *factor theorem.* This is just a generalised version of the principle established above for quadratics, and it provides a method of factorising any polynomial $P(x)$ which has simple factors. The following is one statement of the theorem.

If $x = a$ is a root of the equation $P(x) = 0$,
then $x - a$ is a factor of $P(x)$.

A briefer way of stating that $x = a$ is a root of the equation $P(x) = 0$ is the simple statement that $P(a) = 0$. Hence we have the following condensed version of the factor theorem.

If $P(a) = 0$, then $x - a$ is a factor of $P(x)$.

▷**Example 7**

Factorise $x^3 + 2x^2 - 5x - 6$.
The method, in effect, is to try to find a root of the equation $x^3 + 2x^2 - 5x - 6 = 0$. It is only necessary to try factors of the final constant 6, so a reasonable procedure is to substitute for x in turn the values 1, 2, 3, -1, -2, -3, in the expectation that one of them will make the expression zero. Calling the expression $P(x)$, we have

$$P(1) = 1 + 2 - 5 - 6 \neq 0,$$
$$P(2) = 8 + 8 - 10 - 6 = 0.$$

We have found that $x = 2$ is a root of the equation $P(x) = 0$, and it follows by the factor theorem that $x - 2$ is a factor of $P(x)$. We therefore have

$$x^3 + 2x^2 - 5x - 6 = (x - 2)(\qquad).$$

The second pair of brackets must contain a quadratic function of x, and this can be found by inspection. To obtain x^3 and -6 when the right-hand side is multiplied out, we must have x^2 and $+3$ as the first and last terms:

$$x^3 + 2x^2 - 5x - 6 = (x - 2)(x^2 \quad ? \quad +3).$$

We can obtain the middle term, which is a term in x, by considering how to get the correct x^2 term when the right-hand side is multiplied out. We need $+2x^2$, and so far have $-2x^2$. Hence we must obtain another $+4x^2$, and this can be achieved by placing $+4x$ in the remaining space:

$$x^3 + 2x^2 - 5x - 6 = (x - 2)\underset{\underset{+4x^2}{\llcorner -2x^2 \lrcorner}}{(x^2 + 4x + 3)}.$$

The correctness of this reasoning can be checked by considering the terms in x. When the right-hand side is multiplied out the terms in x are $+3x$ and $-8x$, and these do give the required $-5x$.

In this case the factorisation can be taken a stage further since the quadratic $x^2 + 4x + 3$ can be factorised. The final answer is

$$(x - 2)(x + 3)(x + 1). \qquad \triangleleft$$

Finding the quadratic expression which occupies the empty pair of brackets in the last example really amounts to dividing the polynomial $x^3 + 2x^2 - 5x - 6$ by $x - 2$. This technique will probably seem difficult at first, but it can easily be mastered with practice and is much quicker than the usual long division procedure. Two more examples of the technique are now provided.

▷ Example 8

Divide $6x^3 - 11x^2 - 4x + 4$ by $2x - 1$.
By considering the x^3 and constant terms we obtain

$$6x^3 - 11x^2 - 4x + 4 = (2x - 1)(3x^2 \quad ? \quad - 4).$$

Now consider how the correct x^2 can be obtained when the right-hand side is multiplied out. We need $-11x^2$ and so far have $-3x^2$. Hence another $-8x^2$ is needed, and this can be obtained by placing $- 4x$ in the remaining space:

$$6x^3 - 11x^2 - 4x + 4 = (2x - 1)\underset{\underset{-8x^2.}{\llcorner -3x^2 \lrcorner}}{(3x^2 - 4x - 4)}. \qquad \triangleleft$$

▷ Example 9

Divide $4x^3 - 7x - 3$ by $2x - 3$.
We immediately have

$$4x^3 - 7x - 3 = (2x - 3)(2x^2 \ ? \ + 1).$$

Now the left-hand side has no x^2 term, so $0x^2$ must be obtained when the brackets are multiplied out. So far we have $-6x^2$, and can obtain another $+6x^2$ by inserting $+3x$ in the remaining space:

$$4x^3 - 7x - 3 = (2x - 3)\ (2x^2 + 3x + 1).$$

(The answers to both examples 8 and 9 can be checked by considering the x terms.)

In the final example in this chapter, we are given two of the factors of a polynomial and have to find two of its coefficients. The question is very similar in type to example 6.

▷ Example 10

Find a and b, given that $x + 1$ and $x - 3$ are factors of the expression $2x^3 + ax^2 + bx + 3$.
Since $x + 1$ is a factor of the expression, the expression is equal to zero when $x = -1$. Hence

$$-2 + a - b + 3 = 0$$
$$\therefore a - b = -1. \qquad (1)$$

Similarly, since $x - 3$ is a factor, the expression is equal to zero when $x = 3$:

$$54 + 9a + 3b + 3 = 0$$
$$\therefore 9a + 3b = -57$$
$$\therefore 3a + b = -19. \qquad (2)$$

We now solve the pair of simultaneous equations (1) and (2).

$$(1) + (2): \ 4a = -20$$
$$\therefore \ a = -5.$$

Substituting -5 for a in (1):

$$-5 - b = -1$$
$$\therefore b = -4.$$

EXERCISE 21b

In questions 1–9, state the missing expressions.

1 $x^2 + 8x + 12 = (x + 2)(\qquad)$ 2 $x^2 - 3x - 18 = (x + 3)(\qquad)$

3 $2x^2 - 13x - 24 = (x - 8)(\qquad)$ 4 $6x^2 - 23x + 20 = (2x - 5)(\qquad)$

5 $x^3 + 5x^2 + 7x + 2 = (x + 2)(\qquad)$ 6 $x^3 - 2x^2 + 4x - 3 = (x - 1)(\qquad)$

7 $2x^3 + x^2 - 13x - 15 = (2x + 3)(\qquad)$ 8 $9x^3 - 7x + 2 = (3x - 1)(\qquad)$

9 $x^3 + 8 = (x + 2)(\qquad)$.

In questions 10–18, fully factorise the given expressions.

10 $x^3 + 3x^2 - x - 3$ **11** $x^3 - 4x^2 + x + 6$ **12** $x^3 - 3x + 2$ **13** $x^3 - 7x - 6$
14 $2x^3 - 5x^2 - 4x + 3$ **15** $2x^3 - x^2 - 8x + 4$ **16** $3x^3 + 2x^2 - 37x + 12$
17 $x^3 - 27x - 54$ **18** $4x^3 - 16x^2 - x + 4$.

In questions 19–24, find k and then fully factorise P(x).

19 $P(x) = x^3 + kx^2 - 6x + 8$. One factor is $x - 1$.
20 $P(x) = x^3 - 2x^2 + kx + 6$. One factor is $x + 2$.
21 $P(x) = 2x^3 + x^2 + kx - 9$. One factor is $x - 3$.
22 $P(x) = kx^3 - 7x + 2$. One factor is $x + 1$.
23 $P(x) = 2x^3 - x^2 - kx + 18$. One factor is $x + 3$.
24 $P(x) = 6x^3 - kx^2 + x - 2$. One factor is $x + 2$.

In questions 25–30, use the given information to find a and b.

25 $x - 1$ and $x + 1$ are factors of $3x^3 + ax^2 + bx + 1$.
26 $x + 1$ and $x - 2$ are factors of $ax^3 + bx^2 - 5x + 6$.
27 $x - 1$ and $x + 2$ are factors of $x^3 + ax^2 + bx + 2$.
28 $x + 1$ and $x - 3$ are factors of $3x^3 - ax^2 + bx - 12$.
29 $x + 2$ and $x + 3$ are factors of $2x^3 + 9x^2 - ax + b$.
30 $x + 1$ and $x + 2$ are factors of $ax^3 + 4x^2 - 9x + b$.

22 Binary Operations

When we write, for example, $3 + 5 = 8$, we are using the operation *addition* to obtain the number 8 from the two numbers 3 and 5. The operation is the *rule or procedure* by which 8 is obtained from 3 and 5, and it is called a *binary* operation because it applies to any *two* elements from the set $\mathbf{R}$ of real numbers. An operation which applies to just one element, such as *squaring,* or *taking the sine,* is called a *unary* operation.

The important operations addition, multiplication and so on have special symbols such as $+$ and $\times$. Other operations are usually denoted by $*$ or o. Thus $a \text{ o } b$ stands for the element produced by applying the operation o to the pair of elements a and b taken in that order.

▷ Example 1

The operation o is defined by the rule $x \text{ o } y = x - 2y$. Find (a) $2 \text{ o } -3$, (b) $4 \text{ o } (-5 \text{ o } 2)$. (c) Solve the equation $x \text{ o } 5 = 2 \text{ o } x$.

(a) To obtain $2 \text{ o } -3$ we use the rule $x \text{ o } y = x - 2y$, replacing x by 2 and y by -3:

$$2 \text{ o } -3 = 2 - 2(-3) = 2 + 6 = 8.$$

(b) As in ordinary algebra the expression in brackets is worked out first:

$$-5 \text{ o } 2 = -5 - 2(2) = -9.$$

Now we have

$$4 \text{ o } (-5 \text{ o } 2) = 4 \text{ o } -9 = 4 - 2(-9) = 22.$$

(c) Since $x \text{ o } 5 = x - 10$ and $2 \text{ o } x = 2 - 2x$, the equation is equivalent to

$$x - 10 = 2 - 2x.$$
$$\text{Hence} \quad 3x = 12 \text{ and } x = 4. \qquad \triangleleft$$

Most important mathematical operations apply to numbers, but not all do. A binary operation exists whenever there is a rule or procedure for combining any two elements of a set to produce a third entity. (This third entity may or may not be a member of the original set.) An operation is always defined *on a set*, and, strictly, the operation is not fully defined until the set has been stated. Of course many operations are defined on $\mathbf{R}$, and this is often taken for granted. But a full definition of a binary operation contains both a rule for combining pairs of elements and a statement of the set from which these elements are to be taken.

When an operation does not apply to numbers, it is often convenient to define the operation by means of a *combination table.* The next example illustrates the use of such a table.

▷Example 2

The operation ∗ *is defined on the set {a, b, c} by the combination table below. (a) Find (a* ∗ *b)* ∗ *c. (b) Solve the equation x* ∗ *x* = *c.*

∗	a	b	c
a	b	c	a
b	a	c	b
c	c	a	b

(a) The table gives $a * b = c$, and $c * c = b$. Hence

$$(a * b) * c = c * c = b.$$

(b) The table gives $a * a = b$, $b * b = c$ and $c * c = b$. Hence there is just one solution of the equation $x * x = c$, namely $x = b$. (Note that there are two solutions of $x * x = b$, and no solutions of $x * x = a$.) ◀

Modular arithmetic

Modular or 'clock' arithmetic is a simplified form of arithmetic in which only a few whole numbers are used. In 'arithmetic modulo 4' (or 'mod 4' arithmetic), for example, we only use the four digits 0, 1, 2, 3. To obtain, say, 2×3 in this system, we multiply 2 by 3 in the usual way and then take the *remainder after dividing by 4.* Thus $2 \times 3 = 2$. Similarly $2 + 3 = 1$, $3^3 = 3$ and $2^3 = 0$. When a negative number arises we subtract the first multiple of 4 below the number. Thus $1 - 3 = 2$ and $2 - 3 = 3$.

The following combination tables are for the operations *addition mod 4* and *multiplication mod 5*, respectively:

+ mod 4	0	1	2	3
0	0	1	2	3
1	1	2	3	0
2	2	3	0	1
3	3	0	1	2

× mod 5	0	1	2	3	4
0	0	0	0	0	0
1	0	1	2	3	4
2	0	2	4	1	3
3	0	3	1	4	2
4	0	4	3	2	1

▷Example 3

Use the table given above to solve the following equations in mod 5: (a) $3x^2$ = 2, (b) $3x + 4 = 3$.

(a) We begin by looking along the horizontal line starting with 3 to find a value for x^2. Since $3 \times 4 = 2$ it follows that $x^2 = 4$. Now we try to find a value for x by looking for a number which gives 4 when multiplied by itself. There are two such numbers, and we have $x = 2$ or 3.

(b) Subtracting 4 from both sides we obtain $3x = 4$. Now looking along the horizontal line beginning with 3 we find that $3 \times 3 = 4$; hence $x = 3$. ◀

EXERCISE 22a

The operations are defined on **R** unless otherwise stated.

1 $x \circ y = 2x - 3y$. Find (a) $4 \circ 1$, (b) $-1 \circ 2$, (c) $1\frac{1}{2} \circ 1\frac{1}{3}$, (d) $(1 \circ 2) \circ -4$,
(e) $1 \circ (2 \circ 3)$.
2 $x * y =$ the average of x and y. Find (a) $-6 * 2$, (b) $(4 * 12) * -4$,
(c) $(5 * 5) * (-7 * -11)$.
3 $x \circ y = \frac{x}{y}$. Find (a) $(4 \circ 2) \circ 6$, (b) $9 \circ (15 \circ 10)$, (c) $(3 \circ 6) \circ (2 \circ 8)$.
4 Find in mod 7: (a) $5 + 6$, (b) 4×6, (c) 2^4, (d) $2 - 5$.
5 $x \circ y = 3x + y$. Solve the equations (a) $x \circ 2 = 14$, (b) $4 \circ x = 9$, (c) $x \circ 4 = 6 \circ x$,
(d) $8 \circ x = x \circ 2$.
6 Find in mod 9: (a) 8×7, (b) 5^3, (c) $3 - 7 - 8$, (d) $7 - 4^2$.
7 $x * y = x - xy$. Solve the equations (a) $x * 3 = 4$, (b) $x * 5 = 3 * x$,
(c) $x * x = 2 * 4$.
8 $x \circ y = x^y$. Find (a) $(2 \circ 3) \circ 2$, (b) $4 \circ (2 \circ -1)$, (c) $(27 \circ \frac{2}{3}) \circ (4 \circ -\frac{1}{2})$. Solve
the equations (d) $2 \circ x = \frac{1}{4}$, (e) $25 \circ x = 125$.
9 The operation $*$ is defined on the set $\{p, q, r\}$ by the following combination
table:

$*$	p	q	r
p	r	p	q
q	q	p	r
r	q	r	p

Find (a) $(p * r) * q$, (b) $(r * p) * (p * p)$. Solve the equations (c) $p * x = q$,
(d) $r * (x * x) = q$.
10 Solve the following equations in mod 5: (a) $x + 4 = 3$, (b) $3x = 1$,
(c) $x^2 = 1$, (d) $4x + 3 = 0$.
11 The operation o is defined on **N** by the rule $x \circ y = \sqrt{xy}$ to the nearest
whole number. Find (a) $12 \circ 8$, (b) $25 \circ 9$. Solve the equations (c) $x \circ 10 = 5$,
(d) $20 \circ x = 12$, (e) $4 \circ x = 7$.
12 Solve the following equations in mod 7: (a) $5x = 6$, (b) $3x = 4$, (c) $x^2 = 1$, (d) $4x + 4 = 3$, (e) $1 - 6x = 4$.
13 $x * y = x - 2y$. Express y in terms of x, given that (a) $x * y = y * x$,
(b) $4x * y = 2y * x$.
14 $x \circ y = x^2 - 2y$. Solve the equations (a) $x \circ x = 8$, (b) $2 \circ x = 1 \circ 3x$,
(c) $2x \circ x = 6$, (d) $(3x \circ 2x) - (2x \circ 3x) = 3$.

Properties of operations

Closure

The element produced when two elements are combined may or may not
be a member of the set on which the operation is defined. If it *is* a member
of this set, *for all combinations of elements*, the set is said to be *closed*
under the operation, and the operation is said to possess the property of
closure.

Example

The set **N** is closed under addition because whenever two natural
numbers are added another natural number is obtained. This set is not

closed under subtraction, however, because a negative number is obtained whenever a larger natural number is subtracted from a smaller.

Commutativity

In general, the *order* in which two elements are combined matters. Thus for example $2 - 5$ is not the same as $5 - 2$. When the order does *not* affect the result of an operation, for all combinations of elements, the operation is said to be *commutative.*

Examples

Since $a + b = b + a$ and $ab = ba$ for all real numbers, the operations addition and multiplication are commutative. Subtraction and division, however, are not commutative.

Associativity

Consider the expression $(a \circ b) \circ c$. This tells us to combine a and b by the operation o, and then combine the resulting element with c. To evaluate $a \circ (b \circ c)$, on the other hand, we begin by combining b with c, and then combine a with the result. If $(a \circ b) \circ c$ is equal to $a \circ (b \circ c)$, for all combinations of elements in the set on which o is defined, the operation o is said to be *associative* over the set. In these circumstances the brackets are not needed and we can write simply $a \circ b \circ c$.

Examples

The operation addition is clearly associative. We know, for example, that $2 + 7 + 10$ is equal to 19 whether we begin by adding 2 to 7 or begin by adding 7 to 10. Similarly, multiplication is associative. Consider however the expression $24 \div 6 \div 2$. If we begin by dividing 24 by 6 the final answer is 2, while if we begin by dividing 6 by 2 the final answer is 8. It follows that the operation of division is not associative and that expressions of the form $a \div b \div c$ are ambiguous. Subtraction is also not associative, though there is a convention which gives a definite meaning to expressions such as $a - b - c$. This expression is considered to consist of the three terms a, $-b$ and $-c$, added together. Since addition is associative, the ambiguity is removed.

Identity element

A set on which a binary operation is defined may or may not contain an identity element for the operation. This is an element which leaves all elements unchanged when combined with them in either order. Thus an identity element e for the operation o is one for which $a \circ e = e \circ a = a$ for all elements a.

Examples

Addition has the identity element 0 and multiplication has the identity element 1. Subtraction and division, however, have no identity elements.

Inverse elements

When a set has an identity element e for a particular operation, each element may or may not possess an inverse element. The inverse of the element a, for the operation o, is the element a' which has the property that $a \, o \, a' = a' \, o \, a = e$.

Examples

The inverse element of 5, under addition, is -5. This is because the identity element for addition is zero, and $-5 + 5 = 5 + -5 = 0$. The inverse of 5 under multiplication is $\frac{1}{5}$ since $5 \times \frac{1}{5} = \frac{1}{5} \times 5 = 1$.

▷ Example 4

The operation $*$ is defined on $\mathbf{R}$ by $x * y = 2xy$. Find (a) the identity element, (b) the inverse of $\frac{1}{8}$.
(a) Let the identity element be e; then

$$x * e = x$$
$$\therefore \ 2xe = x$$
$$\therefore \ e = \tfrac{1}{2}.$$

(Since multiplication is commutative we do not need to check that $e * x = x * e$.)
(b) Let the inverse of $\frac{1}{8}$ be a; then

$$a * \frac{1}{8} = \frac{1}{2}$$

$$\therefore \ 2a \times \frac{1}{8} = \frac{1}{2}$$

$$\therefore \ a = 2. \qquad \qquad ◁$$

Groups

A set is called a group under a binary operation if the following properties are present.

(1) The set is closed under the operation.
(2) The operation is associative over the set.
(3) There is an identity element.
(4) Every element has an inverse.

(Note that the operation need not be commutative. If it is, the group is called a commutative group.)

Deducing properties of operations from combination tables

We can easily tell whether or not an operation has each of the special properties *except associativity* by examining its combination table. The following example illustrates the procedure.

▷ Example 5

(a) Prove that the set {1, 2, 3, 4} is a commutative group under multiplication mod 5, and find the inverses of 2 and 4. (b) Prove that the set {1, 2, 3, 4, 5} is not a group under multiplication mod 6. (It may be assumed that these operations, like ordinary multiplication, are associative.)

(a) The combination table is as follows.

× mod 5	1	2	3	4
1	1	2	3	4
2	2	4	1	3
3	3	1	4	2
4	4	3	2	1

(1) Since there are no elements in the table other than 1, 2, 3, 4, the set is closed under multiplication mod 5.

(2) We are assuming that the operation is associative.

(3) By examining the first row and the first column, we can see that 1 is an identity element.

(4) Every element is easily seen to have an inverse. For example, since $2 \times 3 = 3 \times 2 = 1$, the elements 2 and 3 are inverses of each other. Also since $4 \times 4 = 1$, 4 is its own inverse.

The table thus displays the defining properties of a group. The group is commutative since the table is *symmetrical about the leading diagonal* — that is the diagonal from the top left-hand corner to the bottom right. This symmetry shows that in all cases $a \times b = b \times a$.

(b) Since $3 \times 2 = 0$ under multiplication mod 6, and 0 is not an element of the set {1, 2, 3, 4, 5}, the property of closure is missing and it follows that the set is not a group.

Note: We cannot create a group by simply adding 0 to the set. Since $0 \times a = 0$ for all elements a, and 1 is the identity for multiplication, 0 has no multiplicative inverse.   ◀

EXERCISE 22b

1 Say whether or not each of the following sets is closed under the given operation. (a) **Z** under division, (b) {even numbers} under multiplication, (c) {1, 2, 3, 4} under 'taking the average', (d) **R** under 'taking the square root of the product, (e) **Q** under division, (f) {multiples of 3} under addition, (g) {1, 3, 5, 7, 9} under multiplication mod 10, (h) {integers from 1 to 8 inclusive} under multiplication mod 9.

2 Say whether or not each of the following operations is commutative.
(a) $x \circ y =$ the average of x and y, (b) $x \circ y = x - y$, (c) $x \circ y = xy + 2x + 4y$,
(d) $x \circ y = x^2y + xy^2$, (e) $x \circ y = 2x - y^2 + 2y - x^2$.

3 The operation ∗ is defined on **R** by $x * y = x + y - 4$. Find (a) the identity element, (b) the inverses of 7, 10 and −5, (c) the element which is its own inverse.

4 The operation o is defined on **R** by $x \circ y = \frac{1}{3}xy$. Find (a) the identity element, (b) the inverses of 6 and −9.

5 Say whether or not each of the following sets is a group under addition.
(a) **R** (b) **N** (c) **Z** (d) **Q** (e) {0, ±3, ±6, ±9 . . .} (f) {0, ±1, ±3, ±5 . . .}.

6 Say whether or not each of the following sets is a group under multiplication. (a) {±1, ±2, ±3 . . .} (b) **R** (c) {rational numbers excluding zero}.

7 Assuming the property of associativity, show that the set {0, 1, 2, 3, 4} is a commutative group under addition mod 5. State the inverses of 1 and 3.

8 Assuming the associative property, show that the set {1, 2, 3, 4, 5, 6} is a commutative group under multiplication mod 7. State the inverses of 3, 4 and 5.

9 Show that the set {1, 2, 3, 4, 5, 6, 7} is not a group under multiplication mod 8.

10 The operation o on the set {p, q, r, s, t} is defined by the following table:

o	p	q	r	s	t
p	r	s	t	p	q
q	s	t	p	q	r
r	t	p	q	r	s
s	p	q	r	s	t
t	q	r	s	t	p

(a) Assuming the asociative property, show that the set is a group under o.
(b) Name the identity element and the inverses of p and r.
(c) Solve the equation $x \circ x \circ t = r$.

23 Graphs of Equations

Axes, quadrants

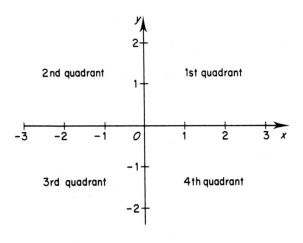

Fig. 23.1

Fig. 23.1 shows a pair of perpendicular lines called *co-ordinate axes*. In this case the horizontal axis is called the *x-axis*, as it is graduated in values of *x*, and the vertical axis is called the *y-axis*. The point *O*, at which both *x* and *y* are zero, is called the *origin*.

The scales along the two axes need not be the same, but the scale must be the same throughout the x-axis and throughout the y-axis.

The axes divide the whole plane into four *quadrants*, called the 1st, 2nd, 3rd and 4th quadrants as shown.

The co-ordinates of a point

Every point has an *x*-value and a *y*-value, called the *co-ordinates* of the point. As shown in Fig. 23.2 each point is labelled by placing the two co-ordinates in brackets, with the *x*-value first.

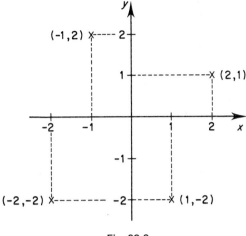

Fig. 23.2

The distance apart of two points

Suppose we require the distance apart of the two points A (2,1) and B (6,4).

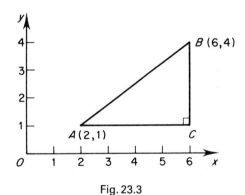

Fig. 23.3

It is clear from Fig. 23.3 that the required distance AB can be obtained by Pythagoras' theorem if we can find AC and BC. Now AC is in fact the *difference between the value of x at B and the value of x at A*, that is $6 - 2 = 4$, and BC is the difference in the y-values at B and A, that is $4 - 1 = 3$. Hence we have

$$AB^2 = 4^2 + 3^2 = 25,$$
$$\therefore \ AB = 5.$$

This result can be generalised. If d is the distance apart of any two points (x_1, y_1) and (x_2, y_2), Pythagoras' theorem gives

$$d = \sqrt{(x_1 - x_2)^2 + (y_1 - y_2)^2}$$

or

$$d = \sqrt{(\text{difference of } x\text{'s})^2 + (\text{difference of } y\text{'s})^2}.$$

Thus for example the distance between the points $(5, -2)$ and $(3, -6)$ is

$$\sqrt{(5-3)^2 + (-2+6)^2} = \sqrt{4+16}$$
$$= \sqrt{20} \text{ or } 2\sqrt{5}.$$

When two points lie in a horizontal or vertical line the above formula is not needed. Consider for example the points $(-1,3)$ and $(4,3)$ (Fig. 23.4).

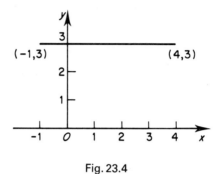

Fig. 23.4

Clearly the distance apart is simply the difference in the x-values, namely $4 - (-1) = 5$.

The mid-point of the line joining two points

Consider once more the points A $(2,1)$ and B $(6,4)$, and let their mid-point be P.

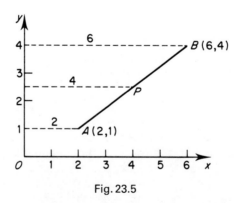

Fig. 23.5

Fig. 23.5 shows that the x-value at P is halfway between the values of x at A and B. Now the number which is halfway between two other numbers is their *average* (or mean), and the average is calculated by adding the two numbers together and dividing by 2. It follows that the x-value at P is $\dfrac{2+6}{2} = 4$, and since similar reasoning applies to the y-values, P is the point $(4, 2\frac{1}{2})$.

In general, the mid-point of the line joining the points (x_1, y_1) and (x_2, y_2) is

$$\left(\frac{x_1 + x_2}{2}, \frac{y_1 + y_2}{2}\right)$$

or

(average of x's, average of y's).

EXERCISE 23a

Mark the following sets of 3 points on graph paper, and decribe the triangles formed when they are joined:
1 (0,0), (3,0) and (0,2)   **2** (−2,3), (2,−3) and (6,3)   **3** (0,−1), (−3,2) and (0,5).

Mark the following sets of 4 points on graph paper, and describe the quadrilaterals formed when they are joined:
4 (−2,−1), (−2,1), (3,−1), (3,1)   **5** (−4,0), (−2,2), (1,0), (3,2)
6 (−4,2), (−1,3), (1,1), (1,−3).

In each of the following questions find (a) the distance apart of the given pair of points (leaving the answer in square root form where appropriate), (b) the mid-point of the line joining the points:
7 (0,6) and (8,0)   **8** (1,4) and (5,7)   **9** (−3,2) and (5,2)
10 (4,2) and (9,14)   **11** (1,0) and (5,1)   **12** (2,−5) and (2,11)
13 (3,0) and (4,−1)   **14** (3,−3) and (−1,3).

In the following questions use the given information to find the point P.
15 A is the point (2,3) and P is a point on OA produced such that $OP = 2\,OA$.
16 A is the point (−1,−5) and P is a point on AO produced such that $OP = 3\,OA$.
17 A is the point (−3,4), B is (5,4), and P is a point on AB produced such that $AB = BP$.
18 A is the point (8,12), and P is a point on OA such that $OP = \frac{3}{4}OA$.
19 A is the point (0,2), B is the point (4,−2), and P is the point at which the line AB meets the x-axis.
20 A is the point (3,0), B is the point (9,0), and APB is an isosceles triangle with a right angle at P.

Graphs of equations

An equation of the form $y = f(x)$ in general has an infinite number of solutions, each of which consists of a pair of x and y values. For example some of the solutions of the equation $y = x^2$ could be expressed as (0,0), (1,1), (2,4) and (3,9). The graph of this equation is the set of points representing all these ordered pairs with respect to a pair of co-ordinate axes. This set of points forms a smooth, infinitely long curve, part of which has the form shown in Fig. 23.6. The values of x and y at every point on this graph satisfy the equation $y = x^2$, and the graph is therefore described as that of $y = x^2$ or $f(x) = x^2$. It can also be described as that of the function $f: x \rightarrow x^2$.

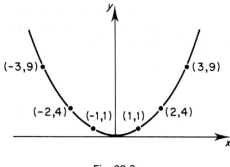

Fig. 23.6

All graphs of simple equations are either straight lines or smooth curves. The above graph, like those of all *quadratic* functions, is a *parabola*.

The gradient of a straight line graph

Gradient is a measurement of *steepness*. Think for the moment of a straight line graph as an inclined road, and suppose that a person moves from a point A on the road to a point B (Fig. 23.7).

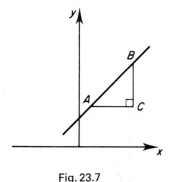

Fig. 23.7

In moving from A to B the person travels a certain distance horizontally (AC in Fig. 23.7), and a certain distance vertically (BC). The horizontal distance is in fact the increase in the value of x, and the vertical distance is the increase in the value of y. Now clearly the steeper the graph is, the greater will be the vertical distance for a given horizontal distance, and we therefore obtain a measurement of steepness, or gradient, by dividing the vertical distance by the horizontal distance. This gives us our definition of gradient:

$$\text{gradient } (m) = \frac{\text{increase in } y}{\text{increase in } x}.$$

In Fig. 23.7 the graph slopes to the right, and both x and y increase as we move from A to B. Hence m is positive. Suppose, however, that the graph slopes to the left (Fig. 23.8).

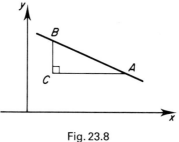

Fig. 23.8

As we move from A to B in this case, x decreases while y increases, and the above definition consequently gives a negative value for the gradient. We therefore have the following rule:

**graph sloping upwards to the right: gradient positive,
graph sloping upwards to the left: gradient negative.**

When a straight line graph is inclined at 45° to the axes its gradient is clearly 1 or −1. Hence the gradient is numerically more than or less than 1 according to whether the line is inclined at more than or less than 45° to the x-axis.

Examples

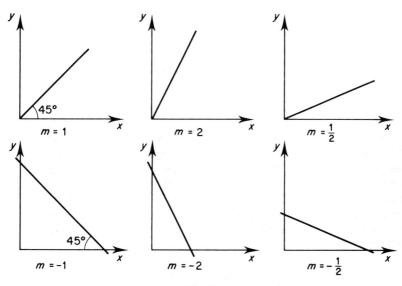

Fig. 23.9

The gradient of a curved graph

When a graph is curved the gradient varies from point to point. The gradient at any given point is defined to be the gradient of the *tangent* to the graph at that point (Fig. 23.10).

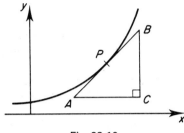

Fig. 23.10

Gradient at P = gradient of line AB
$$= \frac{BC}{AC}.$$

▷**Example 1**

Find the gradients of the lines joining (a) (0,0) and (4,2), (b) (2,1) and (6, −5).

(a) When we move from the first point to the second the increase in x is 4 and the increase in y is 2. Hence

$$m = \frac{\text{increase in } y}{\text{increase in } x} = \frac{2}{4} = \frac{1}{2}.$$

(b) Here the increase in x is 4 and the increase in y is $-5 - 1 = -6$. Hence

$$m = \frac{\text{increase in } y}{\text{increase in } x} = \frac{-6}{4} = -1\frac{1}{2}.$$ ◁

Accurate drawing and sketching

It is important to distinguish between drawing a graph accurately, on graph paper, and sketching a graph. To draw a graph accurately we begin by making a table which consists of a few convenient values of x — such as 0, 1, 2, etc. — together with the corresponding values of y or f(x). A possible table for the equation $y = x^2$ is the following.

x	−4	−3	−2	−1	0	1	2	3	4
y	16	9	4	1	0	1	4	9	16

Having made the table we use it to draw the graph as accurately as possible on graph paper. To *sketch* a graph, however, we do not normally make a table and we do not use graph paper. Instead we simply draw a rough outline of the graph, showing any special features, and put in the co-ordinates of a few important points such as those at which the graph cuts the axes. In this book we shall consider how to sketch graphs of linear and quadratic equations, which are respectively straight lines and parabolas.

Straight-line graphs

Any expression of the form $mx + c$, where m is not zero, is called an expression of degree 1 or a *linear* expression. The expression is called linear because the graph of the equation $y = mx + c$ is a straight line. It can be shown that the gradient of the line is m, and since $y = c$ when $x = 0$, c is the intercept (distance cut off) on the y-axis:

> **The general linear equation $y = mx + c$ represents a straight-line graph of gradient m which cuts the y-axis at the point $(0,c)$.**

Fig. 23.11 shows the effect on a graph of varying c while m is kept constant and varying m while c is kept constant:

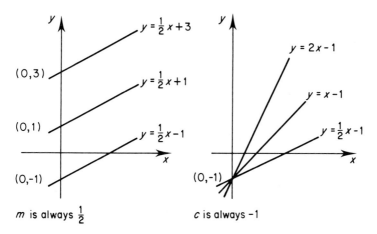

Fig. 23.11

Using the values of m and c gives us one method of sketching a straight-line graph. We can also sketch a graph of this kind, however, by obtaining any *two* points on it. The easiest points to find are usually those at which $x = 0$ and $y = 0$, that is the points at which the graph cuts the y-axis and the x-axis, respectively.

▷ Example 2

Sketch the graph of $2y + x = 4$, by two methods.
Method (a)
Re-arranging the equation into the form $y = mx + c$, we have

$$2y = -x + 4$$
$$\therefore \ y = -\tfrac{1}{2}x + 2.$$

It follows that the gradient m is $-\frac{1}{2}$ and $c = 2$. Since the gradient is negative the graph slopes to the left, and as the numerical value of the gradient is $\frac{1}{2}$ the inclination of the graph to the x-axis is less than 45°. Also, since $c = 2$ the graph cuts the y-axis at (0,2) (Fig. 23.12).

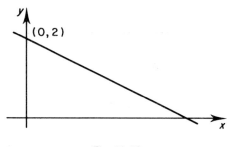

Fig. 23.12

Method (b)
Letting $x = 0$, we have $2y = 4$ and $y = 2$; hence the graph cuts the y-axis at (0,2).

Letting $y = 0$, we have $x = 4$; hence the graph cuts the x-axis at (4,0). Using the two points (0,2) and (4,0) we can sketch the graph (Fig. 23.13).

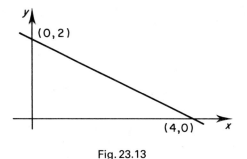

Fig. 23.13

Method (b) in Example 2 is probably the easier of the two — particularly when the equation is not given in the form $y = mx + c$ — but since the idea of *gradient* is important, both methods should be understood.

Horizontal and vertical lines

Horizontal and vertical lines are special cases, and their equations do not have the usual form $y = mx + c$. Consider a horizontal line which is 4 units above the x-axis. Since the equation of a line is simply an equation which is true for all the points on the line, and y is equal to 4 for all the points on this particular line, we say that $y = 4$ is the equation of the line. Similarly, a vertical line which is 6 units to the left of the y-axis has the equation $x = -6$ (Fig. 23.14).

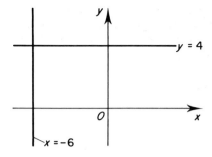

Fig. 23.14

In general, vertical and horizontal lines have equations of the form $x = c$ and $y = k$, respectively, where c and k are constants. The gradient of a horizontal line is zero, and that of a vertical line is 'infinity'.

Parallel lines

Parallel lines clearly have the same gradient, and their equations therefore have the same values of m. The following pairs of lines are parallel:

$$y = 2x - 3, \quad 2y = x - 1, \quad x + y + 1 = 0, \quad y = 12, \quad x = -5,$$
$$y = 2x + 5, \quad 4y = 2x, \quad 2y = 3 - 2x, \quad y = -3, \quad 2x = 9.$$

The points of intersection of graphs

Consider the graphs of $y = 2x$ and $y = x^2$ (Fig. 23.15).

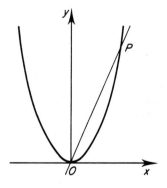

Fig. 23.15

At every point on the straight-line graph the equation $y = 2x$ is true, and at every point on the parabola the equation $y = x^2$ is true. It follows that *both* equations are true at the points of intersection of the two graphs, namely O and P. Now equations which are *both true at the same time* are called *simultaneous* equations, and we know how to solve equations of this kind. Consequently we have a method for finding points of intersection of graphs:

To find the points of intersection of the graphs of $y = f(x)$ and $y = g(x)$, regard these two equations as simultaneous, and solve the pair of simultaneous equations by one of the standard methods.

If both equations are given with y as the subject, as is often the case for equations of graphs, y can be eliminated immediately to give $f(x) = g(x)$. Thus in the above example we have $2x = x^2$, which is a quadratic equation with solutions of 0 and 2. Since $y = 0$ when $x = 0$ and $y = 4$ when $x = 2$, the points of intersection are (0,0) and (2,4).

▷**Example 3**

Find the points of intersection of (a) the lines $y = 3x - 1$ and $y = 6x + 5$, (b) the line $y = 3 - x$ and the curve $y = x^2 - 3x$.

(a) At the point of intersection the equations are simultaneously true; hence

$$6x + 5 = 3x - 1$$
$$\therefore \ 3x = -6$$
$$\therefore \ \ x = -2.$$

Substituting -2 for x in either equation gives $y = -7$, so the point of intersection is $(-2,-7)$.

(b) Again eliminating y, we have

$$x^2 - 3x = 3 - x$$
$$\therefore \ x^2 - 2x - 3 = 0$$
$$\therefore \ (x - 3)(x + 1) = 0$$
$$\therefore \ x = 3 \text{ or } -1.$$

Substituting 3 for x in the equation $y = 3 - x$ we have $y = 0$, and substituting -1 for x we have $y = 4$. Hence the points of intersection are (3,0) and $(-1,4)$.   ◀

EXERCISE 23b

In questions 1–10, find the gradients of the lines joining the given pairs of points.

1 (0,0) and (2,8)   **2** (0,0) and (12,4)   **3** (0,0) and $(-3,6)$
4 (0,0) and $(8,-6)$ **5** (1,1) and (4,7)   **6** (2,1) and (8,5)
7 (3,10) and (1,8)   **8** (2,3) and $(-6,13)$ **9** $(-5,1)$ and $(-7,6)$
10 $(-\frac{1}{2}, -2\frac{1}{2})$ and $(3,-\frac{1}{2})$.

In questions 11–16, find the values of m and c.

11 $y = 3x - 2$ **12** $y = 4 - x$ **13** $x + y + 5 = 0$ **14** $2y = 3x - 4$
15 $5x + 3y = 1$ **16** $\dfrac{3y}{2} - \dfrac{x}{4} - 1 = 0$.

Sketch the graphs of the equations given in questions 17–20, putting in the points where the graphs meet both axes, and stating the values of m.

17 $y = 2x + 4$ **18** $y = 2 - \dfrac{x}{2}$ **19** $4x + 2y = 6$ **20** $15 - 3y = 3x$.

In questions 21–26, say whether or not the pairs of equations represent parallel lines.

21 $y = 5 - x$ and $y = 2 - x$ **22** $y = 2x + 3$ and $3y = 6x - 1$
23 $2y + x = 1$ and $4y + 3 = 2x$ **24** $2y = 7$ and $y - 2 = 0$
25 $x - 5 = 0$ and $y = x$ **26** $2x - 3y - 5 = 0$ and $6y = 12 - 4x$.

In questions 27–34, find the points of intersection of the graphs of the given pairs of equations.

27 $y = 2x - 1$ and $y = x + 3$ **28** $y = x^2$ and $y = 3x$
29 $2y = 1 - x$ and $x + y = 2$ **30** $y = x^2 + 5x$ and $y = 2x + 4$
31 $y = x^2 - 2x$ and $y = -1$ **32** $y = x^2 - x - 2$ and $y = 4$
33 $y = 4x^2 - 1$ and $y = 4x - 2$ **34** $y = 5 + x - x^2$ and $x = 1$.

In questions 35–46, say whether the statements are true (T) or false (F).

35 The graph of $3x - 1 = 2y$ meets the x-axis at $(\frac{1}{3},0)$.
36 All straight lines through the origin have equations of the form $y = kx$.
37 The gradient of the graph of $2x = 1$ is zero.
38 The graphs of $y = x^2 - 2x$ and $y = -5$ meet at two points.
39 The graphs of $y = 1 - x$ and $x = 2 - y$ never meet.
40 All straight-line graphs which do not cut the x-axis have equations of the form $y = k$.
41 The graphs of $y = 4$ and $y = x^2$ meet at $(2,4)$ only.
42 The graphs of $y = 3x - 4$ and $2y + 8 = x$ meet on the y-axis.
43 The equation of the y-axis is $y = 0$.
44 The straight-line graph which passes through $(2,0)$ and has a gradient of 4 cuts the y-axis at $(0,8)$.
45 The lines with equations $y - 2x = 4$, $x + 2 = 0$ and $y = x + 2$ are concurrent (meet at a point).
46 The points $(-1,0)$, $(0,2)$ and $(2,4)$ are collinear (on a straight line).

Some special features of curved graphs

Turning points

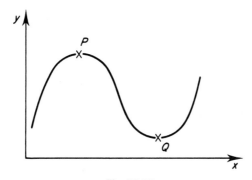

Fig. 23.16

A point such as P, at which the value of y is greater than its value at surrounding points, is called a *maximum* point, and a point such as Q is called a *minimum* point (Fig. 23.16). Both kinds of point are known as *turning points.* Since the tangents to the graph are horizontal at these points, *the gradient at turning points is zero.*

Symmetry

Consider the equation $y = x^2$. When $x = 2$ or -2, $y = 4$, and when $x = 3$ or -3, $y = 9$. So changing the sign of x does not affect the value of y, and hence every point on the graph is accompanied by its reflection in the y-axis (Fig. 23.17).

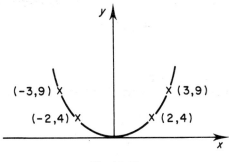

Fig. 23.17

It follows that the graph is symmetrical about the y-axis. Generalising the reasoning just given, we have the following two principles.

> **If the equation of a graph contains only even powers of x,**
> **the graph is symmetrical about the y-axis.**
> **If the equation of a graph contains only even powers of y,**
> **the graph is symmetrical about the x-axis.**

Points of intersection with the axes

We have already seen that a straight-line graph can usually be sketched by finding its points of intersection with the two axes. These points in fact help with the sketching of nearly all graphs, and they are found by using the following simple principle.

> **A graph meets the x-axis when $y = 0$, and the y-axis when $x = 0$.**

Graphs of quadratic functions

The graph of any equation of the form $y = ax^2 + bx + c$ is a *parabola*, which has a maximum or minimum according to the following rule.

> **x^2 term positive: parabola has a minimum,**
> **x^2 term negative: parabola has a maximum.**

The parabola also has an *axis of symmetry*, which passes through its turning point (Fig. 23.18).

Since all graphs of quadratic functions are parabolas, these graphs can usually be sketched by finding their points of intersection with the x-axis.

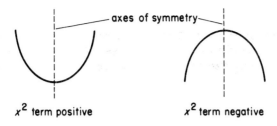

axes of symmetry

x^2 term positive x^2 term negative

Fig. 23.18

▷Example 4

Sketch the graph of $y = x^2 - 2x - 3$.
The graph cuts the x-axis when $y = 0$, that is when

$$x^2 - 2x - 3 = 0$$
$$\therefore \ (x - 3)(x + 1) = 0$$
$$\therefore \ x = 3 \text{ or } -1.$$

The graph is a parabola, and since the x^2 term is positive the parabola has a minimum (Fig. 23.19).

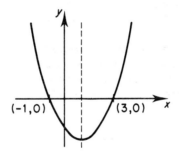

(The axis of symmetry is midway between the points (-1,0) and (3,0), and its equation is therefore $x = 1$)

Fig. 23.19

◁

The next example deals with some special cases in which it is best to find the point of intersection with the y-axis.

▷Example 5

Sketch the graphs of (a) $y = 2x^2$, (b) $y = x^2 + 2$, (c) $y = -1 - 3x^2$.
In all cases of this kind, in which there is *no x term*, the graph is *symmetrical about the y-axis*.

In (a),   when $x = 0, y = 0,$
in (b),   when $x = 0, y = 2,$
and in (c),   when $x = 0, y = -1.$

The graphs are therefore as shown in Fig. 23.20.   ◁

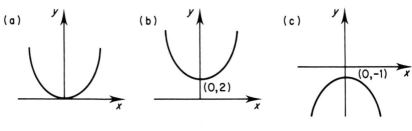

Fig. 23.20

Quadratic inequalities

Sketching graphs of quadratic functions provides an easy method of solving quadratic inequalities. The procedure will be illustrated by examples.

▷ **Example 6**

Solve the inequality $x^2 - x < 2$.
First we move all the terms to one side and factorise. As in the case of quadratic equations, it is usually convenient to choose the side on which the x^2 term is positive:

$$x^2 - x - 2 < 0$$
$$\therefore (x - 2)(x + 1) < 0.$$

Now consider the graph of $y = (x - 2)(x + 1)$. This is a parabola which cuts the x-axis at $(2,0)$ and $(-1,0)$, and since we have chosen to make the x^2 term positive, it must have a minimum rather than a maximum (Fig. 23.21).

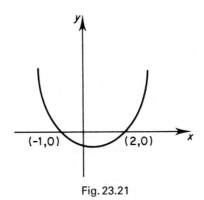

Fig. 23.21

Now since we have let $y = x^2 - x - 2$, the inequality to be solved can be expressed as $y < 0$. This is true for the part of the graph which lies below the x-axis, so the solution of the inequality is

x lies between -1 and 2,

or, more briefly,

$$-1 < x < 2.$$

▷ **Example 7**

Solve the inequality $8 - x^2 < 2x$.
Again making the x^2 term positive, we have

$$x^2 + 2x - 8 > 0$$
$$\therefore \ (x + 4)(x - 2) > 0.$$

Now consider the graph of $y = (x + 4)(x - 2)$ (Fig. 23.22).

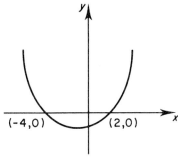

Fig. 23.22

The inequality to be solved is equivalent to $y > 0$, and this is true when

$$x < -4 \text{ or } x > 2. \qquad \triangleleft$$

▷ **Example 8**

Solve the inequalities (a) $x^2 - 2x + 5 < 0$, (b) $x^2 - 2x + 5 > 0$.
Again we consider the graph of $y = $ LHS. To find the points of intersection with the x-axis we have to solve the quadratic equation $x^2 - 2x + 5 = 0$. This clearly cannot be solved by factors, and the quadratic formula gives

$$x = \frac{2 \pm \sqrt{(-16)}}{2}.$$

Since there is no (real) square root of -16, the quadratic equation has no (real) solutions, and it follows that the graph does not cut the x-axis at all (Fig. 23.23).

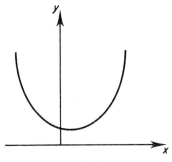

Fig. 23.23

The solutions to (a) and (b) are therefore 'no values of x' and 'all values of x', respectively. ◁

EXERCISE 23c

Sketch the graphs of the equations given in questions 1–10, putting in the points where the graphs meet the x-axis.

1 $y = x^2 - x - 6$ **2** $y = x^2 + 3x - 4$ **3** $y = x^2 - 4x + 3$ **4** $y = 2 - x - x^2$
5 $y = 10 + 3x - x^2$ **6** $y = x^2 - 3x$ **7** $y = -6 + 5x - x^2$ **8** $y = 2x - 4x^2$
9 $y = 2 + 3x - 2x^2$ **10** $y = 1 - 5x + 4x^2$.

Sketch the graphs of the equations given in questions 11–15, putting in the point at which each graph meets the y-axis.

11 $y = x^2 + 3$ **12** $y = 5 - x^2$ **13** $y = 3x^2$ **14** $y = 2x^2 - 1$ **15** $y = -x^2 - 4$

In questions 16–20, state the equations of the axes of symmetry of the graphs.

16 $y = x^2 - 6x + 5$ **17** $y = 12 + 4x - x^2$ **18** $y = 9x - 3x^2$ **19** $y = 2 - x^2$
20 $y = 4x^2 - 3x$.

In questions 21–24, say whether or not the graphs meet the x-axis. (Use the quadratic formula.)

21 $y = x^2 + 3x + 4$ **22** $y = 2x^2 - 7x + 8$ **23** $y = 8 - x - x^2$
24 $y = -3 + 5x - x^2$.

In questions 25–35, solve the quadratic inequalities.

25 $x^2 - 2x - 15 < 0$ **26** $x^2 + 4x - 5 > 0$ **27** $x^2 + 7 > 8x$ **28** $x^2 < 5x$
29 $x^2 - 4 < 0$ **30** $3 - x^2 < 2x$ **31** $x^2 + 5x + 7 < 0$ **32** $4x < 6x^2$
33 $15 - 2x^2 > x$ **34** $2x^2 > 4x - 5$ **35** $18x - 8x^2 < 9$.

In questions 36–46, say whether the given statements are true (T) or false (F).
36 The graph of $y = 2x - x^2$ is symmetrical about the line $x = 1$.
37 The graph of $y = x^2 + 5$ does not meet the x-axis.
38 The turning point of the graph of $y = 5 - 4x - x^2$ lies on the line $x = 2$.
39 The graph of $y = x^2 + x + 3$ meets the y-axis at (3,0).
40 All equations of the form $y = kx^2$ have graphs which are symmetrical about the y-axis.
41 The graph of $y = 1 - x + 3x^2$ has a maximum point.
42 The graph of $y = x^2 - 11x + 30$ does not cut the y-axis.
43 The graph of $y = (1 - 3x)(2x + 1)$ has a minimum point.
44 The x-axis is a tangent to the graph of $y = 4x^2 + 4x + 1$.
45 The graph of $y = 4x^2 - 1$ has a turning point at $(0, -1)$.

Accurate graphs

Up till now we have considered only graph sketching, and not the plotting of an accurate graph from a table of x and y values. The following points should be noted with regard to the technique of plotting accurate graphs.

(1) The points obtained from the table should be clearly marked on the graph paper with dots or crosses, and *not rubbed out* after the graph is drawn.
(2) A *smooth* curve, with no sudden changes of direction, should be drawn through the points in pencil. It is best to begin by drawing the graph very lightly; then the shape of the correct curve will usually become clear and the curve can be drawn with a sharp pencil.
(3) If one of the points appears not to lie on the correct curve, its co-ordinates should be re-calculated.

(4) At particularly curved parts of the graph, e.g. near turning points, it is often advisable to add extra points to the table.

(5) If the scales to be used are not stated in the question, the axes should be graduated so that (a) the values of x and y at all points are easy to read off, (b) the graph fills as much of the paper as possible.

Making a table

Equations of graphs are sometimes quite complicated and the construction of a table requires care. The calculations are made easier by the following kind of table, which is for the graph of $y = 2x - 5 + \dfrac{7}{x}$:

x	0.75	1	1.5	1.75	2	2.25	2.5	3	4
$2x$	1.5	2	3	3.5	4	4.5	5	6	8
-5	-5	-5	-5	-5	-5	-5	-5	-5	-5
$\dfrac{7}{x}$	9.33	7	4.67	4	3.5	3.11	2.8	2.33	1.75
y	5.83	4	2.67	2.5	2.5	2.61	2.8	3.33	4.75

Each column gives the values of $2x$, -5 and $\dfrac{7}{x}$, and these are *added* to obtain y, any minuses in the equation being already written into the table.

The graph has a turning point near to $x = 2$, and more points have been calculated in this region than in the less curved region between $x = 3$ and $x = 4$.

The part of the graph obtained from the table is shown in example 9 below.

Deductions from graphs

When an accurate graph has been drawn it can be used to solve various kinds of problem, some of which are illustrated by the following examples.

▷ **Example 9**

Use the graph of $y = 2x - 5 + \dfrac{7}{x}$ to find

(a) the minimum value of $2x - 5 + \dfrac{7}{x}$ and the value of x at which it occurs,

(b) the roots of the equation $2x + \dfrac{7}{x} = 8.5$,

(c) the range of positive values of x for which $2x - 5 + \dfrac{7}{x}$ is less than $6 - x$.

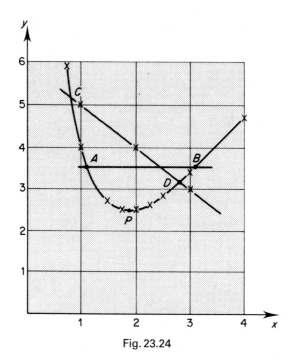

Fig. 23.24

(a) Since $y = 2x - 5 + \dfrac{7}{x}$, the minimum value of $2x - 5 + \dfrac{7}{x}$ is the minimum value of y, that is the value of y at the turning point P. From the graph (Fig. 23.24) this is 2.5 (approximately) and the corresponding value of x is 1.9.

(b) To solve the equation $2x + \dfrac{7}{x} = 8.5$ we must relate this equation to the equation of the graph. Subtracting 5 from both sides we have $2x - 5 + \dfrac{7}{x} = 3.5$, and this is the equation of the graph with 3.5 replacing y. We therefore find the values of x at the points where $y = 3.5$, that is the values at A and B. These are approximately 1.1 and 3.1.

(c) First we draw the graph of $y = 6 - x$. This is a straight line, and it can therefore be drawn by finding any two points on it. As a check, however, it is best to calculate three points:

x	1	2	3
y	5	4	3

This graph cuts the first graph at C and D. Now $2x - 5 + \dfrac{7}{x}$ is less than $6 - x$ for all values of x at which the curved graph is below the straight line graph, that is for the range $0.8 < x < 2.85$ (approximately). ◁

▷ **Example 10** (more difficult)

Draw the graph of $y = 2x - \dfrac{4}{x}$ for the range $x = 0.5$ to $x = 3$. (a) Use the graph to estimate the positive square root of 2. (b) Find the gradient of the graph at the point where $x = 1$. (c) By drawing a certain straight line to intersect the first graph, find a solution of the equation $8x - \dfrac{4}{x} = 12$.

x	0.5	1	1.5	2	2.5	3
$2x$	1	2	3	4	5	6
$-\dfrac{4}{x}$	-8	-4	-2.67	-2	-1.6	-1.33
y	-7	-2	0.33	2	3.4	4.67

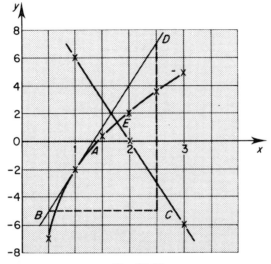

Fig. 23.25

(a) We have to find a solution of the equation $x^2 = 2$. It is not immediately clear how to reduce the equation of the graph to this equation, but a general rule in cases of this kind is to try letting y equal zero. The equation of the graph then becomes

$$0 = 2x - \frac{4}{x}$$
$$\text{i.e.} \quad 0 = 2x^2 - 4$$
$$\text{i.e.} \quad x^2 = 2.$$

It follows that we must find the value of x at the point A where $y = 0$ (Fig. 23.25). This is about 1.4, which is in fact a reasonable estimate of the square root of 2.

(b) To find the gradient at the point where $x = 1$ we first draw the tangent at this point (BD). Now taking a *large* right-angled triangle (BCD) we calculate the value of the fraction

$$\frac{\text{increase in } y}{\text{increase in } x} \left(\frac{CD}{BC} \right).$$

This gives the gradient of the tangent BD, and the gradient of the curved graph is defined to be equal to that of the tangent. We have

$$CD = 7 - -5 = 12,$$
$$BC = 2.5 - 0.5 = 2.$$

Hence the required gradient is $\dfrac{12}{2} = 6$.

(c) At the points of intersection of two graphs their equations are simultaneously true. Hence we treat the equation of the graph and the equation to be solved as simultaneous in order to find the equation of the required straight line:

$$y = 2x - \frac{4}{x} \qquad (1)$$

$$12 = 8x - \frac{4}{x} \qquad (2)$$

Now the non-linear term $\frac{4}{x}$ is eliminated.

$$(1) - (2): \quad y - 12 = -6x$$
$$\text{i.e.} \quad y = -6x + 12.$$

It follows that if we draw the graph of $y = -6x + 12$, the equation $12 = 8x - \frac{4}{x}$ will be true at the point of intersection of this graph with that of $y = 2x - \frac{4}{x}$. In fact the two graphs meet at the point E, and the value of x here is about 1.8. This is therefore the required solution. ◁

EXERCISE 23d (Do not draw any graphs to answer the questions in this exercise.)

In each of questions 1–6 the equations of a pair of graphs are given. Obtain in its simplest form the equation in x which is true at the points of intersection of the graphs.

1 $y = x^2$ and $y = 2x - 3$ **2** $y = 2x^2 - 1$ and $y = 3 + x$
3 $y = x^3 - 2$ and $y = 2x^3 + x^2$ **4** $y = \frac{1}{2}(x^3 - x^2 + 1)$ and $y = x^2 + 1$
5 $y = \frac{2}{x}$ and $y = 3x - 1$ **6** $y = x - \frac{3}{x}$ and $y = 1 - x$.

7 State the values of y which must be taken on the graph of $y = x^2 - 3x + 1$ to obtain solutions of the following equations: (a) $x^2 - 3x + 1 = 0$, (b) $x^2 - 3x = 0$, (c) $x^2 - 3x = 5$, (d) $x^2 = 2 + 3x$.
8 State the values of y which must be taken on the graph of $y = \frac{1}{2}(x^2 + 2x)$ to obtain solutions of the following equations: (a) $x^2 + 2x = 0$, (b) $x^2 + 2x = 4$, (c) $x^2 + 2x - 10 = 0$, (d) $x^2 + 2x + 8 = 0$.

In each of questions 9–12, obtain in its simplest form the equation in x which is true at the points where the given graph meets the x-axis.
9 $y = \frac{x^2}{2} - 3$ **10** $y = \frac{3}{x} - x$ **11** $y = \frac{1}{x^2} - \frac{x}{3}$ **12** $y = \frac{x^2}{5} - \frac{2}{x}$.

In each of questions 13–16 an equation of a graph and an equation to be solved are given. Obtain in each case the equation of the straight line whose points of intersection with the graph give the roots of the equation to be solved.
13 $y = x^2 - \frac{1}{x}$, $x^2 - \frac{1}{x} = 2x$ **14** $y = x^2 + 2x$, $x^2 + x = 5$
15 $y = 2x - \frac{3}{x}$, $4x - \frac{3}{x} = 2$ **16** $y = \frac{x^3}{2} - x$, $x^3 + 3x = 4$.

EXERCISE 23e (Draw accurate graphs.)

1 Draw the graph of $y = 7x - 2x^2$ for the range $x = 0$ to $x = 4$. Read off the values of y when x is 0.8, 1.7, 2.3, and state the value of x at which y is a maximum.

2 Draw the graph of $y = 3x^2 - 4x$ for the range $x = -2$ to $x = 4$, and use the graph (a) to solve the equation $3x^2 - 4x = 2$, (b) to solve the equation $3x^2 - 4x = 10$, (c) to find the minimum value of $3x^2 - 4x$.

3 Draw the graph of $y = 6x - x^2$ for the range $x = 0$ to $x = 6$, and use the graph to solve the inequalities (a) $6x - x^2 > 7$, (b) $6x - x^2 < 3$.

4 Draw the graph of $y = \frac{1}{2}(2x^2 - 12x + 15)$ for the range $x = 0$ to $x = 6$. Estimate (a) the minimum value of y, (b) the solutions of the equation $2x^2 - 12x + 7 = 0$.

5 Draw the graph of $y = 5 + 3x - x^2$ for the range $x = -2$ to $x = 5$, and estimate its gradient at the points where (a) $x = 0.5$, (b) $x = 2.4$. Also (c) use the graph to solve the inequality $3x - x^2 > 1$.

6 Draw the graph of $y = x^2 - 2x - 6$ for the range $x = -3$ to $x = 5$, and use the graph to solve the equations (a) $x^2 - 2x = 6$, (b) $x^2 - 2x = 4$. Draw also the graph of $y = x$ to intersect the first graph, and hence (c) obtain solutions to the equation $x^2 - 3x - 6 = 0$.

7 Draw the graph of $y = 5x^2 - x^3$ for the range $x = 0$ to $x = 5$, and find (a) the range of values of x for which $5x^2 - x^3$ is greater than 10. Draw also the graph of $y = x + 9$ and hence find (b) the range of values of x for which $5x^2 - x^3$ is greater than $x + 9$.

8 Draw the graph of $y = x^3$ for the range $x = 0$ to $x = 3$ and use it to find (a) 2.3^3, (b) $\sqrt[3]{20}$. Draw also the graph of $y = 5x + 2$ and hence obtain (c) a solution of the equation $x^3 - 5x - 2 = 0$.

9 Draw the graph of $y = x^3 - 6x^2$ for the range $x = 0$ to $x = 7$, and find (a) its gradient at the point where $x = 2$, (b) the minimum value of y. By drawing a certain straight line to intersect the first graph, obtain a solution of the equation $x^3 - 6x^2 + 10x - 20 = 0$.

10 Draw the graph of $y = x + \dfrac{2}{x}$ for the range $x = 0.5$ to $x = 4$, and use it to estimate (a) the minimum value of $x + \dfrac{2}{x}$, (b) the solutions of the equation $x + \dfrac{2}{x} = 4$. Draw also the graph of $y = 5x$ to intersect the first graph and hence obtain (c) a solution of the equation $2x^2 = 1$.

11 Draw the graph of $y = \dfrac{3}{x} - x$ for the range $x = 1$ to $x = 3$, and use it to estimate (a) the positive square root of 3. By drawing a certain straight line to intersect the graph, obtain (b) a solution of the equation $\dfrac{3}{x} - 3x + 2 = 0$.

12 Draw the graph of $y = \dfrac{x^2}{8} - \dfrac{4}{x}$ for the range $x = 1$ to $x = 5$, and find (a) its gradient at the point where $x = 4$. Also (b) use the graph to estimate the cube root of 32.

13 Draw the graph of $y = 10 - x - \dfrac{5}{x}$ for the range $x = 0.5$ to $x = 8$. (a) Estimate the maximum value of y and the value of x at which it occurs. (b) Measure the gradient at the points where $x = 1.5$ and $x = 4$. (c) Obtain solutions of the equation $x + \dfrac{5}{x} = 7$.

14 Draw the graph of $y = \dfrac{10}{x} + 2x - 8$ for the range $x = 0.5$ to $x = 8$. Estimate

(a) the range of positive values of x for which $\dfrac{10}{x} + 2x - 8$ is less than 8,

(b) the gradient of the graph at the point where $x = 4.6$. By drawing a certain straight line to intersect the graph, obtain (c) solutions of the equation $\dfrac{10}{x} + 4x = 18$.

24 Linear Programming

Practical problems often involve quantities whose values are restricted or *constrained* so that they have to lie within certain ranges. Here are some examples of the constraints which a firm might impose on the quantities under its control:

(1) At least 500 articles must be manufactured each week.
(2) The profit must be at least £200 per article.
(3) The total number of employees must not exceed 60.
(4) The number of women employed must be at least half the number of men.

In addition, there are some obvious restrictions which do not arise by choice, such as the fact that the number of employees cannot be negative or fractional! When a number of constraints of this kind operate at the same time, it can be quite a complicated matter to decide which values of the variables are the most suitable for achieving the firm's objectives. A general technique for solving this kind of problem is called *linear programming*, and in real problems, involving many variables, it normally requires the use of computers. Provided that the number of variables is limited to two, however, a graphical approach can be used, and this is the approach which will be adopted here.

The kind of constraints or restrictions given in the above examples can usually be expressed in the form of *linear inequalities*. Take for example the condition that the number of employees must not exceed 60. If we let the number of employees be x, this condition can be expressed as $x \leq 60$. Since in addition x clearly cannot be negative or fractional, the complete condition governing values of x is 'x is an integer such that $0 \leq x \leq 60$'.

Now whereas linear *equations* can be represented graphically by straight lines, linear inequalities can be represented by *regions bounded by straight lines*. We begin by considering this technique.

Half-planes

Consider the simple inequality $y > 2$. At all points on the graph of $y = 2$, the value of y is 2 and the graph is therefore a horizontal straight line. Clearly therefore y is greater than 2 at every point above the line, and this semi-infinite region represents the inequality $y > 2$. Regions of this kind, which stretch to infinity in one direction only, are called *half-planes*. We cannot shade the whole of such a region, so it is customary to indicate the region by shading its *outer* boundary; the region itself is left clear (Fig. 24.1).

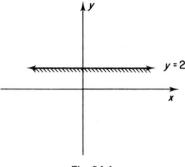

Fig. 24.1

Now consider the region defined by the inequality $y < 2x$. The value of y is equal to $2x$ at all points on the straight line $y = 2x$, and since y is a vertical distance, y will be less than $2x$ at all points *below* the line (Fig. 24.2).

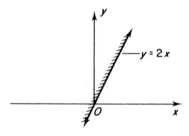

Fig. 24.2

Finally consider the inequality $x + 2y > 4$. Writing this as $x > 4 - 2y$ and remembering that x denotes a horizontal distance, we see that x is greater than $4 - 2y$ at all points to the *right* of the line $x = 4 - 2y$ (Fig. 24.3).

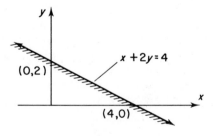

Fig. 24.3

Alternatively we could express the inequality as $y > 2 - \dfrac{x}{2}$, which would tell us to take all points *above* the line. Yet another method of deciding which half-plane is required is to substitute the co-ordinates of the origin into the inequality, and see whether the inequality is then true or false. Here we obtain $0 > 4$, which is false, so the origin is *not* in the half-plane required.

Open and closed regions

We saw in chapter 12, when considering ranges of values on number-lines, that such ranges may or may not include the end-points. For example, the range indicated by $x \leqslant 3$ includes the number 3; the range indicated by $x < 3$ does not. In the former case the range (or interval) is said to be *closed* at its upper end while in the latter case the range is said to be *open*.

Regions can also be open or closed. For example the region indicated by $x - 2y > 3$ does not include the points on the line $x - 2y = 3$, and is said to be open, while the region indicated by $x - 2y \geqslant 3$ does include the points on the line and is said to be closed.

It is seldom necessary to indicate in diagrams whether regions are open or closed, but when this is considered desirable there are several possible methods. One is to use pencil lines to indicate open intervals and ink lines for closed ones, and another is to use dotted and unbroken lines, respectively.

Regions defined by simultaneous inequalities

In practical problems many constraints, each expressible as an inequality, operate simultaneously. We therefore need to be able to locate graphical regions at which several inequalities are simultaneously true.

▷ Example 1

Indicate the region at which the inequalities $x > 0$, $y > 0$, $x + y < 4$ and $y + 3x < 6$ are simultaneously true.
The region is bounded by the x-axis, the y-axis and the lines $x + y = 4$, $y + 3x = 6$ (Fig. 24.4).

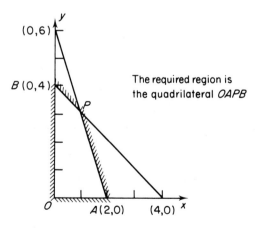

The required region is the quadrilateral *OAPB*

Fig. 24.4

The lines can be sketched by finding their points of intersection with the axes, as shown. If the co-ordinates of P are required they can be found by solving the simultaneous equations $x + y = 4$, $y + 3x = 6$. The solutions are in fact $x = 1$, $y = 3$; so P is the point (1,3).   ◁

▷ Example 2

Find the inequalities which are simultaneously true for the region OAB indicated in Fig. 24.5.

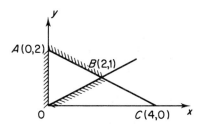

Fig. 24.5

We require first the equations of the lines *OA*, *AB* and *OB*. *OA* is the y-axis, with equation $x = 0$. The gradient of *AB* is $-\frac{1}{2}$, and since this line cuts the y-axis at $(0,2)$, $c = 2$. Hence from the standard equation $y = mx + c$, the equation of *AB* is

$$y = -\tfrac{1}{2}x + 2 \text{ or } 2y + x = 4.$$

The line *OB* has a gradient of $\frac{1}{2}$, and since it passes through the origin, $c = 0$. Hence the equation of *OB* is

$$y = \tfrac{1}{2}x \text{ or } 2y = x.$$

It follows that the inequalities which define the indicated region are

$$x > 0, 2y + x < 4 \text{ and } 2y > x. \qquad \triangleleft$$

All the points in the regions considered in these examples satisfy all the inequalities which define the regions. In general, however, not all the points within a region provide equally suitable solutions to practical problems. In most cases, for example, the solutions have to be *integers* (whole numbers), and this means that we are limited to the lattice of points at which both *x* and *y* are integers (Fig. 24.6).

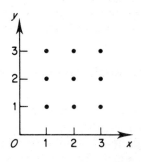

Fig. 24.6

▷ Example 3

Find (a) the set of points with integer co-ordinates within the region defined by the inequalities $y \leqslant 3x$, $y + 2x \leqslant 8$ and $3y \geqslant 2x$. From this set find also the point or points at which (b) $y + x = 4$, (c) $y + 3x$ is a maximum.

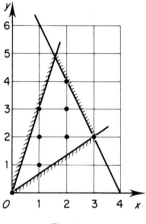

Fig. 24.7

Since the graph of $y + 2x = 8$ cuts the y-axis at the point where $y = 8$, which is inconveniently far from the region we are concerned with, the graph is best drawn by making a short table:

x	1	2	3
y	6	4	2

The other two graphs pass through the origin, and only one other convenient point is required in each case (Fig. 24.7).

(a) Note that points *on* the boundary lines are in this case included in the defined region. There are 8 points with integer co-ordinates in the region, namely (0,0), (1,1), (1,2) (1,3) (2,2), (2,3), (2,4) and (3,2).
(b) Taking each point in turn and calculating $x + y$, we find that the points for which $x + y = 4$ are (1,3) and (2,2).
(c) In this question there are only 8 points to consider, and by trial and error it is easy to discover that the maximum value of $y + 3x$ is provided by the point (3,2), and is 11. When there are inconveniently many points to consider we need the more systematic approach which is explained in the next section.   ◁

The general method for obtaining maximum and minimum values

In the last example we were interested in the maximum value of $y + 3x$ within the given region, and found the value by trying a few likely points. We shall now look at a more general approach to this kind of problem, which is needed when there are many candidate points and the 'trial and error' method is less suitable.

Consider the graphs of the following set of equations:

$$y + 3x = 1,$$
$$y + 3x = 2,$$
$$y + 3x = 3, \text{etc.}$$

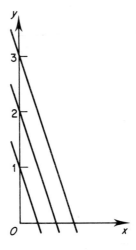

Fig. 24.8

The graphs (Fig. 24.8) all have the same gradient (-3) and they cut the y-axis at the points (0,1) (0,2) and (0,3), respectively. The set of graphs thus forms a family of parallel lines, each of which has an equation of the form $y + 3x = k$. Now as the value of k (and thus $y + 3x$) increases, the diagram shows that the graph of $y + 3x = k$ moves further away from the origin. It follows that to obtain the maximum value of $y + 3x$ within a region, *we take the member of the family of lines which is as far as possible from the origin and which passes through an acceptable point in the region*. If we require the minimum value of $y + 3x$ we take the line which is as *near* as possible to the origin and passes through an acceptable point.

Maximum and minimum values usually occur at *points where boundary lines meet*, if these points provide acceptable values of the quantity in question. This is illustrated in the following example.

▷ Example 4

An infinite region is defined by the inequalities $y \geqslant 0$, $x \geqslant 1$ and $3y + 4x \geqslant 12$. Obtain the minimum value of $y + 3x$ in this region (a) if there are no other restrictions on x and y, (b) if x and y must be integers.

We require the line with equation $y + 3x = k$ which is as near as possible to O and which passes through an acceptable point in the given region. The dotted lines in Fig. 24.9 show some members of this family of lines, and it is clear that if all the points in the region are acceptable, the line through P is the nearest. Now P is the point at which the equations $x = 1$ and $3y + 4x = 12$ are simultaneously true, i.e. the point $(1,2\frac{2}{3})$. This is a point at which x and y are not both integers, so it is acceptable in case (a) but not in case (b).

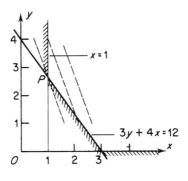

Fig. 24.9

(a) As just explained, the minimum value of $y + 3x$ occurs at the point P, where $x = 1$ and $y = 2\frac{2}{3}$. The minimum value is thus $2\frac{2}{3} + 3 = 5\frac{2}{3}$.

(b) The point or points required must have integer co-ordinates and lie on a line $y + 3x = k$ which is as near to O as possible. There are now several approaches. If a large accurate graph has been drawn, it is often possible to look at all the lines of the required gradient (here -3) which pass through points with integer co-ordinates. If there is an inconveniently large number of these points, however, a better method may be to draw one line accurately and then use a ruler and set-square to 'translate' the line until it is as near to O as possible and passes through a point or points with integer co-ordinates. The above diagram (Fig. 24.9) is not drawn accurately on graph paper, and we shall simply take the two points with integer co-ordinates which are near to P and calculate $y + 3x$ for each. Taking the point $(2,2)$, $y + 3x = 8$, and taking the point $(1,3)$, $y + 3x = 6$. Hence the minimum value of $y + 3x$ when x and y are integers is 6. ◁

EXERCISE 24a

1 Draw sketches indicating the half-planes representing the following inequalities, and say in each case whether the origin is in the region:
(a) $x > 3$, (b) $y < 4$, (c) $y > 3x + 1$, (d) $y < x - 2$, (e) $2x - y > 4$,
(f) $2y - 3 > x$, (g) $3y + 4x - 7 < 0$.
2 Draw sketches indicating the (infinite) regions representing the following simultaneous inequalities, and give the co-ordinates of the points of intersection of the boundary lines:
(a) $x > 1$, $x + y > 3$, (b) $y < 6$, $y > 2x$, (c) $x + 2y < 4$, $x + y < 3$,
(d) $2x - y + 3 < 0$, $2y + 5x < 15$, (e) $y + 3 > 3x$, $x + 4 < 2y$.
3 Draw sketches indicating the (enclosed) regions representing the following simultaneous inequalities, and give the co-ordinates of the vertices of the regions:
(a) $x > 0$, $y > 0$, $y < 4 - 2x$, (b) $2y > x$, $x > 0$, $y < 2$,
(c) $y < 8$, $y < 2x$, $2y - 3x + 2 > 0$, (d) $5x - 2y - 1 < 0$, $3x + 2y < 7$, $x + 1 > 0$.
4 Find the inequalities which define the regions indicated in Fig. 24.10. (The boundary lines are not included.)

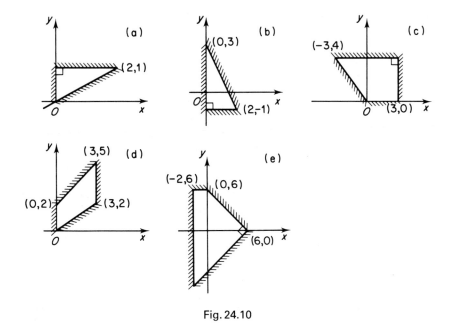

Fig. 24.10

In the remaining questions graph paper may be needed.

5 (a) List the points with integer co-ordinates within the region defined by the inequalities $x > 0$, $y > 0$, $y < x + 2$, $x + y < 5$. From the points listed find (b) the maximum value of $y + 2x$, (c) the minimum value of $x + 2y$, (d) the maximum value of $3y - x$.

6 Given that $x \geqslant 0$, $y \geqslant 0$, $y + 2x \geqslant 4$ and $3y + 2x \geqslant 6$, find the minimum values of (a) $x + y$, (b) $x + 3y$, (c) $3x + y$.

7 Given that $x \geqslant 0$, $y \leqslant 2\frac{1}{2}$, $x \leqslant 2$ and $2y \geqslant x$, find (a) the maximum value of $4y + 3x$, (b) the minimum value of $y - 2x$, (c) the maximum value of $2y - 3x$.

8 Repeat question 7, given that x and y must be integers.

9 Given that $4y - 10x \leqslant 15$, $x + y \leqslant 5$, $y \geqslant x$ and $y \geqslant 0$, find (a) the maximum value of $y + 2x$, (b) the maximum value of $2y - 5x$, (c) the minimum value of $3y + 4x$.

10 Repeat question 9, given that x and y must be integers.

Practical problems

The main task in practical linear programming problems (as in most algebra problems — see chapter 16) is to 'translate' statements in ordinary English into the language of algebra. In chapter 16 the statements led to equations; here they lead to *inequalities in two variables*. The following simple example shows how a statement in ordinary language can lead to an inequality.

> *A housewife has up to £2 to spend on loaves of bread which cost 40 p each and bottles of milk which cost 20 p each.*

In order to express this statement algebraically we must first introduce letters to denote variables. Here it is obvious that the variables must be the number of loaves and the number of bottles of milk, so we let these two quantities be x and y respectively. Since the loaves cost 40 p each the total amount spent on loaves is (40x) p, and since the bottles of milk cost 20 p the total amount spent on milk is (20y) p. The housewife can spend up to £2 or 200 p, so we have the inequality

$$40x + 20y \leqslant 200.$$

With regard to this inequality, it is worth noting the following points:
(1) The *units* are consistent. Each term represents a number of *pence* and it would be possible to add the unit p to each term without falsifying the inequality.
(2) It is permissible to divide both sides of an inequality by any *positive* quantity, so the above inequality can be simplified to $2x + y \leqslant 10$.

Linear programming problems involve two or more linear inequalities, and, as already explained, these can be represented graphically by regions bounded by straight lines. In practical problems the variables are often limited to integral values, and this means that acceptable solutions are represented graphically by points with integer co-ordinates. We have seen that maximum and minimum values are usually given by the points of intersection of the boundary lines, so it is generally advisable to determine whether or not these lines meet at points with integer co-ordinates. If they do, the points of intersection themselves provide the values of x and y giving maxima and minima, while if they do not, the required values are usually near the points of intersection. In the latter case it is necessary to pick out the points with integer co-ordinates in the vicinity of the points of intersection, and consequently the scales on the x- and y-axes should be chosen so as to make these points easy to locate. It is also advisable if possible to use the same scale on the two axes, since the gradients of lines are then more easily calculated or estimated.
When the boundary lines meet at points with integer co-ordinates it is sometimes possible to avoid drawing an accurate graph on graph paper. The co-ordinates of the points of intersection can be found by solving simultaneous equations, and it may be possible to tell from a sketch which points are required. In any case, it is advisable to draw a sketch before the accurate graph is drawn, in order to plan out the positions of the axes and decide on the most convenient scales.
The following example illustrates most of the techniques which arise in elementary problems.

▷ Example 5

A firm employs skilled workers and apprentices. The skilled workers each turn out on average 20 grade A products and 4 grade B products per week, while the apprentices turn out on average 12 grade A products and 7 grade B products. The firm has contracted to supply at least 600 grade A products and 200 grade B products each week, and it has room for up to 60 workers. The number of skilled workers is never more than three times the number of apprentices or less than half of this number.

Let the number of skilled workers be x and the number of apprentices be y, and indicate on a graph the region within which acceptable pairs of values of x and y lie. Use the graph to answer the following questions:

(a) If there are 25 skilled workers, what is the minimum possible number of apprentices?

(b) What is the maximum number of grade A products that can be produced per week?

(c) What is the minimum total number of employees?

(d) If the skilled workers earn twice the wage of the apprentices, what values of x and y give the minimum total wage bill?

The first task is to express the given information as a set of inequalities. Let us begin by using the fact that at least 600 grade A products are required per week. The skilled workers produce a total of $20x$ grade A products, and the apprentices produce a total of $12y$, so we have $20x + 12y \geq 600$, or, dividing by 4, $5x + 3y \geq 150$. Similarly, by considering the grade B products, we have $4x + 7y \geq 200$. The total number of workers cannot be greater than 60, so $x + y \leq 60$. From the fact that the number of skilled workers is never more than three times the number of apprentices it follows that $x \leq 3y$, and as there are at least half as many skilled workers as apprentices, $x \geq \dfrac{y}{2}$ or $2x \geq y$. It is important to remember also to note the more obvious restrictions over which the firm has no control. In this case we have $x \geq 0$ and $y \geq 0$ (which turn out in fact not to be relevant in this problem), and also the fact that x and y must be integers, which is always important because it restricts the acceptable solutions.

Five inequalities have emerged from the given information, and we therefore draw graphs (Fig. 24.11) of the five corresponding equations, namely

$$5x + 3y = 150 \text{ (the line } ST)$$
$$4x + 7y = 200 \ (PT),$$
$$x + y = 60 \ (RQ),$$
$$x = 3y \ (PQ),$$
$$2x = y \ (SR).$$

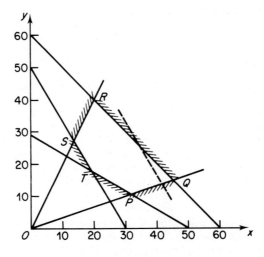

Fig. 24.11

The outer boundaries of the required region are shaded. Note that all the boundaries are included in the region.

(a) If there are 25 skilled workers the value of x is 25, and we are therefore limited to points within the allowed region which are on the straight line $x = 25$. The minimum integral value of y on this line is 15; hence the minimum number of apprentices is 15.

(b) The total number of grade A products manufactured in a week is $20x + 12y$. Now consider the set of straight lines whose equations are $20x + 12y = k$. These lines are all parallel to the line ST, with gradients of $-\frac{5}{3}$. One of them is shown (dotted) in the diagram. We require the member of this family of lines which passes through an acceptable point in the region and is as far as possible from O, and since the point Q has integer co-ordinates the required line is the one passing through Q. At Q the values of x and y are 45 and 15, respectively, so the maximum number of grade A products is $(20 \times 45) + (12 \times 15) = 1080$.

(c) The total number of employees is $x + y$, so we consider the family of straight lines $x + y = k$, which have a gradient of -1. (These lines are not shown.) We require the minimum value of $x + y$, and therefore look for the member of this family which is as near as possible to O. Sliding a ruler over the graph paper (freehand gives sufficient accuracy) shows that the line through T is the nearest, but since T does not have integer co-ordinates this point itself does not provide an acceptable solution. We therefore either look for points with integer co-ordinates which are on the nearest line to O and just inside T, or simply work out $x + y$ for all likely points in the vicinity of T. Either method shows that the 5 points (22,16), (21,17), (20,18), (19,19) and (18,20) all give the value 38 for the minimum number of employees.

(d) If the skilled workers earn twice the wage of the apprentices, then for every 1 unit earned by an apprentice a skilled worker earns 2 units, and it follows that the total earnings are proportional to $2x + y$. This means that we require the values of x and y for which $2x + y$ is a minimum, and we therefore consider the family of straight lines $2x + y = k$. The nearest of these lines to the origin passes through S, which does not have integer co-ordinates, and examination of the points near to S shows that the points (14,27) and (15,25) give the minimum value of $2x + y$. The firm should therefore employ either 14 skilled workers and 27 apprentices or 15 skilled workers and 25 apprentices in order to have the smallest possible wage bill.   ◀

EXERCISE 24b

1 Articles of type A weigh 4 g each and cost 5 p, while articles of type B weigh 1 g each and cost 10 p. The total weight must not exceed 85 g and the total cost must not exceed £1.50. Find the maximum possible total number of articles that can be bought.

2 A boy can spend up to 15 minutes and 45 p eating sweets and chocolates. Sweets cost 1 p each and last for 30 seconds, while chocolates cost 2 p each and last for 20 seconds. The boy gets three times as much pleasure from chocolates as from sweets. How many of each should he eat if (a) he wants the total number to be as great as possible, (b) he wants as much enjoyment as possible?

3 A boy giving a birthday party is allowed to invite up to 25 children, of whom at least 5 must be girls. He decides to have at least as many boys as girls, and at least 15 guests altogether. The cost of entertaining a boy is $1\frac{1}{2}$ times that of entertaining a girl. Find (a) the maximum number of boys he can have if he invites 7 girls, (b) the minimum number of boys if he invites 9 girls, (c) the numbers of boys and girls for which the cost to his parents is a minimum, (d) the numbers for which the cost is a maximum.

4 Food X contains 5 units of vitamin A and 2 units of vitamin B per kilogram, while food Y contains 4 units of vitamin A and 6 units of vitamin B per kilogram. The foods are used to produce a mixture which has to contain at least 23 units of vitamin A and at least 24 units of vitamin B. Working to the nearest 0.1 kg find the combinations that provide (a) the minimum total weight of food, (b) the minimum cost, given that X is twice as expensive as Y.

5 An examination paper contains short questions of which a maximum of 10 can be attempted and long questions of which a maximum of 6 can be attempted. The examination lasts for 3 hours and a certain candidate takes an average of 8 minutes to complete each of the short questions and 20 minutes to complete each of the long ones. On average he obtains 3 marks for each short question and 6 marks for each long one. Find the numbers of the two types he should attempt (a) to obtain maximum marks, (b) to take the minimum time if he is satisfied w 'th 45 marks.

6 A man drinks beer which cosi ; 50 p a pint and lager which costs 75 p. He spends up to £15 a week on drinking, always spending at least as much on lager as beer but never drinking more than three times as much lager as beer. Find (a) the maximum number of pints of beer he can drink in a week if he drinks 20 pints altogether, (b) the number of pints of each if he drinks as great a total quantity as possible, (c) the number of pints of each he should drink to gain the maximum enjoyment, given that he gets twice the enjoyment from lager that he gets from beer.

7 A taxi company has up to £60 000 to spend on cars, and it decides to buy a combination of 4-seaters costing £3000 each and 6-seaters costing £4000 each. The company must be able to carry at least 50 passengers at any one time. It decides that at least 2 6-seaters are essential, but that it should have at least as many 4-seaters as 6-seaters. Find (a) the maximum number of 4-seaters if 5 of the 6-seaters are bought, (b) the minimum total number of cars, (c) the numbers of the two types for which the total number is a maximum, (d) the numbers of the two types for which running costs are a minimum, given that the large cars cost twice as much to run as the small ones.

8 A firm has to produce at least 300 articles per week and has room for up to 60 employees. The men earn £80 per week and produce an average of 10 articles each, while the women earn £60 and produce an average of 6 articles each. The firm's policy is to employ at least as many men as women, but not more than twice as many men. Find (a) the number of articles produced per week if there are as few employees as possible, (b) the total wage bill if as many women as possible are employed, (c) the maximum possible wage bill, (d) the minimum number of men required if 390 articles are to be produced by the firm.

9 A library has up to £100 to spend on books on cricket and football. The cricket books cost on average £2.50 and the football books cost £2. No more than 25 of either are bought and the ratio of one type to the other must not be more than 3 : 1. Let the number of cricket books be x and the number of football books be y, and find (a) the values of x and y giving the maximum enjoyment if (i) the cricket books are twice as popular as those on football, (ii) the football books are twice as popular as those on cricket, (b) the values of x and y if the number of cricket books exceeds the number of football books by as large a number as possible.

10 A firm has £500 with which to manufacture a batch of two types of articles. Articles of type A cost £30 each to make and articles of type B cost £20 each to make. The firm employs 36 workers, and while in the time available a single worker can make a type A article, two workers are required to make one of type B. The batch must contain at least 4 type A articles, and not more than twice as many type A's as type B's. Find (a) the maximum number of type A's if 10 type B's are made, (b) the maximum number of type B's if 5 type A's are made. Find also the numbers of each type which give the maximum profit if (c) A's and B's provide an equal profit, (d) A's provide twice as great a profit as B's, (e) B's provide three times as great a profit as A's.

25 Some Elementary Geometry

Geometry is a *logical* subject. It is built up from a few basic statements called *axioms* which are either self-evident or true by definition. All other geometrical statements are derived from these axioms.

Particularly important geometrical statements are called *theorems*. These are treated as standard geometrical facts and they are used in problem-solving and in proving other theorems. A familiar example is the theorem that the angles in a triangle add up to 180°. Theorems are normally learned by heart and quoted without proof when they are used to solve geometrical problems. The order in which they themselves are proved is important because once a theorem has been proved it becomes available for use in the proof of other theorems. Thus the theorems form a kind of structure, the ones proved later depending on those proved earlier with all resting ultimately on the basic axioms. Writing out the proof of a theorem used to be an important examination requirement, but is now seldom demanded. It is still essential, however, to learn the geometrical facts which the theorems state.

In this section we shall deal almost entirely with *plane* and not solid geometry. Normally therefore the lines in the diagrams can be considered to lie in the plane of the paper on which they are drawn.

Terms and conventions

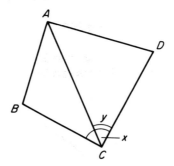

Fig. 25.1

Fig. 25.1 illustrates some standard conventions used in geometry which students often ignore. *Points*, such as *A, B, C, D*, are always denoted by *capital* letters. When the whole figure is named, the letters must be in the *same order* as the points in the diagram. Thus the above figure could be denoted by *ABCD* or *ADCB* or *DCBA*, etc., but *not*, for example, by *ABDC*. To name the angle at *D*, we can write either angle *ADC* or angle *CDA* or simply angle *D*. We cannot, however, denote any of the angles at *A* and *C* by angle *A* or angle *C*, because there is more than one angle at each of these points. When *single small letters* are used to denote angles, as at *C*, the extent of each angle should always be indicated by means of a small arc. Thus in Fig. 25.1 *x* denotes the whole angle *BCD*— as the arc indicates —while *y* denotes angle *ACD*.

A *vertex* is a point where two or more lines cross. In Fig. 25.1, *A*, *B*, *C* and *D* are all vertices.

A *line* is strictly considered to be a straight line which is infinitely long in both directions, and a *half-line* or *ray* is a line which is infinitely long in one direction only (Fig. 25.2). An arrow on a line can be used to show that it extends to infinity.

line   half-line

Fig. 25.2

A part of a line, such as a side of a triangle, is strictly called a *line-segment* and denoted by a symbol such as *AB*. The symbol *AB* is used in slightly different ways, however: sometimes it means the segment *AB*, sometimes the length of the segment, and sometimes the whole line of which the segment is a part.

The expression *produce the line AB* means *extend the line-segment through the end point B* (Fig. 25.3).

A   *B*   *A*   *B*

AB is produced.   *BA* is produced.

Fig. 25.3

An *acute* angle is one which is less than 90°, an *obtuse* angle is between 90° and 180°, and a *reflex* angle is between 180° and 360° (Fig. 25.4).

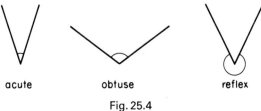

acute   obtuse   reflex

Fig. 25.4

Two angles which have a sum of 90° are called *complementary*, and two angles which have a sum of 180° are called *supplementary*.

A triangle is *equilateral* if all its sides are equal, isosceles if two (or more) are equal, and *scalene* if all its sides are of different length. A triangle is *acute-angled* if all its angles are acute, *right-angled* if it has a right angle, and *obtuse-angled* if it has an obtuse angle.

A *median* of a triangle is a line from a vertex to the mid-point of the opposite side, and an *altitude* is a line from a vertex which meets the opposite side at right angles (Fig. 25.5).

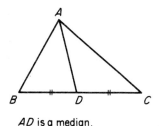

AD is a median.   *AD* is an altitude.

Fig. 25.5

A *polygon* is any plane closed figure bounded by straight lines. Triangles and quadrilaterals are thus polygons, but the term is usually used for figures with more than 4 sides.

Interior and exterior angles of polygons are illustrated by the following diagram (Fig. 25.6).

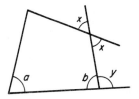

a and *b* are interior angles.
x and *y* are exterior angles.

Fig. 25.6

As shown, an exterior angle is an angle between a side and the produced part of an adjacent side.

A *regular* polygon is one whose sides and angles are all equal.

Elementary properties

Students using this book will almost certainly be familiar with elementary geometrical properties such as those involving angles in triangles, angles made by parallels, etc., and we shall now simply summarise these (Figs. 25.7–25.17).

Vertically opposite angles

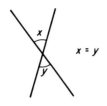

$x = y$

Fig. 25.7

Adjacent angles on a straight line

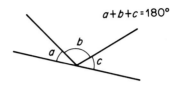

$a+b+c = 180°$

Fig. 25.8

Angles at a point

$a + b + c = 360°$

Fig. 25.9

Angles in a triangle

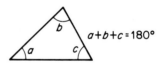

$a+b+c = 180°$

Fig. 25.10

Exterior angle of a triangle

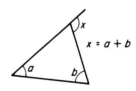

$x = a + b$

Fig. 25.11

Right-angled triangle

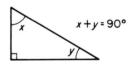

$x+y = 90°$

Fig. 25.12

Base angles of isoceles triangle

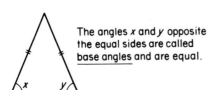

The angles x and y opposite
the equal sides are called
base angles and are equal.

Fig. 25.13

Angles in a quadrilateral

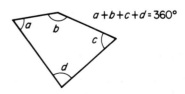

$a+b+c+d = 360°$

Fig. 25.14

Alternate angles   *Corresponding angles*

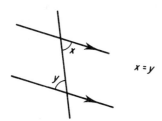   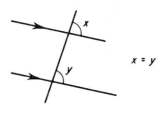

$x = y$ $x = y$

Fig. 25.15   Fig. 25.16

Interior opposite angles (or 'allied angles')

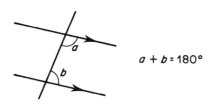

$a + b = 180°$

Fig. 25.17

Angles in a polygon

We can derive a formula for the sum of the angles in an n-sided polygon by splitting the polygon into triangles and using the fact that angles in a triangle add up to 180°.

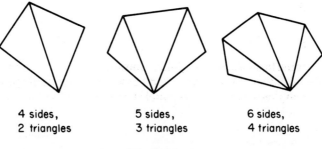

| 4 sides, | 5 sides, | 6 sides, |
| 2 triangles | 3 triangles | 4 triangles |

Fig. 25.18

It should be clear from the examples given in Fig. 25.18 that an n-sided polygon can be split into $(n - 2)$ triangles, and thus that the formula for the sum of the angles is $(n - 2)180°$. This is usually expressed as follows.

The sum of the angles in a polygon is (2n − 4) right angles.

Regular polygons

The above formula is not essential in dealing with *regular* polygons since we can obtain the value of each interior angle by putting in the centre of the polygon and then splitting the polygon into isosceles triangles. Consider for example a regular pentagon (Fig. 25.19).

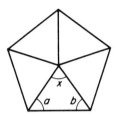

Fig. 25.19

We have $x = \dfrac{360°}{5} = 72°$ (angles at a point), and thus $a = b = \dfrac{180° - 72°}{2} = 54°$ (base angles of isosceles triangle). Hence each interior angle of the pentagon is 108°.

The parallelogram family

This consists of the ordinary parallelogram, the rhombus, the rectangle and the square. These figures have the following properties.

Ordinary parallelogram

Opposite sides parallel and equal, opposite angles equal, diagonals bisect each other, diagonals bisect the whole figure in area. (No axes of symmetry.)

Rhombus

All the properties of the ordinary parallelogram together with the following: all sides equal, diagonals meet at right angles, diagonals bisect the interior angles. Also, each diagonal is an axis of symmetry.

Rectangle

All the properties of the ordinary parallelogram together with the following: all interior angles 90°, diagonals equal in length. The perpendicular bisectors (or *mediators*) of the sides are axes of symmetry.

Square

All the properties of the rhombus and the rectangle.

Two other important figures

The *trapezium* is a quadrilateral with (at least) *one* pair of parallel sides. An *isosceles trapezium* is one in which the non-parallel sides are equal in length. The latter figure has one axis of symmetry, namely the perpendicular bisector of the parallel sides (Fig. 25.20).

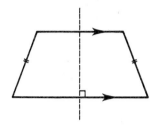

Fig. 25.20

The *kite* can be regarded as two isosceles triangles with a common base. Its diagonals meet at right angles, and *one* of the diagonals is an axis of symmetry (Fig. 25.21).

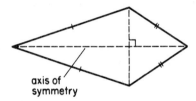

Fig. 25.21

Presentation of solutions to geometrical problems

The following rules may be helpful.
(1) Use small letters for angles wherever possible. The method involving three capitals may be needed when several angles at the same point have to be named.
(2) Put into the diagram as much of the given information as possible. For example equal sides and parallels can often be indicated without confusion. State other information under the heading *Given*.
(3) A line which is added to a diagram to help solve a problem is called a *construction*. It is usual to use dotted lines for constructions.
(4) Make the reasoning as clear as possible, paying particular attention to the order of the steps. When one step follows from the previous step indicate this by either of the symbols ∴ (*therefore*) or ⇒ (*implies*, or *which implies that*). Whenever a standard fact or property is used, put the appropriate reference in brackets after the statement.
(5) *Name* the part of the figure referred to whenever this will avoid confusion. For example, if a diagram contains more than one triangle, the reason (angles in triangle *ABC*) is likely to be more helpful than simply (angles in triangle).

Simple numerical problems

▷ **Example 1**

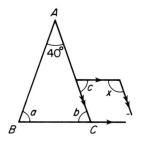

Fig. 25.22

Given AB = AC, and the parallels shown.
To find x

  $a = b = 70°$ (base angles of isosceles triangle)
  $\therefore c = 70°$ (alternate angles)
  $\therefore x = 180° - 70° = 110°$ (interior opposite angles). ◁

▷ **Example 2**

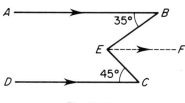

Fig. 25.23

To find angle BEC
(The line *EF*, parallel to *AB* and *DC*, is added to the figure.)

  Angle *BEF* = 35° (alternate angles),
  angle *CEF* = 45° (alternate angles)
  $\therefore$ angle *BEC* = 80°. ◁

EXERCISE 25a

In questions 1–12, find the angles labelled *x* and *y*, giving reasons. Add capital letters for points and small letters for other angles as required.

1

2

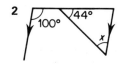

3

4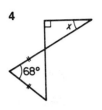

5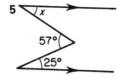

6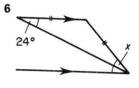

7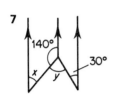

8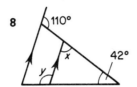

9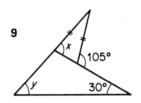

10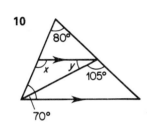

11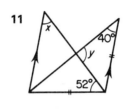

12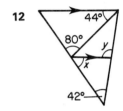

13 *ABCD* is a parallelogram. Angle *BDC* = 30° and angle *BAD* = 50°. Find angles *ABC* and *ADB*.

14 The diagonals of a rectangle *ABCD* cut at *E*. Angle *AEB* = 110°. Find angle *BCE*.

15 *ABCD* is a rhombus in which angle *ADC* = 112°. Find angles *BAC* and *CBD*.

16 *A, B, C* are consecutive vertices of a regular hexagon (6-sided polygon). Find angle *BAC*.

17 Find the value of each interior angle of a regular 10-sided polygon.

18 *A, B, C* are consecutive vertices of a regular pentagon, and *ABE* is an equilateral triangle inside the pentagon. Find angle *CAE*.

19 The sum of the angles in a polygon is 1800°. Find the number of sides.

20 *ABCD* is a square and *AD* is produced to *F*. The bisector of angle *CBD* meets *AC* at *E* and the bisector of angle *BDF* at *G*. Find angles *AEB* and *DGB*.

21 *A, B, C, D* are consecutive vertices of a regular hexagon. The bisector of angle *ABC* meets *AD* at *E*. Find angle *BED*.

22 *ABCD* is a square and *BEC* is an equilateral triangle outside the square. Find angles *BAE* and *AEC*.

23 *A, B, C, D* are consecutive vertices of a regular 10-sided figure with centre *O*. *BO* meets *AD* at *E*. Find angles *ADB* and *OED*.

24 *A, B, C* are consecutive vertices of a regular 8-sided figure with centre *O*, and the bisector of angle *BOC* meets *AC* at *D*. Find angle *ADO*.

Simple algebraic problems and proofs

▷Example 3

The angles of a pentagon are x°, 2x°, (x − 20)°, (x + 50)°, (x + 60)°. Find the largest angle.
Since the sum of the angles in a pentagon is (10 − 4) right angles = 540°, we have

$$6x + 90 = 540$$
$$\therefore \ 6x = 450$$
$$\therefore \ \ \ x = 75.$$

It follows that the largest angle is 2x°, that is 150°. ◁

▷Example 4

ABC is a triangle in which AB = AC. The bisector of angle ABC meets AC at D. Prove that angle ADB = 3 × angle ABD.

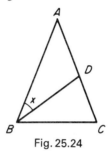

Fig. 25.24

Given AB = AC.
Proof
Let angle *ABD = x*, as shown (Fig. 25.24). Then we have

        angle *CBD = x* (as *DB* bisects angle *ABC*)
$\therefore$ angle *BCD* = angle *ABC* = 2x (base angles of isosceles triangle)
$\therefore$ angle *ADB* = angle *CBD* + angle *BCD* = 3x (exterior angle of
                                    triangle *BCD*),

    that is angle *ADB* = 3 × angle *ABD*. ◁

▷Example 5

In Fig. 25.25, DA = DB = DC, as shown. Prove that angle BAC = 90°.

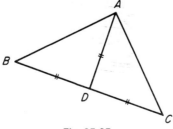

Fig. 25.25

Proof

angle DAC = angle DCA (base angles of isosceles triangle DAC)
and angle DAB = angle DBA (base angles of isosceles triangle DAB)
Hence we can let angle DAC = angle DCA = $x°$ and angle DAB = angle DBA = $y°$ (Fig. 25.26).

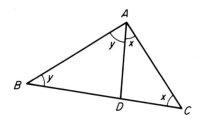

Fig. 25.26

Now we have

$2x + 2y = 180$ (angles in triangle ABC)
$\therefore$ $x + y = 90$
$\therefore$ angle $BAC = 90°$. ◁

EXERCISE 25b

In questions 1–3, find x.

1

2
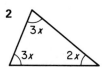

3
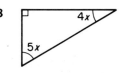

4 The angles of a quadrilateral are $x°$, $(x - 15)°$, $(x + 5)°$, $(x + 30)°$. Find the smallest angle.
5 The angles of a hexagon are $x°$, $x°$, $2x°$, $(2x - 50)°$, $(x - 10)°$, $(x + 20)°$. Find the largest angle.
6 A quadrilateral has a right angle and the other angles are in the ratio 2:3:4. Find the largest angle.
7 EB bisects angle ABC and EC bisects angle BCD. Prove that angle $BEC = 90°$.

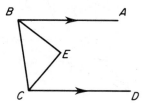

8 Express *y* in terms of *x*.

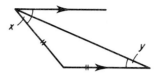

9 (a) Express *p* and *q* in terms of *x*.
(b) Find *x* if *p* = 2*q*.

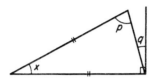

10 A triangle *ABC* has a right angle at *B* and *D* is a point on *AC* such that angle *DBC* = angle *BAC*. Prove that angle *BDC* = 90°.

11 *ABCD* is a rhombus. Letting angle *BAC* = *x*, express in terms of *x* (a) angle *ABD*, (b) angle *BCD*.

12 (a) Express *r* and *s* in terms of *x*.
(b) Find *x* if *DA* bisects angle *BAC*.

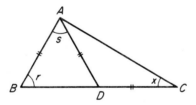

13 *ABCD* is a quadrilateral in which angles B and D are right angles. If *DC* is produced to *E* prove that angle *BCE* = angle *BAD*.

14 *ABCD* is a kite in which *AB* = *BC*, *AD* = *CD* and angle *BAD* = 120°. Letting angle *ADB* = *x*, express in terms of *x* as simply as possible (a) angle *BAC*, (b) angle *CBD*.

15 The side *BC* of a triangle *ABC* is produced to *D*. The bisector of angle *ACB* meets *AB* at *E* and *BE* = *CE*. Prove that angle *ACD* = angle *BEC*.

16 Prove that angle *BCD* = 2 × angle *BAD*.

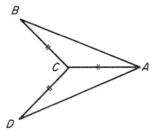

17 *ABCD* is a trapezium in which angle *A* = angle *D* = 90° and *BC* = *DC*. Prove that angle *BCD* = 2 × angle *ADB*.

18 ABCD is a parallelogram in which *AB* = 2*AD* and *E* is the mid-point of *AB*. Prove that *ED* bisects angle *ADC*.

19 *FB* bisects angle *ABD* and angle *BDE* = 3 × angle *BCD*. Prove that angle *BCD* + angle *FBA* = 90°.

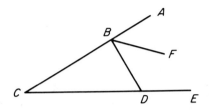

20 In a quadrilateral *ABCD*, *AB* = *AD*, *DB* = *DC* and angle *ABC* = 90°. Prove that angle *BAD* = 2 × angle *BCD*.

26 Congruence and Similarity

Definition of congruence

Two plane figures are congruent if one will fit exactly on top of the other, possibly after one of the figures is turned over. The symbol for 'is congruent to' is ≡ , which should not be confused with =. The latter symbol, when applied to geometrical figures, means 'equals in area'.

Congruent triangles

Congruent triangles are particularly important because they are used in geometrical proofs. The conditions for two triangles to be congruent are as follows.

(1) All three pairs of sides are equal. This is called the **SSS** case (Fig. 26.1).

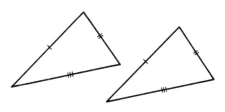

Fig. 26.1

(2) Two pairs of sides are equal, and the angles between these sides (the 'included' angles) are equal. This is called the **SAS** case (Fig. 26.2).

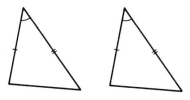

Fig. 26.2

(3) Two pairs of angles are equal, and one pair of sides in the same positions relative to the angles are equal. This case is denoted either by **AAS** or **ASA**, according to the positions of the equal sides (Fig. 26.3).

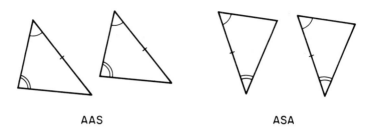

AAS   ASA

Fig. 26.3

(4) Equality of two sides and a non-included angle does not in general prove congruence, but there is one exceptional case. Two triangles are congruent if they each have a right angle, and if the two sides opposite the right angles together with one other pair of corresponding sides are equal. Since the side opposite the right angle is called the *hypotenuse* of a right-angled triangle, this is called the **RHS** case (right angle, hypotenuse, side) (Fig. 26.4).

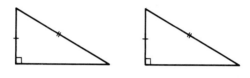

Fig. 26.4

The use of congruent triangles in geometrical proofs

Congruent triangles provide a powerful method of proving geometrical results for the following reason. If two triangles are congruent they are equal in *six* important ways since three pairs of sides and three pairs of angles are equal. To prove the congruence, however, we need only to establish *three* of these equalities, so three other geometrical facts follow from the congruence.

With regard to the method of presentation of proofs by congruent triangles, the following points should be noted.

(1) The two triangles should be named at the beginning of the proof, with the letters in corresponding order. Thus, for example, if we start 'In the triangles *ABC, PQR*. . .', this indicates that angle A = angle P, etc., and that $AB = PQ$, etc.

(2) The three equalities which prove congruence should then be listed, each being followed, if necessary, by a reason in brackets. If one of the equalities needs several steps to prove it, the proof is best given before the three equalities are listed, so that the three equalities can be kept together.

(3) If a line segment AB is a complete side of both triangles, we write 'AB is common' as one of the reasons for congruence. Common angles can also occur.

(4) After it has been stated that the triangles are congruent, the abbreviated reason SSS, SAS, etc. should be given.

▷**Example 1**

The following diagram shows a triangle in which AB = AC. Prove that
(a) CP = BQ, (b) PQ is parallel to BC, (c) BR = CR.

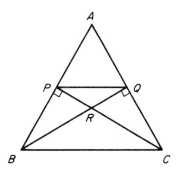

Fig. 26.5

Given AB = AC and the right angles shown.
To prove (a) *CP = BQ*, (b) *PQ* is parallel to *BC*, (c) *BR = CR*.
Proof

(a)   In the triangles *BCP, CBQ*,
                     BC is common,
          angle *ABC* = angle *ACB* (base angles of isosceles triangle *ABC*),
          angle *BPC* = angle *CQB* (both right angles),
               ∴ the triangles are congruent, AAS,
               ∴ *CP = BQ*.

(b) Also from the congruent triangles we have *BP = CQ*, and since *AB = AC*
it follows that *AP = AQ*.

$$\text{Hence angle } APQ = \text{angle } AQP = \frac{180° - \text{angle } A}{2} \text{ (base angles of}$$
$$\text{isosceles triangle } APQ\text{).}$$

$$\text{But angle } ABC = \text{angle } ACB = \frac{180° - \text{angle } A}{2} \text{ (base angles of isosceles}$$
$$\text{triangle } ABC\text{)}$$

               ∴ angle *APQ* = angle *ABC*
               ∴ *PQ* is parallel to *BC* (corresponding angles equal).

(c)   In the triangles *BRP, CRQ*,
                     BP = CQ (proved),
          angle *BPR* = angle *CQR* (both right angles),
          angle *BRP* = angle *CRQ* (vertically opposite angles),
               ∴ the triangles are congruent, AAS,
               ∴ *BR = CR*.   ◁

EXERCISE 26a

In questions 1–9 decide whether the given conditions prove that the two
triangles *ABC, PQR* are congruent. If so, answer by giving the appropriate
reason, e.g. SAS; if not, answer 'No'.

1 angle A = angle Q, AB = PQ, BC = PR.
2 $AB = QR$, $BC = RP$, $AC = QP$.
3 angle A = angle Q, angle B = angle R, angle C = angle P.
4 angle C = angle P, $BC = PR$, $AC = PQ$.
5 angle A = angle P, angle C = angle R, $AB = PQ$.
6 angle B = angle P, angle C = angle R, $AB = PR$.
7 angle B = angle R = 90°, $AC = PQ$, $AB = PR$.
8 angle A = angle P = 90°, $AB = PQ$, $AC = PR$.
9 angle B = angle Q, angle C = angle P, $BC = PQ$.

10 Prove (a) that the base angles of an isosceles triangle are equal, (b) that a triangle with a pair of equal angles is isosceles. (Drop a perpendicular.)
11 $AC = BD$ and $AE = BE$. Prove that triangles ABD, BAC are congruent.

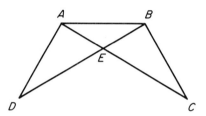

12 BDE is an equilateral triangle. Prove that $AB = CD$.

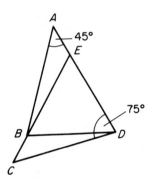

13 $ABCD$ is a kite in which $AB = AD$ and $BC = DC$. Prove that AC bisects angles BAD and BCD.
14 Given that E is the mid-point of AC, prove that it is also the mid-point of BD.

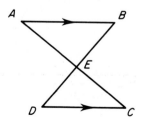

15 $AB = AC$, angle B = angle C and CA bisects angle BAE. Prove that (a) $BD = CE$, (b) angle ADE = angle AED.

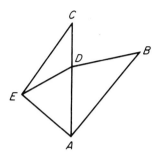

16 Prove that if the diagonals of a quadrilateral bisect each other, the quadrilateral is a parallelogram (that is, its opposite sides are parallel).

17 O is the centre of both circles. Prove that $AB = CD$.

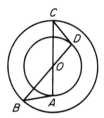

18 Prove (a) that a perpendicular from the centre of a circle to a chord bisects the chord, (b) that if the perpendiculars from the centre to two chords are equal, the chords are equal.

19 ABC is a triangle in which $AB = AC$. P, Q, R are the mid-points of BC, AC, AB, respectively. Prove that angle ARP = angle AQP.

20 $AB = AC$ and C is the mid-point of BE. Prove that $BF = CD$.

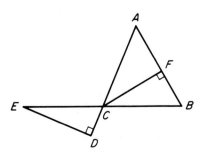

21 *BCEF* is a parallelogram and angle *DCE* = angle *BFE*. Prove that *AB* = *CD*.

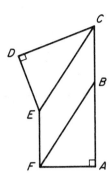

22 *AB* = *BC*. Prove that *AE* = *BD*.

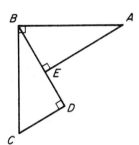

23 *AB* = *AC* and *AD* = *AE*. Prove that triangles *ABD*, *ACE* are congruent.

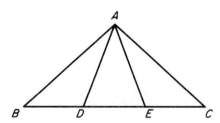

24 *AB* = *AD* and angle *BAC* = angle *ADE*. Prove that *AC* = *DE*.

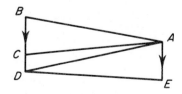

25 *ABCD* is a parallelogram in which angle *BAD* is obtuse, and *E* is a point on *CD* such that *AE* = *AD*. Prove (a) that triangles *ADC*, *EAB* are congruent, (b) that triangles *AEB*, *BCA* are congruent.

26 Angle EAD = angle EDA and angle EBC = angle ECB. Prove that $AB = DC$.

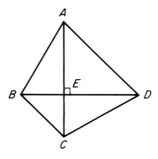

27 $AD = AE = CD$, and $BD = EF$. Prove that angle BCD = angle EAF.

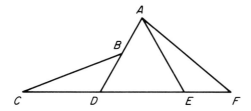

28 DA bisects angle BAF and $DB = DE$. Prove that $CB = EF$. (Two pairs of congruent triangles are involved here.)

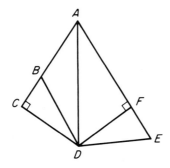

29 Angle CBD = angle CDB. Prove that $AC = DE$.

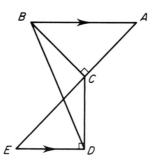

30 $AB = DE$, angle EAC = angle ACE and angle BAE = angle CED. Prove that (a) AB is parallel to DC, (b) $DC = DF$.

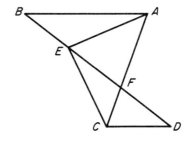

Similarity

Definition

Similar figures are figures with the same *shape*, and this in general means (a) that corresponding angles are equal, (b) that the ratios of all corresponding lengths are equal.

Consider for example the following two similar quadrilaterals (Fig. 26.6):

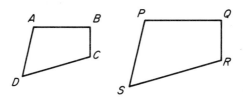

Fig. 26.6

It follows from the similarity of the figures that
(a) angle A = angle P, angle B = angle Q, angle C = angle R, angle D = angle S;

(b) $\dfrac{AB}{PQ} = \dfrac{BC}{QR} = \dfrac{CD}{RS}$, etc.

It is important to realise that *all* ratios of corresponding lengths are equal. Thus in the above example the diagonals PR and AC are in the same ratio as the sides, as are the perimeters of the two figures.

Note that it is normally possible for figures to have their corresponding angles equal without being similar. Consider for example the following rectangles (Fig. 26.7):

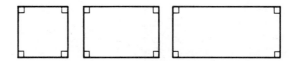

Fig. 26.7

All the angles are right angles, but since the ratios of the sides differ the shapes are not the same. *Triangles* are an important exception to this rule: they cannot have their corresponding angles equal without being similar.

Similar triangles

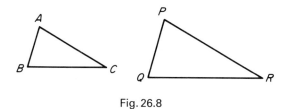

Fig. 26.8

Any of the following sets of two conditions prove the similarity of the triangles *ABC, PQR* shown in Fig. 26.8:

(1) Two pairs of angles are equal, e.g. angle A = angle P and angle B = angle Q.

(2) There is one pair of equal angles, and the ratios of the sides which include these angles are equal. E.g. angle A = angle P and $\dfrac{AB}{PQ} = \dfrac{AC}{PR}$.

(3) The ratios of all corresponding sides are equal, i.e. $\dfrac{AB}{PQ} = \dfrac{AC}{PR} = \dfrac{BC}{QR}$.

Similar triangles are important because, like congruent triangles, they are used to prove geometrical theorems. Some of these proofs will be given in later chapters. In proving triangles similar, method (1) above is by far the most commonly used. Method (3) will not be used at all in this book and can be safely ignored.

Similar triangles should *always* be named with their letters in corresponding order. This enables the equal ratios to be written down without reference to the figure. For example, if triangles *BFR, CQV* are similar and their letters are in corresponding order, it follows immediately that

$$\frac{BF}{CQ} = \frac{FR}{QV} = \frac{BR}{CV}.$$

▷ **Example 2**

In Fig. 26.9 the angles are equal as shown. Find x and y.

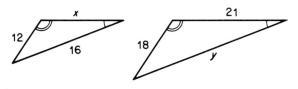

Fig. 26.9

The two corresponding sides of 12 and 18 give us the ratios of all corresponding lengths. We have

$$\frac{x}{21} = \frac{12}{18} = \frac{2}{3}$$

$$\therefore \quad x = \frac{2 \times 21}{3} = 14.$$

Also $\frac{y}{16} = \frac{18}{12} = \frac{3}{2}$

$$\therefore \quad y = \frac{3 \times 16}{2} = 24.$$

▷ **Example 3**

In Fig. 26.10, find x and y.

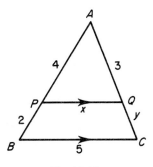

Fig. 26.10

The triangles *ABC*, *APQ* are similar since angle *A* is common and angle *ABC* = angle *APQ* (corresponding angles). Hence

$$\frac{AP}{AB} = \frac{PQ}{BC}$$

i.e. $\frac{4}{6} = \frac{x}{5}$

$$\therefore x = \frac{20}{6} = 3\tfrac{1}{3}.$$

Also $\frac{AC}{AQ} = \frac{AB}{AP}$

i.e. $\frac{AC}{3} = \frac{6}{4}$

$$\therefore AC = \frac{18}{4} = 4\tfrac{1}{2}$$

$$\therefore y = 4\tfrac{1}{2} - 3 = 1\tfrac{1}{2}.$$

▷ Example 4

With angles equal as shown in Fig. 26.11, find AC.

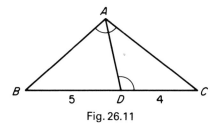

Fig. 26.11

The two triangles CAB, CDA are similar since angle C is common and angle BAC = angle ADC. Here it is difficult to tell from the diagram which ratios are equal and which involve the quantities given and required, so we begin by using the orderings CAB, CDA to write down all three equal ratios:

$$\frac{CA}{CD} = \frac{CB}{CA} = \frac{AB}{DA}.$$

We are not interested in AB or DA, so we ignore the final ratio. Substituting numbers where possible into the remaining equation, we have

$$\frac{CA}{4} = \frac{9}{CA}$$
$$\therefore CA^2 = 36$$
$$\therefore CA = 6.$$ ◁

▷ Example 5

In the diagram given in Fig. 26.12, prove that AB is parallel to DC and find the value of $\frac{AB}{CD}$.

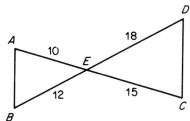

Fig. 26.12

Proof

In the triangles ABE, CDE,
angle AEB = angle CED (vertically opposite angles)
and $\dfrac{AE}{CE} = \dfrac{BE}{DE} = \dfrac{2}{3}$.

Hence the triangles are similar and angle B = angle D. It follows that AB is parallel to DC (alternate angles equal) and that

$$\frac{AB}{CD} = \frac{AE}{CE} = \frac{2}{3}.$$ ◁

Note on ratios of lengths

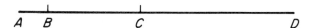

Suppose we are told that in the above line $AB:BC:CD = 1:3:5$, and we require some other ratio, say $AC:CD$. The simplest method is to regard the *actual* lengths as 1, 3 and 5 — which they are, on a suitable scale — and then any other ratio can be read off immediately:

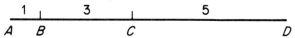

We have $AC:CD = 4:5$, and also, for example, $AB:BD = 1:8$ and $BC:AD = 3:9 = 1:3$.

EXERCISE 26b

In questions 1–9 find x and y. Equal angles are shown.

1

2

3

4

5

6

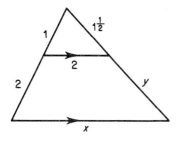

7

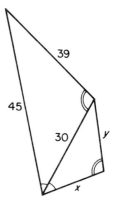

8

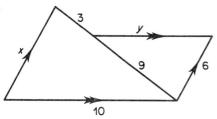

9

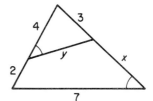

10 Find $\dfrac{AB}{AC}$, $\dfrac{AB}{BC}$, $\dfrac{AE}{ED}$.

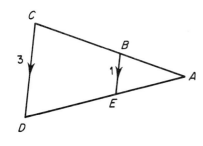

11 Find $\dfrac{BE}{CD}$ and $\dfrac{AE}{ED}$.

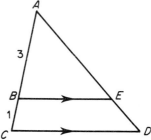

12 $DF = 3FB$. Find $\dfrac{BE}{CD}$, $\dfrac{AC}{AB}$, $\dfrac{AE}{ED}$.

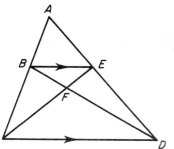

13 $AB = 1\frac{1}{2}BC$.
Find $\dfrac{BG}{CD}$, $\dfrac{AG}{GD}$, $\dfrac{GE}{AF}$, $\dfrac{DE}{EF}$.

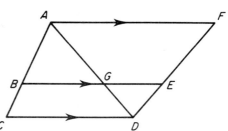

14 $\frac{AB}{FC} = \frac{5}{3}$.

Find $\frac{ED}{DC}$ and $\frac{EC}{DB}$.

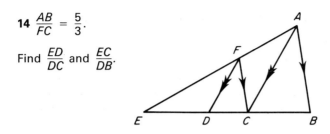

In questions 15–19 name the triangles similar to triangle *ABC* with the letters in the correct order.

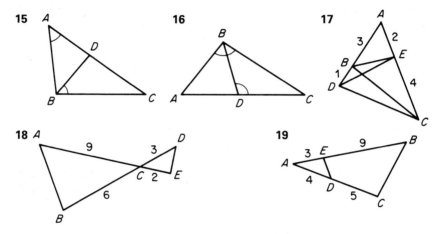

20 *ABCD* is a quadrilateral in which *CA* bisects angle *BAD*, and angle *ABC* = angle *ACD*. Prove two triangles similar and hence that $AC^2 = AB.AD$.

21 *ABC* is a triangle and *D* a point on *AC* such that angle *ABD* = angle *ACB*. Prove that $AB^2 = AD.AC$.

22 *E* is a point on the side *CD* of a parallelogram *ABCD*, and *AE* produced meets *BC* produced at *F*. Prove that $AB.AD = DE.BF$.

23 The diagonals *AC*, *BD* of a quadrilateral *ABCD* meet at *E*. If $AE.EC = BE.ED$, prove that angle *CAD* = angle *CBD*.

24 In a triangle *ABC* the bisector of angle *BAC* meets *BC* at *D*, and *DA = DC*. By proving two triangles similar show that $AB^2 = BD.BC$.

25 *BE* and *CD* are altitudes of a triangle *ABC*. Prove that $AD.AB = AE.AC$.

Areas and volumes of similar figures

Consider two squares whose lengths are 1 cm and 3 cm (Fig. 26.13).

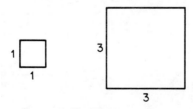

Fig. 26.13

The areas of the squares are 1 cm^2 and 9 cm^2, and we thus have

ratio of lengths $= 1:3$,
ratio of areas $= 1:9$.

This example illustrates the general principle that *the ratio of the areas of all similar figures is the square of the ratio of corresponding lengths*. The principle is difficult to prove rigorously, but one reasonable explanation of it is the following.

Any geometrical figure can be divided up into a large number of small squares. Usually of course there will be a small remainder when this is done, but as there is no limit to the smallness of the squares this remainder can be made as near to zero as we like. Now let the figure be enlarged by a factor k — that is, let all its lengths become k times as great — so that we have a similar figure with the same number of squares. Since each square has increased in area by a factor k^2 the whole figure must have increased in area by this factor, and thus the ratio of the areas is the square of the ratio of corresponding lengths.

A similar argument shows that the ratio of the *volumes* of similar solid figures is the *cube* of the ratio of corresponding lengths; so that, for example, if two similar solids have lengths in the ratio 1:5, their volumes will be in the ratio 1:125. The two principles can be more briefly expressed as follows.

Given a pair of similar figures, let pairs of corresponding lengths, areas and volumes, respectively, be l_1 and l_2, A_1 and A_2, V_1 and V_2. Then we have

$$\frac{A_1}{A_2} = \left(\frac{l_1}{l_2}\right)^2,$$
$$\frac{V_1}{V_2} = \left(\frac{l_1}{l_2}\right)^3.$$

There are many different kinds of problem on this topic, some examples of which now follow.

▷ **Example 6**

Two similar buckets have heights in the ratio 2:3. If the capacity of the smaller bucket is 4 litres, what is the capacity of the larger bucket?
The ratio of the volumes is $(2:3)^3 = 8:27$. Hence the volume of the larger bucket is $\frac{27}{8}$ times that of the smaller, that is

$$\frac{27}{8} \times 4 \text{ litres} = 13\tfrac{1}{2} \text{ litres.} \qquad \triangleleft$$

▷ **Example 7**

In Fig. 26.14, AB = 2BC. Find the ratio of triangle ABE to quadrilateral BCDE.

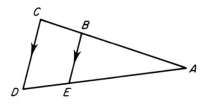

Fig. 26.14

The similar triangles are *ABE, ACD*. Letting *AB* = 2 units and *BC* = 1 unit we see that $\frac{AB}{AC} = \frac{2}{3}$, and since *AB* and *AC* are corresponding sides of the similar triangles it follows that the ratio of their areas is $(2:3)^2 = 4:9$. If therefore we let triangle *ABE* = 4 units of area, we have triangle *ACD* = 9 units and quadrilateral *BCDE* = 5 units. The required ratio is therefore 4:5.   ◁

▷ **Example 8**

How many spheres of radius 3 cm must be melted down to make one sphere of radius 15 cm?
Comparing one sphere of radius 3 cm with one of radius 15 cm we see that the ratio of corresponding lengths is 1:5. Since all spheres are similar it follows that the ratio of the volumes is $(1:5)^3 = 1:125$ and thus that 125 of the smaller spheres are needed to make one of the larger.   ◁

▷ **Example 9**

If the ratio of the surface areas of two similar solids is k:1, what is the ratio of their volumes?
Here we must begin by finding the ratio of corresponding lengths. To do this we take the *square root* of the ratio of the areas:

$$\text{Ratio of corresponding lengths} = k^{1/2}:1$$
$$\therefore \text{ ratio of volumes} = (k^{1/2}:1)^3$$
$$= k^{3/2}:1.$$ ◁

▷ **Example 10**

If it takes 5 minutes to fill a certain tank with water, how long would it take to fill a similar tank of 4 times the base area?

$$\text{Ratio of corresponding areas} = 4:1$$
$$\therefore \text{ ratio of corresponding lengths} = 2:1$$
$$\therefore \text{ ratio of volumes} = 8:1.$$

It would therefore take $8 \times 5 = 40$ minutes to fill the larger tank.   ◁

EXERCISE 26c

1 Two circles have radii in the ratio 1:2. What is the ratio of (a) the circumferences, (b) the areas?

2 The perimeters of two similar rectangles are 6 cm and 9 cm. What is the ratio of (a) the diagonals, (b) the areas?

3 The areas of two circles are 16 cm² and 25 cm². What is the ratio of (a) the diameters, (b) the circumferences?

4 Two spheres have diameters in the ratio 1:3. Find the ratio of (a) the surface areas, (b) the volumes.

5 The surface areas of two cubes are 4 cm² and 9 cm². Find the ratio of (a) the side-lengths, (b) the volumes.

6 The surface areas of two similar solids are 18 cm² and 50 cm². What is the ratio of their volumes?

7 A sphere of radius 6 cm is melted down and made into spheres of radius 2 cm. How many spheres are obtained?

8 Two similar containers have heights in the ratio 4:5. If the smaller container holds 32 litres, what does the larger hold?

9 ABC is a triangle and D, E are points on AB, AC, respectively, such that DE is parallel to BC. Find the ratio of triangle ADE to quadrilateral $DBCE$ if
(a) $\dfrac{DE}{BC} = \dfrac{3}{4}$, (b) $AD:DB = 3:2$, (c) $EC = \dfrac{3AC}{5}$.

10 Two cubes have surface areas of 15 cm² and 60 cm². How many of the smaller type would be needed to make 5 of the larger?

11 It takes a man 2 minutes to walk round a circular lawn. How long would it take him to walk round a similar lawn of $2\frac{1}{4}$ times the area?

12 It takes 3 pots of paint to decorate the walls of a certain room. How many pots would it take to decorate a similar room of $1\frac{1}{3}$ times the height?

13 With the notation of question 9, what is $\dfrac{AD}{DB}$ if quadrilateral $DBCE$ is
(a) 3 times triangle ADE, (b) $4\frac{4}{9}$ times triangle ADE?

14 Two similar containers have base areas of 1200 cm² and 2700 cm². If the larger container holds 36 litres what does the smaller hold?

15 The volumes of two similar solids are 2 cm³ and $6\frac{3}{4}$ cm³. What is the ratio of their surface areas?

16 $ABCD$ is a trapezium in which AB is parallel to DC and the diagonals meet at E. (a) If $BD = 3BE$ and the area of triangle ABE is 4 cm², what is the area of triangle DEC? (b) If triangle DEC is $2\frac{1}{4}$ times triangle ABE, what is $AC:AE$?

17 It costs 36 p to paint a cylinder of length 10 cm. How much does it cost to paint 20 similar cylinders of length 15 cm?

18 192 lead spheres, each with a surface area of 45 cm², are melted down and re-cast into 81 spheres, all of the same size. What is the surface area of each new sphere?

19 ABC is a triangle and D is a point on AC such that angle ABC = angle ADB. (a) if $AB = 1\frac{1}{4}AD$ and the area of triangle ABD is 8 cm², what is the area of triangle BCD? (b) If the ratio of triangle BCD to triangle ABD is 16:9 and $BC = 30$ cm, what is the length of BD?

20 ABC is a triangle and D a point on AC such that angle ABD = angle ACB. (a) if $AB:AC = 2:3$ what is the ratio of triangle ABD to triangle BCD? (b) If triangle ABD is $1\frac{2}{7}$ times triangle BCD and $AB = 12$ cm, what are the lengths of AC and AD?

27 Reflection, Rotation, Symmetry

Transformation geometry

A transformation is the geometrical equivalent of an algebraic function or mapping. Under an algebraic function, every element of a set of numbers, usually $\mathbf{R}$, is linked or 'mapped' to one definite number called its image. Similarly, under a geometrical transformation, every member of a set of points — usually all the points in a plane — is mapped to one definite image point. Transformations are denoted by capital letters, and if T is a particular transformation, T(P) stands for the image of the point P under the transformation. The original point P is called the object point. We also write $P \rightarrow P'$ which means that P is mapped to P'. T^{-1} denotes the inverse transformation of T, so that if T maps P to P', the transformation T^{-1} maps P' to P.

It will be noticed that the notation used for transformations corresponds exactly to that used for functions, and the correspondence extends also to combinations of transformations. If T and W are two separate transformations, TW means W *followed by* T, and TW(P) denotes the image of P under the transformation W followed by the transformation T. The symbol T^2 means T *followed by* T, and T^3, T^4, etc. are similarly defined.

Transformations sometimes leave certain points unchanged. These points are said to be *invariant* under the transformation, and any other features which are left unaltered by a transformation, such as distance or angle, are also described as invariant. The *identity transformation*, denoted by I, leaves all points unchanged. It sometimes occurs as the result of combinations of transformations.

We study a transformation by examining its effects on particular lines and figures. All the transformations we shall consider will be *linear*, which means that they map straight lines to straight lines, and lines which are originally parallel will always remain parallel. In this chapter we shall look at two transformations which are closely associated with *symmetry*, and which also have one other special feature. This is that they map all figures to *congruent* figures. Transformations of this kind are called *isometries*.

Reflection

A reflection is a transformation which is completely defined by specifying one line called the *axis of reflection* or *mirror-line*. If A is any point and A' is its image, A' is the *mirror-image* of A in the axis of reflection, and the axis is thus the mediator of AA' (Fig. 27.1). Since the image of A' is clearly

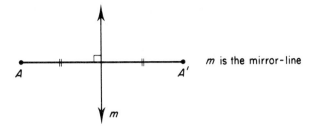

m is the mirror-line

Fig 27.1

A, the inverse of a reflection is the same transformation as the original reflection.

All points on the mirror-line are invariant under a reflection, so *m* is an invariant line. Lines perpendicular to the mirror-line are also invariant, though it should be noted that only one point of such a line — its point of intersection with the mirror-line — is individually invariant. All other points are mapped to different points on the line. A line of this kind is said to be *invariant but not point invariant.*

▷ Example 1

ABC is a right-angled triangle in which A is the point (1,1), B is (3,1) and C is (3, −1). Find the images of A, B, C, and thus of the triangle, under reflection in (a) the y-axis, (b) the line y = 3. Show the images in a sketch.

(a) Let the images of *A, B, C* be *A′, B′, C′*. The image of a point under reflection in the y-axis is clearly obtained by changing the sign of the value of *x*. Hence *A′* is (−1,1), *B′* is (−3,1) and *C′* is (−3,−1).

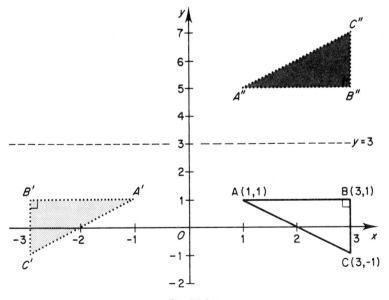

Fig. 27.2

(b) Let the images be A'', B'', C''. The vertical distance between A and the horizontal line $y = 3$ is 2, and the image is the same distance from the line on the other side of it. Hence A'' is (1,5) and, by similar reasoning, B'' is (3,5) and C'' is (3,7).

The positions of the object figure and its images are as shown in Fig. 27.2.

This example shows that a geometrical figure is mapped to a congruent figure by reflection, and thus that reflection is an *isometry*.   ◄

▷ Example 2

Denoting reflection in the x-axis by X and reflection in the line y = x by P, find (a) XP(A), where A is the point (3, 1), (b) PX(A).

(a) XP(A) means *apply P and then X to the point A.* Consider the effect of reflecting A in the line $y = x$ (Fig. 27.3):

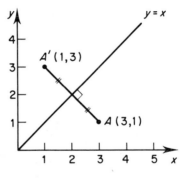

Fig. 27.3

It is clear from the symmetry of the diagram that *the x and y co-ordinates are interchanged by reflection in the line y = x.* Thus A' is the point (1,3).

Having applied transformation P to A, we now apply X, that is reflect A' in the x-axis. This gives XP(A) = (1,−3).

(b) PX(A) means *apply X and then P to A.* Reflecting A(3,1) in the x-axis we obtain (3,−1), and reflecting this point in the line $y = x$ we have PX(A) = (−1,3).

(This example shows that, as in the case of composition of functions, the *order* in which two successive transformations are performed in general makes a difference.)   ◄

EXERCISE 27a

In this exercise X = reflection in the x-axis, Y = reflection in the y-axis, W = reflection in the line $y = x$ and S = reflection in the line $y = 3$.

1 Draw on graph paper the rectangle $ABCD$, where A is the point (2,1), B is (4,1), C is (4,2) and D is (2,2). Draw also the image of the rectangle under (a) X, (b) Y, (c) S, stating the co-ordinates of the image points in each case.

2 Draw on graph paper the triangle ABC, where A is the point (−1,−3), B is (2,−3) and C is (2,−5). Draw also the image of the triangle under (a) X, (b) Y, (c) W, stating the co-ordinates of the image points in each case.

3 Draw on graph paper the triangle ABC, where A is the point $(4,0)$, B is $(4,1)$ and C is $(2,0)$. Draw also the image of the triangle under (a) X, (b) W, (c) WX, (d) XW, stating the co-ordinates of the image points in each case.

4 Draw on graph paper the triangle ABC, where A is the point $(1,0)$, B is $(2,0)$ and C is $(2,1)$. Draw also the image of the triangle under (a) S, (b) WS, (c) SW, stating the co-ordinates of the image points in each case.

In the remaining questions only rough diagrams should be drawn when needed.

5 Find the images of the following points under X: (a) $(0,4)$, (b) $(0,-3)$, (c) $(2,0)$, (d) $(2,1)$, (e) $(-1,5)$, (f) $(-3,-4)$, (g) (a,b).

6 Find the images of the following points under Y: (a) $(3,0)$, (b) $(-1,0)$, (c) $(2,3)$, (d) $(0,5)$, (e) $(-4,1)$, (f) $(-5,-2)$, (g) (a,b).

7 Say which of the following points are invariant under (a) X, (b) Y: $(2,1)$, $(0,-3)$, $(1,1)$, $(2,0)$, $(0,-5)$, $(0,0)$, $(-5,5)$, $(-6,0)$.

8 Find the images of the following points under reflection in the line $x = 1$: (a) $(0,0)$, (b) $(0,-2)$, (c) $(3,0)$ (d) $(-2,3)$, (e) $(1,3)$, (f) $(-5,-4)$.

9 Find the images of the following points under reflection in the line $y = -2$: (a) $(0,1)$, (b) $(3,0)$, (c) $(3,-2)$, (d) $(4,-1)$, (e) $(5,-7)$, (f) $(-5,8)$.

10 Say which of the following points are invariant under (a) reflection in the line $x = 1$, (b) reflection in the line $y = -2$: $(-1,2)$, $(3,-2)$, $(1,0)$, $(-1,4)$, $(1,-2)$, $(0,-2)$.

11 Say which of the following lines are invariant under reflection in (a) the line $x = 1$, (b) the line $y = -2$: $x = 4$, $y = 2x$, $y - 3 = 0$, $2x - 1 = 0$, $y + x = 0$, $y + 2 = 0$.

12 Find the images of the following points under reflection in the line $y = x$: (a) $(2,1)$, (b) $(3,3)$, (c) $(5,2)$ (d) $(-2,4)$, (e) $(-1,-2)$, (f) (a,b).

13 Find the images of the following points under reflection in the line $y = -x$: (a) $(0,2)$, (b) $(3,0)$, (c) $(2,1)$, (d) $(-3,1)$ (e) $(-4,-7)$, (f) (a,b).

14 Each of the following mappings is a reflection in a certain mirror-line. Find the equation of the mirror-line in each case: (a) $(2,0) \rightarrow (4,0)$, (b) $(-5,0) \rightarrow (1,0)$, (c) $(0,3) \rightarrow (0,9)$, (d) $(2,3) \rightarrow (8,3)$, (e) $(3,4) \rightarrow (3,-6)$, (f) $(-2,5) \rightarrow (-2,-3)$.

15 Find (a) XY$(2,1)$, (b) YX$(2,1)$, (c) WX$(3,-5)$, (d) XW$(3,-5)$, (e) XS$(0,2)$, (f) SX$(0,2)$, (g) $X^2(1,3)$, (h) $Y^5(4,1)$.

16 Find (a) XY(a,b), (b) YX(a,b), (c) WX(a,b), (d) XW(a,b).

17 Say which of the following combinations of transformations are equal to the identity transformation: Y^4, XY, W^7, S^2, WXWX, XYXY.

18 Say whether the following statements are true (T) or false (F): (a) the line $x = 2$ is invariant under reflection in the line $y = 3$, (b) SY = YS, (c) the point $(-1,4)$ is invariant under reflection in the line $y - x = 3$, (d) for any pair of reflections A and B, AB = BA, (e) for any reflection R, $R^8 =$ I, (f) all lines of the form $y + x = k$ are invariant under W, (g) for any pair of reflections A and B, ABBA = I.

Rotation

A rotation is a transformation which is defined by stating a point — the *centre of rotation* — and an angle. A positive angle denotes an anticlockwise rotation about the centre of rotation and a negative angle denotes a clockwise rotation. Fig. 27.4 shows the effect on a point A of a rotation of θ about a centre of rotation O.

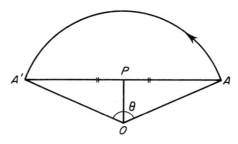

Fig. 27.4

The arc AA' is part of a circle of centre O, so A and A' are equidistant from O. The perpendicular OP from O to AA' bisects AA' (congruent triangles); hence OP is the mediator of AA'. In general therefore *the mediator of the line joining a point and its image passes through the centre of rotation*. There is only one invariant point under a rotation (other than one of 0° or 360°), namely the centre of rotation.

A rotation of 360° is usually called a *full-turn*, one of 180° a *half-turn*, and so on. Thus for example a negative quarter-turn is a clockwise rotation of 90°.

The inverse of a rotation — the transformation which takes an image point back to its object point — is simply a rotation of the same angle but in the opposite direction. Thus if Q denotes a positive quarter-turn about some point, Q^{-1} is a negative quarter-turn about the same point.

When a whole figure is rotated about a point it is not difficult to see that both shape and size are preserved and thus that the transformation is an isometry. The effect is just the same as that of swinging a physical object on the end of a rotating arm or rope (Fig. 27.5).

Fig. 27.5

It can also be shown quite easily that all lines in the figure turn through the same angle, namely the angle through which the arm is rotated.

Location of the centre of rotation

Whenever a plane figure moves from *any* initial position to *any* final position with some turn, the effect is that of a pure rotation about some central point. This point can be located by taking any two points in the figure, A, B, together with their images A', B', and drawing the mediators of AA' and BB'. The centre of rotation lies at the point of intersection of the two mediators.

The half-turn

A half-turn is a turn through 180° (in either direction) and it has the special property of mapping every line to a parallel line. Fig. 27.6 shows the effect of rotating a line-segment AB through 180° about a point O.

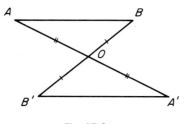

Fig. 27.6

Since length is preserved under rotation, $OA = OA'$, $OB = OB'$ and $AB = A'B'$. Hence the triangles OAB, OA'B' are congruent and angle $A =$ angle A'. These are alternate angles, so it follows that AB is parallel to B'A'.

Fig. 27.6 also shows that the image of a point A under a half-turn about O can be obtained by joining AO and producing this line a distance equal to AO. In these circumstances A' can be described as the image of A under *reflection in O*.

▷ Example 3

OAB is a triangle in which O is the origin, A the point (0,2) and B the point (2,1) (Fig. 27.7). Obtain the image of the triangle under (a) a rotation of 90° about O, (b) a half-turn about the point P(2,0).

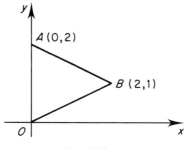

Fig. 27.7

(a) The angle of rotation is positive so the turn is anticlockwise. O is invariant and A clearly maps to (−2,0). The line OB rotates to a position at which the angle it makes with the y-axis is equal to the angle it initially made with the x-axis. This occurs when the image B' is the point $(-1,2)$ (Fig. 27.8).

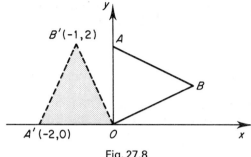

Fig. 27.8

(b) The best method of obtaining the image of a point under a half-turn is to join the point to the centre of rotation and produce the line obtained the same distance beyond the point. Since $P(2,0)$ is the centre of rotation it follows that this must be the mid-point of AA'', BB'', OO'', where A'', B'', O'' are the images of A, B, O. Hence A'' is the point $(4,-2)$, B'' is $(2,-1)$ and O'' is $(4,0)$ (Fig. 27.9).

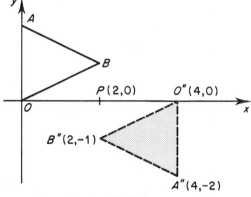

Fig. 27.9

Note that all line-segments are parallel to their images under this half-turn. For example, OB is parallel to $B''O''$. ◁

▷ Example 4

Letting T denote a positive quarter-turn about the point (3,1), find T(A) where A is the point (4,3), and T^{-1} (B) where B is the point (5,0).

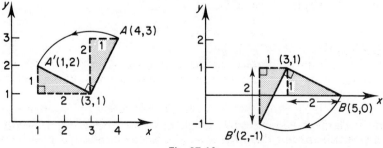

Fig. 27.10

Fig. 27.10 is self-explanatory. In each case the co-ordinates of the image point are calculated by using the congruence of the right-angled triangles shown. We thus obtain $T(A) = (1,2)$ and $T^{-1}(B) = (2,-1)$. ◁

▷ **Example 5**

Under rotation about a certain point, $A(5,4) \rightarrow A'(5,0)$ and $B(2,0) \rightarrow B'(0,0)$. Find the centre of rotation.
The centre of rotation lies on the mediator of the line joining any point and its image. Here we can draw the mediators of AA' and BB' (Fig. 27.11).

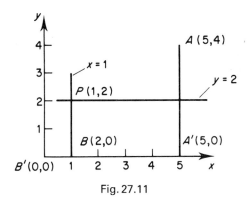

Fig. 27.11

The mediators are the lines $x = 1$ and $y = 2$, and they meet at the point $P(1,2)$. This is the centre of rotation. ◁

Combinations of transformations

A combination (or 'product') of two or more transformations can always be regarded as a single transformation. A simple example is the reflection of a point in the x-axis followed by the reflection of its image in the y-axis. We have

$$YX(a,b) = Y(a,-b) = (-a, -b).$$

Now the single transformation which maps (a,b) to $(-a,-b)$ is a half-turn about the origin O (or reflection in O). If, therefore, we denote this transformation by H, we can write

$$YX = H.$$

It can in fact be shown quite easily that a product of two reflections in any two perpendicular lines is equivalent to a half-turn about their point of intersection.
  Another simple example is the product of two rotations about the same point. This is clearly equivalent to a single rotation through an angle equal to the algebraic sum of the original angles. Thus for example if we denote a half-turn about O by H and a quarter-turn about O by Q, we can form the

following equalities:

$$Q^2 = (Q^{-1})^2 = H,$$
$$Q^4 = H^2 = I,$$
$$QH = Q^3 = Q^{-1},$$
etc.

To deal with more complicated cases it is often helpful to take a simple figure, such as a triangle, and construct its images under the successive transformations on graph paper. This usually enables us to 'see' the single transformation which is equivalent to the combination of transformations. A more formal method, which must be used if a proof of the result is required, is to apply the successive transformations to the general point (a,b), as in the first example above. Both methods are illustrated by the following example.

▷ Example 6

Draw the triangle ABC, where A is the point (3,1), B is (4,1) and C is (4,3). By constructing the successive images A'B'C' and A''B''C'' under reflection in the line y = x (W) followed by a positive quarter-turn about the origin (Q), find the single transformation which is equivalent to QW. Obtain the same result by applying QW to the point (a,b).

First method

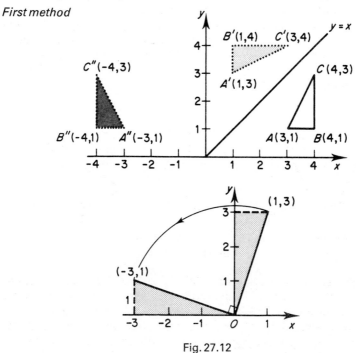

Fig. 27.12

As explained in Example 2, to reflect a point in the line $y = x$ we simply interchange the co-ordinates of the point. The method for rotating a point through 90° about O is illustrated by the second diagram of Fig. 27.12, which shows how the image of the point (1,3) is obtained. When the triangle *ABC* and the final image triangle $A''B''C''$ are compared, it can be seen that the single transformation which is equivalent to QW is *reflection in the y-axis*.

Second method

The rules for the transformations W and Q can be expressed as follows.

In words:

W: Interchange the co-ordinates.

Q: Interchange the co-ordinates and then change the sign of the first co-ordinate.

In symbols:

$W(a,b) = (b,a)$,

$Q(a,b) = (-b,a)$.

We therefore have

$QW(a,b) = Q(b,a) = (-a,b)$,

and since $Y(a,b) = (-a,b)$ it follows once more that QW = Y.   ◁

Direct and opposite isometries

Any transformation which maps a figure to a congruent image, such as reflection and rotation, is called an *isometry*. Suppose now that we have a piece of cardboard which fits over the object figure exactly, and we have to move the cardboard until it fits exactly over the image figure with each point over its image point. If this can be done purely by *sliding the cardboard over the paper, without turning it over*, the transformation is called a *direct* isometry. If, however, the cardboard has to be turned over before it will fit on the image figure, the transformation is called an *opposite* isometry (Fig. 27.13).

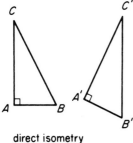

direct isometry

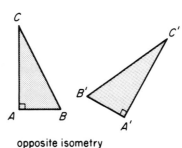

opposite isometry

Fig. 27.13

In a direct isometry the letters ABC ... and $A'B'C'$ ... are either clockwise or anticlockwise in both figures, while in an opposite isometry the letters are clockwise in one figure and anticlockwise in the other.

Consider now a product of transformations. Clearly a product of direct isometries can only produce another direct isometry, while a product of opposite isometries will be direct or indirect according to whether the number of transformations is even or odd. This gives us a check on the correctness of an 'equation' relating transformations, such as QW = Y. The left-hand side of this equation is a product of a direct and an opposite isometry, and is therefore equivalent to an opposite isometry. The right-hand side is also an opposite isometry so the check is successful.

The inverse of a product of transformations

We saw when considering functions (see chapter 20) that since fg means 'do g and then f', the inverse function $(fg)^{-1}$ must be equivalent to the reverse procedure, namely 'do the inverse of f then the inverse of g'. Hence $(fg)^{-1} = g^{-1}f^{-1}$. The same reasoning applies to transformations, so if R, S and T are any transformations, we have

$$(ST)^{-1} = T^{-1}S^{-1},$$
$$(RST)^{-1} = T^{-1}S^{-1}R^{-1},$$
etc.

EXERCISE 27b

In addition to the symbols used in exercise 27a, Q and H denote a positive quarter-turn and a half-turn about O, respectively, and V denotes reflection in the line $y = -x$.

1 Draw on graph paper the triangle OAB, where A is the point $(1,0)$ and B is $(0,2)$. Draw also the image of the triangle under (a) Q, (b) H, (c) Q^{-1}, stating the co-ordinates of the images of A and B in each case.

2 Draw on graph paper the triangle ABC, where A is the point $(0,1)$, B is $(-3,1)$ and C is $(-1,2)$. Draw also the image of the triangle under (a) Q, (b) a half-turn about the point $(1,1)$, stating the co-ordinates of the images of A, B, C in each case.

3 Find the images of the following points under H: (a) $(3,0)$, (b) $(0,-2)$, (c) $(3,5)$, (d) $(-4,1)$, (e) (a,b).

4 Find the images of the following points under Q: (a) $(5,0)$, (b) $(0,3)$, (c) $(0,-2)$, (d) $(3,1)$, (e) $(-2,5)$, (f) $(-4,-1)$, (g) (a,b).

5 Find the images of the following points under Q^{-1}: (a) $(0,2)$, (b) $(1,4)$, (c) $(-3,-2)$, (d) $(2,-5)$, (e) (a,b).

6 Find the images of the following points under a half-turn about the point $(2,1)$: (a) $(2,0)$, (b) $(0,1)$, (c) $(4,2)$, (d) $(6,1)$ (e) $(3,2)$ (f) $(-3,4)$, (g) $(-5,-8)$.

7 Find the images of the following points under a negative (clockwise) quarter-turn about the point $(3,0)$: (a) $(5,0)$, (b) $(3,2)$, (c) $(-1,0)$, (d) $(0,1)$, (e) $(2,2)$.

8 Each of the following mappings is the result of a half-turn about a point. Find the co-ordinates of the point. (a) $(3,1) \rightarrow (3,-1)$, (b) $(1,2) \rightarrow (5,2)$, (c) $(2,3) \rightarrow (-2,-3)$, (d) $(5,1) \rightarrow (7,3)$, (e) $(-2,9) \rightarrow (-8,-3)$.

9 Find the centres of rotation about which the following pairs of mappings occur: (a) $(2,0) \rightarrow (4,0)$ and $(5,1) \rightarrow (5,3)$, (b) $(2,2) \rightarrow (2,0)$ and $(1,-1) \rightarrow (-1,1)$, (c) $(-1,-1) \rightarrow (1,1)$ and $(2,0) \rightarrow (2,4)$, (d) $(-3,0) \rightarrow (3,6)$ and $(3,2) \rightarrow (5,0)$.

10 Under a rotation of $30°$ about A, $B \rightarrow B'$ and $C \rightarrow C'$ (Fig. 27.14). Find angle B and angle C'.

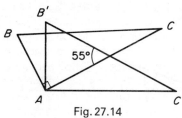

Fig. 27.14

11 The triangle shown in Fig. 27.15 is given a positive rotation about A equal to angle ACB. $B \rightarrow B'$ and $C \rightarrow C'$. Given that angle $BB'C' = 145°$, find angle CAB'.

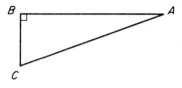

Fig. 27.15

12 Simplify (a) Q^8, (b) H^5, (c) Q^3H, (d) $(Q^{-1})^3$, (e) H^3Q^6, (f) $(Q^{-1}H)^{-1}$.

13 Draw on graph paper the triangle OAB, where A is the point $(-2,0)$ and B is $(0,1)$. Draw its image under W, and then draw the image of this image under X. State (a) the co-ordinates of the final images of A and B, (b) the single transformation which is equivalent to XW.

14 The triangle OAB of question 13 is reflected in the line $y = 1$ and then the image is reflected in the y-axis. Draw the triangle and the two images on graph paper and state (a) the co-ordinates of the final images of O, A, B, (b) the single transformation which is equivalent to the product of the two transformations.

15 Draw on graph paper the triangle OAB, where A is the point $(0,-3)$ and B is $(1,-3)$. The triangle is rotated through $+90°$ about O, and then the image is reflected in the line $y = x$. Draw the two images and state (a) the co-ordinates of the final images of A and B, (b) the single transformation which is equivalent to WQ.

16 Draw on graph paper the triangle ABC, where A is the point $(-1,0)$, B is $(-2,0)$ and C is $(-2,1)$. The triangle is subjected to the transformation V and then its image is subjected to Q^{-1}. Draw the two images and state (a) the co-ordinates of the final images of A, B, C, (b) the single transformation which is equivalent to $Q^{-1}V$.

17 Write down the results of applying X, Y, W, V, Q, Q^{-1} and H to the point (a,b), and use these results to obtain the single transformations which are equivalent to (a) YW, (b) XQ^{-1}, (c) $Q^{-1}X$, (d) YH, (e) VY, (f) QV, (g) HW, (h) WQ^{-1}.

18 ABC is an equilateral triangle with centre O. P_a = reflection in OA, P_b = reflection in OB, P_c = reflection in OC and T = rotation of $+120°$ about O. Express in terms of T the single transformations which are equivalent to (a) P_aP_b, (b) P_aP_c, (c) $(P_cP_b)^2$.

19 Say whether the following transformations are direct or opposite isometries: (a) QX, (b) YW, (c) HYQ, (d) X^5, (e) $Q^{-1}H^3V^5$.

20 The triangle shown in Fig. 27.16 is reflected about the bisector of angle A and then the image is given a half-turn about A. If the final image is $AB'C'$, find angle $B'C'C$.

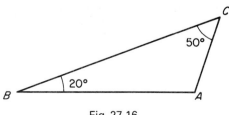

Fig. 27.16

Line symmetry

A figure which is *invariant under reflection* is said to be symmetrical about the mirror-line. This kind of symmetry is called line symmetry (or *bilateral* symmetry) and when it exists the mirror-line is called the *line of symmetry* or the *axis of symmetry*. For a figure to be invariant under reflection every part of the figure has to be accompanied by its image under the reflection, and this means that we can produce a symmetrical pattern from any figure about any line simply by adding its image (where this does not already exist) under reflection in the line.

Example

The capital letter **A** already has symmetry about a vertical axis. To produce a figure with symmetry about the central horizontal axis we add the image of the letter under reflection in this axis (Fig. 27.17). The dotted lines are axes of symmetry.

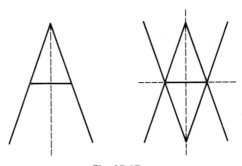

Fig. 27.17

Examples of geometrical figures with line symmetry

(a) The *isosceles triangle* has one axis of symmetry, and the *rhombus* (which can be regarded as a pair of isosceles triangles in two different ways) has both diagonals as axes of symmetry (Fig. 27.18).

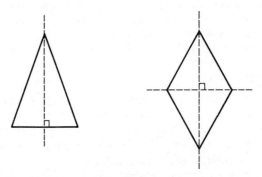

Fig. 27.18

(b) The *circle* has symmetry about all diameters, and thus possesses an infinite number of axes of symmetry (Fig. 27.19).

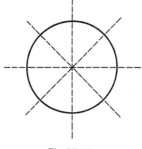

Fig 27.19

(c) *Regular polygons* have the mediators of all their sides as axes of symmetry.

▷ **Example 7**

What is the equation of the axis of symmetry of the pattern of points A(0,1), B(1,−1), C(3,−1), D(4,1)? What points must be added to this pattern to produce symmetry about the line y = 1?

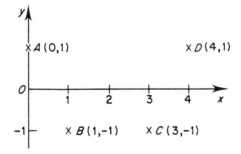

Fig. 27.20

It can be seen from Fig. 27.20 that the axis of symmetry is the mediator of *AD* and *BC*, that is the line $x = 2$. To produce a pattern with symmetry about the line $y = 1$ we add, where necessary, the images of the points in this line. *A* and *D* are on the line and are therefore their own images, so we need only add the images of *B* and *C*. These are (1,3) and (3,3).   ◀

Rotational symmetry

A figure which is *invariant under rotation* (other than a rotation of 360°) is said to have rotational symmetry about the central point. What this means is that when the figure is rotated, each part of the figure moves into the position of another identical part. So each part of the figure must be accompanied by its image under the rotation.

   If a half-turn is the smallest rotation which will bring each part of the figure into the position of an identical part, the figure is said to have rotational symmetry of *order 2*. If a quarter-turn is required the order is 4, and so on (Fig. 27.21).

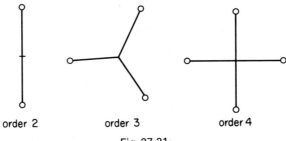

order 2   order 3   order 4

Fig. 27.21

Rotational symmetry can also be looked at in the following way. If we think of the whole plane as divided into equal *sectors*, a figure with rotational symmetry has identical patterns or figures in each sector. The number of sectors is the order of the symmetry. Fig. 27.22 shows eight equal sectors, each of which contains the same simple pattern. The whole figure therefore has rotational symmetry of order 8:

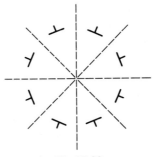

Fig. 27.22

Point symmetry

A figure which is *invariant under a half-turn* is said to have point symmetry. The reason is that invariance under a half-turn about *O* means that each point is accompanied by its image under reflection in *O* (Fig. 27.23).

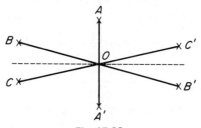

Fig. 27.23

Any figure with rotational symmetry of *even order* will be invariant under a half-turn and thus have point symmetry. So the diagrams above with orders 2, 4 and 8 have point symmetry while the diagram with order 3 does not.

Examples of figures with rotational symmetry

(a) Consider a *parallelogram ABCD* whose diagonals meet at *E* (Fig. 27.24).

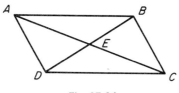

Fig. 27.24

Since *E* is the mid-point of both diagonals we have *AE* = *EC* and *BE* = *ED*. Hence *C, D* are the images of *A, B* under a half-turn about *E*, and, as straight lines map to straight lines under rotation (and all elementary transformations), it follows that every point in the figure is accompanied by its reflection in *E*. Hence *the parallelogram has rotational symmetry of order 2 about the centre of its diagonals*. (This is a form of point symmetry.)

(b) By similar reasoning to that given for the parallelogram the capital letters **N** and **Z** have point symmetry about their centres.

(c) All *regular polygons* have rotational symmetry about their centres. The order is equal to the number of sides.

(d) *Circles* have rotational symmetry of infinite order about their centres.

Symmetry of solid figures

The ideas about symmetry developed above for plane figures can easily be extended to apply to solid figures. Just as line symmetry means that a figure is invariant under reflection in a line, *plane* symmetry means that a solid is invariant under reflection in a plane. And whereas rotational symmetry of a plane figure means that the figure is invariant under rotation about a point, rotational symmetry of a solid means that the figure is invariant under rotation about an *axis*.

Consider, for example, a cuboid (rectangular block) (Fig. 27.25).

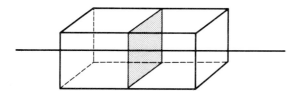

Fig. 27.25

The cuboid has plane symmetry about each of the three planes through the centre which are parallel to the faces of the cuboid. It also has rotational symmetry of order 2 about each of the three axes through the centre which are parallel to the edges. One plane and one axis of symmetry are shown in Fig. 27.25.

Point symmetry of solid figures cannot be defined in terms of rotation, but it does correspond to the second definition of point symmetry for plane figures given above. A solid figure has point symmetry about a point O if every point of the figure is accompanied by its image under reflection in O.

The cuboid has point symmetry about its centre.

EXERCISE 27c

1 Which of the capital letters B, E, H, O, S, T have (a) just one axis of symmetry, (b) more than one axis, (c) rotational symmetry?

2 Name the quadrilateral formed by the points $A(1,0)$, $B(0,2)$, $C(1,4)$, $D(2,2)$, and state the equations of its axes of symmetry.

3 Say which of the following have point symmetry: a rectangle, a running track, an equilateral triangle, a wheel with 5 evenly spaced spokes.

4 Find the equation of the axis of symmetry of the triangle formed by the points $(0,3)$, $(5,1)$, $(5,5)$.

5 Which six points must be added to $(0,1)$ and $(2,1)$ to produce a pattern with rotational symmetry of order 4 about the origin?

6 Give the equations of the axes of symmetry of the square formed by the points $(0,0)$, $(4,0)$, $(4,4)$ and $(0,4)$.

7 How many planes of symmetry does a cube have?

8 What points must be added to $(5,1)$ $(0,-3)$, $(-2,0)$, $(1,1)$ to produce a pattern with symmetry about (a) the line $y = 1$, (b) the line $y = x$?

9 Name quadrilaterals with symmetry about (a) just one axis, that axis being a diagonal, (b) just one axis, that axis not being a diagonal.

10 Find the equations of the axes of symmetry of the polygon formed by the points $(1,1)$, $(2,4)$, $(4,4)$, $(5,1)$, $(4,-2)$ and $(2,-2)$.

11 State (a) the number of planes of symmetry, (b) the number of axes of symmetry, of a right pyramid on a square base.

12 What points must be added to the origin to produce rotational symmetry of order 4 about the point $(1,2)$?

13 Find the equation of the axis of symmetry of the triangle formed by the points $(0,0)$, $(0,5)$, $(4,3)$.

14 A quadrilateral is formed by the points $A(1,-1)$, $B(-2,1)$, $C(1,6)$ and another point D. If AC is an axis of symmetry, find the co-ordinates of D and name the quadrilateral.

15 Describe the axis or axes of symmetry of (a) a line-segment, (b) a pair of infinitely long non-parallel lines.

16 What points must be added to $(2,5)$, $(-1,3)$, $(4,-2)$ to produce point symmetry about (a) $(0,0)$, (b) $(2,5)$?

17 Say which of the following words or combinations of letters have (a) symmetry about a horizontal axis, (b) symmetry about a vertical axis, (c) rotational symmetry: DID, OXO, AHA, SOS, MUM.

18 ABC is a triangle and D is the mid-point of BC. Under a half-turn about D, $A \rightarrow A'$, $B \rightarrow B'$, $C \rightarrow C'$. Say whether the following statements are true (T) or false (F): (a) B' and C are coincident, (b) $ABA'C$ is a parallelogram, (c) $DA = DB$ $\Leftrightarrow$ $ABA'C$ is a rectangle, (d) angle $BAC = 90°$ $\Leftrightarrow$ $ABA'C$ is a square, (e) $ABA'C$ is a rhombus $\Leftrightarrow$ DA bisects angle BAC.

19 The figure shown in Fig. 27.26 is symmetrical about O. Find x and y.

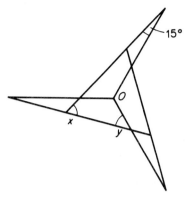

Fig. 27.26

20 $ABCD$ is a parallelogram in which the diagonals meet at E. Say whether the following statements are true (T) or false (F): (a) $AB = AD$ ⇔ symmetry about AC, (b) rotational symmetry of order more than 2 ⇔ $ABCD$ is a square, (c) angle $AEB = 90°$ ⇔ the diagonals are the only axes of symmetry, (d) $ABCD$ is a square ⇔ there are axes of symmetry parallel to both sides.

28 The Circle

The circle is a *locus*, that is a clearly defined set of points. It is *the locus of points which are equidistant from a fixed point*, the fixed point being called the *centre* and the distance of the points from it being called the *radius*. The definition can be expressed more briefly in set notation as $\{P:OP = r\}$, that is, 'the set of points P such that $OP = r$'. Here O denotes the centre and r the radius, and it can be assumed throughout this chapter that a point O inside a circle is the centre of the circle.

Elementary properties

There are three elementary properties of the circle which we shall state without proof (Fig. 28.1):
(1) *The perpendicular from the centre to a chord bisects the chord.*
(2) *A tangent meets the radius to its point of contact at right angles.*
(3) *The two tangents from an external point to a circle are equal in length.*

 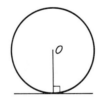 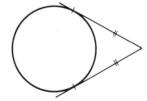

Fig. 28.1

(A tangent is a line which *touches* a circle, that is it meets the circle in one point only.)

Arcs and segments

A chord other than a diameter divides a circle into a *major arc* and a *minor arc*, and it divides the region inside the circle into a *major segment* and a *minor segment* (Fig. 28.2).

Note: Three letters are needed to name an arc unambiguously, though it is generally understood that when only two letters are used the minor arc is meant. It follows that three letters *must* be used to name a major arc.

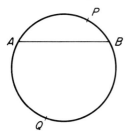 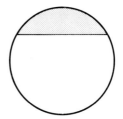

APB is a minor arc
AQB is a major arc

The shaded region is a minor segment
The unshaded region is a major segment

Fig. 28.2

Angles subtended by an arc

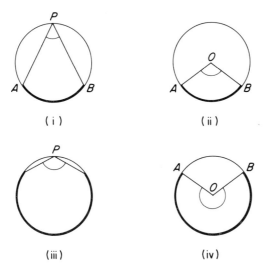

Fig. 28.3

In Fig. 28.3 (i), angle APB is *the angle subtended at the circumference by the minor arc AB*. (This angle can also be described as the angle *in the segment APB*.) In Fig. 28.3 (ii), angle AOB is the angle *subtended at the centre* by arc AB. Diagrams (iii) and (iv) show what happens when the arc is major. The angle subtended at the circumference becomes obtuse instead of acute, and the angle at the centre becomes *reflex*. The latter case should be particularly noted.

Arc theorems

There are six theorems concerning angles subtended by arcs. We shall state them without proof.

Angle at centre = twice angle at circumference

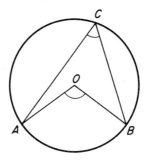

Fig. 28.4

The theorem states that

angle AOB = 2 × angle ACB.

Angles subtended at the circumference by the same arc are equal

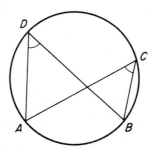

Fig. 28.5

The theorem states that

angle ADB = angle ACB.

The angle subtended at the circumference by a diameter is 90°.

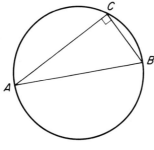

Fig. 28.6

AB is a diameter. The theorem states that

$$angle\ ACB = 90°.$$

The opposite angles of a cyclic quadrilateral are supplementary

A cyclic quadrilateral is one which can be *inscribed in a circle,* that is drawn inside a circle with all its vertices on the circumference. See Fig. 28.7.

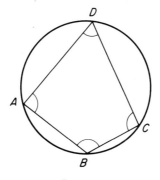

Fig. 28.7

The theorem states that

$$angle\ A + angle\ C = 180°,$$
$$angle\ B + angle\ D = 180°.$$

An interior angle of a cyclic quadrilateral equals the opposite exterior angle

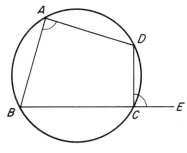

Fig. 28.8

The theorem states that

angle A = angle DCE.

The alternate segment theorem

A tangent to a circle and a chord through the point of contact are drawn. The chord (TC in Fig. 28.9) divides the circle into two segments:

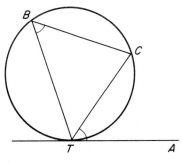

Fig. 28.9

The theorem states that the angle between the tangent and the chord is equal to the angle subtended by the chord in the other or 'alternate' segment. That is

angle ATC = angle B.

Numerical problems

Note: In addition to the properties of the circle given above, whenever the centre occurs in a problem *isosceles triangles* are likely to be present. This is because the centre is equidistant from all points on the circumference.

▷**Example 1**

Given that AB is a diameter, find angle BAC and angle CAD (Fig. 28.10).

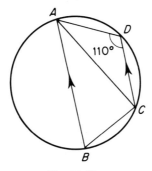

Fig. 28.10

Angle $ABC = 180° - 110° = 70°$
(opposite angles of cyclic quadrilateral)
and angle $ACB = 90°$ (subtended by diameter).
Hence angle $BAC = 20°$ (angles in triangle ABC).
Also angle $BAD = 180° - 110° = 70°$
(interior opposite angles),
∴ angle $CAD = 70° - 20° = 50°.$ ◁

▷**Example 2**

Find angle AOB (Fig. 28.11).

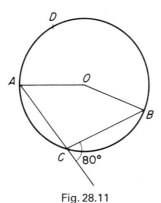

Fig. 28.11

Angle $ACB = 180° - 80° = 100°$
(adjacent angles on straight line),
∴ *reflex* angle $AOB = 2 \times 100° = 200°$
(angle at centre, arc ADB)
∴ *obtuse* angle $AOB = 360° - 200° = 160°$ (angles at a point).   ◁

▷ Example 3

Find angle ETB (Fig. 28.12).

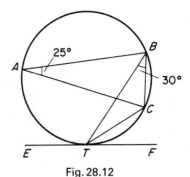

Fig. 28.12

Angle BTC = angle A = 25° (arc BC)
and angle CTF = angle CBT = 30°
(alternate segment theorem),
∴ angle ETB = 180° − 55° = 125°
(adjacent angles on straight line).   ◁

▷ Example 4

Find angle D and angle A (Fig. 28.13).

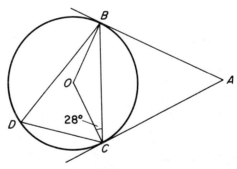

Fig. 28.13

Angle OBC = angle OCB = 28°
(base angles of isosceles triangle OBC),
∴ angle O = 124° (angles in triangle OBC),
∴ angle D = $\dfrac{124°}{2}$ = 62°
(angle at centre, arc BC).

Also angle ABC = angle ACB = 62°
(alternate segment theorem),
∴ angle A = 56° (angles in triangle ABC).   ◁

Note: Small letters can be used for angles if preferred. They have not been used in the above examples so as to keep the diagrams simple and clear.

EXERCISE 28a (easy numerical problems)

O always denotes the centre.

1 Find angle *D* and angle *B*.

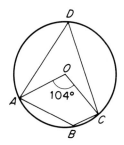

2 Find angle *D*, angle *C* and angle *B*.

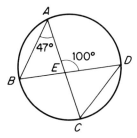

3 Find angle *O*, angle *D* and angle *B*.

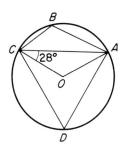

4 *AC* is a diameter. Find angle *BAC*.

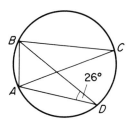

5 Find angle *C* and angle *EBD*.

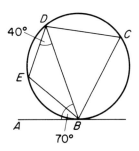

6 Find reflex angle *O* and obtuse angle *O*.

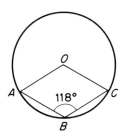

7 Find angle *D*.

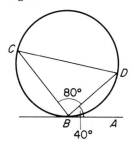

8 Find angle *B*.

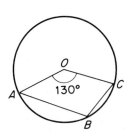

9 Find angle *ACD*.

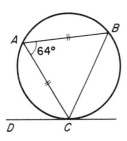

10 Find angle *ABE*.

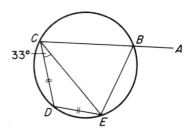

11 Find angle *C*, angle *D* and angle *E*.

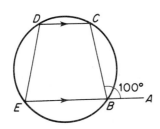

12 *CE* is a diameter. Find angle *BDE*, angle *BEC* and angle *BFE*.

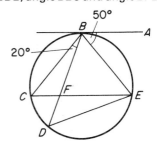

13 Find angle *B* and angle *O*.

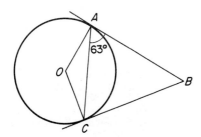

14 Find angle *CED*.

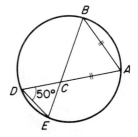

15 Find angle *BAE*.

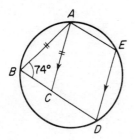

16 Find angle *ABO*.

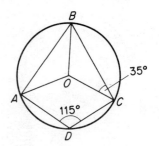

17 Find angle *AEC*, angle *COE* and angle *DCE*.

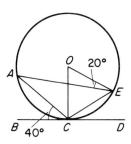

18 Find angle *OBC* and angle *AOD*.

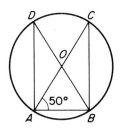

19 *AC* is a diameter. Find angle *A* and angle *CBD*.

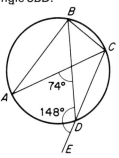

Find angle *C*.

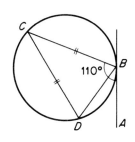

21 *BD* is a diameter and *AC = AD*. Find angle *BDC*.

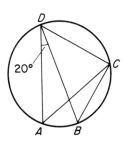

22 Find angle *DBE*.

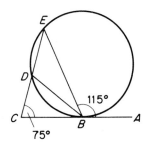

23 *EB = EC*. Find angle *CDA* and angle *AEB*.

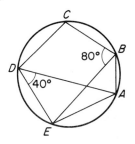

24 Find angle *EDF*.

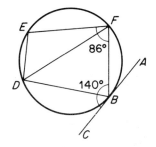

EXERCISE 28b (harder numerical problems)

1 Find angle *COE* and angle *COD*.

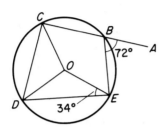

2 *CA = CD*. Find angle *BAC*.

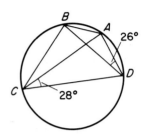

3 Find angle *D* and angle *DCE*.

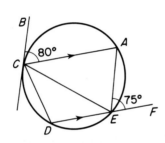

4 Find angle *BEC* and angle *DCF*.

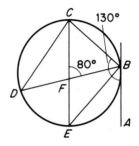

5 Find angle *DCB*.

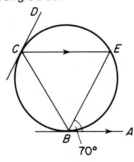

6 Find angle *OBA* and angle *ABC*.

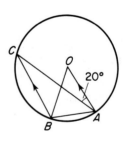

7 Find angle *OBA*.

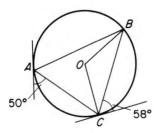

8 *AD* is a diameter. Find angle *CAD* and angle *BCA*.

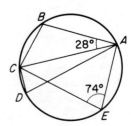

9 Find angle *ACD*.

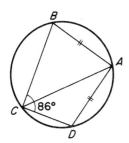

10 Find angle *C* and angle *CEF*.

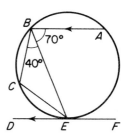

11 Find angle *ACB* and angle *OAC*.

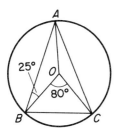

12 Find angle *AOB* and angle *OCB*.

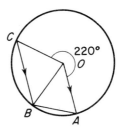

13 Find angle *DCF* and angle *FCB*.

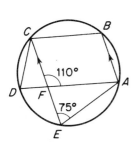

14 Find angle *A* and angle *ABE*.

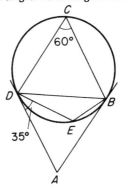

15 Find angle *EDF* and angle *CBF*.

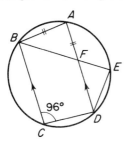

16 Find angle *ACB*.

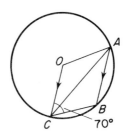

17 Find angle *ABE* and angle *CED*.

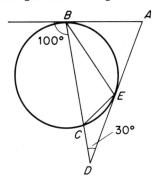

18 Find angle *ODE* and angle *OAB*.

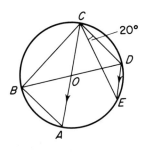

19 Find angle *ABC*.

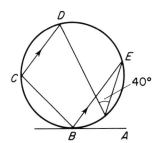

20 Find angle *CBE*.

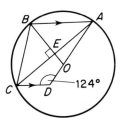

Converse theorems and proofs

The converse of the theorem 'If a triangle has two equal sides it has two equal angles' is 'If a triangle has two equal angles it has two equal sides.' The converse of a theorem does not *follow* from the original theorem, and if the converse is true it is a *separate theorem* which needs to be proved separately. The converses of the arc theorems are in fact all true, and thus are theorems themselves. Once again we shall merely state the theorems, omitting the proofs.

(1)

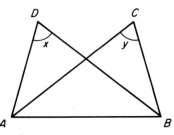

Fig. 28.14

If in Fig. 28.14 it can be shown that $x = y$, we can proceed as follows. *Since $x = y$ and these angles are both subtended by AB, the quadrilateral ABCD is cyclic.*

(2)

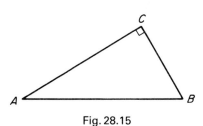

Fig. 28.15

If in Fig. 28.15 it can be shown that angle $C = 90°$, we can conclude that AB *is a diameter of circle ABC.*

(3)

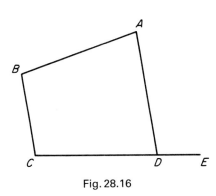

Fig. 28.16

If in Fig. 28.16 it can be shown either that angle A + angle $C = 180°$ or that angle B = angle ADE, we can conclude that *ABCD is a cyclic quadrilateral.*

(4)

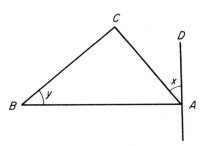

Fig. 28.17

If in Fig. 28.17 it can be shown that $x = y$, we can proceed as follows. *DA is a tangent to the circle on whose circumference points A, B and C lie (converse of the alternate segment theorem).*

The worked examples which follow involve both the main theorems and the converse theorems.

▷ Example 5

In a quadrilateral ABCD, CB = CD, angle BAD = 100° and angle BDC = 50°. Prove that the quadrilateral is cyclic and find angle BAC.

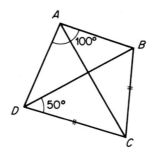

Fig. 28.18

Angle CBD = 50° (base angles of isosceles triangle CBD),
∴ angle BCD = 80° (angles in triangle CBD).

Hence angle BAD + angle BCD = 180° and it follows that the quadrilateral is cyclic. A circle can therefore be drawn around the quadrilateral and all the circle theorems are applicable. In particular,

angle BAC = angle BDC = 50° (arc BC). ◁

▷ Example 6

The altitudes BD, CE of a triangle ABC meet at F. Prove (a) that angle DEF = angle DAF, (b) that angle CBD = angle CED.

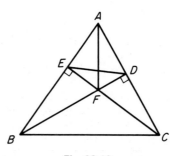

Fig. 28.19

(a) Since angle AEF = angle ADF = 90°, angle AEF + angle ADF = 180° and quadrilateral $ADFE$ is cyclic. Hence a circle can be drawn around the quadrilateral and we have

angle DEF = angle DAF (arc DF).

(b) Since angle BEC = angle BDC and these angles are both subtended by BC, quadrilateral $BCDE$ is cyclic and a circle can be drawn around it. Hence

angle CBD = angle CED (arc CD). ◁

▷ **Example 7**

Prove that the line ABC in Fig. 28.20 touches the circle BEF.

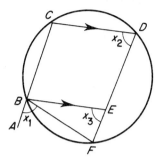

Fig. 28.20

$x_1 = x_2$ (exterior angle of cyclic quadrilateral *BCDF*)
and $x_2 = x_3$ (corresponding angles).
∴ $x_1 = x_3$
∴ *ABC* touches circle *BEF* (converse of alternate segment theorem).

◁

EXERCISE 28c

1 The diagonals of a quadrilateral *ABCD* meet at *E*, and *CB* = *CE*. *DA* is produced to *F*. If angle *BCE* = 80° and angle *CAF* = 130°, prove that the quadrilateral is cyclic and find angle *ADB*.

2 *ABCD* is a cyclic quadrilateral in which *AB* is parallel to *DC*. Prove that angle *C* = angle *D*.

3 *ABCD* is a quadrilateral in which *AB* = *AC*. The diagonals meet at *E*, and *DC* is produced to *F*. Angle *CBD* = 25°, angle *AEB* = 95° and angle *BCF* = 65°. Prove that the quadrilateral is cyclic and find angle *ADB*.

4 The diagonals of a cyclic quadrilateral *ABCD* meet at *E*, and *EA* = *ED*. Prove that *AD* is parallel to *BC*.

5 *ABC* is a triangle and *D* is a point on *BC*. Angle *BAC* = 95°, angle *ADB* = 85° and angle *ACD* = 40°. Prove that *CA* is a tangent to circle *ABD*.

6 The tangents from an external point *A* to a circle of centre *O* meet the circle at *B* and *C*. Prove that quadrilateral *ABOC* is cyclic and hence prove that if *D* is the mid-point of *AO*, *DA* = *DB*.

7 *ABCD* is a quadrilateral in which *AB* = *AC* and *AB* is parallel to *DC*. Angle *BAC* = 40° and angle *CAD* = 30°. Prove that the quadrilateral is cyclic and hence prove that *BA* = *BD*.

8 *A*, *B*, *C*, *D* are consecutive vertices of a regular polygon, and *AC* cuts *BD* at *E*. Prove that *BC* touches circle *ABE*.

9 In a quadrilateral *ABCD*, *AB* = *AD* and angle *C* = 2 × angle *ABD*. Prove that the quadrilateral is cyclic.

10 *ABC* is a triangle in which *AB* = *AC*. *P* and *Q* are points on *AB*, *AC* such that *PQ* is parallel to *BC*. Prove that angle *CPQ* = angle *CBQ*.

11 *ABCD* is a rhombus in which angle *A* is obtuse. The diagonals meet at *E*, and *F* is the foot of the perpendicular from *C* to *AB*. Prove that *BFEC* is a cyclic quadrilateral and hence prove that angle *EBF* = angle *EFC*.

12 The diagonals of a quadrilateral *ABCD* meet at *E*. If *EA* = *EB* and *EC* = *ED*, prove that angle *DAC* = angle *DBC*.

13 The tangent at *A* to a circle *ABC* meets *BC* produced at *D*. If *AC* = *AD*, prove that *BA* = *BD*.

14 *O* is the centre of a circle *ABC* in which *BA* = *BC* and *BC* is parallel to *AO*. Prove that angle *ACB* = 30°.

15 *ABCD* is a quadrilateral in which angle *B* and angle *D* are right angles and *E* is the mid-point of *AC*. Prove that angle *ABE* = angle *BDC*.

16 *ABCD* is a cyclic quadrilateral in which *AB* = *AD*. *E* is a point on *CD* such that *AE* = *AD* and *AE* is parallel to *BC*. Prove that *BD* bisects angle *ADC*.

17 The side *DA* of a quadrilateral *ABCD* is produced to *E* and *F* is a point on *CD* such that *FA* is parallel to *CB*. If angle *BAE* = angle *C*, prove that *BA* touches circle *ADF*.

18 *ABCD* is a quadrilateral in which *DB* = *DC* and *E* is a point on *CD* such that *BE* is parallel to *AD*. If angle *ABD* = angle *CBE*, prove that quadrilateral *ABCD* is cyclic.

19 *ABCD* is a cyclic quadrilateral in which *DB* = *DC*. The bisector of angle *BAC* meets *BC* at *E*. Prove that angle *DAE* = 90°.

20 The tangent at *A* to a circle *ABCD* meets *CD* produced at *E*. *AC* bisects angle *BCD* and *CA* = *CE*. Prove that *CA* bisects angle *BAE*.

Contact of circles

Two circles may *touch* either internally or externally. In either case they have a *common tangent at the point of contact*, which is at right angles to the line joining the centres (Fig. 28.21).

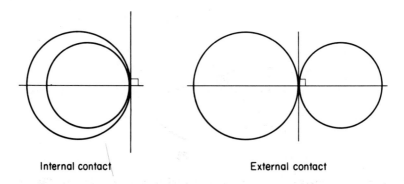

Internal contact   External contact

Fig. 28.21

It is worth noting also that the other two tangents which can be drawn from a point on the common tangent are equal in length. This follows immediately from the theorem that tangents from an external point to a circle are equal (Fig. 28.22).

$$\text{Since}\quad AB = AC$$
$$\text{and}\quad AD = AC,$$
$$\text{it follows that}\quad AB = AD.$$

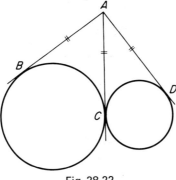

Fig. 28.22

Tangent and chord theorems

The arc theorems dealt with *angles*; the remaining circle theorems are concerned with *lengths*. They are proved by similar triangles, and since the arc theorems are needed to prove the similarity, the tangent and chord theorems must necessarily follow and not precede the arc theorems.

The first theorem is called the *intersecting chord theorem*, and it concerns two chords of a circle which meet *inside* the circle. When the chords meet outside the circle — that is, after being produced – the corresponding theorem is proved as part of a more general theorem called the *tangent–secant theorem*.

Intersecting chord theorem — chords meeting inside circle

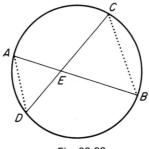

Fig. 28.23

AB and CD are *any* two chords meeting inside the circle (Fig. 28.23).

To prove AE.EB = DE.EC

Proof

> In the triangles *AED, CEB*,
> angle A = angle C (arc *DB*),
> angle D = angle B (arc *AC*),
> ∴ the triangles are similar,
> ∴ $\dfrac{AE}{EC} = \dfrac{DE}{EB} \left(= \dfrac{AD}{CB} \right)$,
> ∴ $AE.EB = DE.EC$.

The tangent – secant theorem

A *secant* is simply a line cutting across a circle; in other words a line obtained by producing a chord (*CBA* in Fig. 28.24).

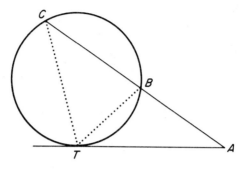

Fig. 28.24

To prove $AT^2 = AB.AC$

Proof

In the triangles $ATB, ACT,$
angle A is common,
angle ATB = angle C (alternate segment theorem),
∴ the triangles are similar,
∴ $\dfrac{AT}{AC} = \dfrac{AB}{AT}$
∴ $AT^2 = AB.AC.$

Now since the product $AB.AC$ is equal to AT^2 for *any* secant from A, we can immediately derive the second intersecting chord theorem. This deals with the case of two chords meeting outside the circle, that is two secants (Fig. 28.25).

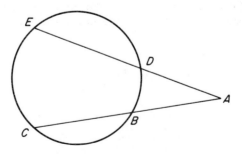

Fig. 28.25

The theorem states that $AB.AC = AD.AE$. This can be memorised as follows: *part outside circle times whole secant is constant.*

The three theorems are summarised in Fig. 28.26:

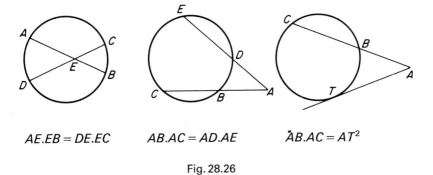

$$AE.EB = DE.EC \qquad AB.AC = AD.AE \qquad \grave{A}B.AC = AT^2$$

Fig. 28.26

Converse theorems

The converses of all three tangent and chord theorems are true, and thus are theorems themselves:

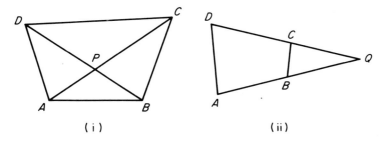

(i)   (ii)

Fig. 28.27

If it can be shown that $AP.PC = BP.PD$ in Fig. 28.27 (i) or that $QB.QA = QC.QD$ in Fig. 28.27 (ii), we can proceed as follows. *ABCD is a cyclic quadrilateral (converse of intersecting chord theorem).*

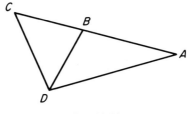

Fig. 28.28

If in Fig. 28.28 it can be show that $AB.AC = AD^2$, we can proceed as follows. *AD is a tangent to circle BCD (converse of tangent-secant theorem).*

▷**Example 8**

Fig. 28.29 shows a segment of a circle of radius 5 cm. The width of the segment is 8 cm, as shown, and the height is x cm. Find x.

Fig. 28.29

Completing the circle, we have the diagram shown in Fig. 28.30.

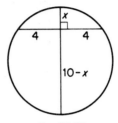

Fig. 28.30

The vertical line is a diameter since it bisects the chord and is perpendicular to it, and since the radius of the circle is 5 cm the diameter is 10 cm. Applying the intersecting chord theorem, we obtain

$$x(10 - x) = 16$$
$$\therefore \ x^2 - 10x + 16 = 0$$
$$\therefore \ (x - 2)(x - 8) = 0$$
$$\therefore \ x = 2 \text{ or } 8.$$

Clearly we require the smaller value; hence $x = 2$.   ◁

▷**Example 9**

Find x in the two diagrams shown in Fig. 28.31.

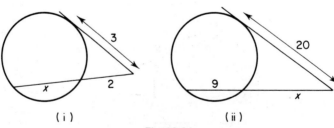

(i)   (ii)

Fig. 28.31

In each case we use the tangent–secant theorem. Diagram (i) gives a linear equation and diagram (ii) a quadratic.

From diagram (i):
$$2(2 + x) = 9$$
$$\therefore \ 2 + x = 4\tfrac{1}{2}$$
$$\therefore \ x = 2\tfrac{1}{2}.$$

From diagram (ii):
$$x(x + 9) = 400$$
$$\therefore \ x^2 + 9x - 400 = 0$$
$$\therefore \ (x + 25)(x - 16) = 0$$
$$\therefore \ x = 16 \text{ (discarding the negative solution)}. \ ◁$$

▷ Example 10

In Fig. 28.32, prove that the points B, C, G, F are concyclic. (Concyclic points are points through which a circle can be drawn.)

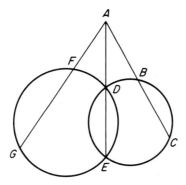

Fig. 28.32

Proof

> $AB.AC = AD.AE$ (intersecting chord theorem — circle $BCED$),
> $AF.AG = AD.AE$ (intersecting chord theorem — circle $FGED$),
> $\therefore$ $AB.AC = AF.AG$,
> $\therefore$ B, C, G, F are concyclic (converse of intersecting chord theorem). ◁

Some questions involving lengths of chords, etc. have to be done either by the direct use of similar triangles or by combining the use of similar triangles with that of the tangent and chord theorems. The final example in this chapter illustrates this type of problem.

▷ Example 11

In Fig. 28.33, find x and y.

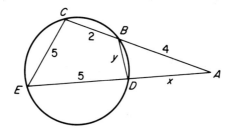

Fig. 28.33

We can find x by using the intersecting chord theorem:

$$x(x + 5) = 4 \times 6 = 24$$
$$\therefore \ x^2 + 5x - 24 = 0$$

from which $x = 3$.

To find y we must notice that triangles ABD, AEC are similar since angle A is common and angle ABD = angle AEC (exterior angle of cyclic quadrilateral). Since $\dfrac{AB}{AE} = \dfrac{4}{8} = \dfrac{1}{2}$, we have

$$\frac{y}{5} = \frac{1}{2}$$
$$\therefore \ y = 2\tfrac{1}{2}$$

◀

EXERCISE 28d

In questions 1–10, find x and y.

1

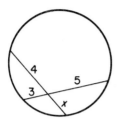

2

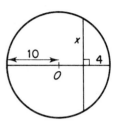

3

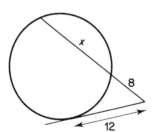

4

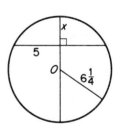

5

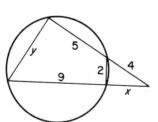

6

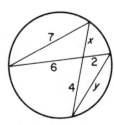

7

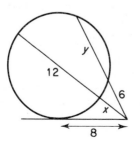

8

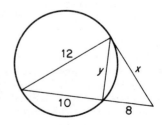

9

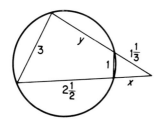

10

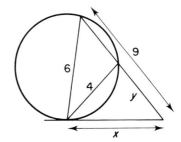

11 P and Q are centres. $AC = 12, AD = 18, DE = 14, QG = 10$. Find $AB, AG, AF,$ BP.

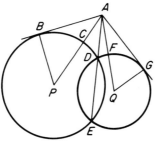

12 $AB = 4, GC = 4, CF = 1$ and the length of the tangent from A to circle BFE is 6. Find BC, CD and DE.

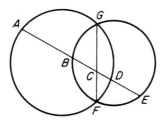

13 Two chords of a circle, CB and ED, meet when produced at A. (a) Prove that triangles ADC, ABE are similar. (b) If $AB = 2\frac{1}{2}, BC = 3\frac{1}{2}, AD = 2$ and $BE = 5$, find DE and CD.

14 The sides AB, DC of a quadrilateral ABCD are produced to meet at E. If $AB = CE = 4, BE = 3$ and $CD = 1\frac{1}{4}$, prove that angle A = angle BCE.

15 ABC is a triangle in which $AB = 4$ and $BC = 8$. If D is the point on BC such that $BD : DC = 1 : 3$, prove that angle BAD = angle C.

16 Two lines, AB and CD, of lengths 12 and 15, meet at E. This point bisects AB and divides CD in the ratio 1 : 4. Prove that angle BAC = angle BDC.

17 ABC is a triangle and D, E are points on AB, AC such that angle A + angle ADE + angle B = 180°. Prove that $AD.AB = AE.AC$.

18 In a kite ABCD, $AB = AD$. If the diagonals meet at E and $AE.EC = BE.ED$, prove that angle B is a right angle.

19 ABC is a triangle in which $AB = AC$, and D is a point on BC such that $DA = DB$. Prove that $BA^2 = BD.BC$.

20 Two circles touch externally at T, and from a point A on the common tangent at T two other tangents AB, AC are drawn to touch the circles at B and C. BC meets AT at D. (a) Prove that angle CAT = 2 × angle CBT. (b) If $BD = 8, DC = 6$ and $TD = 3$, find AD.

29 Area, Intercepts, Bisectors

Area

It is convenient to have formulae for the areas of all standard figures, and here we shall consider the main figures which arise in elementary geometry, namely the rectangle, parallelogram, triangle, trapezium and kite. We shall take the formula for the rectangle — length × breadth — as basic and show briefly how the other formulae are derived from it.

Parallelogram

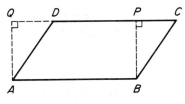

Fig. 29.1

It is easy to show that triangles *BPC, AQD* (Fig. 29.1) are congruent, and hence triangle *BPC* could be removed and placed in the position of triangle *AQD* without affecting the area. This would give a rectangle of area *AB.BP,* and if we regard *AB* as the *base* of the parallelogram, *BP* is its *perpendicular height.* It follows that

$$\textbf{area of parallelogram} = \textbf{base} \times \textbf{height,}$$
$$\text{or} \quad \boldsymbol{A = bh.}$$

Triangle

We saw in chapter 27 that a triangle together with its image under a half-turn forms a parallelogram.

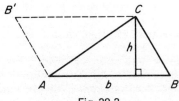

Fig. 29.2

Since the triangle and its image are congruent (Fig. 29.2), it follows that

area of triangle $= \frac{1}{2}$ base $\times$ height,
or $A = \frac{1}{2}bh$.

Trapezium

A trapezium can be split into two triangles by a diagonal (Fig. 29.3).

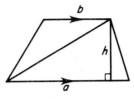

Fig. 29.3

The height of both the triangles is h; hence the sum of their areas is $\frac{1}{2}ah + \frac{1}{2}bh = \frac{1}{2}(a + b)h$. This can be expressed as follows:

area of trapezium $=$ average of parallel sides $\times$ height,
or $A = \frac{1}{2}(a + b)h$.

Kite

A kite can be split into two identical triangles by a diagonal *(AB* in Fig. 29.4).

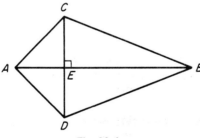

Fig. 29.4

The area of triangle *ABC* is $\frac{1}{2}AB.EC$; hence the area of the kite is $\frac{1}{2}AB \times 2EC$ or $\frac{1}{2}AB.DC$. In words,

area of kite $= \frac{1}{2}$ product of diagonals.

Deductions from the triangle result

The formula for the area of a triangle is easily the most important of those derived above because the triangle is the most commonly occurring standard figure. Two deductions from the triangle formula are the following:

(1) Triangles with the same base which lie between the same parallels are equal in area (Fig. 29.5).

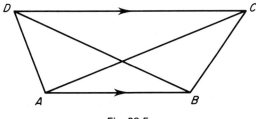

Fig. 29.5

Triangle ABC = triangle ABD (same base, same parallels).
The reason is that if the triangles lie between the same parallels they must have equal heights.

(2) When triangles have the same height, the ratio of their areas equals the ratio of their bases (Fig. 29.6).

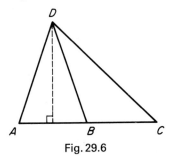

Fig. 29.6

If we regard AB and BC as their bases, triangles ABD, BCD have the same height (the perpendicular shown), and hence

$$\frac{\triangle ABD}{\triangle BCD} = \frac{AB}{BC}.$$

This second result is particularly important and often arises in problems. The following examples are typical.

▷ **Example 1**

In the trapezium shown in Fig. 29.7, $AB = 2DC$. Prove that triangle $DEC = \frac{1}{9}$ trapezium ABCD.

First we must note that triangles ABE, CDE are similar and that since $AB = 2DC$, $BE = 2ED$ and $AE = 2EC$.
   Now consider the triangles BEC, DEC. If we take BE and DE as their bases, the perpendicular from C to BD is the height of both triangles. Hence since $BE = 2ED$, we have

$$\triangle BEC = 2 \triangle DEC.$$

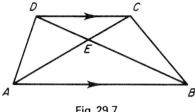

Fig. 29.7

Similarly, triangles *AED, DEC* can be compared by regarding *AE* and *EC* as their bases. We have

$$\triangle AED = 2 \triangle DEC \text{ (base } AE = 2EC \text{, same height)}.$$

Finally triangles *AEB, AED* can be compared by regarding *BE* and *ED* as their bases:

$$\triangle AEB = 2 \triangle AED \text{ (base } BE = 2ED \text{, same height)}.$$

Now it is convenient to let the smallest of these triangles, *DEC*, have an area of 1 unit; then the areas of the other triangles are as shown in Fig. 29.8.

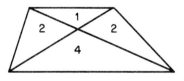

Fig. 29.8

Clearly the area of the whole trapezium is 9, and hence triangle $DEC = \frac{1}{9}$ of the trapezium. ◀

▷**Example 2**

In Fig. 29.9, CT:BT = 3:2. Find the ratio AB:BC.

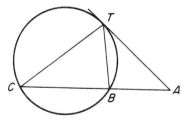

Fig. 29.9

In this case triangles *ACT, ATB* are similar and since *TC* and *TB* are corresponding sides, the ratio of the sides of the similar triangles is 3:2. Hence the ratio of the areas is $(3:2)^2 = 9:4$, and it follows that if we let triangle *ATB* equal 4 units in area, triangle *ACT* will be 9 and therefore triangle *TBC* will be 5 (Fig. 29.10):

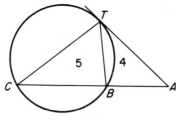

Fig. 29.10

Now if *AB* and *BC* are regarded as the bases of triangles *ATB* and *TBC*, the triangles have the same height, namely the perpendicular from *T* to *AC* (not shown). It follows that the ratio of the bases is equal to the ratio of the areas, and we have

$$AB{:}BC = 4{:}5. \qquad \triangleleft$$

Intercept theorems

There are various intercept theorems, but we shall give (without proof) only the simplest ones which refer to the triangle. The theorems are stated with reference to Fig. 29.11.

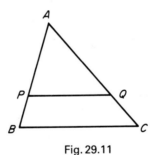

Fig. 29.11

(1) **If *PQ* is parallel to *BC*, then** $\dfrac{AP}{PB} = \dfrac{AQ}{QC}$.

(This theorem is sometimes called *the* intercept theorem.)

(2) **If** $\dfrac{AP}{PB} = \dfrac{AQ}{QC}$**, then *PQ* is parallel to *BC*.**

[Theorem (2) is clearly the converse of theorem (1)].

(3) **If *P* and *Q* are the mid-points of *AB* and *AC*, then**
 (a) ***PQ* is parallel to *BC*,**
 (b) ***PQ* = ½*BC*.**

Theorem (3) is called the *mid-point theorem*.

All three theorems follow from the similarity of triangles *APQ*, *ABC*.

Bisector theorems

The bisector theorems again relate ratios of lengths. There are two theorems, one concerning the bisector of an interior angle of a triangle, and the other concerning the bisector of an exterior angle. We shall prove only the former.

The internal bisector theorem

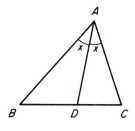

Fig. 29.12

The theorem states that the internal bisector of angle A divides BC internally in the same ratio as that of the two sides containing the angle. That is,

$$\frac{DB}{DC} = \frac{AB}{AC}.$$

The usual method of proof involves similar triangles, but a more interesting approach is based upon the final result on area obtained above (page 262).

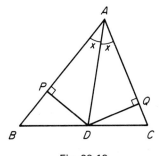

Fig. 29.13

Consider triangles ABD, ACD (Fig. 29.13). If we regard BD and DC as their bases the triangles have the same height, namely the perpendicular from A to BC. Hence

$$\frac{\triangle ABD}{\triangle ACD} = \frac{BD}{DC}.$$

If, however, we regard AB and AC as bases, PD and QD are the heights and these are equal from the congruence of triangles APD, AQD (SAA). Hence

$$\frac{\triangle ABD}{\triangle ACD} = \frac{AB}{AC}.$$

It follows immediately that $\dfrac{BD}{DC} = \dfrac{AB}{AC}$.

Internal and external division of a line

The ratio in which the point D divides BC internally in Fig. 29.13 could be expressed as

distance from point to B : distance from point to C.

When the point D is on BC produced, the same expression gives the ratio in which the point is said to divide the line externally. For example, if D divides BC externally in the ratio 3:1, D is positioned as shown in Fig. 29.14:

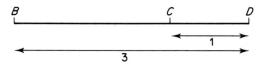

Fig. 29.14

The external bisector theorem

When the angle A of a triangle ABC is bisected externally, the point D divides BC externally (Fig. 29.15).

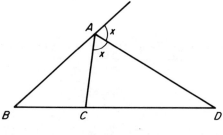

Fig. 29.15

The external bisector theorem states that DA divides BC *externally* in the ratio of the two sides containing the angle, and this gives exactly the same equation as the internal bisector theorem, namely

$$\frac{DB}{DC} = \frac{AB}{AC}.$$

▷ Example 3

ABC is a triangle in which AB = 5, AC = 3, BC = 6 (Fig. 29.16). The internal and external bisectors of angle A meet BC at D and E. Find (a) DB, (b) EC.

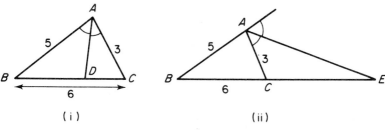

Fig. 29.16

(a) By the internal bisector theorem, *D* divides *BC* in the ratio 5:3. One method of dividing 6 in the ratio 5:3 is to add up 5 and 3, obtaining 8; then divide 8 into 6, etc (see chapter 2). The other method, which is more generally applicable, is to let the required length (*BD*) be *x* and write down an equation involving *x*:

$$\frac{x}{6-x} = \frac{5}{3} \quad \text{(internal bisector theorem)}$$
$$\therefore \ 3x = 30 - 5x$$
$$\therefore \quad x = 3\tfrac{3}{4}.$$

(b) Letting *EC* = *y* and applying the external bisector theorem, we have

$$\frac{y+6}{y} = \frac{5}{3}$$
$$\therefore \ 3y + 18 = 5y$$
$$\therefore \quad y = 9.$$

▷ Example 4

In Fig. 29.17, DA bisects angle BAC, CD = 1½DB and AB = 20 cm. Find CE.

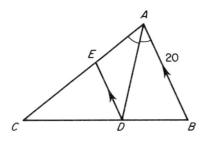

Fig. 29.17

First we use the internal bisector theorem to find AC:

$$\frac{AC}{AB} = \frac{CD}{DB}$$

i.e. $\dfrac{AC}{20} = \dfrac{3}{2}$

$\therefore \; AC = 30$ cm.

Now we apply the first intercept theorem. Letting $CE = x$ cm, we have

$$\frac{x}{30-x} = \frac{3}{2}$$

$\therefore \; 2x = 90 - 3x$

from which $x = 18$.

Hence $CE = 18$ cm. ◀

▷ Example 5

Fig. 29.18 shows a parallelogram in which 3AD = 4AF. Equal angles are indicated. Find the ratio EF:FB.

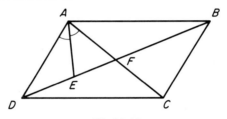

Fig. 29.18

Since $\dfrac{AD}{AF} = \dfrac{DE}{EF}$ (internal bisector theorem), $\dfrac{DE}{EF} = \dfrac{4}{3}$. Let $DE = 4$ units and $EF = 3$ units; then since F is the mid-point of DB, $FB = 7$ units. Hence $EF:FB = 3:7$. ◀

▷ Example 6

In Fig. 29.19 D is the mid-point of BC, and PD, QD bisect angles ADB, ADC as shown. Prove that PQ is parallel to BC.

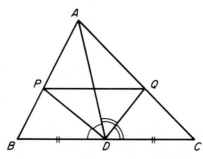

Fig. 29.19

Proof

$$\frac{DB}{DA} = \frac{BP}{PA} \text{ (internal bisector theorem)}$$

$$\text{and } \frac{DC}{DA} = \frac{CQ}{QA} \text{ (internal bisector theorem).}$$

But $DB = DC$ (given)

$$\therefore \frac{BP}{PA} = \frac{CQ}{QA}$$

$\therefore$ *PQ* is parallel to *BC*.

(The final step follows from the second intercept theorem.) ◁

EXERCISE 29a (bisector theorems)

Note: The bisector theorems are probably the most difficult of the theorems dealt with in this chapter and so the whole of this exercise is devoted to them.

Equal angles are marked. Where no instructions are given, find the quantities indicated by the letters in the diagram.

1

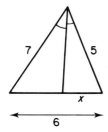

2

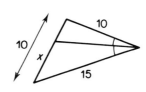

3

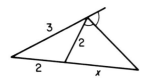

4

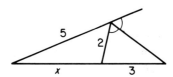

5

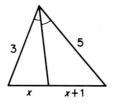

6

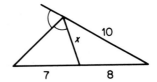

7
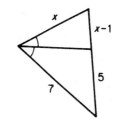

8 $AB:AC = 2:3$. Find $DB:BC$.
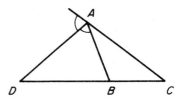

9 $BC:CD = 7:6$. Find $AB:AC$.
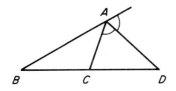

10 $BC = 2\frac{1}{2}DC$ and $AC = 60$. Find AB.
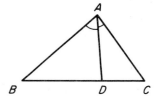

11 $PS = 1\frac{2}{5}QS$ and $QR = 30$. Find PQ.   **12** $CD = 5BC$ and $AB = 90$. Find AC.

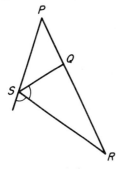
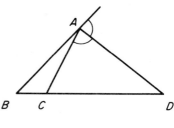

Questions 13–20 refer to a triangle *ABC,* in which the internal and external bisectors of angle *A* meet *BC* and *BC* produced at *P* and *Q*, respectively.

13 $AB = 1\frac{1}{2}AC$ and $BC = 25$. Find *PC* and *CQ*.

14 $AB = 1\frac{1}{3}AC$ and $BP = 20$. Find *BQ*.

15 $5AC = 3AB$ and $BC = 40$. Find *PQ*.

16 $BC = CQ$. Find *AB:AC* and *BP:BC*.

17 $QC:QB = 2:3$. Find *BP:PQ*.

18 $BC = 3PC$. Find *PC:CQ*.

19 $QC = 5CP$. Find *AB:AC*.

20 $CP = \frac{1}{4}QP$. Find *AC:AB*.

EXERCISE 29b (miscellaneous)

Note: In this exercise there is sometimes a choice between using one of the intercept theorems and using similar triangles.

1 $AB = 2$ cm, $BC = 3$ cm, $AF = 3$ cm. Find the areas of BCDE, ADC, ACDE.

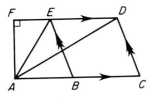

2 Find the ratios of the areas of
(a) triangles ABC and ACE and
(b) triangles ABD and ABE.

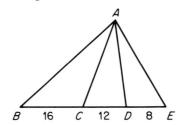

3 $BC = 2AB$ and $\triangle BCD = 12$ cm². Find the areas of triangles BCE, ABE.

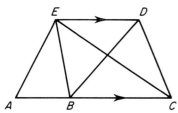

4 The tangents at A, B to a circle of centre O meet at D. $AB = 5$ cm and $OD = 8$ cm. Find the area of quadrilateral ABDO.

5 $BD = DC$, $AE = \frac{1}{2}EC$. The area of triangle $ABC = 48$ cm². Find the areas of triangles ABD, AED.

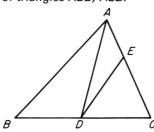

6 Find x and y.

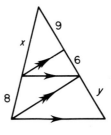

7 Find x.

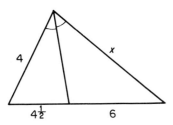

8 E is the mid-point of BC and $3AC = 7AB$. Find the ratio of $\triangle ABD : \triangle ADE$.

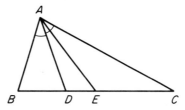

9 $AB:BC = 3:2$ and the area of triangle $ABE = 12$ cm². Find the areas of triangle DEC and quadrilateral $BCDE$.

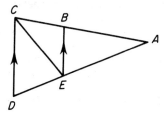

10 $BA:BC = 4:3$, $AD = 35$ and the area of quadrilateral $FEDC = 66$. Find AE and the area of triangle AEF.

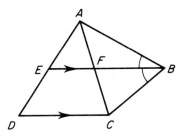

11 Find x.

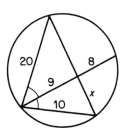

12 $BF = \dfrac{FD}{3}$. Find (a) $BE:CD$, (b) $AB:BC$, (c) $\triangle BCF:\triangle BEF$, (d) $\triangle ABE$:quadrilateral $BCDE$.

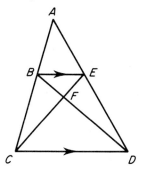

13 (a) $p:q = 3:2$, $s = 4$; find r.
(b) $r = s = 4$, $p = 6$; find q.
(c) $BD = 4BC$, $q = 12$; find p.
(d) Express s in terms of p, q, r.

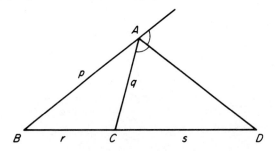

14 In a triangle ABC, D is the mid-point of AB and E is a point on AC such that $AE = \frac{1}{2}EC$. Letting the area of triangle $ADE = 1$, find the areas of triangles CED and CBD. What fraction is triangle ADE of triangle ABC?

15 In a triangle ABC, D is a point on AB such that $AD = 2DB$, and E is a point on BC such that $BE = 2EC$. Prove that $\triangle BDE:\triangle ABC = 2:9$. (Proceed as in question 14.)

16 The diagonals of a parallelogram $ABCD$ meet at F and the internal bisector of angle DAF meets DF at E. (a) Given that $3AF = 2AD$, find $EF:FB$. (b) Given that $EF = 1$, $AF = 1\frac{1}{2}$ and $FB = 3$, find AD. (c) Given that triangle $ABC = 40$ cm^2 and $AD:AF = 5:3$, find the area of triangle ADE.

17 In a triangle ABC the internal bisectors of angle A and angle B meet BC and AC at D and E, respectively. $AB = 2$, $BD = 1$, $DC = 3$. Find AE and EC.

18 P, Q, R are the mid-points of BC, CA, AB in a triangle ABC. Prove that triangle $PQR = \frac{1}{4}$ triangle ABC.

19 From an external point A, a tangent AT and a secant ABC are drawn to a circle BCT. Given that $4 \triangle BCT = 5 \triangle ABT$, find the ratios $AB:BC$, $AB:AT$, $TC:TB$.

20 In a triangle ABC, the internal bisector of angle C meets AB at P, and Q is a point on BC such that PQ is parallel to AC. If $\triangle PCQ : \triangle PBQ = 4:3$, find $AC:CQ$.

21 In a triangle ABC, D is a point on AC such that angle $ADB =$ angle ABC. Given that $4BC = 5BD$, use an area method to find $CD:DA$.

22 In a triangle ABC, P is the mid-point of AB, Q is a point on BC such that $BQ = \frac{1}{2}QC$, and R is a point on AC such that QR is parallel to BA. What fraction of triangle ABC is quadrilateral $APQR$?

23 In a triangle ABC, the external bisector of angle A meets BC produced at D, and E is a point on AD such that EC is parallel to AB. Prove that
$$\frac{AC}{DE} = \frac{AB}{AD}.$$

24 D, E are points on the sides AB, AC of a triangle ABC. $AD = 2DB$ and $\triangle BCD = 1\frac{1}{2} \triangle CDE$. Prove that DE is parallel to BC.

25 ABC is a triangle in which $AB = AC$. The internal bisector of angle B meets AC at D, and E is a point on AB such that ED is parallel to BC. Prove that
$$\frac{AB}{AE} = \frac{BC}{DC}.$$

30 Loci and Constructions

Loci

A locus is *a clearly defined set of points*. The best examples of loci we have met so far are graphs. We saw in chapter 23 that an equation relating x and y, such as $y = x^2$, defines a set of points (x,y) which forms a curve or line, while an inequality such as $y < 3x$ defines a region. These sets of points are both loci since they are clearly defined by their equations or inequalities. In this chapter all the two-dimensional loci we shall consider — those lying entirely in one plane — will be lines or curves, and they will be defined by *explicit* laws or sets of conditions rather than by means of equations. Thus for example if the law governing a set of points is that each of them is the same distance from a fixed point, the locus they form is a circle. When a locus is a line or curve it is often convenient to regard the locus as a *path* which is traced out by a single moving point. The point must however move in a law-governed and not a random way if the path is to count as a locus.

When the set of points is not confined to a plane but can range throughout space, the locus is three-dimensional and normally takes the form of a *surface* rather than a line or curve. Often the law which defines a two-dimensional locus also defines a simple three-dimensional equivalent; for example, the locus in three dimensions of points equidistant from a fixed point is a *spherical surface* rather than a circle.

Below are listed the main two-dimensional loci which should be learned, along with the corresponding three-dimensional loci when these exist. In each case the law or set of conditions is stated and then the locus is described. The loci are of two types: those in which the form of the line or curve is obvious from the statement of the law, and slightly more complicated cases in which the locus is less directly defined.

Directly defined loci

(1) **Law**: the distance from a fixed point is constant.
Locus: a circle whose centre is the fixed point.
In 3-D: a spherical surface whose centre is the fixed point.

(2) **Law**: the distance from a fixed line is constant.
Locus: two lines, both parallel to the fixed line.
In 3-D: a cylindrical surface whose central axis is the fixed line.

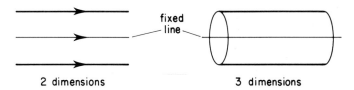

2 dimensions   3 dimensions

Fig. 30.1

Both the lines and the surface are of course infinitely long.

(3) **Law**: the points of the locus are equidistant from two fixed points.
Locus: the mediator of the line joining the fixed points.
In 3-D: the plane which bisects the line joining the points at right angles.

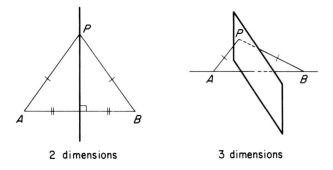

2 dimensions   3 dimensions

Fig. 30.2

For all points P on both loci, $AP = BP$.

(4) **Law**: the points of the locus are equidistant from two fixed parallel lines.
Locus: another parallel line, midway between the fixed lines.
In 3-D: a plane, parallel to the fixed lines, which cuts the plane containing them at right angles.

(*Note:* the 'distance from a point to a line' means the *perpendicular* distance.)

(5) **Law**: the points of the locus are equidistant from two fixed non-parallel lines.
Locus: the two bisectors of the angles between the lines.

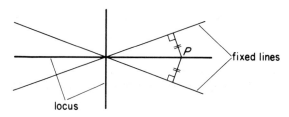

Fig. 30.3

Indirectly defined loci

(6) The locus of the centre of a circle of constant radius which touches a fixed line

The way to discover the nature of the locus is to draw the circle in a few different positions, and link up the centres. This will give the path traced out by the centre, considered as a single moving point (Fig. 30.4).

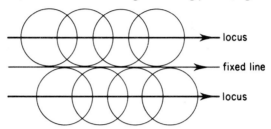

Fig. 30.4

The locus is clearly identical to (2) above, namely two parallel lines. It is worth noting also that the locus in 3-D of the centre of a sphere of fixed radius which touches a plane is two parallel planes.

(7) The locus of the centre of a circle which touches a fixed line at a fixed point (Fig. 30.5).

Here the radius of the circle is variable:

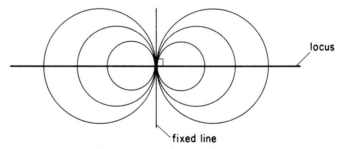

Fig. 30.5

The locus is clearly the perpendicular to the fixed line at the fixed point.

(8) The locus of the centre of a circle of constant radius which touches a fixed circle (Fig. 30.6).

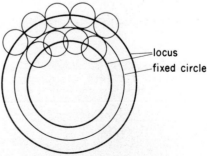

Fig. 30.6

The locus is two concentric circles.

(9) The locus of the centre of a circle of constant radius which passes through a fixed point (Fig. 30.7).

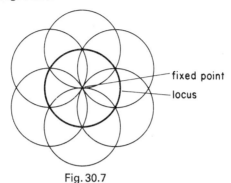

Fig. 30.7

The locus is another circle, of centre the fixed point, with the same radius as the given circle.

(10) The locus of the mid-point of a chord of constant length in a fixed circle (Fig. 30.8).

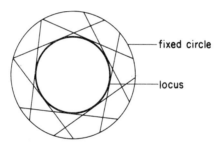

Fig. 30.8

The locus is a circle with the same centre as the fixed circle.

(11) The locus of the point P which moves in such a way that the area of triangle APB is constant, A and B being fixed points (Fig. 30.9).

Since triangles with the same base and the same area must have the same height, the locus of P is a pair of lines parallel to AB.

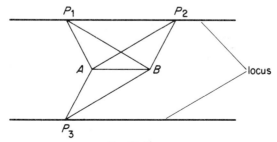

Fig. 30.9

Triangles ABP_1, ABP_2, ABP_3 all have the same area.

(12) The locus of the point *P* which moves in such a way that angle *APB* is constant, *A* and *B* being fixed points (Fig. 30.10).

Here the geometry of the circle tells us that the locus is a pair of circular arcs.

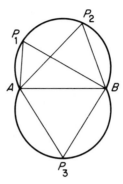

Fig. 30.10

Angles AP_1B, AP_2B, AP_3B are all equal as they are all subtended by AB. The locus is a pair of major arcs if the given angle is acute, and a pair of minor arcs if the angle is obtuse. An important special case is that in which the given angle is 90°. The locus is then a complete circle, of which AB is a diameter.

EXERCISE 30a

1 Describe the locus of the mid-points of a set of parallel chords of a fixed circle.

2 A ball can roll on a horizontal plane. Describe the locus of its highest point.

3 Describe the locus of the centre of a circle which touches two non-parallel lines.

4 Describe the locus of the point of intersection of two tangents of constant length to a fixed circle.

5 A ball can roll so as to be in contact with the floor and at least one vertical wall of a square room. Describe the locus of its centre.

6 Two fixed lines meet at right angles at A. B is a fixed point on one line and P is a variable point on the other. Describe the locus of the mid-point of BP.

7 A is a fixed point on a fixed line, and AP is at right angles to the line. Describe the locus of P (in 3-D) when (a) AP is of constant length, (b) the length of AP is unrestricted.

8 A and B are fixed points. Describe the locus of the point P such that angle ABP is constant, (a) if the points A, B, P are restricted to one plane, (b) if they are not so restricted.

9 Describe the locus (in 2-D) of the centre of a circle which passes through two fixed points A and B.

10 Describe the locus (in 3-D) of the centre of a sphere of fixed radius which touches (a) a fixed line, (b) a fixed sphere externally.

11 Q is the point of contact of the tangent from an external point P to a fixed circle. Describe the locus of P if QP is of constant length.

12 Describe the locus in 3-D of a point which is equidistant from all the four lines of a square.

13 *P* is a variable point on a fixed plane, and *A* is a fixed point which is not on the plane. Describe the locus of the mid-point of *AP* if (a) *AP* is constant, (b) *AP* is of any length.

14 *A*, *B*, *C* are fixed points such that angle *ABC* = 90°. Describe the locus of a point *P* such that (a) *ABCP* is a cyclic quadrilateral, (b) *ABCP* is a quadrilateral of constant area.

Constructions

A construction is an accurate geometrical drawing. The main instruments used are the compass and the straightedge, though it is normal practice in examinations for any instruments not explicitly forbidden to be allowed. All construction lines and arcs should be shown and not rubbed out. Accuracy is improved (a) by using a hard pencil, (b) by taking as large a radius as convenient for each circular arc. When graph paper is allowed, the lines on the paper can be used wherever appropriate. For example, all the lines on graph paper are either parallel or perpendicular, and this can sometimes avoid the necessity for constructing parallels or right angles. Also, if the graph paper is graduated in centimetres, any simple lengths in centimetres can be obtained from the paper rather than by using a ruler.

Basic techniques

The following elementary constructions require the use of an ungraduated straightedge and a compass only. The diagrams are almost self-explanatory and additional explanation is therefore kept to a minimum.

1 The bisector of an angle

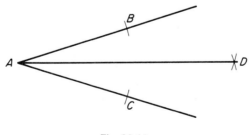

Fig. 30.11

The compass point is placed at *A*, then at *B* and *C*. Finally *A* and *D* are joined.

2a The perpendicular from a point to a line

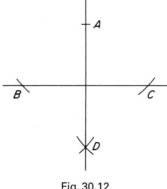

Fig. 30.12

A is the given point and *BC* is the given line. The compass point is placed at *A*, then at *B* and *C*.

2b Reflection

If the radius is kept the same throughout in construction 2, *D* is the image of *A* under reflection in the line. To obtain the image of a line, we construct the images of any two points on the line.

3 The perpendicular to a line from a point on the line

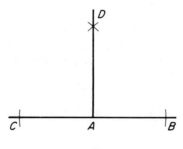

Fig. 30.13

This is simply the bisector of an angle of 180°.

By combining this construction with 1 we can construct angles of 45°, $22\frac{1}{2}°$, etc.

4 The perpendicular bisector (mediator) of a line-segment

Two arcs with centre *A* and two with centre *B* are drawn (Fig. 30.14).

This construction can be used (a) to find the mid-point of a line-segment, (b) to find a centre of rotation, given two successive positions of a line-segment (see chapter 27).

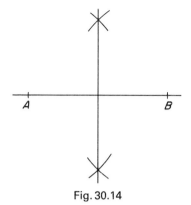

Fig. 30.14

5 An angle equal to a given angle

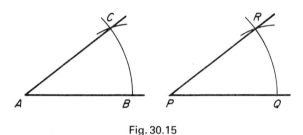

Fig. 30.15

We start with the given angle *BAC* and a point *P* on a line at which an equal angle is required.

The compass point is placed at *A* and then at *P*, and equal arcs are drawn. Then the point is placed at *B*, and a radius of *BC* is obtained. Finally the point is placed at *Q*, and an arc of equal radius is drawn to give *R*. Angle *QPR* is equal to angle *BAC*.

6a A line parallel to a given line through a given point

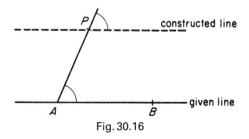

Fig. 30.16

A line through *P* parallel to *AB* can be obtained by using construction 5 to construct an angle at *P* corresponding to angle *PAB*. (Alternate angles can also be used.) The method involving sliding a set-square along a straightedge is quicker, however, and should be used unless disallowed.

6b A line parallel to a given line at a given distance from the line

Fig. 30.17

With the compass point at any two convenient points on the given line, two arcs are drawn, of radius the given distance. A line is then drawn linking the highest points of the arcs.

7 An angle of 60°

Effectively we construct an equilateral triangle:

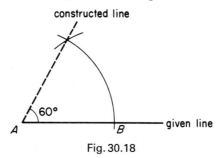

Fig. 30.18

AB is the radius of both arcs.

By combining this construction with 1 we can construct angles of 30°, 15°, etc.

8a Division of a line-segment into a given number of equal parts

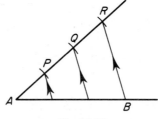

Fig. 30.19

To divide *AB* into three equal parts we draw another line through *A*, and using any convenient radius, mark off three equal lengths *AP*, *PQ*, *QR* with a compass. Then we join *B* and *R*, and construct parallel lines as shown in Fig. 30.19.

8b Division of a line-segment in a given ratio

To divide a line-segment in the ratio 3:2 (for example), we use the method of 8a to divide the segment into *five* equal parts, but only draw the required two parallels.

More complicated constructions involving the basic techniques

9 The circumscribed circle of a triangle

The circumscribed circle (or circumcircle) of a triangle *ABC* passes through *A*, *B* and *C*, and its centre is thus equidistant from these three points. The locus of all points equidistant from *A* and *B* is the mediator of *AB*; hence *the point of intersection of any two mediators* is equidistant from *A*, *B*, and *C* and is thus the circumcentre of the triangle (Fig. 30.20).

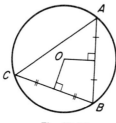

Fig. 30.20

O is the circumcentre of triangle *ABC*.

10 The inscribed circle of a triangle

The inscribed circle (or incircle) of a triangle touches all the three sides and therefore the centre is equidistant from the sides. Now all the points on the bisector of an internal angle are equidistant from the two sides containing the angle; hence *the point of intersection of two internal bisectors* is equidistant from all three sides (Fig. 30.21).

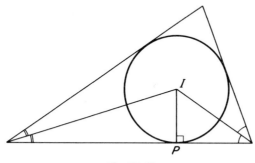

Fig. 30.21

To construct the incircle we bisect two internal angles and thus obtain the *incentre, I*. Then we drop a perpendicular (see construction 2) from *I* to any side of the triangle to obtain a point such as *P* above. Then *IP* is the radius of the required circle.

11 The tangent to a circle at a point on its circumference

Let *P* be the point on the circumference; then since the tangent at *P* is perpendicular to the radius *OP* we obtain the tangent by using construction 3 to draw a line through *P* perpendicular to *OP* (Fig. 30.22).

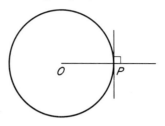

Fig. 30.22

12 A tangent from an external point to a circle

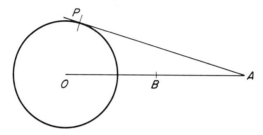

Fig. 30.23

The external point is *A*. The method is to use construction 4 to find the mid-point *B* of *OA*; then to draw an arc of the circle of centre *B* and radius *BA* to cut the given circle at *P*. Since *OA* is a diameter it subtends a right angle at *P*; hence *AP* is the required tangent.

13 A segment of a circle containing a given angle

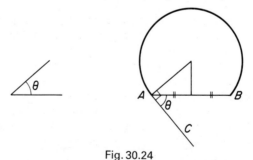

Fig. 30.24

We are given an angle θ (which could also be given numerically) and a line-segment *AB*. The task is to construct an arc at all points of which *AB* subtends an angle of θ. First we construct the angle *CAB* equal to θ (using a protractor if θ is given numerically), then the mediator of *AB* and the perpendicular to *AC* at *A*. These lines meet at the centre of the required arc. (The proof rests on the alternate segment theorem; *CA* is a tangent to the constructed arc.)

14 A triangle equal in area to a given quadrilateral

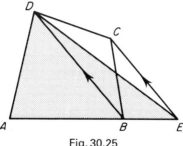

Fig. 30.25

The quadrilateral is *ABCD*. We draw the diagonal *DB* and construct the line through *C* parallel to *DB* to meet *AB* produced at *E*. Then *AED* (shaded) is the required triangle. This is because triangle *BDC* = triangle *BDE* (same base *DB*, same parallels) and if these are added in turn to triangle *ABD* we obtain the quadrilateral *ABCD* and the triangle *AED*.

15 A square equal in area to a given rectangle

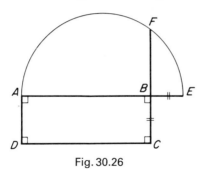

Fig. 30.26

ABCD is the given rectangle. We produce *AB* to *E*, where *BE* = *BC*, and construct the semicircle on *AE*. If *CB* produced meets the semicircle at *F*, *BF* is the side of the required square. The proof rests on the intersecting chord theorem: since the diameter *AE* bisects the chord *BF*, we have $AB.BE = BF^2$ and hence $AB.BC = BF^2$.

The last three of the above constructions are quite difficult. One of the best ways to learn them is to draw plenty of *rough* diagrams, in various positions, and think out the procedure each time. Once the procedure is learned it is relatively easy to perform an accurate construction.

Construction of geometrical figures from given numerical data

A *triangle* has a definite shape and size when a set of information of the form SSS, SAS, etc. is given, and it is then easy to construct the triangle using ruler, compass and protractor. When another kind of figure has to be constructed it is often necessary to begin by constructing a triangle, the standard properties of the figure being used to complete the construction.

The method should be planned out with the aid of a rough diagram before the accurate drawing is started.

▷ Example 1

Construct a rhombus ABCD in which AC = 8 cm and BD = 5 cm.
    The rough diagram, which is used to plan out the method, is shown in Fig. 30.27.

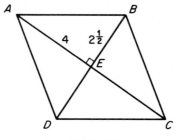

Fig. 30.27

Since the diagonals meet at right angles and bisect each other we have enough information to construct triangle *AEB*. The figure can be completed by producing *AE* 4 cm and *BE* $2\frac{1}{2}$ cm.   ◁

The use of loci in constructions

We have already seen that to locate either the circumcentre or the incentre of a triangle we find the point of intersection of two loci. This idea arises frequently in constructions, as the following examples show.

▷ Example 2

Draw two lines AB, BC meeting at 50°. Construct a point which is equidistant from the two lines and 3 cm from AB. Hence draw a circle of radius 3 cm which touches AB and BC.

Again we plan out the method with the help of a rough diagram (Fig. 30.28).

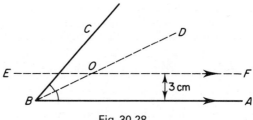

Fig. 30.28

The dotted line *BD*, which bisects angle *ABC*, is part of the locus of points equidistant from *AB* and *BC*, and *EF* is part of the locus of points 3 cm from *AB*. Hence both conditions are satisfied at the point of intersection *O*, and the circle of centre *O* with radius 3 cm clearly touches both *AB* and *BC*.

Notes:
(a) The line *EF* can be drawn by using construction 6b.
(b) After the point *O* has been obtained, it is essential to drop a perpendicular to either *BA* or *BC* before drawing the required circle. (See construction 10.) ◁

▷ Example 3

Draw lines AB, BC such that AB = 5 cm, BC = 7 cm and angle ABC = 60°. Construct the circle which passes through A and touches BC at C. Construct also a point D on this circle such that triangle BCD = triangle BCA.

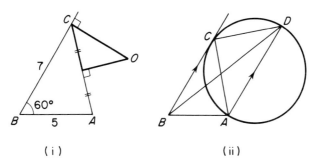

(i)   (ii)

Fig. 30.29

The required circle passes through *A* and *C*, and its centre is therefore on the mediator of *AC*. Also the centre of any circle which touches *BC* at *C* is on the perpendicular to *BC* at *C*. It follows that the required centre *O* is at the point of intersection of these lines (Fig. 30.29 (i)).

The locus of all points *P* such that triangle *BCP* = triangle *BCA* is a pair of lines parallel to *BC*. We require the line which intersects the circle, and this is shown in Fig. 30.29 (ii). In this diagram we have triangle *BCD* = triangle *BCA* (same base, *BC*, same parallels). ◁

EXERCISE 30b (easy constructions)

Protractors and graduated rulers should be used only to construct the given angles and lengths.

1 Draw a line of length 5 cm and divide it using a set square and a compass in the ratio 2:3. Check the accuracy by measurement.
2 Construct the circumcircle of a triangle with sides of 5 cm, 6 cm and 7 cm. Measure its radius.
3 Construct a parallelogram *ABCD* in which *AB* = 7 cm, *BC* = 5 cm and angle *ABC* = 70°. Measure *BD*.
4 Construct the incircle of a triangle with sides of 8 cm, 9 cm and 10 cm. Measure its radius.
5 Construct a parallelogram with a side of 6 cm and diagonals of 8 cm and 6 cm. Measure the other side.
6 Draw a circle of radius 3 cm and construct a tangent to it from a point 5 cm from the centre. Measure the length of the tangent and check the accuracy by Pythagoras' theorem.
7 Without using a protractor construct a triangle with angles of 30°, 60° and 90°. Check the accuracy with a protractor.

8 Construct a rhombus with diagonals of 7 cm and 6 cm. Measure the length of its side.

9 Construct an angle of 75° and check the accuracy with a protractor.

10 Construct a trapezium $ABCD$ in which AB is parallel to DC, $AB = 9$ cm, $BC = 5$ cm, $CD = 4$ cm, $DA = 3$ cm. Measure the distance apart of the parallels.

11 Draw a line AB of length 4 cm. Without using a protractor construct an arc of a circle at all points of which AB subtends an angle of 60°.

12 Without using a protractor construct a triangle ABC in which $AB = 7$ cm, $AC = 8$ cm and angle $A = 45°$. Construct also the internal bisector of angle A, letting it cut BC at D. Measure BD.

13 Construct the circumcircle of a triangle ABC in which $AB = 3$ cm, $BC = 5$ cm and angle $B = 100°$. Construct also a point D on the circle such that triangle $ABC =$ triangle BCD. Measure AD.

14 Draw a rectangle with length 7 cm and breadth 5 cm, and find by construction the length of the side of a square of equal area.

15 Draw a pair of lines meeting at 65° and construct a circle of radius 2 cm which touches them both.

16 Draw a line AB of length 6 cm and construct a circle of radius 4 cm which passes through A and B. Construct also the two points P and Q on this circle such that $\triangle ABP = \triangle ABQ = 15$ cm^2. Measure PQ.

17 Construct a quadrilateral $ABCD$ in which $AB = 8$ cm, angle $A =$ angle $B = 70°$, $BC = 6$ cm and $BD = 8.5$ cm. By using the diagonal BD and producing AB, construct a triangle ADE of equal area to the quadrilateral. Measure BE.

18 Draw lines AB, BC with $BC = 5$ cm and angle $ABC = 75°$. Construct two points P and Q, both of which are $2\frac{1}{2}$ cm from C and $3\frac{1}{2}$ cm from AB. Measure PQ.

19 Draw a triangle ABC in which $AB = 4.5$ cm, $BC = 5.8$ cm and angle $B = 90°$. Construct a point P which is equidistant from B and C and from AB and AC. Measure AP.

20 Draw lines AB, BC with $AB = 4$ cm, $BC = 3$ cm and angle $ABC = 90°$. Construct a circle which passes through A and touches BC at C. Measure its radius.

EXERCISE 30c (harder constructions)

Protractors and graduated rulers should be used only to construct the given angles and lengths.

1 Draw a triangle ABC in which $AB = 9$ cm, $BC = 4$ cm and angle $B = 70°$. Construct the circumcircle of the triangle and also the point D on the circle such that $DA = DB$ and angle $ADB =$ angle ACB. Measure BD.

2 Draw a triangle ABC in which $AB = 5$ cm, $BC = 8$ cm and $AC = 7$ cm. Construct the circumcircle of the triangle and the tangent to the circle at B. Construct also the point D on the tangent such that angle BCD is acute and triangle $ADB =$ triangle ACB. Measure BD.

3 Without using a protractor construct lines AB, BC such that angle $ABC = 120°$, $AB = 7.5$ cm and $BC = 9$ cm. Construct the circle which passes through A and touches BC at B, and also the other tangent to this circle from C. Let this tangent touch the circle at D, and measure AD.

4 Draw a triangle ABC in which $AB = 12$ cm, $AC = 9$ cm and angle $A = 65°$. Construct the incircle of the triangle, letting its centre be I and letting its points of contact with AB and AC be D and E respectively. Construct the two points P and Q inside the triangle which are such that angle $DPE =$ angle

$DQE = \frac{1}{2}$ angle DIE and P and Q are both 2 cm from BC. Measure PQ.

5 Draw a straight line and take a point P 6 cm from it. Construct a circle of radius 4 cm which passes through P and touches the line. Construct the tangent at P and let it meet the line at Q. Measure PQ.

6 Draw lines AB and BC with angle $ABC = 50°$ and $AB = 8$ cm. Construct (a) the locus of the centre of a circle which touches both lines and lies within the acute angle ABC, (b) the locus of the centre of a circle which touches AB at A. Hence construct the circle which touches AB at A and also touches BC. Measure its radius.

7 Take a point P 5 cm from a straight line. Draw the circle with centre P and radius 4 cm. Construct the two circles of radius 2 cm which touch this circle externally and also touch the line. Measure the distance apart of their centres and check the result by calculation.

8 Draw a line AB of length 10 cm and construct an arc at all points of which AB subtends an angle of 70°. On this arc construct a point C such that $AC = 6$ cm and a point D such that triangle $ABC =$ triangle ABD. Measure AD.

9 Draw a circle of radius 5 cm. Without using a protractor construct four points A, B, C, D which lie on the circle in this order and are such that $AC = 8$ cm, $AB = BC$ and angle $ABC = 2 \times$ angle ACD. Measure AD.

10 Draw lines AB, AC meeting at 90°, letting $AC = 8$ cm. Take a point D on AC such that $AD = 3$ cm and construct a circle to touch AB and pass through C and D. Let the point of contact with AB be E and construct a point F on the circle such that triangle $DEF =$ triangle DEC. Measure CF.

11 Draw a triangle ABC with $AB = 10$ cm, angle $A = 50°$ and angle $B = 60°$. Construct the point D on BC such that angle $ADB = 90°$ and also the point E on AC such that $AE = DE$. Measure BE.

12 Without using a protractor construct a quadrilateral $ABCD$ in which $AB = 6$ cm, $BD = 7$ cm, angle $ABD = 75°$, angle $BDC =$ angle BAD and C is equidistant from AB and AD. Measure AC.

13 Draw a triangle ABC in which $AB = AC = 7$ cm and angle $A = 100°$. Without further use of a protractor construct a point D such that $BD = 5$ cm and angle $ACB =$ angle ADB. Measure AD.

14 Draw circles of radii 2 cm and 3 cm with their centres 10 cm apart. Construct a circle of radius 6 cm which touches the smaller circle internally and the larger circle externally.

15 Draw a triangle ABC in which $AB = 5$ cm, $BC = 3$ cm and angle $B = 90°$. Construct the circle which passes through C and touches AB at A. Without using a protractor construct the point D such that angle $ADC =$ angle BAC and angle $DCA =$ angle ACB. Measure CD.

31 Right-Angled Triangles

Definitions of sine, cosine, tangent

The study of trigonometry usually begins with right-angled triangles, and is based on the idea that if one angle is given in addition to the right angle, the *shape* of the triangle is determined. This means that when one angle is given *the ratio of any pair of sides is fixed,* the value of the ratio depending on the value of the given angle.

The important ratios are known as the *sine* (sin), *cosine* (cos) and *tangent* (tan) of the given angle, and are defined as follows (see Fig. 31.1):

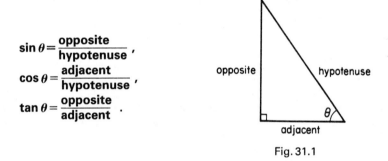

$$\sin \theta = \frac{\text{opposite}}{\text{hypotenuse}},$$

$$\cos \theta = \frac{\text{adjacent}}{\text{hypotenuse}},$$

$$\tan \theta = \frac{\text{opposite}}{\text{adjacent}}.$$

Fig. 31.1

The word SOHCAHTOA provides a popular method of memorising these definitions. The letters of this word stand for sine, opposite, hypotenuse, cosine, adjacent, etc.

Pythagoras' theorem

This theorem gives the relationship between the sides of a right-angled triangle (Fig. 31.2).

Pythagoras' theorem states that

$$a^2 + b^2 = c^2.$$

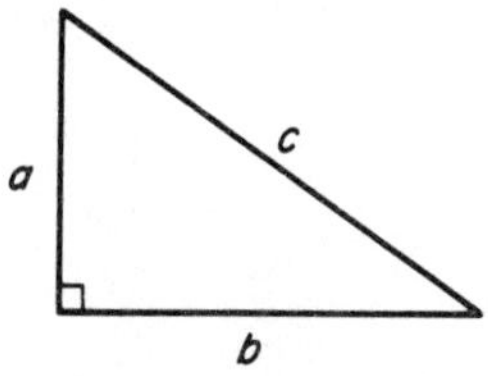

Fig. 31.2

The area of a right-angled triangle

The two short sides of a right-angled triangle can be regarded as the triangle's base and height, so the area of the triangle can be calculated easily if these sides are known. With the notation of Fig. 31.2 we have

$$A = \frac{1}{2}ab.$$

Inverse trigonometric functions

From the equation sin $30° = \frac{1}{2}$, it follows that $30°$ is *the angle whose sine is* $\frac{1}{2}$. There are two alternative symbols for 'the angle whose sine is', namely *sin*$^{-1}$ and *arc sin*. We shall use the latter symbol in this book, and thus write, for example, *$30° = arc\ sin\ \frac{1}{2}$*. In general, the two statements $y = \sin x$ and $x = arc \sin y$ are equivalent to each other.

From the theory of functions (chapter 20), we can see that if f is the function *sin,* then *arc sin* is the inverse function f^{-1}. Similarly *arc cos* and *arc tan* are the inverse functions of *cos* and *tan.*

It is important to realise that sin x is only meaningful if x is an angle, while arc sin x is only meaningful if x is a fraction or decimal such as 0.5.

▷Example 1

In Fig. 31.3, find x and y.

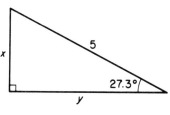

Fig. 31.3

To find x	*To find y*
$\sin 27.3° = \frac{x}{5}$	$\cos 27.3° = \frac{y}{5}$
$\therefore\ x = 5 \sin 27.3°$	$\therefore\ y = 5 \cos 27.3°$
$= 2.29$ to 3 s.f.	$= 4.44$ to 3 s.f.

▷Example 2

In Fig. 31.4, find AC and the area of the triangle.

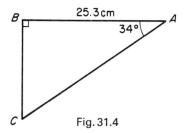

Fig. 31.4

To find AC	*To find the area*
$\cos 34° = \dfrac{25.3}{AC}$	$\tan 34° = \dfrac{BC}{25.3}$
$\therefore\ AC\cos 34° = 25.3$	$\therefore\ BC = 25.3\tan 34°$
$\therefore\ AC = \dfrac{25.3}{\cos 34°}$	$\therefore\ \text{area} = \frac{1}{2} \times 25.3 \times 25.3\tan 34°$
$= 30.5$ cm to 3 s.f.	$= 216$ cm^2 to 3 s.f.

◀

▶ Example 3

In Fig. 31.5, find BC and θ.

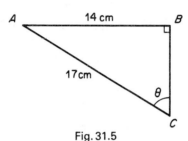

Fig. 31.5

To find BC	*To find θ*
By Pythagoras,	$\sin \theta = \dfrac{14}{17}$
$BC^2 = 17^2 - 14^2$	
$= 289 - 196$	$\therefore\ \theta = \arcsin \dfrac{14}{17}$
$= 93$	
$\therefore\ BC = 9.64$ cm to 3 s.f.	$= 55.4°$ to 3 s.f.

◀

Right-angled triangles obtained by construction

Isosceles triangles

To deal with an isosceles triangle we *drop a perpendicular* to obtain two identical right-angled triangles.

▶ Example 4

ABC is a triangle (Fig. 31.6) in which AB = AC = 17 cm and angle A = 54°. Find BC.

Let $\dfrac{BC}{2} = x$, as shown (Fig. 31.6). Then we have

$$\sin 27° = \frac{x}{17}$$
$$\therefore\ x = 17\sin 27°$$
$$\therefore\ BC = 34\sin 27°$$
$$= 15.4 \text{ cm to 3 s.f.}$$

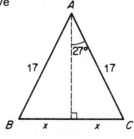

Fig. 31.6

◀

Since the *rhombus* can be regarded as a pair of isosceles triangles it can be treated in the same way.

▷Example 5

Find the angles of a rhombus of side 23 cm, one of whose diagonals is 14 cm.

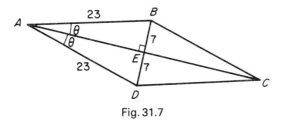

Fig. 31.7

From triangle *ABE (Fig. 31.7)* we have

$$\sin \theta = \frac{7}{23}$$

$$\therefore \quad \theta = \arcsin \frac{7}{23} = 17.72°$$

$$\therefore \quad \text{angle } BAD = 2\theta = 35.4° \text{ to 3 s.f.}$$

Also   angle $ABC = 180° - 35.4°$ (interior opposite angles)

$$= 144.6°,$$
$$= 145° \text{ to 3 s.f.} \qquad \blacktriangleleft$$

Trapeziums

The usual way to deal with a trapezium is to draw one or more perpendiculars from one of the parallel sides to the other.

▷Example 6

Fig. 31.8 shows an isosceles trapezium ABCD in which AB is parallel to DC, AB = 15 cm, AD = BC = 12 cm and angle D = angle C = 50°. Find the area of the trapezium.

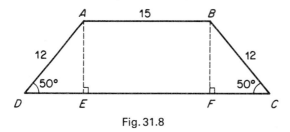

Fig. 31.8

We can find the area of the trapezium either by using the formula *average of parallel sides × height* or by adding the areas of the two triangles to that of the rectangle. For both methods we require *AE* and *DE.*

From triangle ADE we have $\sin 50° = \dfrac{AE}{12}$; hence $AE = 12 \sin 50° = 9.193$ cm to 4 s.f.

Similarly $DE = 12 \cos 50° = 7.713$ cm to 4 s.f.

$$\begin{aligned}
\text{Hence trapezium } ABCD &= 2 \text{ triangle } ADE + \text{rectangle } ABFE \\
&= (7.713 \times 9.193) + (15 \times 9.193) \\
&= 209 \text{ cm}^2 \text{ to 3 s.f.}
\end{aligned}$$ ◁

Other occurrences of right angles

In addition to those already mentioned, the following common occurrences of right-angles should be noted.
(1) The angles of a square or rectangle.
(2) The angle subtended by the diameter of a circle.
(3) The angle between a tangent and a radius.
(4) The angles in the isosceles triangles formed by radii or tangents. (These right angles are obtained by dropping perpendiculars.)

Standard notation for a triangle

The standard way to label a triangle (right-angled or otherwise) is to let the small letters *a, b, c* stand for the lengths of the sides opposite the vertices *A, B, C,* respectively:

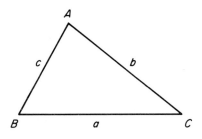

Fig. 31.9

This notation is used in the following exercise.

EXERCISE 31a

Give the answers to 3 s.f. When two answers are required, do not use the first answer to obtain the second unless this is essential.

Questions 1–12 refer to a triangle *ABC* with a right angle at *C*.
1 $c = 14$, angle $A = 65°$. Find a and b.
2 $c = 0.58$, angle $B = 27.3°$. Find a and b.
3 $a = 38.4$, angle $A = 70°$. Find b and c.
4 $a = 237.6$, angle $B = 80.6°$. Find b and c.
5 $a = 4$ cm, $b = 7$ cm. Find angle A and the area of the triangle.
6 $b = 2.8$ cm, $c = 4.9$ cm. Find a and the area of the triangle.

7 $a = 429, c = 673.2$. Find angle B and b.
8 $b = 0.07, c = 0.12$. Find angle A and a.
9 $a = 1.27$ m, $b = 83.4$ cm. Find c and the area of the triangle.
10 $a = 0.29, c = 0.47$. Find b and angle A.
11 $a = 2500, b = 3000$. Find c and angle B.
12 $b = 935$ m, angle $A = 68.4°$. Find c and the area of the triangle, working in kilometres.

Questions 13–17 refer to an isosceles triangle ABC in which $AB = AC$.
13 $c = 32, a = 26$. Find angle A.
14 $c = 15$, angle $A = 40.6°$. Find a.
15 Angle $A = 58°, a = 17$. Find c.
16 $c = 0.724$, angle $C = 67°$. Find a.
17 $c = 2043, a = 3598$. Find angle C.

18 $ABCD$ is a trapezium in which AB is parallel to DC, $AB = BC = AD = 10$ and angle $D = 60°$. Find CD.
19 $ABCD$ is a trapezium in which AB is parallel to DC, angle $B =$ angle $C = 90°$, angle $D = 80°$, $AB = 12$ and $CD = 17$. Find BC and AD.
20 $ABCD$ is a rhombus in which $AB = 25$ and $BD = 18$. Find angle A and AC.
21 $ABCD$ is a trapezium in which AB is parallel to DC, $AB = 104, DC = 193$ and angle $C =$ angle $D = 72°$. Find AD.
22 Find the area of a rhombus with diagonals of 18 cm and 12 cm.
23 Find the area of a rhombus with sides of 20 cm and a shorter diagonal of 14 cm.
24 ABC is a circle in which AB is a diameter, $AC = 17$ cm and angle $BAC = 29°$. Find the radius.
25 The tangents from a point A to a circle of centre O touch the circle at B and C. If the radius is 2 cm and angle $BAC = 50°$ what is the area of the kite $ABOC$?
26 $ABCD$ is a trapezium in which AB is parallel to DC, angle $A =$ angle $D = 90°, AB = 15, CD = 12$ and $AD = 14$. Find angle C and BC.
27 What angle is subtended at the centre of a circle of radius 8 cm by a chord of length 7 cm?
28 What angle is subtended at the circumference of a circle of diameter 15 cm by a chord of length 9 cm?

Special right-angled triangles

The 3, 4, 5 triangle

Since $3^2 + 4^2 = 5^2$, a triangle with sides of 3, 4 and 5 is right-angled by the converse of Pythagoras' theorem. This kind of triangle often arises in problems and it is important to be familiar with it. Triangles with sides of 6, 8 and 10, or 9, 12 and 15, or, more generally, $3k$, $4k$ and $5k$, are also regarded as 3,4,5 triangles.

Other triangles of a similar kind

There is an infinite number of different kinds of triangles in which the side-lengths a, b, c are integers and $a^2 + b^2 = c^2$. The 3,4,5 triangle is the simplest, but others worth remembering are those with sides of 5, 12, 13 and also 7, 24, 25 and 8, 15, 17.

The 30°, 60°, 90° triangle

If we bisect one of the angles of an equaliteral triangle we obtain two identical triangles with angles of 30°, 60° and 90°. It is convenient to let the sides of the equilateral triangle be 2 units in length since one of them is bisected (Fig. 31.10).

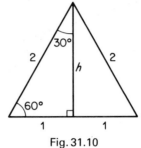

Fig. 31.10

From the right-angled triangle shown we have immediately

$$\sin 30° = \cos 60° = \tfrac{1}{2}.$$

This result should be known by heart. The other trigonometric ratios for 30° and 60° (which are treated as standard results in *A*-level courses) can be obtained by using Pythagoras' theorem to calculate the height of the triangle:

$$h^2 = 2^2 - 1^2 = 3$$
$$\therefore \ h = \sqrt{3}.$$

It follows that $\sin 60° = \cos 30° = \dfrac{\sqrt{3}}{2}$, $\tan 30° = \dfrac{1}{\sqrt{3}}$ and $\tan 60° = \sqrt{3}$.

The right-angled isosceles triangle (Fig. 31.11)

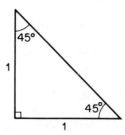

Fig. 31.11

From this triangle we obtain immediately

$$\tan 45° = 1,$$

which should be learned by heart. Since, by Pythagoras, the hypotenuse is $\sqrt{2}$, we also have $\sin 45° = \cos 45° = \dfrac{1}{\sqrt{2}}$.

Deducing one trigonometric ratio from another

If we are given a trigonometric ratio as a simple fraction — for example, $\sin \theta = \frac{1}{3}$ — we can deduce values for the other ratios by drawing a right-angled triangle and using Pythagoras' theorem (Fig. 31.12).

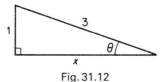

Fig. 31.12

By Pythagoras we have $x^2 = 9 - 1 = 8$; hence $x = \sqrt{8}$ or $2\sqrt{2}$. It follows that $\cos \theta = \frac{2\sqrt{2}}{3}$ and that $\tan \theta = \frac{1}{2\sqrt{2}}$.

Often the triangle drawn is one of the special kinds of triangle considered above. Suppose, for example, that $\cos \theta = 0.28$. Expressing this as a fraction we have $\frac{28}{100} = \frac{7}{25}$, and this means that the triangle to be drawn is a 7, 24, 25 triangle (Fig. 31.13)

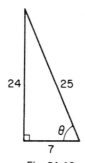

Fig. 31.13

It follows that $\sin \theta = \frac{24}{25}$ (or 0.96) and $\tan \theta = \frac{24}{7}$ or $3\frac{3}{7}$.

When special right-angled triangles occur in problems, the use of tables or calculators can often be avoided.

▷ Example 7

In Fig. 31.14, angle BAC = 45° and angle BAD = arc sin 0.8. Find CD.

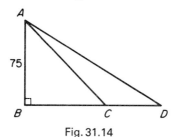

Fig. 31.14

The method is to use triangles *ABC, ABD* to obtain *BC* and *BD,* and then subtract. Since triangle *ABC* is a right-angled isosceles triangle we have immediately *BC* = 75. To obtain *BD* we need tan *BAD,* and since sin $BAD = \frac{8}{10} = \frac{4}{5}$, we can deduce the value of tan *BAD* by drawing a 3,4,5 triangle (Fig. 31.15).

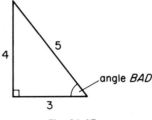

Fig. 31.15

Clearly tan $BAD = \frac{4}{3}$, and we can therefore proceed as follows.

$$\tan BAD = \frac{BD}{75}$$
$$\therefore \ BD = 75 \tan BAD$$
$$= 75 \times \frac{4}{3}$$
$$= 100.$$

It follows that $CD = 100 - 75 = 25$.   ◄

EXERCISE 31b

Do not use tables or a calculator in this exercise. Where appropriate, leave answers in terms of square roots.

1 $\sin \theta = \frac{5}{13}$. Find $\cos \theta$ and $\tan \theta$.

2 $\tan \theta = 2$. Find $\sin \theta$ and $\cos \theta$.

3 $\cos \theta = 0.6$. Find $\sin \theta$ and $\tan \theta$.

4 $\sin \theta = \frac{1}{\sqrt{5}}$. Find $\cos \theta$ and $\tan \theta$.

5 $\tan \theta = 1\frac{7}{8}$. Find $\sin \theta$ and $\cos \theta$.

6 $\cos \theta = \frac{\sqrt{7}}{4}$. Find $\sin \theta$ and $\tan \theta$.

7 *ABC* is a triangle in which angle $B = 90°$, angle $A = $ arc tan 2.4 and $AC = 195$ cm. Find *AB*.

8 *ABC* is a circle in which *AB* is a diameter, $AC = 9$ cm and angle $B = 30°$. Find the radius.

9 *ABC* is a triangle in which angle $C = 90°$, angle $B = $ arc sin $\frac{8}{17}$ and $BC = 60$ cm. Find *AB*.

10 *ABC* is a triangle in which angle $B = 90°$, $\sin C = 0.8$ and $BC = 30$ cm. Find the area of the triangle.

11 The sides of a rhombus *ABCD* are all 15 cm and angle $BDC = $ arc tan 0.75. Find *AC* and *BD*.

12 ABC is a triangle of area 25 cm² in which angle $C = 90°$ and tan $A = 2$. Find BC.

13 $ABCD$ is a trapezium in which angle B = angle $C = 90°$, angle A = arc tan 2, $AB = 15$ cm and $CD = 9$ cm. Find BC.

14 ABC is a triangle in which D is the foot of the perpendicular from A to BC. Angle B = arc sin $\frac{12}{13}$, angle $C = 45°$ and $BD = 10$ cm. Find CD.

15 $ABCD$ is a trapezium in which $AB = AD = BC = 10$ cm and angle C = angle D = arc tan $1\frac{1}{3}$. Find CD.

16 Find the side of rhombus with a diagonal of 10 cm and an area of 120 cm².

17 Find the length of a chord which subtends an angle of arc tan 2.4 at the circumference of a circle of radius 65 cm.

18 ABC is a triangle in which angle $B = 90°$, $AC = 1$ m and $BC = 60$ cm. D is a point on AB such that tan $BDC = 1.2$. Find AD.

19 A triangle ABC of area 270 cm² has a right angle at B, and angle A = arc sin $\frac{5}{\sqrt{34}}$. Find AB.

20 B and C are the points of contact of the tangents from a point A to a circle of centre O. $AB = 16$ cm and the area of the quadrilateral $ABOC$ is 192 cm². Find AO.

21 ABC is a triangle in which $AC = 30$ cm, sin $B = \frac{4}{7}$ and sin $C = \frac{2}{3}$. Find AB. (Drop a perpendicular.)

22 $ABCD$ is a rhombus in which $BD = 35$ cm and angle ABD = arc sin 0.96. Find AB and AC.

23 $ABCD$ is a quadrilateral in which angle ABD = angle BCD = 90°, $CD = 15$ cm, angle $CBD = 30°$ and angle ADB = arc sin $\frac{\sqrt{7}}{4}$. Find AD.

24 ABC is a triangle in which $AB = 12$ cm, angle $B = 90°$ and angle C = arc cos 0.8. D is a point on BC such that angle ADB = arc cos $\frac{1}{\sqrt{5}}$. Find AC and CD.

Practical applications involving right-angled triangles

Bearings

Bearings are measurements of *direction*. A bearing of zero indicates the direction *due north*, and the bearing of any other direction is the angle between the direction and due north, measured clockwise from due north.

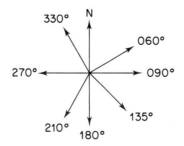

Fig. 31.16

In stating a bearing it is usual to give three figures; thus for example the direction *due east* is indicated in Fig. 31.16 by the bearing 090°. It is sufficiently accurate for most purposes to give bearings to the nearest degree.

There are two commonly used expressions involving bearings which it is important to understand, namely *travelling on a bearing* and *the bearing of one point from another.* The first presents no problems; for example a ship which is sailing south-west could be said to be sailing *on a bearing of 225°* (Fig. 31.17).

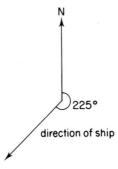

Fig. 31.17

Now suppose that *the bearing of a point A from a point B is 070°.* Here we work from *B* (not *A*) and measure 70° clockwise from due north. This gives the direction of *A* (Fig. 31.18).

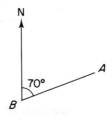

Fig. 31.18

If we require the bearing of *B* from *A* we work from *A* (Fig. 31.19).

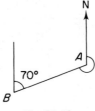

Fig. 31.19

The reflex angle shown is 360° − 110° = 250°, and this is the bearing of *B* from *A*.

The nautical mile and the knot

The nautical mile (n.m.) is a unit which is often used in navigation, and it therefore arises frequently in problems involving bearings. The nautical mile is about 6080 feet, and thus somewhat greater than the ordinary or statute mile which is 5280 feet. The *knot* is a unit of *speed* and is equal to 1 nautical mile per hour.

▷**Example 8**

A ship sails at 30 knots for 3 hours on a bearing of 280° from a point A to a point B. It then turns through a clockwise angle of 90° and sails at 25 knots for 4 hours, finally reaching a point C. Find (a) the distance AC, (b) the bearing of C from A, (c) how far C is to the west of A.

Since knots = n.m./h, the ship sails $3 \times 30 = 90$ n.m. in the first 3 hours and $4 \times 25 = 100$ n.m. in the next four hours.

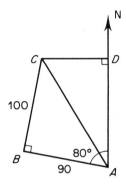

Fig. 31.20

(a) Using Pythagoras' theorem we have $AC = \sqrt{90^2 + 100^2} = 134.5$ n.m. or 135 n.m. to 3 s.f.
(b) The bearing of C from A is the reflex angle *DAC*. To calculate this we begin by finding angle *BAC*:

$$\tan BAC = \frac{100}{90}$$
$$\therefore \text{ angle } BAC = \arctan \frac{100}{90} = 48.01°.$$

Now we have

$$\text{angle } DAC = 80° - 48.01° = 31.99°$$

and hence

$$\text{reflex angle } DAC = 360° - 31.99°$$
$$= 328° \text{ to 3 s.f.}$$

(c) The required distance is *CD*, and we find this by working on the right-angled triangle *ACD*:

$$\sin DAC = \frac{CD}{AC}$$
$$\therefore\ CD = AC \sin DAC$$
$$= 134.5 \sin 31.99°$$
$$= 71.3 \text{ n.m. to 3 s.f.} \qquad \triangleleft$$

Angles of elevation and depression

Suppose that an observer *O* looks at a point *P* which is at a different horizontal level from himself. If *P* is above *O*, the angle between *OP* and the horizontal is called the *angle of elevation of P from O*, and if *P* is below *O* this angle is called the *angle of depression of P from O* (Fig. 31.21).

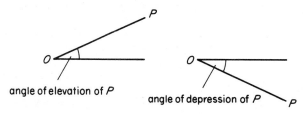

angle of elevation of *P*   angle of depression of *P*

Fig. 31.21

It is essential to remember that both angles are between a direction and the *horizontal*.

▷ Example 9

A point O at ground level is 5 m from a wall containing a window. The angles of elevation from O of the bottom and top of the window are 20° and 28°. What is the vertical length of the window?

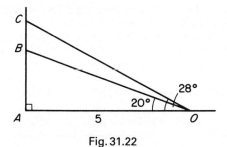

Fig. 31.22

We require *BC* (Fig. 31.22), and the method is to use the two right-angled triangles *OAB* and *OAC* to obtain *AB* and *AC*. We then find *BC* by subtracting.

$$\text{Using triangle } OAB, \quad \tan 20° = \frac{AB}{5}$$
$$\therefore\ AB = 5 \tan 20°$$
$$= 1.820 \text{ m.}$$

Using triangle OAC, $\tan 28° = \dfrac{AC}{5}$

$$\therefore \ AC = 5\tan 28°$$
$$= 2.659 \text{ m.}$$

It follows that the vertical length of the window, BC, is $2.659 - 1.820 = 0.839$ m to 3 s.f.   ◀

EXERCISE 31c

When a bearing is required, it should be given to the nearest degree. Otherwise answers should be given to 3 s.f., as usual.

1 A man walks 8 km due east, then 5 km due north. Find his final distance and bearing from the starting point.

2 From a point on the ground which is 15 m from the foot of a vertical building, the angle of elevation of the top of a building is 53°. Find the height of the building.

3 A boat is 75 m from a cliff of height 50 m. What is the angle of depression of the boat from the top of the cliff?

4 The bearing of A from B is 140°. What is the bearing of B from A?

5 A ship sails at 20 knots for 3 hours on a bearing of 040°. How far is it then to the east of the starting point?

6 A car which is initially 20 miles due north of a town T travels 30 miles due east. What is its final bearing from T?

7 A man walks from a point P on a bearing of 030°. What is his shortest distance from a point which is 50 m due north of P?

8 An aeroplane flies 400 km on a bearing of 290°, then 100 km due east. How far west of the starting point is its final position?

9 A picture hanging on a wall has a vertical length of 80 cm. From a point on the ground which is 2 m from the foot of the wall, the angle of elevation of the bottom of the picture is 44°. What is the angle of elevation of the top of the picture?

10 A man is 4 km from his house on a bearing of 270° from it. If he travels 7 km due south what is his new bearing from the house?

11 From the top of a building 30 m high a man sees two people, both due east of him, with angles of depression of 52° and 47°. How far apart are they?

12 A ship sailing at 12 knots on a bearing of 312° observes a lighthouse on a bearing of 270°. Three hours later the bearing of the lighthouse is 180°. Find (a) the final distance of the ship from the lighthouse, (b) their shortest distance apart.

13 A man looks at a point 5 m above the level of his eye whose angle of elevation from his eye is 32°. He walks towards the point until the angle of elevation is 54°. How far does he walk?

14 The bearing of a ship from a port P, 50 n.m. away, is 320°. The ship sails on a bearing of 060° until it is due north of P. How far is it then from P?

15 Two points A and B are 12 m apart on the same horizontal level. A point P lies between A and B, 6 m below them in the same vertical plane. If the angle of depression of P from A is 37°, what is the angle of depression of P from B?

16 The distance and bearing of an aeroplane from a point P are 120 km and 054°. If the plane flies due west at 600 km h^{-1} for 15 minutes, what will be its final distance and bearing from P?

17 A boy in a tree 16 m above the ground sees a friend walking towards the tree at 0.8 m s^{-1}. If the friend is initially 24 m from the tree, how long does it take, to the nearest second, for his angle of depression from the boy in the tree to become 60°?

18 From a certain point on the ground, the angle of elevation of the top of a tree 20 m high is 30°. What is the angle of elevation from a point twice as far from the tree?

19 A ship sails at 35 knots on a bearing of 045°, then turns through an anticlockwise angle of 90° and sails at the same speed until it reaches a point 120 n.m. due north of its starting point. How long does the complete journey take, to the nearest minute?

20 A ladder inclined at 60° to the horizontal reaches a point 7 m up a vertical wall. How far must the base be moved inwards to make the top reach a point 8 m high?

21 ABC is a horizontal triangle in which $AB = 18$ m, $BC = 17$ m and $CA = 13$ m; and BP and CQ are vertical posts whose feet are at B and C. If the angles of elevation of P and Q from A are 32° and 24° respectively, what is the angle of elevation of P from Q?

22 AP is a vertical post, of height 4 m, with its foot A on the ground. From points B and C on the ground, which are respectively due west and due south of the post, the angles of elevation of P are 25° and 40°. Find BC and the bearing of C from B.

23 From the top of a lighthouse L, of height 35 m, a boat is sighted on a bearing of 240° with an angle of depression of 15°. If the boat sails due east, find (a) its angle of depression when it is at its closest point to L, (b) the distance it has travelled when its angle of depression is 10°.

32 General Definitions of Sine, Cosine, Tangent

To extend the application of trigonometry beyond right-angled triangles we need definitions of sine, cosine and tangent which apply to all angles and not just those which are acute. The more general definitions are designed in such a way that when the angle *is* acute, the old definitions in terms of the sides of a right-angled triangle are still valid.

The new definitions involve an *x*-axis and a *y*-axis. Consider an arm *OP* of length *r* which can rotate about the origin *O*. Let the arm start along the positive *x*-axis and rotate anticlockwise through an angle of θ (Fig. 32.1).

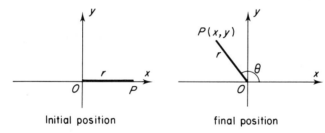

Initial position   final position

Fig. 32.1

(The arm is considered to turn through a positive angle when it rotates anticlockwise, and a negative angle when it rotates clockwise.)

Letting the end *P* of the arm be the point (x, y), as shown, we now define the sine, cosine and tangent of the angle θ as follows:

$$\sin\theta = \frac{y}{r} \qquad \cos\theta = \frac{x}{r} \qquad \tan\theta = \frac{y}{x}$$

Let us consider what these definitions mean. It is easy to see that when θ is acute, the definitions reduce to the ones we used earlier in terms of opposite, hypotenuse, etc. This is because the lengths *x*, *y* and *r* can be regarded as the adjacent, opposite and hypotenuse in a right-angled triangle (Fig. 32.2).

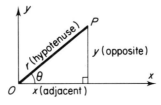

Fig. 32.2

It can be seen from Fig. 32.2 that the new definition of sine $\left(\dfrac{y}{r}\right)$ gives the same result as the one we used previously $\left(\dfrac{\text{opposite}}{\text{hypotenuse}}\right)$.

To show what the new definitions amount to when θ is not acute, let us take an example. Suppose that θ is 140° (Fig. 32.3).

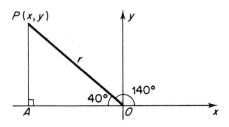

Fig. 32.3

The definition of $\sin\theta$ is $\dfrac{y}{r}$, and $\sin 140°$ is thus $\dfrac{AP}{OP}$. (Note that y is *positive* with the above position of P.) Now $\dfrac{AP}{OP}$ is simply $\dfrac{\text{opposite}}{\text{hypotenuse}}$ for the angle of 40° in the right-angled triangle OAP, and we therefore have

$$\sin 140° = \sin 40°.$$

The definition of $\cos\theta$ is $\dfrac{x}{r}$, and since $x = -OA$, $\cos 140° = -\dfrac{OA}{OP}$, that is $-\dfrac{\text{adjacent}}{\text{hypotenuse}}$ for the angle of 40° in the triangle OAP. Hence

$$\cos 140° = -\cos 40°.$$

Finally since $\tan\theta = \dfrac{y}{x}$, $\tan 140° = -\dfrac{AP}{OA} = -\dfrac{\text{opposite}}{\text{adjacent}}$ for the angle of 40°. Hence

$$\tan 140° = -\tan 40°.$$

The example illustrates the general fact that the sine, cosine or tangent of a non-acute angle is *numerically* the same as the sine, cosine or tangent of the acute angle between the arm and the x-axis, and that it is only the *sign* of the ratio which has to be decided by considering x and/or y. The following procedure can be used to deal with any angle:

(1) Find the acute angle between the arm and the x-axis.
(2) Take the sine, cosine or tangent of this angle.
(3) Insert a positive or negative sign according to the following rules: sin depends on y, cos depends on x, tan depends on both x and y.

▷**Example 1**

Find cos 240°.
The position of the arm is as shown in Fig. 32.4.

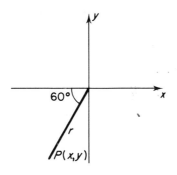

Fig. 32.4

The acute angle between the arm and the x-axis is clearly 60°; hence cos 240° is *numerically* equal to cos 60°. To determine the sign we note that cos is defined as $\frac{x}{r}$ and thus has the same sign as x. (r is just the length of the arm, and is always positive). Since x is negative in Fig. 32.4 we have

$$\cos 240° = - \cos 60° = - 0.5.$$ ◁

▷**Example 2**

Find tan 335°.
The position of the arm is as shown in Fig. 32.5.

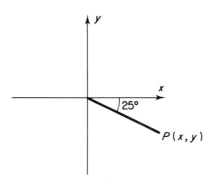

Fig. 32.5

Clearly tan 335° is numerically equal to tan 25°. Since $\tan \theta = \frac{y}{x}$, the sign of tan depends on both x and y, and in Fig. 32.5 x is positive and y is negative. Hence tan 335° is negative and we have

$$\tan 335° = - \tan 25° = - 0.466 \text{ to 3 s.f.}$$ ◁

Here are some more examples:

Second quadrant	**Third quadrant**	**Fourth quadrant**
$\sin 160° = + \sin 20°$	$\sin 230° = - \sin 50°$	$\sin 300° = - \sin 60°$
$\cos 110° = - \cos 70°$	$\cos 200° = - \cos 20°$	$\cos 310° = + \cos 50°$
$\tan 100° = - \tan 80°$	$\tan 240° = + \tan 60°$	$\tan 320° = - \tan 40°$

It will be noticed that each of the ratios sin, cos and tan is positive in *one* quadrant other than the first. An alternative to the above method of deciding the signs of the ratios is simply to learn by heart the quadrant in which each particular ratio is positive. A popular method of doing this is to place the letters of the word CAST in the positions shown in Fig. 32.6.

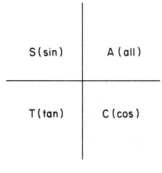

Fig. 32.6

Now each letter tells us which ratio is *positive* in the quadrant in which it stands.

Angles of 0°, 90°, 180°, 270°

When the rotating arm is in one of the horizontal or vertical positions it makes angles of 0°, 90°, 180°, 270°, etc. with the positive x-axis. We shall now show that the trigonometric ratios of these angles have the special values 0, ±1, or ∞.

Angles of 0° and 180°

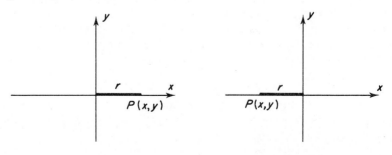

Fig. 32.7   Fig. 32.8

Since in Fig. 32.7, $x = r$ and $y = 0$, we have

$$\sin 0° = 0, \cos 0° = 1, \tan 0° = 0.$$

Since in Fig. 32.8, $x = -r$ and $y = 0$, we have

$$\sin 180° = 0, \cos 180° = -1,$$
$$\tan 180° = 0.$$

Angles of 90° and 270°

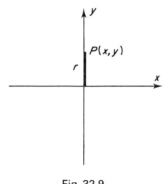

Fig. 32.9   Fig. 32.10

Since in Fig. 32.9, $x = 0$ and $y = r$, we have

$$\sin 90° = 1, \cos 90° = 0,$$
$$\tan 90° = \infty.$$

Since in Fig. 32.10, $x = 0$ and $y = -r$, we have

$$\sin 270° = -1, \cos 270° = 0,$$
$$\tan 270° = \infty.$$

Note: 'Infinity' is not a proper number, and since $\tan 90° = \dfrac{r}{0}$ we should strictly say that $\tan 90°$ is meaningless or indeterminate. As the angle θ approaches 90°, however, $\tan \theta$ does become greater and greater without limit, and, '$\tan 90° = \infty$' can be regarded as a shorthand way of saying this.

The periodic nature of the trigonometric functions

A function $f(x)$ is said to be *periodic* if its value is unchanged whenever a certain definite quantity is added to the value of x. More briefly, $f(x)$ is periodic if $f(x + c) = f(x)$ and c is the smallest value for which this is true. The constant c is called the *period* of the function.

Now whenever 360° is added to the value of θ, the position of the rotating arm does not change and thus the values of $\sin \theta$ and $\cos \theta$ are unaltered. For example,

$$\sin 390° = \sin 30° = \tfrac{1}{2}.$$

It follows that the functions $\sin \theta$ and $\cos \theta$ are periodic with a period of 360°.

Since the value of $\tan \theta$ is unchanged when 180° is added to the value of θ, this function is periodic with the smaller period of 180°.

The importance of obtuse angles

In practical applications of trigonometry (such as are considered in the next chapter), angles between 90° and 180° occur rather often. It is therefore worth treating the following three results as standard and learning them by heart.

$$\sin \theta = \sin (180° - \theta),$$
$$\cos \theta = -\cos (180° - \theta),$$
$$\tan \theta = -\tan (180° - \theta).$$

For example, sin 160° = sin 20°, cos 160° = −cos 20°, tan 160° = −tan 20°.

▷ Example 3

θ is an obtuse angle such that tan θ = −0.75. Find (a) tan(180° − θ), (b) sin θ, (c) cos θ.

(a) The sine, cosine and tangent of the obtuse angle θ are *numerically* equal to the sine, cosine and tangent of the acute angle 180° − θ, and all the trigonometric ratios of an acute angle are positive. Hence

$$\tan(180° - \theta) = 0.75.$$

(b) First we draw a right-angled triangle containing the acute angle 180° − θ. Since tan(180° − θ) = 0.75, we can let the opposite and adjacent sides be 3 and 4, respectively (Fig. 32.11).

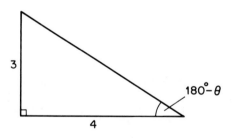

Fig. 32.11

Clearly the hypotenuse is 5, so $\sin(180° - \theta) = \dfrac{3}{5}$. Since sin θ = sin(180° − θ), it follows that $\sin \theta = \dfrac{3}{5}$.

(c) From Fig. 32.11 it follows that $\cos(180° - \theta) = \dfrac{4}{5}$, and cos θ = −cos(180° − θ).

$$\text{Hence } \cos \theta = -\frac{4}{5}. \qquad \blacktriangleleft$$

The final example in this chapter deals with a *trigonometric equation* in which the unknown quantity is an angle.

▷**Example 4**

Solve the equation cos θ = −0.64, for the range 0° ≤ θ ≤ 360°.

First we use trigonometric tables or a calculator to find the *acute* angle whose cosine is 0.64. This is 50.2° to 3 s.f. Next we determine the quadrants in which cos θ is negative. Since cos θ depends upon *x* for its sign, it is negative in the second and third quadrants. Now 50.2° has to be the acute angle between the rotating arm and the *x*-axis; hence the arm can be in either of the two positions shown in Fig. 32.12.

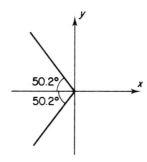

Fig. 32.12

It follows that θ (which is the angle between the arm and the *positive* x-axis) can have either of the values 180° − 50.2° and 180° + 50.2°. That is, θ = 130° or 230° to 3 s.f.   ◁

EXERCISE 32

Do not use tables or a calculator for questions 1–29.

In questions 1–12, express the given quantities in terms of acute angles.
1 sin 200°   **2** cos 300°   **3** tan 130°   **4** cos 205°   **5** sin 285°   **6** tan 218°
7 sin 104°   **8** cos 98°   **9** tan 323°   **10** cos 247°   **11** sin 198°   **12** cos 289°

In questions 13–16, state which quadrant θ lies in.
13 sin θ is positive, cos θ is negative.
14 tan θ is positive, sin θ is negative.
15 tan θ is negative, cos θ is positive.
16 sin θ is negative, cos θ is negative.

17 Given that $\sin \theta = \frac{5}{13}$ and θ is acute, find cos(180° − θ).
18 Given that cos θ = − 0.6 and θ is obtuse, find sin θ and tan θ.
19 Given that sin 60° = 0.87, find sin 240° and sin 300°.
20 Given that cos 28° = 0.88, find cos 152° and cos 332°.
21 Given that tan 320° = −0.84, find tan 220°.
22 Given that sin 40° = 0.64, find sin 140° and sin 320°.
23 Given that cos 205° = − 0.91, find cos 335°.
24 *x* and *y* are adjacent angles on a straight line. Given that $\cos y = \frac{7}{25}$, find sin *x* and tan *x*.

25 *ABCD* is a parallelogram. Given that $\tan B = -\dfrac{5}{12}$, find $\sin D$ and $\cos A$.

26 *ABCD* is a cyclic quadrilateral in which $\cos C = \dfrac{8}{17}$. Find $\tan A$ and $\sin A$.

27 *ABC* is a triangle with a right angle at *B*, and *D* is a point on *BC* such that $\tan DAB = 1\frac{1}{3}$. Find $\cos ADC$.

28 *ABCD* is a parallelogram in which *E* is the foot of the perpendicular from *D* to *AB*. $AD = 68$ cm and $\tan ADC = -1\frac{7}{8}$. Find *AE*.

29 *ABC* is a triangle with a right angle at *B*, and *D* is the mid-point of *BC*. Given that $AB = 9$ cm and angle $ADC =$ arc sin 0.6, find *BC*.

In questions 30–40, solve the equations (to 3 s.f. where appropriate) for the range $0° \leqslant \theta \leqslant 360°$.

30 $\sin \theta = -0.5$ **31** $\cos \theta = 0$ **32** $\tan \theta = 3$ **33** $\tan \theta = 0$

34 $\cos \theta = -0.47$ **35** $\sin \theta = -1$ **36** $\tan \theta = -1.8$ **37** $\cos \theta = 1$

38 $\sin \theta = 0.35$ **39** $\cos \theta = 0.73$ **40** $\tan \theta = 1$.

33 The General Triangle

A triangle is fixed in shape and size when one of the sets of three pieces of information of the form SSS, SAS, etc. is given. Finding the other three sides and angles is known as *solving* the triangle, and if the triangle is not right-angled or isosceles this process requires the use of two formulae called the *sine formula* and the *cosine formula.*

The sine formula

The triangle *ABC* is lettered in the standard way, with *a, b, c* standing for the lengths of the sides opposite the vertices *A, B, C*. To prove the sine formula we put in any altitude, letting its length be *h* (Fig. 33.1).

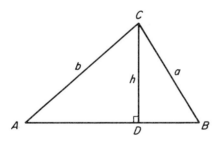

Fig. 33.1

From triangle *ADC*, $\sin A = \dfrac{h}{b}$; hence $h = b \sin A$.

From triangle *BDC*, $\sin B = \dfrac{h}{a}$; hence $h = a \sin B$.

It follows that $a \sin B = b \sin A$, and thus that

$$\frac{a}{\sin A} = \frac{b}{\sin B}.$$

By drawing another altitude we can prove that either of these expressions is equal to $\dfrac{c}{\sin C}$; hence we have

$$\frac{a}{\sin A} = \frac{b}{\sin B} = \frac{c}{\sin C}.$$

This is the sine formula. It is often needed in its inverted form, and can also be stated in this way:

$$\frac{\sin A}{a} = \frac{\sin B}{b} = \frac{\sin C}{c}$$

The sine formula is applicable when the information given about a triangle includes *a side and the angle opposite to it*. In particular, it is applicable when the given information has the AAS form, as in the following example.

▷Example 1

In the triangle shown in Fig. 33.2, find x.

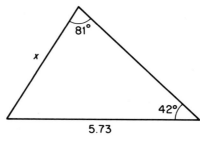

5.73

Fig. 33.2

By the sine formula we have

$$\frac{x}{\sin 42°} = \frac{5.73}{\sin 81°}$$
$$\therefore x = \frac{5.73 \sin 42°}{\sin 81°}$$
$$= 3.88 \text{ to } 3 \text{ s.f.} \quad \triangleleft$$

In the next example the information given has the SSA form. It will be remembered from chapter 26 (dealing with congruence) that two sides and a non-included angle do not in general prove two triangles to be congruent or fix the size and shape of a single triangle. However, more than one triangle cannot *always* be constructed from information of the SSA form, and in particular when the given angle is obtuse only one triangle is possible. The following example illustrates this.

▷Example 2

In Fig. 33.3 find θ.

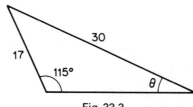

Fig. 33.3

By the sine formula we have

$$\frac{\sin\theta}{17} = \frac{\sin 115°}{30}$$

$$\therefore \;\; \sin\theta = \frac{17\sin 115°}{30}\left(= \frac{17\sin 65°}{30}\right)$$

$$= 0.5136$$

$$\therefore \;\; \theta = \arcsin 0.5136.$$

We see now how the possibility of two different triangles can sometimes arise. This equation has *two* solutions of less than 180°, one in the first quadrant and one in the second. It is only because this particular triangle already has one obtuse angle that the higher value of θ can be rejected. We have in fact

$$\theta = 30.9° \text{ to 3 s.f.}$$

Note: The step in which sin 115° is replaced by sin 65° (shown in brackets above) is not essential if calculators with trigonometric functions are being used. Books of tables, however, normally only give acute angles.   ◀

EXERCISE 33a

In questions 1–5 find the quantities indicated by letters.

1

2

3

4

5

The remaining questions refer to a triangle ABC.

6 $a = 37$ cm, angle $B = 66°$, angle $C = 59°$. Find b and c.

7 $b = 9.83$ cm, angle $B = 116°$, angle $C = 28°$. Find a and c.

8 $b = 1.6$ cm, $c = 8.7$ mm, angle $B = 130°$. Find angle C.

9 $a = 93$ cm, $c = 1.2$ m, angle $C = 104°$. Find angle A.

10 $b = 87$ cm, $a = 1.5$ m, angle $A = 140°$. Find angle B.

The cosine formula

This formula can be regarded as an extension of Pythagoras' theorem to non-right-angled triangles. It is proved by using Pythagoras' theorem.

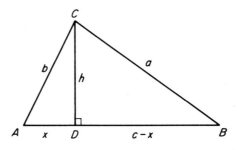

Fig. 33.4

Applying Pythagoras' theorem to triangle BDC (Fig. 33.4) we have

$$a^2 = h^2 + (c - x)^2$$
$$= h^2 + c^2 + x^2 - 2cx.$$

But from triangle ADC we have $h^2 + x^2 = b^2$ and also $x = b\cos A$. Hence

$$a^2 = b^2 + c^2 - 2bc\cos A$$

This is the first form of the cosine formula. This form can also be stated in either of the following equivalent ways:

$$b^2 = c^2 + a^2 - 2ca\cos B$$
$$c^2 = a^2 + b^2 - 2ab\cos C$$

The first form of the cos formula is used when the information given is of the SAS kind, as illustrated by the next two examples.

▷ **Example 3**

In Fig. 33.5, find x.

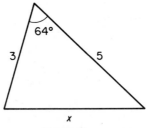

Fig. 33.5

By the cos formula we have

$$x^2 = 3^2 + 5^2 - (2 \times 3 \times 5\cos 64°)$$
$$= 34 - (30\cos 64°).$$

(The brackets are not essential but are put in to emphasise that the 30 must not be subtracted from the 34. This is a common mistake.)

$$\text{Hence } x^2 = 20.85$$
$$\therefore \ x = 4.57 \text{ to 3 s.f.}$$

Notes
(1) It is important to learn to write down the first step in this kind of question without reference to the general cos formula in terms of *a, b, c,* etc. This can easily be done with practice on numerical examples.
(2) If we need to solve the above triangle fully, we use the sine formula to find one of the two unknown angles. This is possible after we have found *x* since the information then includes a side and the angle opposite to it.   ◀

▷ **Example 4**

Find x in Fig. 33.6.

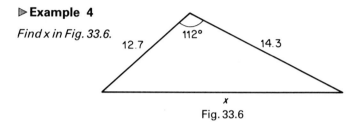

Fig. 33.6

By the cos formula we have

$$x^2 = 12.7^2 + 14.3^2 - (2 \times 12.7 \times 14.3 \cos 112°).$$

Since $\cos 112° = -\cos 68°$, the sign of the whole term in brackets changes from minus to plus:

$$x^2 = 12.7^2 + 14.3^2 + (2 \times 12.7 \times 14.3 \cos 68°)$$
$$= 161.3 + 204.5 + 136.1$$
$$= 501.9$$
$$\therefore \ x = 22.4 \text{ to 3 s.f.}$$ ◀

The cosine formula for the SSS case

In order to deal with triangles in which the given information has the SSS form, we need to transform the first cosine formula and have cos *A* as the subject. By elementary algebra we obtain

$$\cos A = \frac{b^2 + c^2 - a^2}{2bc}$$

This is the cosine formula in its second form. Again it is more important to learn to apply the formula directly to numerical examples than to learn it in its general form.

▷ **Example 5**

In Fig. 33.7, find angles A and B.

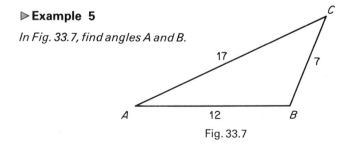

Fig. 33.7

To find angle A
By the cos formula we have

$$\cos A = \frac{12^2 + 17^2 - 7^2}{2 \times 12 \times 17}$$
$$= 0.9412$$
$$\therefore \text{ angle } A = \text{arc cos } 0.9412$$
$$= 19.7° \text{ to 3 s.f.}$$

To find angle B
We could now use the sine formula to find angle B since we have a side and the angle opposite to it. It is probably better to use the cosine formula again, however, for the following reasons.
(1) If the angle is obtuse the cosine formula will reveal this immediately since the cosine of an obtuse angle is negative.
(2) If we use the sine formula we are relying on a previous answer which may be incorrect and is in any case only accurate to a certain number of significant figures.
By the cos formula we have

$$\cos B = \frac{12^2 + 7^2 - 17^2}{2 \times 12 \times 7}$$
$$= -0.5714$$
$$\therefore \text{ angle } B = \text{arc cos } (-0.5714)$$
$$= 125° \text{ to 3 s.f.}$$

◀

The area of a triangle

The basic formula $\frac{1}{2} base \times height$ can seldom be applied directly to a non-right-angled triangle because we are usually given sides and angles of the triangle rather than its perpendicular height. Consequently the formula is converted into a more convenient form for use on non-right-angled triangles.

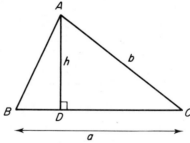

Fig. 33.8

From triangle ADC (Fig. 33.8), $\sin C = \dfrac{h}{b}$, from which $h = b \sin C$. Hence we have

$$A = \tfrac{1}{2} a h$$
$$\text{i.e. } A = \tfrac{1}{2} a b \sin C$$

In other words, the area equals $\frac{1}{2}$ *the product of any two sides and the sine of the angle between them.* The formula is therefore applicable when we have information in SAS form.

▷**Example 6**

Find the area of the triangle shown in Fig. 33.9.

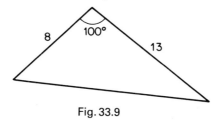

Fig. 33.9

$$\text{Area} = \tfrac{1}{2} \times 8 \times 13 \sin 100°$$
$$= 52 \sin 80°$$
$$= 51.2 \text{ to 3 s.f.}$$ ◁

EXERCISE 33b

In questions 1–8 find the quantities indicated by letters.

1

2

3

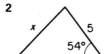

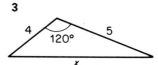

4

5

6

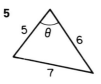

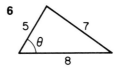

7

8

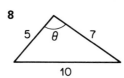

The remaining questions refer to a triangle *ABC*.

9 $b = 5.2$ cm, $c = 3.5$ cm, angle $A = 70°$. Find a and the area.

10 $a = 1.05$ cm, $c = 7.2$ mm, angle $B = 43.6°$. Find b and the area in mm².

11 $a = 1.3$ m, $b = 84$ cm, angle $C = 126°$. Find c and the area in m².

12 $a = 16.2$, $b = 9.4$, $c = 15$. Find angles A and B.

13 $a = 5.19$, $b = 9.15$, $c = 11.3$. Find angle C.

14 $a = 27.4$, $b = 52.3$, $c = 34.8$. Find angle B.

15 $a = 12$ cm, $b = 11$ cm, $c = 9$ cm. Find angle A and the area.

16 $a = 14$ cm, $b = 10$ cm, $c = 7$ cm. Find angle A and the area.

17 $a = 9.6$ mm, $b = 1.3$ cm, $c = 7.4$ mm. Find all the angles and the area in mm².

18 $a = 1.68$ m, $b = 97$ cm, $c = 83.2$ cm. Find all the angles and the area in cm².

Practical applications

Many practical problems involve triangles, and since the sine and cosine formulae are needed to solve all triangles which are neither right-angled nor isosceles, it is clear that these formulae will be frequently applicable to practical situations. The example below concerns *bearings*, which often arise in practical problems. In bearings questions it is generally best to put in north–south lines at all relevant points and look for alternate angles.

▷Example 7

A ship sails for 2 hours at 25 knots on a bearing of 305° from a point A to a point B. It then sails on a bearing of 070° for 2½ hours at 30 knots to a point C. Find (a) the distance AC, (b) the bearing of C from A, (c) how far C is to the east of A.

We need a set of information in one of the forms SAS, AAS, etc. to fix triangle *ABC*. Fig 33.10 shows how this is obtained. Vertical (or N–S) lines are drawn through *A* and *B*, and we use alternate angles and adjacent angles on a straight line to obtain one of the angles of triangle *ABC*.

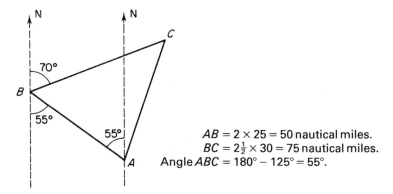

$AB = 2 \times 25 = 50$ nautical miles.
$BC = 2\frac{1}{2} \times 30 = 75$ nautical miles.
Angle $ABC = 180° - 125° = 55°$.

Fig. 33.10

(a) By the cos formula we have

$$AC^2 = 50^2 + 75^2 - 2 \times 50 \times 75 \cos 55°.$$
$$= 2500 + 5625 - 4302$$
$$= 3823$$
$$\therefore AC = 61.83 \text{ n.m. or } 61.8 \text{ n.m. to 3 s.f.}$$

(b) The bearing of *C* from *A* is angle *CAN*. To find this we first obtain angle *BAC*. By the sin formula we have

$$\frac{\sin BAC}{75} = \frac{\sin 55°}{61.83}$$
$$\therefore \sin BAC = \frac{75 \sin 55°}{61.83}$$
from which angle $BAC = 83.53°$.

It follows that the bearing of *C* from *A* is $83.53° - 55° = 28.53°$, that is 029° to the nearest degree.

(c) We have to find CD in the diagram shown in Fig. 33.11.

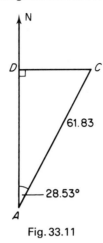

Fig. 33.11

Since this is a right-angled triangle we use the *definition* sine $= \dfrac{\text{opposite}}{\text{hypotenuse}}$ and not the sine formula.

$$\sin 28.53° = \frac{CD}{61.83}$$
$$\therefore\ CD = 61.83 \sin 28.53°$$
$$= 29.5 \text{ n.m. to 3 s.f.} \qquad \blacktriangleleft$$

EXERCISE 33c

(In many of the following questions a rough diagram should be drawn before the final neat diagram.)

1 A batsman standing 16.5 m from the bowler's wicket hits a ball 40 m. Find (a) its final distance from the bowler's wicket if it is hit at 34° to the line joining the wickets. (b) the angle at which it must be hit if it is to finish 35 m from the bowler's wicket.

2 An observer sights a tower on a bearing of 340°. He moves 100 m due west, and observes the tower again on a bearing of 040°. Find (a) his final distance from the tower, (b) how far south of the tower he is.

3 A golfer's ball is 17 m from the hole. He holes the ball with two straight putts, of 16 m and 1.2 m respectively. Find the angle between the direction of his first putt and the direction of the hole.

4 An observer at the top of a building sees two points A and B on the ground, both due south of him. The points are 20 m apart, and their angles of depression from the observer are 55° and 40°, respectively. Find (a) the distance from A to the top of the building, (b) the height of the building.

5 Two ships A and B sail on bearings of 040° and 110°, respectively. B is initially due north of A, and sails at a speed of 18 knots. Find A's speed if the ships are heading for a collision.

6 A car is driven at 30 km h^{-1} for $2\frac{1}{2}$ hours on a bearing of 055°, and then for half an hour at 80 km h^{-1} on a bearing of 340°. Find (a) its final distance from the starting point, (b) how far east it has travelled. (*Note:* part (b) is best done by using right-angled triangles.)

7 Three roads AB, BC, CA form a triangle in which $AB = 25$ km, $AC = 15$ km and angle $BAC = 37°$. If a car which averages 50 km h^{-1} is forced to travel from A to B via C rather than directly, how much time does it lose to the nearest minute?

8 At noon a ship B is 4 n.m. north-east of a ship A. B is sailing at 5 knots on a bearing of 045° and A is sailing at 15 knots on a bearing of 342°. Find their distance apart at 2 p.m.

9 A town T is 35 km due east of a town P, and another town S, south of the line TP, is 24 km from T and 18 km from P. Find the bearing of S from T.

10 A ship B is initially 20 n.m. north-east of a ship A. If B sails on a bearing of 310° while A sails due south at the same speed of 25 knots, find (a) the time it takes, to the nearest minute, for B to reach a point due north of A, (b) their distance apart at that time to the nearest n.m.

11 A ship starts from a point A which is 5 n.m. from a lighthouse B on a bearing of 225° from B. It sails on a bearing of $157\frac{1}{2}°$ to a point C due south of B, at 15 knots. Find BC and the time of the journey to the nearest minute.

12 A ship P is 40 n.m. due north of a ship Q. The ships sight a lighthouse L on bearings of 220° and 250°, respectively. Find (a) the distance PL, (b) the distance from P to a point which is 100 n.m. due north of L.

13 At 12 noon a lighthouse keeper P sights a ship 25 n.m. away on a bearing of 140°. If the ship is sailing on a bearing of 250° at 15 knots, what is its distance and bearing from P at 3 p.m.?

14 A vertical pole is 25 m high. Two points P, Q on the ground are due south and north-east of the pole, their angles of depression from the top of the pole being respectively 20° and 30°. Find PQ.

15 A ship sailing at 8 knots on a bearing of 306° observes a lighthouse on a bearing of 348°. Two hours later the bearing of the lighthouse is 62°. Find the distance of the ship from the lighthouse at this time, and also the shortest distance between the two.

16 A, B, C are three points on a line of greatest slope of a hillside inclined at 32° to the horizontal, A being at ground level and BC being 225 m. From a point on the ground in the same vertical plane as A, B and C, the angles of elevation of B and C are 12° and 21°. Find AB.

17 Two ships leave harbour together, ship A travelling on a bearing of 330° at 11 knots, and ship B travelling on a bearing of 045°. After 2 hours A observes B on a bearing of 095°. Find the speed of B. At this time A and B also observe beacons due east and due west of them, both of which are due north of the harbour. Find the distance apart of the beacons.

18 From a train travelling north-east at 150 km h^{-1} the bearing at 12 noon of a church steeple is 033°. The train continues at the same speed in the same direction, and 20 minutes later the bearing of the steeple is 341°. Find (a) the shortest distance of the steeple from the train, (b) the time, to the nearest minute, at which the train is due east of the steeple.

19 From a boat at P the bearing of a lighthouse at Q is 112°. The boat sails due north to R, 10 km from the lighthouse, at which the bearing of the lighthouse is 150°. It then sails 8 km north-east to a point S. Find (a) PQ, (b) QS, (c) the bearing of S from P.

20 A ship steams at 15 knots on a bearing of 065° from a port A to a point B 35 n.m. away. Then it steams on a bearing of 332° at the same speed for $32\frac{1}{2}$ n.m. to a point C. Find AC and the bearing of C from A. A second ship leaves A 2 hours after the first, and steams due north so as to be at its nearest point to C when the first ship reaches C. Find the speed of the second ship.

34 Solid Trigonometry

The plane

A plane is a flat surface which extends to infinity in all directions. Any 2-dimensional figure such as a triangle or a rectangle fixes a definite plane, so we can refer to 'the plane ABC', 'the plane PQRS', etc.

Intersection of planes

Any two non-parallel planes meet in a line called the *line of intersection* of the planes (Fig. 34.1).

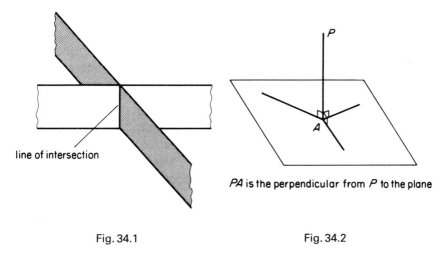

line of intersection

PA is the perpendicular from *P* to the plane

Fig. 34.1   Fig. 34.2

It follows that three planes meet, in general, at a point.

The perpendicular from a point to a plane

From a point not on a plane *one* perpendicular can be drawn to the plane. This line is at right angles to *all* lines in the plane (Fig. 34.2).

The angle between a line and a plane

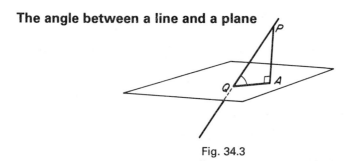

Fig. 34.3

In Fig. 34.3 Q is the point of intersection of the line and the plane. From any other convenient point P on the line, the perpendicular PA to the plane is drawn. Then angle PQA is the angle between the line PQ and the plane.

The line QA is called the *projection* of the line on the plane. It follows that the angle between a line and a plane can be defined as *the angle between the line and its projection on the plane*.

The angle between two planes

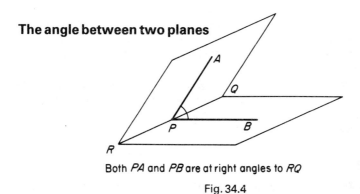

Both *PA* and *PB* are at right angles to *RQ*

Fig. 34.4

First we find the line of intersection of the planes — RQ in Fig. 34.4. Then from any convenient point P on this line we draw two perpendiculars PA, PB to the line, one in each plane. The angle APB between these perpendiculars is the angle between the planes.

The extension of Pythagoras' theorem to 3 dimensions

Pythagoras' theorem can be thought of as providing a formula for the diagonal of a rectangle (Fig. 34.5).

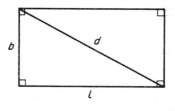

Fig. 34.5

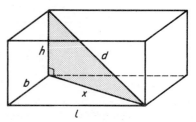

Fig. 34.6

We have $d^2 = l^2 + b^2$, where l and b are the length and breadth of the rectangle.

Consider now a cuboid, with length l, breadth b and height h (Fig. 34.6). We have

$$d^2 = x^2 + h^2,$$

and since $x^2 = l^2 + h^2$, it follows that

$$d^2 = l^2 + b^2 + h^2.$$

This result should be learned by heart. It can be regarded as the 3-dimensional equivalent of the formula given by Pythagoras' theorem for the diagonal of a rectangle.

Worked examples

The following points should be noted:

(1) In drawing solid figures for mathematical work all vertical lines should be drawn vertically, and all parallel lines should be drawn parallel.

(2) In all problems a large, fully labelled 3-dimensional diagram should be drawn. At the relevant stages in the solution it often helps also to draw 2-dimensional sections of this diagram. These should have the same lettering as the main diagram.

(3) Problems on solid trigonometry largely involve *right-angled* triangles, and consequently should normally be solved by the use of Pythagoras' theorem and the *definitions* of sine, cosine and tangent. The sine and cosine *formulae* are seldom required.

▷ Example 1

The diagram (Fig. 34.7) shows a right pyramid on a square base. The sides of the base are all 10 cm and the slant edges are all 12 cm in length. Find (a) the height VE of the pyramid, (b) the angle between each slanting edge and the base, (c) the angle between each slanting face and the base.

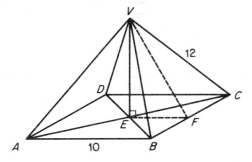

F is the mid-point of *BC*, so *BF* = *CF* = 5 cm

Fig. 34.7

(a) *VE* is required, so we look for a right-angled triangle containing this line. In fact there is a choice of two triangles: we can use triangle *VEF*, in which case EF^2 and VF^2 must first be found, or we can use triangle *VEC*, in which case EC^2

is needed. (Triangle VEA is, of course, congruent to VEC and could also be used.) We shall use the second method, though there is no difference in length between the two.

$EF = FC = 5$ cm, so we can use Pythagoras on triangle EFC to find EC^2 (Fig. 34.8).

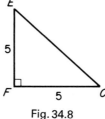

Fig. 34.8

$$EC^2 = 5^2 + 5^2 = 50.$$

There is no need to find the square root of 50, since EC^2 and not EC is needed for the final step. Using triangle VEC we have

$$\begin{aligned} VE^2 &= VC^2 - EC^2 \\ &= 12^2 - 50 \\ &= 94 \\ \therefore \quad VE &= 9.70 \text{ cm to 3 s.f.} \end{aligned}$$

(b) The angle required is angle VCE (or angle VBE, etc.). Since we have all the sides of triangle VCE we can use either sine, cosine or tangent to find this angle.

$$\sin VCE = \frac{\sqrt{94}}{12}$$

from which angle $VCE = 53.9°$ to 3 s.f.

(Note that we use the exact $\sqrt{94}$ rather than the approximate 9.70 here.)

(c) The angle required is angle VFE. From triangle VFE we have

$$\tan VFE = \frac{\sqrt{94}}{5}$$

from which angle $VFE = 62.7°$ to 3 s.f.   ◀

▷ Example 2

The diagram shown in Fig. 34.9 can represent a tent or the roof of a house. ABCD is a rectangle, and ADE and BCF are congruent isosceles triangles equally inclined to the base. $AB = 14$ m, $AD = 6$ m, $EF = 6$ m and the height $EG = 5$ m. Find the angles between the base and (a) the line EA, (b) the plane AED, (c) the plane ABFE.

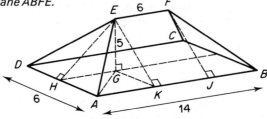

Fig. 34.9

The angles required are angle EAG, angle EHG and angle EKG. To find these we need AG, HG and KG. Since triangle ADE is isosceles, H is the mid-point of AD and hence $AH = 3$ m. Also, by the symmetry of the figure, EF is centrally placed, and since $KJ = EF = 6$ m, $AK = \dfrac{14-6}{2} = 4$ m. It follows that triangle AKG is a 3,4,5 triangle and that $AG = 5$ m.

(a) $\tan EAG = \dfrac{5}{5} = 1$; hence angle $EAG = 45°$.

(b) $\tan EHG = \dfrac{5}{4}$, from which angle $EHG = 51.3°$ to 3 s.f.

(c) $\tan EKG = \dfrac{5}{3}$, from which angle $EKG = 59.0°$ to 3 s.f.   ◀

EXERCISE 34

1 Find the lengths of the diagonals of the cuboids with the following dimensions: (a) 2 cm, 4 cm, 5 cm, (b) 2 cm, 2 cm, 1 cm, (c) 3 cm, 3 cm, 7 cm, (d) 3 cm, 4 cm, 12 cm.
2 The diagram (Fig. 34.10) shows a cuboid in which $AB = 4$, $BC = 3$, $AE = 2$. Find the angles between (a) BE and plane $ABCD$, (b) planes $BEHC$ and $ADHE$, (c) BH and plane $ABCD$, (d) planes $AHGB$ and $EFGH$, (e) AH and plane $ABFE$, (f) planes $ADGF$ and $BCHE$.

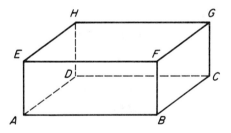

Fig. 34.10

3 A right pyramid stands on a rectangular base with sides of 12 cm and 16 cm. The lengths of the slanting edges are 26 cm. Find the height of the pyramid.
4 A right pyramid of height 12 m stands on a square base of side 8 m. Find the angle between the base and (a) each slanting edge, (b) each slanting face.
5 In Fig. 34.10 $AB = 6$, $BC = 2$ and $AE = 3$. Giving the answers in the form arc sin, arc cos or arc tan of a fraction without square roots, find the angles between (a) BH and plane $EFGH$, (b) planes $AFGD$ and $ADHE$, (c) BH and plane $BCGF$.
6 A right pyramid stands on a rectangular base of length 9 cm and breadth 7 cm. The length of each slanting edge is 10 cm. Find the angle between the base and (a) each slanting edge, (b) the smaller slanting faces.

7 Fig. 34.11 represents a tent on a rectangular base. *ADE* and *BCF* are congruent isosceles triangles equally inclined to the horizontal. *AB* = 8 m, *BC* = 3 m, *EF* = 4 m and the height of the tent is 3 m. Find the angle between the horizontal and (a) plane *ADE*, (b) *AE*, (c) plane *ABFE*.

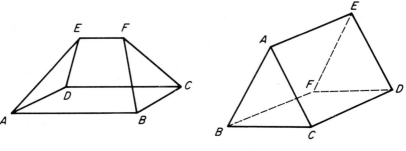

Fig. 34.11   Fig. 34.12

8 *ABC* and *EFD* are congruent vertical isosceles triangles and *BCDF* is a horizontal rectangle in Fig. 34.12. *AB* = *AC* = 17, *BC* = 15 and *CD* = 20. Find the angles between (a) plane *ACDE* and the horizontal, (b) planes *ACDE* and *ABFE*, (c) *CE* and the horizontal.

9 In Fig. 34.13, *ABC* is a vertical isosceles triangle and *BCDE* is a horizontal rectangle. *AD* = *AE* = 5, *DE* = 6 and the plane *ADE* is inclined at 30° to the horizontal. Find (a) *AF*, (b) *AC*, (c) the inclination of *AD* to the horizontal, (d) the inclination of plane *ADC* to the horizontal.

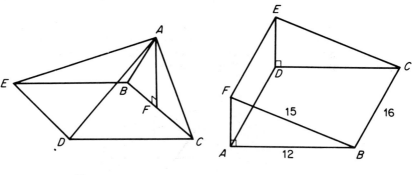

Fig. 34.13   Fig. 34.14

10 *ABC* is a horizontal equilateral triangle of side 8 cm, and *D* is a point 6 cm vertically above *A*. Find the angles between (a) *BD* and the horizontal, (b) plane *BDC* and the horizontal, (c) planes *ABD* and *ACD*.

11 A right pyramid stands on a square base of side 5 cm, and each slanting face is inclined at 75° to the horizontal. Find (a) the height of the pyramid, (b) the length of each slanting edge, (c) the angle between each slanting edge and the horizontal.

12 *ABCD* is a horizontal rectangle (Fig. 34.14) and *ABF*, *DCE* are congruent vertical triangles. Find the angles between (a) plane *FBCE* and the horizontal, (b) *CF* and the horizontal, (c) *BE* and plane *DEC*, (d) *BE* and plane *ADEF*.

13 *ABC* is a horizontal equilateral triangle, and *P* is a point 5 m vertically above *A*. If the angles of elevation of *P* from *B* and *C* are 25°, what is the inclination of the plane *BCP* to the horizontal?

14 The base of a tetrahedron (pyramid on a triangular base) is an equilateral triangle *ABC* of side 8 cm. The mediators of the sides of triangle *ABC* meet at *G*, and the vertex *V* is 12 cm vertically above *G*. Find (a) *AG*, (b) angle *VAG* (c) the angle between each slanting face and the base.

15 In a tent such as the one shown in Fig. 34.11, *AB* = 12 m, *AD* = 10 m, *EF* = 6 m and the triangles *ADE*, *BCF* are inclined at 60° to the horizontal. Find (a) the height of the figure, (b) *AE*, (c) the angle between *CF* and the horizontal, (d) the angle between the opposite faces *ABFE* and *CDEF*.

16 A right pyramid with vertex *E* stands on a rectangular base *ABCD* in which *AB* = 4 and *BC* = 3. The length of each slanting edge is 6.5. Find the angles between (a) *AE* and the base, (b) plane *ABE* and the base, (c) planes *ADE* and *BCE*. Given that *P* is the mid-point of *EC*, find (d) the tangent of angle *PAC* as a simple fraction.

17 *ABCD* and *PQRS* are horizontal squares with sides of 7 and 3, and the height of the figure is $2\frac{1}{2}$ (Fig. 34.15). The edges *AP*, *BQ*, etc. are equally inclined to the horizontal. Find the angles between (a) *AP* and the base, (b) plane *ADSP* and the base, (c) planes *ABQP* and *CDSR*.

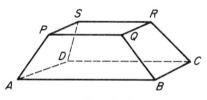

Fig. 34.15

18 The diagram (Fig. 34.16) shows a pyramid on a rectangular base, whose vertex is not directly above the centre of the base. *AV* = *DV* and *BV* = *CV*. Given that plane *AVD* is inclined at 70° to the horizontal, find the inclinations to the horizontal of (a) plane *BVC*, (b) plane *AVB*.

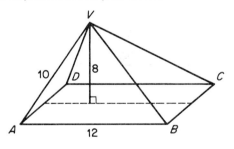

Fig. 34.16

19 Using the diagram given in question 17, *AB* = 20, *PQ* = 14, and the inclination of *AP* to the horizontal is *50°*. Find the angle between each slanting face and the base.

20 *ABCD* and *ABEF* are two rectangular pages of a book. *AB* = 24 cm and *AD* = 18 cm. When the angle between the two pages is 30°, what is the angle between the diagonal *AC* and the plane *ABEF*?

35 Length, Area, Volume, Density

The conversion of units of area and volume

We know that 10 mm = 1 cm; consider now the relationship between the *square millimetre* (written mm²) and the *square centimetre* (cm²) (Fig. 35.1).

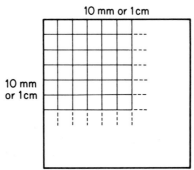

Fig. 35.1

The large square represents 1 square cm, and each small square represents 1 square mm. There are clearly 10² or 100 of the small squares in the large one, and this illustrates the general principle governing the conversion of area units. *If the linear units are in the ratio k:1, the units of area are in the ratio k²:1.* We have in fact

$$1 \text{ cm} = 10 \text{ mm}$$
$$\therefore \ 1 \text{ cm}^2 = 10^2 \text{ mm}^2,$$

$$1 \text{ m} = 100 \text{ cm}$$
$$\therefore \ 1 \text{ m}^2 = 100^2 \text{ cm}^2,$$
$$\text{etc.}$$

In a similar way, by considering a cube, we can show that *if linear units are in the ratio k:1, the corresponding units of volume are in the ratio k³:1.* For example,

$$1 \text{ m} = 100 \text{ cm}$$
$$\therefore \ 1 \text{ m}^3 = 100^3 \text{ m}^3,$$

$$1 \text{ km} = 1000 \text{ m}$$
$$\therefore \ 1 \text{ km}^3 = 1000^3 \text{ m}^3,$$
$$\text{etc.}$$

▷**Example 1**

Express 200 hectares in (a) cm², (b) km².

(a) By definition, 1 hectare $= 10^4$ m²
$\therefore$ 200 hectares $= 200 \times 10^4$ m².
But 1 m² $= 100^2$ cm²
$\therefore$ 200 hectares $= 200 \times 10^4 \times 100^2$ cm²
$= 2 \times 10^2 \times 10^4 \times 10^4$ cm²
$= 2 \times 10^{10}$ cm².

(An answer as large as this is best left in terms of a power of 10.)

(b) As before, 200 hectares $= 200 \times 10^4$ m².
But 1 km² $= 1000^2$ m²
$= 10^6$ m²;
$\therefore$ 200 hectares $= \dfrac{200 \times 10^4}{10^6}$ km²
$= 2$ km². ◀

Standard figures

In chapter 29 we derived formulae for the areas of some simple 2-dimensional figures bounded by straight lines, such as the triangle and the parallelogram. The remaining standard figures are mainly 3-dimensional, and the formulae for their areas and volumes cannot be proved by elementary methods. Consequently in this chapter we shall simply state the formulae and show how they are used in problems.

The circle

When the circumference of a circle is divided by its diameter a constant called π is obtained. This is an *irrational* number, which means that it cannot be expressed as a fraction or as a terminating or recurring decimal. π is *approximately* equal to $\dfrac{22}{7}$ or 3.142. In problems, the value of π to be used is often stated, and then this value must be used. Otherwise the value given by a calculator can be employed. When we are told to take the value as $\dfrac{22}{7}$, it is usually because the 7 will cancel with some other number in the problem.

By definition of π, we have the following alternative formulae for the circumference of a circle:

$$C = 2\pi r, \text{ or } C = \pi d.$$

(These formulae cannot be proved as they are true by definition.)

The formula for the area of a circle (which *can* be proved, though the proof will not be given here) is

$$A = \pi r^2.$$

The cylinder and the prism

The defining feature of these two figures is that they have *the same cross-section throughout.* The cross-section of a cylinder is a circle (or an ellipse), and that of a prism is a polygon. (A polygon is *any* plane figure bounded by straight lines, including the triangle and the quadrilateral.)

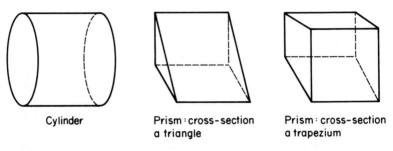

| Cylinder | Prism : cross-section a triangle | Prism : cross-section a trapezium |

Fig. 35.2

The figure formed by the *water in a swimming pool* provides an example of a prism whose cross-section is a trapezium.

For all figures of uniform cross-section the formula for volume is as follows:

Volume = cross-sectional area × length.

In the case of the cylinder this formula becomes

$$V = \pi r^2 h,$$

and in the case of the cuboid the formula gives the elementary result

$$V = lbh.$$

The surface area of a cylinder

Consider a cylinder of radius r and length (or height) h. We can imagine the *curved* surface to be 'unrolled' into a rectangle of length $2\pi r$ (Fig. 35.3).

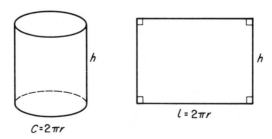

$C = 2\pi r$

$l = 2\pi r$

Fig. 35.3

It follows that the curved surface area is $2\pi r\,h$. The *total* surface area is obtained by adding to this expression the areas of the two circular ends, that is $2 \times \pi r^2$ or $2\pi r^2$.

Curved surface area $= 2\pi r h$.
Total surface area $= 2\pi r h + 2\pi r^2$
[or $2\pi r(r + h)$].

The cone and the pyramid

A *right* cone or pyramid is one in which the slanting edges are all equal in length, so that the vertex (top) is directly above the centre of the base. A right cone is determined by giving any two of the following quantities: *radius of base r, height h, slant length l, semivertical angle* α. These quantities are shown in the first diagram of Fig. 35.4. The other diagrams show a pyramid whose base is a quadrilateral, and the special kind of pyramid called a *tetrahedron*. This has a triangular base, which means that all its four faces are triangles.

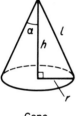

Cone

Pyramid: base
a quadrilateral

Tetrahedron
(pyramid on
triangular base)

Fig. 35.4

The following formula gives the volume of any cone or pyramid:

Volume $= \frac{1}{3}$ area of base $\times$ height.

In the case of the cone this becomes

$$V = \tfrac{1}{3}\pi r^2 h.$$

The surface area of a cone

The formula for the *curved* surface area is in terms of the slant length *l*:

Curved surface area $= \pi rl$.

To obtain the total surface area we add the area of the circular base:

Total surface area $= \pi rl + \pi r^2$.

Frustum of cone or pyramid

A horizontal plane cutting across a cone or pyramid divides the figure into a similar cone or pyramid together with a figure called a *frustum* (Fig. 35.5).

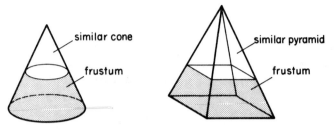

Fig. 35.5

If the volume of the original figure is known, the volume of a frustum can be calculated by using the theory of similar figures (see chapter 26). For example, if the height of the cone removed is half that of the original cone, we have

ratio of lengths of similar figures $= 1:2$
$\therefore$ ratio of volumes of similar figures $= 1:8$

$\therefore$ volume of frustum $= \dfrac{7}{8}$ volume of original cone.

The sphere

The following two formulae give the volume and the surface area of a sphere:

$$V = \frac{4\pi r^3}{3},$$
$$A = 4\pi r^2.$$

Worked examples

As the next two examples illustrate, problems on the standard figures often involve the algebraic technique of transformation of equations.

▷**Example 2**

Find the surface area of a sphere of volume 50 cm².

Using the standard formula for the volume of a sphere we have

$$\frac{4\pi r^3}{3} = 50$$
$$\therefore r^3 = \frac{150}{4\pi}$$
$$\therefore r = \sqrt[3]{\frac{150}{4\pi}} = 2.285.$$

Now using the formula $A = 4\pi r^2$ for the surface area, we have

$$A = 4\pi \times 2.285^2$$
$$= 65.6 \text{ to 3 s.f.}$$

The surface area is therefore 65.6 cm^2 to 3 s.f.   ◁

▷ Example 3

A cone (Fig. 35.6) of radius 5 cm and semivertical angle 25° is melted down and recast into a cylinder of length 8 cm. Find the radius of the cylinder.

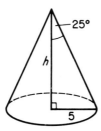

Fig. 35.6

First we find the height of the cone, h cm:

$$\tan 25° = \frac{5}{h}$$
$$\therefore h = \frac{5}{\tan 25°} = 10.723.$$

Now we use the formula $V = \frac{1}{3}\pi r^2 h$ to find the volume of the cone:

$$V = \frac{1}{3}\pi \times 25 \times 10.723 = 280.73.$$

Finally we equate this value to the expression for the volume of a cylinder, and make r the subject:

$$\pi r^2 h = 280.73,$$
$$\text{and since } h = 8, r^2 = \frac{280.73}{8\pi}.$$
$$\text{Hence } r = \sqrt{\frac{280.73}{8\pi}} = 3.34 \text{ to 3 s.f.}$$

The required radius is therefore 3.34 cm to 3 s.f.   ◁

Areas and volumes obtained by subtraction

In certain cases an area or volume is best found by regarding it as the difference between two other areas or volumes. Consider for example a *circular ring* (Fig. 35.7).

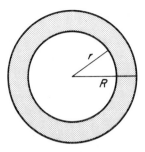

Fig. 35.7

The area of the ring is obtained by subtracting the area of the inner circle from that of the outer:

$$\text{Area} = \pi R^2 - \pi r^2$$
$$= \pi(R^2 - r^2)$$
$$= \pi(R + r)(R - r).$$

This technique should also be used to find the volume of material in a hollow body. If the body is completely enclosed we have the following formula.

Volume of material = outer volume − inner volume.

▶ Example 4

A box made of wood 1 cm thick is 12 cm long, 11 cm wide and 9 cm high. Find the volume of the wood if the box is (a) closed, (b) open.

(a) We must subtract *twice* the thickness of the wood from each outer dimension to obtain the corresponding inner dimension. Hence

$$\text{volume of wood} = \text{outer volume} - \text{inner volume}$$
$$= (12 \times 11 \times 9) - (10 \times 9 \times 7)$$
$$= 1188 - 630 = 558 \text{ cm}^3.$$

(b) In this case only *one* times the thickness of the wood has to be subtracted from the height; hence the volume is $(12 \times 11 \times 9) - (10 \times 9 \times 8) = 468 \text{ cm}^3$. ◀

Density

Density is a property of a *substance* — e.g. iron — and not of a particular sample of that substance. It can be defined as *mass per unit volume*, or by the equation

$$\text{density} = \frac{\text{mass}}{\text{volume}}.$$

The units of density are g cm^{-3}, kg m^{-3}, etc., which are shorthand ways of writing 'grams per cubic centimetre', etc.

Relative density or specific gravity

An indirect way to measure the density of a substance is to compare its density with that of water. This gives the quantity known as *relative density*.

$$\text{Relative density} = \frac{\textbf{mass of a given volume of a substance}}{\textbf{mass of an equal volume of water}}$$

The density of water is usually taken to be 1 g cm^{-3} or 1000 kg m^{-3}. This means that the density of a substance in g cm^{-3} is numerically equal to its relative density. Note, however, that relative density has no units, as it is defined as a mass divided by a mass.

▷Example 5

A pipe of length 12 m has an external radius of 16 cm and is made of metal 2 cm thick with relative density 8.5. Find the mass of the pipe in kilograms.
The cross-section of a pipe is a ring, and we obtain the volume of metal by multiplying the area of the ring by the length of the pipe. Let the outer and inner radii be R cm and r cm, respectively, and let the length be l cm; then we have

$$
\begin{aligned}
\text{volume of metal} &= (\pi R^2 l - \pi r^2 l) \text{ cm}^3 \\
&= \pi l (R + r)(R - r) \text{ cm}^3 \\
&= (\pi \times 1200 \times 30 \times 2) \text{ cm}^3 \\
&= 72\,000\,\pi \text{ cm}^3 = 0.072\,\pi \text{ m}^3.
\end{aligned}
$$

The density of the metal is 8.5 times that of water, that is 8500 kg m^{-3}, and from the definition of density we have mass = density × volume. Hence

$$
\begin{aligned}
\text{mass of metal} &= 0.072\,\pi \times 8500 \\
&= 1920 \text{ kg to 3 s.f.}
\end{aligned}
$$
◁

EXERCISE 35a

Take the density of water to be 1 g cm^{-3} or 1000 kg m^{-3}.

1 Convert (a) 125 mm^2 to cm^2, (b) 0.05 m^2 to cm^2, (c) 0.028 cm^3 to mm^3 (d) 5.7 × 10^8 m^2 to km^2, (e) 3 × 10^{-4} m^3 to cm^3.

2 Taking π to be $\frac{22}{7}$, and without using a calculator, find (a) the circumference, (b) the area, of a circle of radius $3\frac{1}{2}$ cm.

3 Find the area of a circle (a) of radius 5 cm, (b) of circumference 12 cm.

4 If 2.75 kg of a substance has a volume of 750 cm^3, what is the density of the substance in g cm^{-3}?

5 The base of a tetrahedron is 3 cm by 4 cm by 5 cm and its height is 6 cm. Find its volume.

6 Find the radius of a circle of area 80 m^2.

7 If 200 mm^3 of a substance has a mass of 0.04 g, what is the density of the substance in g cm^{-3}?

8 If the relative density of a substance is 4.5, what volume of the substance in cm^3 has a mass of 1.5 kg?

9 A running track consists of straight sections of length 95 m which are 60 m apart, and two semicircular ends. Find (a) the perimeter, (b) the area, of the track.

10 A right pyramid of height 12 cm stands on a square base of side 10 cm. Find (a) the volume, (b) the total surface area, of the pyramid.

11 Find the volume of a sphere of surface area 250 cm^2.

12 The density of a metal is 6 g cm^{-3}. Find (a) the volume in m^3 of 27 000 kg of the metal, (b) the mass of a sphere of radius 3 cm.

13 Taking π to be $\frac{22}{7}$, and without using a calculator, find the curved surface area of a cylinder of length 12 cm and cross-section 616 cm^2.

14 A circular lawn of radius 20 m is surrounded by a path of width 50 cm. Find the area of the path.

15 A cone has a height of 12 cm. What fraction of the volume of the whole cone is that of the frustum of height 4 cm?

16 A closed box is made of wood 0.5 cm thick with relative density 0.75. The external dimensions of the box are 8 cm, 7 cm and 5 cm. Find (a) the volume of the wood, (b) its mass.

17 Find (a) the volume, (b) the curved surface area, of a right cone of height 20 cm and radius 8 cm.

18 Find the volume of a prism of length 25 cm whose cross-section is an equilateral triangle of side 12 cm.

19 Find the total surface area of (a) a cylinder of radius 4 cm and length 7 cm, (b) a solid hemisphere of volume 50 m^3.

20 Find the mass of a cylinder of curved surface area 28 cm^2, length 4.5 cm and density 2.6 g cm^{-3}.

21 An open box made of wood 1 cm thick is 16 cm high, 22 cm long and 20 cm wide. Find the volume of the wood.

22 500 g of metal, of density 8000 kg m^{-3}, is melted down and made into a sphere. Find the radius in centimetres.

23 A pipe of length 1.5 m has an external radius of 20 cm and is made of metal 1 cm thick. Find the volume of the metal.

24 Find the radius of a sphere of mass 2 kg which is made of metal with relative density 9.

25 The fencing around a rectangular plot of land of length 20 m and width 12 m is just sufficient to fence a semicircular plot. What is the area of this plot?

26 Viewed end-on, the vertical cross-section of a shed consists of a rectangle of width 6 m and height 4 m, surmounted by an isosceles triangle of height $4\frac{1}{2}$ m. The length of the shed is 8 m. Find its volume.

27 A metal sphere of radius 6 cm is melted down and made into wire of radius 0.25 cm. What length of wire is obtained, in metres?

28 A swimming pool has a length of 25 m and a width of 12 m. Viewed from the side, it has a cross-section which is a trapezium of height 1.2 m at the shallow end and 3.8 m at the dep end. Find the volume of the pool.

29 Find the mass of water in kg which will fill a cylindrical vessel of radius 20 cm and height 50 cm.

30 *ABCD* is a tetrahedron, the base *ABC* being a horizontal triangle in which $AB = AC = 13$ cm and $BC = 10$ cm. *D* is directly above *A* and $AD = 10$ cm. Find (a) the volume of the tetrahedron, (b) its total surface area.

31 The volume of a cone of height 7 cm is 60 cm^3. Find its slant length.

32 A cylinder of radius 4 cm and height 9 cm is recast into a cone of height 12 cm. *Without using a calculator*, find the radius of the cone.

33 The top of a bucket has a radius of 20 cm and the base has a radius of 10 cm. If the height of the bucket is 40 cm what is its capacity? (Regard the bucket as a frustum and use similarity properties.)

34 A horizontal cylindrical pipe, closed at both ends, has an internal diameter of 4 cm and an internal length of 6 cm. It contains liquid to a depth of 2 cm. When it is poured into a vertical conical vessel the liquid reaches a depth of 9 cm. Without using a calculator, find the radius of the surface of the liquid.

Miscellaneous topics

Submersion

Suppose a body of volume V is completely submerged in a liquid contained in a vessel with uniform cross-section A (Fig. 35.8).

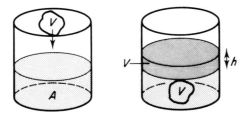

Fig. 35.8

It is clear that the volume of the body is equal to the volume of liquid that it lifts up; hence if the rise in level is h, we have

$$V = A h,$$

$$\text{or } h = \frac{V}{A}.$$

When the submerged body is removed there will be an equal fall in level, and we thus have the following general result.

$$\text{Change in level} = \frac{\text{volume added or removed}}{\text{cross-sectional area}}.$$

▷**Example 6**

A cylindrical vessel of radius 8 cm contains water to a depth of 12 cm. If a metal sphere of radius 6 cm is dropped into the vessel, what will be the new depth of water?

Using the formula for change in level given above together with the formulae for the volume of a sphere and the area of a circle, we have

$$\text{rise in level} = \frac{4\,\pi \times 6^3}{3} \div \pi \times 8^2$$

$$= \frac{4\,\pi \times 6 \times 6 \times 6}{3\,\pi \times 8 \times 8}$$

$$= 4.5 \text{ cm.}$$

(A calculator is not needed here since the fraction can be cancelled.) It follows that the new depth of water is 16.5 cm. ◁

Flow through a pipe or orifice

Suppose that a liquid flowing at v m s^{-1} is being delivered from a pipe of cross-section A m^2. In 1 second the water in v metres of pipe will pass through the end of the pipe (Fig. 35.9).

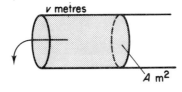

v metres

A m^2

Fig. 35.9

It follows that the volume delivered in 1 second is Av m^3, and we thus have the following general result.

Volume delivered per second = speed × cross-sectional area.

If the liquid is passing through some other orifice such as a nozzle or a hole in a tank, the result still holds, even though the speed at which the liquid passes through the hole may not be equal to its speed just before reaching the hole.

▷ Example 7

A tank measuring 2 m by 2 m by 1.5 m is half full of water. How long does it take to empty through a hole of radius 5 cm if the average speed at which the water passes through the hole is 2 m s^{-1}?

$$\text{Area of hole} = \pi \times 0.05^2 = 0.0025\,\pi\,\text{m}^2,$$
$$\therefore \text{ volume delivered per second (on average)} = 2 \times 0.0025\,\pi$$
$$= 0.005\,\pi\,\text{m}^3.$$
$$\text{But total volume of water} = \tfrac{1}{2} \times 2 \times 2 \times 1.5$$
$$= 3\,\text{m}^3,$$
$$\therefore \text{ time taken for tank to empty} = \frac{3}{0.005\,\pi}$$
$$= 191\,\text{s to 3 s.f.} \qquad ◁$$

Cylinders and spheres in contact

In problems concerning cylinders and spheres in contact it is generally best to put into the diagram all the radii which look relevant, and to join the centres. Remember that *a line joining two centres passes through the point of contact, and its length equals the sum of the two radii.*

▷Example 8

A triangular frame is just large enough to hold three billiard balls. What is the length of the side of the frame in terms of the radius of the balls?

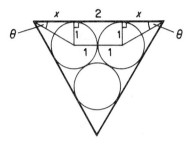

Fig. 35.10

Let the radius of each ball be 1 unit, as shown in Fig. 35.10. The triangle is obviously equilateral; so its angles are 60° and hence $\theta = 30°$. We therefore have

$$\tan 30° = \frac{1}{x},$$
$$\therefore \; x = \frac{1}{\tan 30°} = 1.732,$$
$$\therefore \; \text{side length} = 2 + (2 \times 1.732)$$
$$= 5.46 \text{ to 3 s.f.} \qquad \triangleleft$$

The distance travelled by a rolling wheel

When a wheel turns through one complete revolution, the distance it travels is equal to the circumference of the wheel. We therefore have the following general result.

Distance travelled by rolling wheel = circumference × number of revolutions.

Also, since the speed of the wheel is usually expressed as distance travelled per second, the speed is given by the following formula.

Speed of rolling wheel = circumference × number of revolutions per second.

▷Example 9

A wheel rotates at 750 revolutions per minute in travelling at a speed of 10 m s⁻¹. Find (a) the radius of the wheel, (b) the number of complete revolutions it makes in travelling 65 m.

(a) First we convert the revolutions per minute to revolutions per second:

$$750 \text{ revs per minute} = \frac{750}{60}$$
$$= 12.5 \text{ revs per second.}$$

Now using the formula

$$speed = circumference \times number\, of\, revs\, per\, second,$$

and letting the radius be r metres, we have

$$10 = 2\pi r \times 12.5$$
$$\therefore r = \frac{10}{2\pi \times 12.5} = 0.1273.$$

The radius is therefore 0.1273 m or 12.73 cm

(b) When the wheel travels 65 m the *exact* number of revolutions it makes is obtained by dividing 65 m by the circumference of the wheel. That is

$$\frac{65}{2\pi \times 0.1273} \text{ or } 81.27.$$

It follows that the number of *complete* revolutions made by the wheel is 81. ◀

EXERCISE 35b

Only use a calculator when it is essential.

1 A liquid of density 2.5 g cm^{-3} flows at 20 cm s^{-1} through a pipe of cross-section 5 cm^2. Find (a) the volume delivered in 1 second, (b) the mass delivered in this time.

2 Find the rise in level when 12 spheres of radius 2 cm are completely submerged in the water in a cylindrical vessel of radius 8 cm.

3 Two spheres of radius 10 cm stand in contact on horizontal ground. They support a third sphere, of radius 2.5 cm, which rests in contact with them both. Find the height of the top point of this third sphere.

4 A sphere of radius 6 cm stands half immersed in the liquid in a cylindrical vessel of radius 12 cm. Find the depth of liquid when the sphere is removed.

5 Water flows through a pipe of cross-section 30 cm^2 at a speed of 50 cm s^{-1} into a tank measuring 1 m by 60 cm by 50 cm. Find the time in seconds it takes for the tank to fill.

6 A rectangular frame just holds two balls of radius 1 cm and one of radius 2 cm on a horizontal table. The smaller balls are each in contact with two sides of the frame, the large ball is in contact with one side, and each ball is in contact with each other ball. Find the length and breadth of the frame.

7 A cylindrical vessel of height 50 cm and radius 6 cm contains water to a depth of 10 cm. How many spheres of radius 3 cm must be added to the water to raise its level to the rim of the vessel?

8 Liquid of density 0.5 g cm^{-3} flows out of a hole in a tank at an average speed of 10 cm s^{-1}. After 30 minutes 36 kg of the liquid has been lost. Find the area of the hole.

9 Two spheres of radius 20 cm stand on the ground with their centres 80 cm apart. A third sphere rests in contact with them both with its centre 65 cm above the ground. Find the radius of this sphere.

10 A right cone of height 12 cm and radius 8 cm stands with its circular base in contact with the base of a cylindrical vessel of radius 10 cm. The vessel contains water to a depth of 6 cm. Find the depth when the cone is removed.

11 A tank holding 3 m³ of water empties in 5 minutes through an orifice of area 80 cm². Find the average speed in cm s⁻¹ with which the water emerges.

12 2 kg of metal, of relative density 8, is dropped into a vessel with uniform cross-section which contains water. If the metal is completely submerged and the rise in level is 5 cm, what is the cross-sectional area of the vessel?

13 A wheel has radius of 20 cm. Find (a) the distance the wheel travels in rotating 50 times, (b) the number of complete revolutions it makes in travelling 15 m.

14 The wheels of a car have a diameter of 60 cm. Find (a) the speed of the car if the wheels rotate at 10 revolutions per second, (b) the number of revolutions made per second if the car travels at 90 km h⁻¹.

15 Find the radius of a wheel which rotates at 400 revolutions per minute when travelling at 80 km h⁻¹.

36 Arcs, Sectors, Segments

The length of an arc

The length of a circular arc is directly related to the angle it subtends at the centre of the circle. Consider the examples shown in Fig. 36.1.

Arc = $\frac{1}{4}$ of circumference   Arc = $\frac{1}{2}$ of circumference   Arc = $\frac{3}{4}$ of circumference

Fig. 36.1

In the first diagram, since *90° is a quarter of 360°*, the arc is a quarter of the circumference; in the second diagram, 180° is *half* of 360°, and the arc is half of the circumference. The diagrams thus illustrate the general principle that if the angle at the centre is θ, the arc will be a fraction $\frac{\theta}{360°}$ of the circumference.

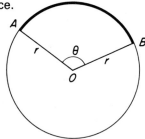

Fig. 36.2

With reference to Fig. 36.2, the general result is

$$\frac{\text{arc } AB}{2\pi r} = \frac{\theta}{360°}.$$

The area of a sector

Again referring to Fig. 36.2, and using similar reasoning to that used to determine the length of an arc, we have

$$\frac{\text{sector } OAB}{\pi r^2} = \frac{\theta}{360°}.$$

The area of a segment

The area of a *minor* segment can be found by treating the segment as the difference between a sector and an isosceles triangle, and that of a *major* segment can be found by regarding the segment as the sum of a sector and an isosceles triangle (Fig. 36.3).

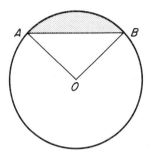

Minor segment = sector
OAB − triangle *OAB*

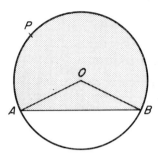

Major segment = sector
OAPB + triangle *OAB*

Fig. 36.3

The area of triangle *OAB* can be obtained from the formula $\frac{1}{2}ab \sin C$. If angle $AOB = \theta$, then triangle $OAB = \frac{1}{2}r^2 \sin \theta$.

▷Example 1

The radius of a circle is 20 cm. Find (a) the length of an arc which subtends an angle of 70° at the centre, (b) the angle subtended at the centre by an arc of length 55 cm.

(a) Let the length of the arc be x cm; then we have

$$\frac{x}{2\pi \times 20} = \frac{70}{360}$$
$$\therefore \ x = \frac{40\pi \times 70}{360} = 24.4 \text{ to 3 s.f.}$$

The arc length is thus 24.4 cm.

(b) Let the required angle be θ; then we have

$$\frac{55}{2\pi \times 20} = \frac{\theta}{360°}$$
$$\therefore \ \theta = \frac{55 \times 360°}{2\pi \times 20}$$
$$= 158° \text{ to 3 s.f.} \qquad \triangleleft$$

▷Example 2

APB is a major arc of a circle, centre O. AB = 12 cm and the radius of the circle is 8 cm. Find the area of (a) the major sector OAPB, (b) the major segment APB.

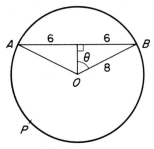

Fig. 36.4

Angle *AOB* must be found, and since triangle *OAB* is isosceles we drop a perpendicular as shown in Fig. 36.4. Then we have

$$\sin\theta = \frac{6}{8} = 0.75$$
$$\therefore \ \theta = 48.59°$$
$$\therefore \ \text{angle } AOB = 97.18°$$
$$\therefore \ \text{reflex angle } AOB = 360° - 97.18°$$
$$= 262.8° \text{ (to 4 s.f.).}$$

(a) We now have

$$\frac{\text{sector } OAPB}{\pi \times 8^2} = \frac{262.8}{360},$$

from which

$$\text{sector } OAPB = 146.8 \text{ cm}^2$$
$$= 147 \text{ cm}^2 \text{ to 3 s.f.}$$

(b) The major segment *APB* is obtained by adding triangle *OAB* to the major sector *OAPB*.

$$\text{Triangle } OAB = \tfrac{1}{2} \times 8^2 \sin 97.18$$
$$= 31.75 \text{ cm}^2.$$
$$\therefore \ \text{segment } APB = 146.8 + 31.75$$
$$= 179 \text{ cm}^2 \text{ to 3 s.f.} \qquad \triangleleft$$

▷**Example 3**

In Fig. 36.5, AD and BC are arcs of circles with centre O. Find the area of the shaded region.

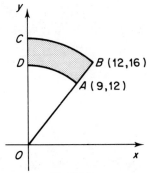

Fig. 36.5

Let E be the foot of the perpendicular from A to the y-axis (Fig. 36.6).

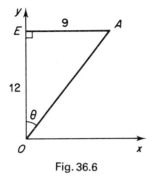

Fig. 36.6

OAE is a 3,4,5 triangle, so $OA = 15$. Also $\theta = \text{arc tan } \frac{3}{4} = 36.87°$, and $OB = \frac{4}{3}OA = 20$.

The area of the shaded region is the difference between the areas of sectors OBC, OAD, and it can be found by calculating the areas of these sectors. A better method, however, is to use the fact that the two sectors are similar. Since the ratio of their sides is 4:3, it follows that the ratio of their areas is 16:9, and thus that the shaded region is $\frac{7}{9}$ of sector OAD. If we use this method, we only have to calculate the area of one of the sectors.

$$\frac{\text{Sector } OAD}{\pi \times 15^2} = \frac{36.87}{360}$$

$$\therefore \text{ sector } OAD = \frac{225\,\pi \times 36.87}{360}$$

$$= 72.39,$$

$$\therefore \text{ shaded region} = \frac{7}{9} \times 72.39$$

$$= 56.3 \text{ to 3 s.f.} \qquad \blacktriangleleft$$

Construction of a cone from a sector

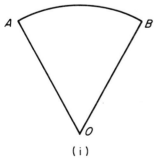
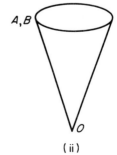

Fig. 36.7

Suppose that the minor sector OAB shown in diagram (i) of Fig. 36.7 is made of cardboard or thin metal. The sector can then be 'rolled' into the cone shown in diagram (ii) by joining the edges *OA, OB.* There are clearly two simple relationships between the dimensions of the cone and the sector, namely

radius *OA* = slant length of cone,
arc length *AB* = circumference of circular base.

The other relationships, involving, for example, the radius and height of the cone, can be derived from these two. The following example demonstrates the procedure.

▷ Example 4

*An arc AB of a circle of centre O and radius 15 cm subtends an angle of 120°
at O. The sector OAB is cut out and rolled into a cone. Find the radius of the
base of the cone and its height.*

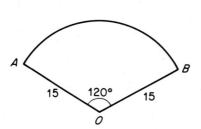
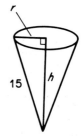

Fig. 36.8

First we find the length of arc *AB*. Since 120° is $\frac{1}{3}$ of 360°, arc *AB* is $\frac{1}{3}$ of the circumference of the circle of centre *O* and radius 15 cm:

$$\text{arc } AB = \frac{2\pi \times 15}{3} = 10\pi \text{ cm.}$$

Now arc *AB* is equal to the circumference of the base of the cone, so we have

$$2\pi r = 10\pi$$
$$\therefore r = 5.$$

The height *h* cm can now be found by Pythagoras' theorem:

$$h^2 = 15^2 - 5^2 = 200$$
$$\therefore h = 14.1 \text{ to 3 s.f.}$$

The radius of the cone is thus 5 cm (exactly), and the height is 14.1 cm to 3 s.f.◁

Note that it will always be possible to cancel π when the arc length of the sector is equated to the circumference of the base of the cone. This often means that an exact answer for the radius can be obtained, and that the use of a calculator can be avoided.

EXERCISE 36

Questions 1–15 refer to an arc ABC which subtends an angle of θ at the centre of a circle of radius r and centre O.

In questions 1–4, find (a) arc ABC, (b) area of sector $OABC$.
1 $\theta = 60°, r = 5$ cm.   **2** $\theta = 77°, r = 25$ cm.   **3** $\theta = 270°, r = 4$ cm.
4 $\theta = 158°, r = 12$ cm.

In questions 5–10, find θ.
5 arc $ABC = 12$ cm, $r = 14$ cm.   **6** arc $ABC = 2\pi$ cm, $r = 12$ cm.
7 sector $OABC = 8$ cm^2, $r = 2$ cm.   **8** sector $OABC = 57$ cm^2, $r = 10$ cm.
9 sector $OABC = 5\pi$ cm^2, $r = 5$ cm.   **10** arc $ABC = 7\pi$ cm, $r = 5$ cm.

In questions 11–15, find r.
11 arc $ABC = 15$ cm, $\theta = 72°$.   **12** sector $OABC = 75$ cm^2, $\theta = 137°$.
13 sector $OABC = 4$ cm^2, $\theta = 90°$.   **14** arc $ABC = 14\pi$ cm, $\theta = 18°$.
15 arc $ABC = 10$ cm, sector $OABC = 30$ cm^2.

16 A chord of a circle of radius 6 cm subtends an angle of 140° at the centre. Find the area of the minor segment cut off by the chord.
17 Find the area of the major segment cut off by a chord of length 8 cm in a circle of radius 8 cm.
18 Find the area of the minor segment cut off by a chord of a circle of radius 10 cm which subtends an angle of 72° at the circumference.
19 AB is an arc of length 2π cm in a circle of radius 3 cm. Find the area of the major segment cut off by the chord AB.
20 A running track consists of two straight sections of length 80 m which are 60 m apart, and two arcs of circles whose centre O is at the centre of the track. Find the perimeter of the track.
21 The minute and hour hands of a clock have lengths of 20 cm and 18 cm, respectively. Find the distances travelled in 1 hour 40 minutes by (a) the tip of the minute hand, (b) the tip of the hour hand.
22 A windscreen wiper consists of a rotating arm of length 50 cm, the outer 30 cm of which carries a rubber blade. Find the area swept out by the blade if the arm rotates through 100°.
23 Two tangents to a circle of radius 10 cm meet at an angle of 60°. Find the area between the tangents and the circle.
24 AB is an arc of a circle of radius 20 cm, the angle it subtends at the centre O being 72°. The sector AOB is cut out and bent round to form a cone. Find the radius of the base of the cone and its height.

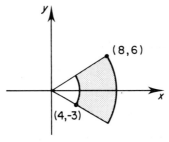

Fig. 36.9

25 In Fig. 36.9, O is the centre of both circular arcs. Find (a) the perimeter, (b) the area, of the shaded region.

26 A cone has height 24 cm and radius 10 cm. If the curved surface is 'unrolled' to form a sector *AOB* of a circle of centre *O*, what is angle *AOB*?

27 A horizontal cylindrical pipe of internal radius 10 cm and internal length 25 cm contains water to a depth of 5 cm. Find the volume of the water.

28 A pendulum of length 50 cm swings through an arc of length 10π cm. If the length of the pendulum is increased to 60 cm while the angle of each swing remains the same, what is the increase in the area swept out?

29 A sector *AOB* in which angle *AOB* = 90° is bent round to form a cone. Prove that the semivertical angle of the cone is arc tan $\frac{1}{4}$.

30 *A*(2,12) and *B*(10,0) are points on a circle of centre *P*(−3,0). Find the length of the minor arc *AB*.

31 In Fig. 36.10, *AB* is a diameter of the circle *ABC*. Find the area of the shaded region.

32 The figure shown (Fig. 36.11) consists of two equal and parallel straight sections and two equal circular arcs. Each arc is part of a circle at the centre of which it subtends an angle of 60°. Find the area of the figure.

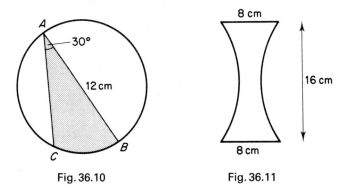

Fig. 36.10   Fig. 36.11

37 Latitude and Longitude

Great and small circles

A *great circle* is a circle on the surface of a sphere whose centre and radius are the same as those of the sphere itself. It is the largest kind of circle that can be drawn on the surface of a sphere. Any other circle on the sphere has a smaller radius and is known as a *small circle* (Fig. 37.1).

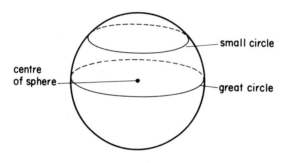

Fig. 37.1

The earth

The earth will be considered here to be an exact sphere (Fig. 37.2). To specify the position of a point on the surface of the earth two sets of circles are used. *Meridians* are circles which pass through the north and south poles, and they are all great circles. *Parallels of latitude* are circles which are perpendicular to the meridians, and only one of them – the *equator* – is a great circle.

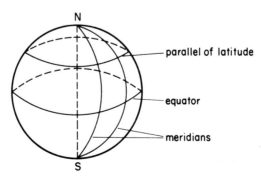

Fig. 37.2

If we think of the north pole as being at the 'top' of the earth, and the south pole as being at the 'bottom', the meridians can be described as vertical circles and the parallels of latitude as horizontal circles. In using this kind of description we are picturing the earth as a model globe set up in the normal way.

The latitude and longitude of a point

The words 'latitude' and 'longitude' are slightly deceptive since latitude tells us how *north or south* a point is, while longitude describes how *east or west* it is. Both latitude and longitude are *angles*. Latitude is measured relative to the equator, and its exact meaning is illustrated by Fig. 37.3. All the points on the upper parallel shown have latitudes of 50°N, and all those on the lower parallel have latitudes of 30°S.

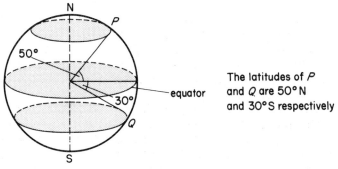

The latitudes of P and Q are 50°N and 30°S respectively

Fig. 37.3

Longitude is measured relative to the semi-meridian known as the *Greenwich meridian* which stretches from the north pole through Greenwich to the south pole. In Fig. 37.4 all the points on the semi-meridian NPS have a longitude of 40°E.

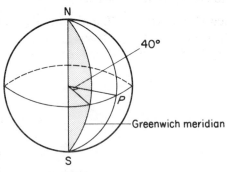

Fig. 37.4

All the diagrams so far have been 3-dimensional, but angles of latitude and longitude are often more conveniently shown in 2-dimensional diagrams. Fig. 37.5(i) represents a view from the 'side' of the earth, and shows just one meridian, while Fig. 37.5(ii) gives a view from 'above' and displays a single parallel of latitude.

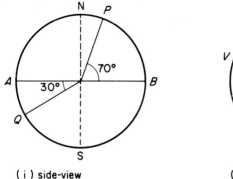
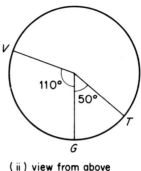

(i) side-view   (ii) view from above

Fig. 37.5

In diagram (i) the equator passes through A and B, and the latitudes of P and Q are respectively 70°N and 30°S. In diagram (ii) the Greenwich meridian passes through G, and the longitudes of T and V are respectively 50°E and 110°W. Diagrams such as (ii), representing views from above the north pole, should always be drawn with the point on the Greenwich meridian at the bottom of the circle.

It will be clear from the examples given that the latitude of a point can vary from 90°N to 90°S, while the longitude can vary from 180°E to 180°W.

By stating the latitude and longitude of a point we completely specify its position on the surface of the earth. Like x and y co-ordinates, the latitude and longitude of a point are often placed in brackets. For example we might have P(25°N, 150°W). When this is done the latitude is always stated first.

The radius of a parallel of latitude

The radius of the earth itself, and thus of all meridians and the equator, is usually taken to be 6370 km and denoted by R. The radius of a parallel of latitude is denoted by r, and its value can be obtained in terms of R as follows.

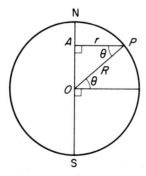

Fig. 37.6

Fig. 37.6 shows a meridian, on which there lies a point P of latitude θ. PA is the radius of the parallel of latitude through P, and PO is the radius of the earth. From triangle OAP we have

$$\cos \theta = \frac{AP}{OP}$$
$$\therefore \ AP = OP\cos \theta$$
that is $\quad r = R\cos \text{latitude.}$

This formula for r should be learned by heart.

Worked examples

Problems on latitude and longitude usually involve journeys on the surface of the earth. In this book we shall only consider journeys along meridians or parallels of latitude, that is N–S or E–W journeys. The problems are solved by the method explained in the last chapter for dealing with circular arcs, based on the equation

$$\frac{\text{arc length}}{2\pi r} = \frac{\theta}{360°}.$$

In all the examples the radius of the earth, R, will be taken to be 6370 km.

▷ Example 1

An aeroplane flies due south from the point A(20°N, 40°W) to B(50°S, 40°W). Find the distance travelled. (Regard the plane's own height as negligible.)

The journey takes place on the 40°W meridian, and we draw a 2-dimensional diagram (Fig. 37.7) showing this meridian only. Since the journey is along a great circle we call the radius R and not r.

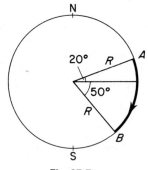

Fig. 37.7

By the standard equation for arc length we have

$$\frac{\text{arc } AB}{2\pi R} = \frac{70}{360'}$$
$$\text{and since } R = 6370 \text{ km,}$$
$$\text{arc } AB = \frac{2\pi \times 6370 \times 70}{360}$$
$$= 7780 \text{ km to 3 s.f.} \qquad \triangleleft$$

▷Example 2

A man travels 25 000 km due west from P(40°S, 30°W) to a point Q. Find the latitude and longitude of Q.

Since the man travels due west his latitude does not change. Hence the journey takes place on the 40°S parallel of latitude and we draw this circle, viewing it from 'above' the north pole and placing the Greenwich meridian at the bottom of the circle. The parallel of latitude is a small circle, so we call the radius *r* (Fig. 37.8).

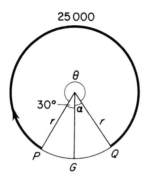

25 000

Fig. 37.8

The longitude of *Q* is the angle α, but we begin by finding the reflex angle θ which is subtended by the arc of length 25 000 km.

$$\frac{\theta}{360°} = \frac{25\ 000}{2\pi r}.$$

Now from the standard equation $r = R \cos$ latitude, we have $r = 6370 \cos 40°$. Hence

$$\theta = \frac{25\ 000 \times 360°}{2\pi \times 6370 \cos 40°}.$$
$$= 293.54°$$
$$\therefore \quad \alpha = 360° - 30° - 293.54° \text{ (angles at a point)}$$
$$= 36.5° \text{ to 3 s.f.}$$

It follows that the latitude and longitude of *Q* are 40°S, and 36.5°E to 3 s.f. ◁

▷Example 3

An aeroplane flies due north from the point A(20°N, 50°W). Staying on the same meridian throughout, it passes over the north pole, and after travelling 15 000 km altogether, finishes at a point B. Find the latitude and longitude of B.

First we consider the meridian along which the plane flies (Fig. 37.9).

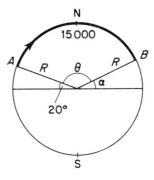

Fig. 37.9

The latitude of B is α, and in order to find α we first calculate θ.

$$\frac{\theta}{360°} = \frac{15\,000}{2\pi \times 6370}$$
$$\therefore \; \theta = \frac{15\,000 \times 360°}{2\pi \times 6370}$$
$$= 134.9°.$$

Hence $\alpha = 180° - 134.9° - 20°$ (adjacent angles on a
straight line)
$= 25.1°$ to 3 s.f.

To find the longitude of B we consider the view from above the north pole (Fig. 37.10).

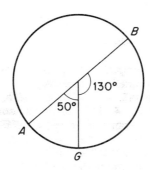

Fig. 37.10

It can be seen from Fig. 37.10 that when the plane passes over the north pole its longitude changes from 50°W to 130°E.

The latitude and longitude of B are therefore 25.1°N (to 3 s.f.) and 130°E.   ◁

▷ Example 4

Two points A and B on the same parallel of latitude are 4000 km apart and their longitudes differ by 70°. Find the latitude of A and B.

Consider the parallel of latitude on which A and B lie. Since the longitudes of A and B differ by 70°, the arc AB subtends an angle of 70° at the centre (Fig. 37.11).

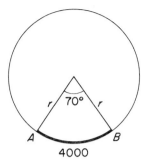

Fig. 37.11

We now have

$$\frac{4000}{2\pi r} = \frac{70}{360}$$

$$\therefore \quad \frac{4000}{2\pi \times 6370 \cos \text{latitude}} = \frac{70}{360}$$

$$\therefore \quad \cos \text{latitude} = \frac{4000 \times 360}{2\pi \times 6370 \times 70}$$

$$\therefore \quad \text{latitude} = 59.1°\text{N or S to 3 s.f.} \qquad \triangleleft$$

EXERCISE 37a

Take the radius of the earth to be 6370 km.

In questions 1–12, find the lengths of the given journeys on the earth's surface. All are along meridians or parallels of latitude.
1 (20°N, 40°W) to (80°S, 40°W). **2** (0°N, 70°E) to (0°N, 10°E).
3 (35°S, 30°E) to (45°N, 30°E). **4** (30°N, 20°W) due south to the equator.
5 From the south pole to the equator. **6** (50°N, 10°E) to (50°N, 80°E).
7 (60°S, 40°E) to (60°S, 10°W).
8 (10°N, 30°E) over the N-pole to (20°N, 150°W).
9 (40°S, 15°W) via the south pole to (10°S, 165°E).
10 (20°S, 50°E) over the N-pole to (10°N, 130°W).
11 (50°N, 40°W) due *west* to (50°N, 50°E).
12 (10°S, 30°E) due *east* to (10°S, 30°W).

In questions 13–20 find the latitude and longitude at the end of each of the given journeys.
13 3000 km due north from (0°N, 20°W).
14 2000 km due east from (0°N, 25°E).
15 6500 km due west from (0°N, 36°E).
16 4500 km due west from (60°S, 30°E).
17 9500 km due west from (30°N, 15°W).
18 12 000 km due north from the south pole along the Greenwich meridian.
19 2700 km due east from (40°S, 138°W).
20 7000 km due east from (20°N, 160°E).

21 A geographical globe has a radius of 10 cm. Find the length of the 35°N parallel of latitude.

22 An aeroplane flies 4000 km due west from a point P with longitude 20°E to a point Q with longitude 50°W. What is the latitude of P and Q?

23 An aeroplane flies 10 000 km from $P(20°N, 55°E)$. It passes over the north pole and finishes at Q, staying on the same meridian throughout. Find the latitude and longitude of Q.

24 A ship sailing at 30 km h^{-1} would take 700 hours to sail right round a certain parallel of latitude. Find this latitude.

25 A man travels 6000 km due east from the point (28°S, 34°W), then 7000 km due north. Find his final latitude and longitude.

26 An aeroplane flies 12 000 km due west from the point (36°S, 116°W), then 1850 km due north. Find its final latitude and longitude.

27 One aeroplane flies due north from $A(0°N, 0°E)$ to $B(30°N, 0°E)$, and then due east to $C(30°N, 40°E)$. Another aeroplane flies due east from A to $D(0°N, 40°E)$, and then due north to C. Calculate the difference in length between the two journeys.

28 One aeroplane flies at an average speed of 800 km h^{-1} direct from $P(30°N, 70°W)$ to $Q(30°N, 110°E)$ via the north pole. Another aeroplane flies due east from P to Q. If the two aeroplanes take the same time, what is the average speed of the second aeroplane?

The nautical mile and the knot

The nautical mile (n.m.) is a unit which simplifies calculations involving journeys on the earth's surface. The definition is as follows.

1 nautical mile is the arc length on a great circle which subtends an angle of 1 minute at the centre of the earth.
(1 minute $= \frac{1}{60}$ of a degree.)

We have already seen (chapter 31) that the *knot* is a unit of speed and equal to 1 nautical mile per hour.

To see why calculations are simpler when the nautical mile is used, consider the journey along the equator from $P(0°N, 20°W)$ to $Q(0°N, 30°E)$ (Fig. 37.12).

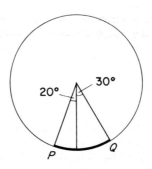

Fig. 37.12

We have

$$\text{arc } PQ \text{ in n.m.} = \text{minutes subtended at centre}$$
$$= 60 \times 50$$
$$= 3000 \text{ n.m.}$$

If the journey takes place on a parallel of latitude rather than a great circle, the calculation is slightly more complicated. Fig. 37.13 shows a parallel of latitude and the equator, both viewed from above the north pole.

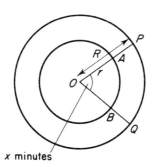

Fig. 37.13

PQ is an arc of a great circle which subtends x minutes at the centre. Hence

$$PQ = x \text{ n.m.}$$

Since the sectors OAB, OPQ are similar, however, we have

$$\frac{AB}{PQ} = \frac{r}{R} = \cos \text{ latitude (since } r = R \cos \text{ latitude)}$$

and hence $AB = PQ \cos \text{ latitude}$

or $AB = x \cos \text{ latitude}.$

There are consequently two standard results, one for journeys along great circles and one for journeys along parallels of latitude.

Great circle journeys: **Arc length in n.m. = minutes subtended at centre.**
Small circle journeys: **Arc length in n.m. = minutes subtended at centre × cos latitude.**

▷ **Example 5**

The point P, with longtidue 18°W, is 2000 n.m. due west of the point Q whose longitude is 30°E. Find the latitude of P and Q.

Consider the parallel of latitude containing P and Q (Fig. 37.14).

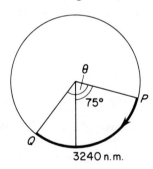

Fig. 37.14

Since arc *PQ* is part of a *small* circle we have

$$\text{arc } PQ = \text{minutes subtended at centre} \times \cos \text{latitude}$$
$$\therefore \quad 2000 = 48 \times 60 \cos \text{latitude}$$
$$\therefore \quad \cos \text{latitude} = \frac{2000}{48 \times 60}$$
$$\therefore \quad \text{latitude} = 46.0° \text{ N or S to 3 s.f.} \quad \triangleleft$$

▷ Example 6

An aeroplane flies 3240 n.m. due west from P(60°S, 75°E) to Q. Find the longitude of Q.

Consider the 60°S parallel of latitude (Fig. 37.15).

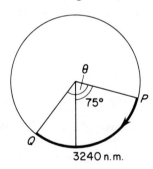

Fig. 37.15

We have

$$\text{arc } PQ = \text{minutes subtended at centre} \times \cos \text{latitude}$$
$$\therefore \quad 3240 = 60 \, \theta \cos 60°.$$

Since $\cos 60° = \frac{1}{2}$ it follows that

$$\theta = \frac{3240 \times 2}{60}$$
$$= 108,$$

and the longitude of Q is therefore $108° - 75° = 33°$ W. $\triangleleft$

The conversion of n.m. to km

An arc of length 1 n.m. on a great circle subtends an angle of $(\frac{1}{60})°$ at the centre of the earth. Hence, letting this arc have a length of x km, we have

$$\frac{x}{2\pi R} = \frac{\frac{1}{60}}{360}$$

$$\therefore \quad x = \frac{2\pi \times 6370}{60 \times 360}$$

$$= 1.85 \text{ to 3 s.f.}$$

It follows that 1 n.m. $\approx$ 1.85 km.

EXERCISE 37b

In questions 1–7, find the lengths of the given journeys in n.m. All are along meridians or parallels of latitude.

1 (30°N, 20°E) to (70°N, 20°E).   **2** (0°N, 26°W) to (0°N, 42°E).

3 From the north pole to the south pole.   **4** (60°N, 70°E) to (60°N, 54°W).

5 (50°N, 110°W) due west to (50°N, 110°E).

6 (20°S, 50°E) over the north pole to (30°S, 130°W).

7 (78°S, 26°E) due east to (78°S, 123°W).

In questions 8–12, find the latitudes and longitudes after the given journeys.

8 9000 n.m. due north from (70°S, 40°W).

9 2700 n.m. due east from (0°N, 10°E).

10 870 n.m. due west from (60°N, 76°W).

11 4000 n.m. due east from (25°N, 52°W).

12 6360 n.m. due south from the north pole along the Greenwich meridian.

13 When a ship sails 1600 n.m. due west its longitude changes by 40°. Find its latitude.

14 The length of a certain parallel of latitude is 5400 n.m. Find the latitude of this parallel.

15 A ship sails 1200 n.m. due west from (0°N, 15°W) and then 1500 n.m. due south. Find its final latitude and longitude.

16 A ship sails due north at 34 knots for 90 hours, finishing at (15°N, 120°W). What was its starting point?

17 An aeroplane takes 12 hours to fly from P(10°N, 100°W) direct to Q(30°N, 80°E) via the north pole. Find its average speed in knots.

18 A ship sails for 300 hours along the 60°S parallel of latitude, changing its longitude by 150°. Find its average speed in knots.

19 One aeroplane flies due east from P(60°N, 40°W) to Q(60°N, 140°E), while another flies from P to Q along a meridian via the north pole. Find the difference in the lengths of their journeys, in n.m.

20 An aeroplane flying due east along the equator at 500 knots takes the same time to change its longitude by 100° as another aeroplane flying due east at 600 knots takes to change its longitude by 150°. Find the latitude of the second aeroplane.

38 Statistics

The ordinary average or arithmetic mean

In everyday life the word *average* denotes a quantity which mathematicians call the *arithmetic mean*. It is given this name to distinguish it from some other forms of average which we shall deal with later. In its ordinary sense the term can be defined as follows.

$$\text{Average (or mean)} = \frac{\text{total quantity}}{\text{number of items}}.$$

For example, the average of 7, 9 and 14 is $\frac{30}{3} = 10$, and if a cricketer scores 12, 38, 72, and 16 in four innings, his average score is $\frac{138}{4} = 34\frac{1}{2}$.

It often happens that we know an average and require the corresponding total quantity. If so we use the following formula, which is derived immediately from the definition.

$$\text{Total quantity} = \text{average} \times \text{number of items}.$$

The following simple example illustrates the use of this formula.

▷Example 1

200 men work in a factory. 50 of them are skilled, and have an average wage of £120, while the other 150 are unskilled with an average wage of £90. What is the factory's total wage bill?

$$\begin{aligned}
\text{Total wage of skilled men} &= \text{average} \times \text{number of men} \\
&= £120 \times 50 = £6000. \\
\text{Total wage of unskilled men} &= £90 \times 150 = £13\,500. \\
\text{Hence total bill} &= £6000 + £13\,500 = £19\,500. \quad \blacktriangleleft
\end{aligned}$$

A common mistake in work on averages is to *average averages*. Suppose, for example, that the average ages of the children in two classes are 12 and 14. It is tempting but wrong to think that the average age of all the children must be the average of these two averages, namely 13. To find the true average we need to know the numbers of children in each class. If these are 30 and 20, respectively, we proceed as follows.

$$\text{Average age} = \frac{\text{total age}}{\text{number of children}} = \frac{(30 \times 12) + (20 \times 14)}{50} = 12.8.$$

This kind of average is sometimes called a *weighted* average. In calculating it we have given more weight to one class than the other because one class contains more children than the other.

In calculating the average of a number of quantities of similar size, it often saves time to work out the average *deviation* from some convenient number. This number is called the *working origin*. The following example illustrates the method.

▷ Example 2

Work out the average of 57, 58.2, 57.6, 59, 55.7, 61 and 58.

Here we might choose 57, 58 or 59 as a working origin. Working from 58 the deviations are as follows:

$$-1, \ 0.2, \ -0.4, \ 1, \ -2.3, \ 3 \text{ and zero.}$$

Now the total deviation is 0.5; hence the average deviation is $\dfrac{0.5}{7} = 0.07$ to 2 d.p., and the average of the original quantities is thus 58.07 to 2 d.p.

(*Note:* This method is useful if a calculator is not available, but if a calculator is being used it is probably quicker simply to sum the original quantities.) ◁

▷ Example 3

A cricketer averages 47 in 12 innings. What must he average in his next 3 innings to bring his average up to 50?

$$\text{Total scored so far} = 47 \times 12 = 564.$$
$$\text{Total required} = 50 \times 15 = 750.$$

Hence the cricketer must score $750 - 564$ runs in his next three innings and thus must average $\dfrac{186}{3} = 62$. ◁

▷ Example 4

The average age of 20 boys and 10 girls is $13\frac{1}{2}$. If the average age of the boys is 14.2, what is that of the girls?

$$\text{Total age of all children} = 13\tfrac{1}{2} \times 30 = 405.$$
$$\text{Total age of boys} = 14.2 \times 20 = 284.$$
$$\therefore \ \text{total age of girls} = 405 - 284 = 121,$$
$$\therefore \ \text{average age of girls} = \frac{121}{10} = 12.1.$$ ◁

▷ Example 5

A bookshelf holds 4 books with 300 pages each and 5 books with 350 pages each. Some books with 150 pages are added and the average number of pages per book becomes 250. How many books are added?

Let the number of books added be x; then we have:

$$\text{Total number of pages} = (4 \times 300) + (5 \times 350) + 150x.$$
$$\text{Total number of books} = 9 + x.$$

Now using the equation

$$\text{total quantity} = \text{average} \times \text{number of items},$$

we obtain

$$1200 + 1750 + 150x = 250(9 + x),$$
$$\text{from which } 100x = 700,$$
$$\text{and hence } x = 7. \qquad \triangleleft$$

▷Example 6

A grocer buys x oranges and y apples, paying an average price of 7 p. If the average price of the oranges is 8 p, what is the average price of the apples in terms of x and y?

$$\text{Total price of all fruit} = 7(x + y) \text{ p.}$$
$$\text{Total price of oranges} = 8x \text{ p.}$$
$$\therefore \text{ total price of apples} = (7x + 7y - 8x) \text{ p}$$
$$= (7y - x) \text{ p,}$$
$$\therefore \text{ average price of apples} = \frac{7y - x}{y} \text{ p.} \qquad \triangleleft$$

EXERCISE 38a

In questions 1–5, find the average of the given numbers without using a calculator.

1 8, 12, 13.   **2** 257 and 269.   **3** 6.3, 5.6, 3.1.   **4** 86, 86.2, 85.4, 87, 86.8.
5 147.5, 148, 143.2, 146, 147, 148.3, 143.4.

6 Two pens cost 20 p each and 3 pencils cost 5 p each. Find the average cost.
7 12 articles are bought at an average price of £4 and 2 more at £11 each. Find the overall average price.
8 A cricketer averages 47 in 5 innings. What must he score in his next innings to bring his average up to 50?
9 What is the average of $\frac{1}{3}$, $\frac{3}{4}$ and $\frac{1}{6}$?
10 A girl's marks in three tests are 18%, 26% and 21%. What must she get in her next test to bring her average up to 30%?
11 Five women have an average age of 25. If a woman of 55 joins them, what is the new average age?
12 What is the average of $1\frac{1}{2}$, $-\frac{5}{8}$, $1\frac{1}{8}$ and $-\frac{2}{3}$?
13 A shopkeeper buys 200 articles at 3 p each and 300 more at an average price of 4 p. If he sells them all at an average price of 5 p, how much profit does he make?
14 A firm employs 40 men at a wage of £75, 25 men at £100 and 15 men at £120. What is the average wage?
15 A shopkeeper buys 250 articles at an average price of 8 p, and sells them for a total price of £30. Find (a) her total outlay, (b) the average price she charges for the articles.
16 In a class of 30 girls, 18 get 50 p pocket money each, 5 get £1 each and the rest get 40 p each. What is the average pocket money?
17 Two boys have an average age of $8\frac{1}{2}$. A third boy joins them, and the average rises to 9. What is his age?

18 A cricketer averages 34 after 5 innings, and after 3 more innings his average drops to 31. How many runs has he scored in the 3 innings?

19 15 men have an average wage of £80. If 10 of them have an average wage of £75, what is the average wage of the rest?

20 A football team sets out to average one point per game over the whole season, during which 42 games are played. If they average only 0.5 points per game for the first 22 games, what must they average for the rest of the season to achieve their original objective?

21 A boy averages 70% at his first 5 tests, then obtains only 10% at the next. What must he average at the next 4 tests to bring his average back to 70%?

22 The average age of Susan and Peter is 7, that of Susan, Peter and Harry is 9, and that of Susan and Harry is 8. How old are Susan, Peter and Harry?

EXERCISE 38b (harder)

1 Write down an expression for the average age of x boys aged 10 and y girls aged 12.

2 Write down an expression for the average wage in pounds of 5 men who earn £x and 7 women who earn £y.

3 20 boys have an average age of 10. How many 15-year-olds must join them to bring the average age up to 11?

4 A cricketer averages 35 in his first 8 innings and 52 in his next 7. What must he average in his next 5 innings to have an overall average of 50?

5 A shopkeeper buys x pens and y pencils. The average price of the pens is 25 p and the overall average price is 15 p. Obtain an expression for the average price of the pencils.

6 20 boys have an average age of $17\frac{1}{2}$ and some girls have an average of 16 years 8 months. If the overall average age is 17, find the number of girls.

7 A woman buys some articles at 50 p each and twice as many at 20 p each. What is the average price of all the articles?

8 The overall average age of 5 boys and 3 girls is x years. Given that the age of each of the girls is y years, obtain an expression for the average age in years of the boys.

9 A girl sets out to average 60% in all her year's maths tests. After averaging only 50% for a certain number of tests, she calculates that she needs to obtain 100% in all the three remaining tests to achieve her original objective. How many tests has she had already?

10 A man buys 12 articles at $12\frac{1}{2}$ p each, 15 at 3 p each and a certain number at 5 p each. The overall average price is $6\frac{1}{2}$ p. How many does he buy at 5 p?

Other kinds of average

An ordinary average or arithmetic mean can sometimes be deceptive in the information it gives. Consider for example the following examination scores of a class of 5 girls:

$$49\%, \ 56\%, \ 53\%, \ 47\%, \ 95\%$$

All but one of the girls has scored around 50%, yet owing to one unusually high score the average is 60% and all but one are apparently 'below average'. Since an average is supposed to serve as a representative of a whole series of values, this is clearly unsatisfactory and explains why other forms of average are sometimes used. The *median* and the *mode* are two kinds of average which, unlike the mean, are unaffected by extreme values.

The median

To find the median of a set of values we first list them in ascending or descending order, and then take the value which lies halfway along the series. If there is an even number of values, we take the mean of the middle two values.

Suppose, for example, that we require the median of the numbers 7, 12, 15, 7, 20, 50, 20, 5. Listing the numbers in ascending order, we have

$$5, \ 7, \ 7, \ 12, \ 15, \ 20, \ 20, \ 50.$$

There are eight numbers altogether, so the middle two are the fourth and the fifth. These are 12 and 15; hence the median is $\frac{12 + 15}{2} = 13\frac{1}{2}$. In this case the median is significantly different from the mean, which is 17.

The mode

The mode of a set of values is the *most frequently occurring* value. For example the mode of 2, 3, 3, 5, 5, 5, 8 is 5. Not all sets of values have modes, and some have more than one mode. For example, the numbers 2, 7, 9, 15 have no mode, and the numbers 2, 3, 3, 7, 9, 9, 12 have the two modes 3 and 9.

The mode is not usually a good representative value for a small set of numbers. Consider the following very similar sets:

$$4, \ 6, \ 10, \ 19, \ 21.$$
$$5, \ 5, \ 10, \ 19, \ 21.$$
$$4, \ 6, \ 10, \ 20, \ 20.$$

Even though there is little essential difference in these sets, and they have the same means and medians, the first has no mode and the second and third have the very different modes of 5 and 20.

The mode can be a useful average when there are large numbers of items. It certainly helps manufacturers of clothes and shoes, for example, to know the most frequently occurring sizes.

Frequency distributions

Suppose a football team plays 20 games in a season, and the manager wants a record of its performance in terms of goals scored. The simplest procedure would be to make a list of the scores in each game, e.g.

$$2, \ 0, \ 1, \ 1, \ 3, \ 0, \ 1, \ 2, \ 2, \ 4,$$
$$0, \ 0, \ 1, \ 3, \ 0, \ 2, \ 3, \ 1, \ 1, \ 2.$$

This list gives all the necessary information, but in an unorganised way: it is said to give the *raw data*. What the manager would probably find more useful, however, is a record of *how many times* the team scored no goals, 1 goal, etc; that is, the *frequency* of each of these scores. This information can be presented in a convenient way by a table called a *frequency table* or a *frequency distribution*:

Number of goals	0	1	2	3	4
Frequency	5	6	5	3	1

From this table the mean score, as well as the median and mode scores, can be calculated quite easily.

Calculation of the mean from a frequency distribution

The mean number of goals scored per game in the above example is obtained from the fraction

$$\frac{\text{total number of goals}}{\text{total number of games}}$$

To see how the total number of goals is calculated consider as an example the third pair of entries in the above table. If the team scores 2 goals 5 times it scores $5 \times 2 = 10$ goals altogether. This indicates that we obtain the total number of goals by multiplying each number in the first row by the corresponding frequency and adding the results.

$$\begin{aligned}\text{Total number of goals} &= (5 \times 0) + (6 \times 1) + (5 \times 2) + (3 \times 3) + (1 \times 4)\\ &= 29.\end{aligned}$$

The total number of games is simply the sum of all the frequencies, that is $5 + 6 + 5 + 3 + 1 = 20$; hence the mean score is $\frac{29}{20} = 1.45$.

The reasoning applied in this example can be generalised. Let x stand for the quantity whose mean is required, and let f stand for frequency. Then we can set out the above kind of calculation more briefly by adding a line to the frequency table giving the values of fx. The following example illustrates the procedure:

x	1	2	3	4	5	
f	7	10	12	9	4	Total 42
fx	7	20	36	36	20	Total 119

The mean value in this case is $\frac{119}{42} = 2.83$ to 2 d.p.

Calculation of the median and the mode from a frequency distribution

Consider the following frequency distribution:

x	0	1	2	3	4
f	10	12	9	9	7

By adding the frequencies we find that there are 47 values altogether and the middle value is therefore the 24th. (This has 23 values above and below it.) Now the first 10 values are zero, the next 12 are 1 and the 24th is one of the next 9 values, all of which are 2. Hence the median is 2. The mode is the most frequently occurring value, and this is clearly 1, which occurs 12 times.

Diagramatic representation of data

Bar charts

Fig. 38.1 gives a simple example of a bar chart, showing the amount of time that a pupil is supposed to spend on different homework subjects.

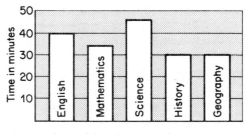

Fig. 38.1

The following points should be noted:
(1) It is only the *lengths* of the bars which give the required measurements; their widths and areas have no significance. In some charts of this kind the bars are reduced to straight lines.
(2) The horizontal axis is not graduated numerically. There is clearly no numerical relationship between school subjects, so no numbers appear on the horizontal axis in the above example. Even when numbers do appear, however, they do not graduate the axis into equal divisions like the numbers on an *x*-axis or number line. Consider for example the bar chart shown in Fig. 38.2, representing the frequencies with which a football team has scored 0, 1, 2, 3 goals.

The numbers on the horizontal axis are not at all like those on a proper number line, where they represent distances from the origin. Here the bars can be drawn at different distances apart, and even their order can, if desired, be changed.

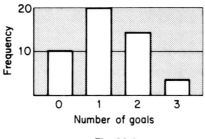

Fig. 38.2

Pie charts

A pie chart is a circular diagram in which quantities are represented by the areas of sectors. This kind of diagram is useful for comparing a small number of quantities which together form a whole or complete set of some kind.

Suppose, for example, that 20 children are asked their favourite school subject and the results are as follows:

English	Mathematics	Science	History
4	5	8	3

To display this information in the form of a pie chart we first divide 360° in the ratio 4:5:8:3. This gives us the angles at the centre of the chart corresponding to each subject.

$$\text{English:} \quad \frac{4}{20} \times 360° = 72°$$

$$\text{Maths:} \quad \frac{5}{20} \times 360° = 90°$$

$$\text{Science:} \quad \frac{8}{20} \times 360° = 144°$$

$$\text{History:} \quad \frac{3}{20} \times 360° = 54°.$$

We can now construct the pie chart as in Fig. 38.3.

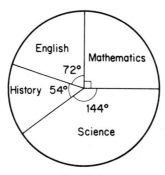

Fig. 38.3

EXERCISE 38c

1 Find the mean, median and mode of each of the following sets of numbers:
(a) 0, 1, 2, 3, 3; (b) 5, 2, 7, 15, 7; (c) 25, 0, 150, 0, 40, 15, 80, 10;
(d) 5, −7, 5, −3, −7, 9, −3, 5; (e) −0.4, 0.6, −0.3, 0.6, −0.1, −0.3, −0.3, 0.6, −0.1, −0.3.

2 A man buys 10 articles at £7 each, 14 articles at £2 each, 9 articles at £4 each and 7 articles at £8 each. Find the mean, median and modal prices.

3 In a test, 2 children get 3 marks, 8 get 4 marks, 6 get 5 marks and 4 get 6 marks. Find the mean, median and modal marks.

4 Given that 40 articles weigh 7 g each, 35 weigh 6 g each, 20 weigh 13 g each and 55 weigh 10 g each, find the mean, median and modal weights.

5 A football team scores no goals 5 times, one goal 8 times and more than one goal 10 times. Which of the three averages can be obtained from this data and what is its value?

6 The marks of five students at a test are 34%, 58%, 47%, 51% and 35%. Find the mean and median marks. If another student joins the group and scores 93%, what are the new mean and median marks?

7 A man buys 10 articles at 5 p each, 25 at 8 p each and another 5 at an average price of 22 p. State the values of the averages which can be found from this data.

8 The homeworks of 30 children are marked out of 10. State the values of the averages that can be found, given that 8 children get below 5, 12 get 5 and 10 get more than 5.

9 A factory employs 9 men at a wage of £120, 4 men at £105 and 3 men at £100. They also employ 4 men whose average wage is £110. State the values of the averages that can be found from this data.

10 The following table shows the percentages of his leisure time that a certain man spends on various activities:

Reading	Television	Gardening	Conversation
5%	50%	35%	10%

Display this information (a) in a bar chart, (b) in a pie chart. State the angles at the centre of the pie chart.

11 A sixth former spends 40% of her study time on maths, 35% on physics and 25% on chemistry. Draw a pie chart to represent this data and state the angles at the centre.

12 The wickets taken by a bowler in a series of cricket matches are as follows:

Wickets	0	1	2	3	4	5	6
Frequency	3	2	5	7	6	4	3

Find the number of matches the bowler played in, and the mean, median and mode of the wickets he took.

13 Given that 2 articles cost 10 p each, 3 cost 11 p each, 4 cost 12 p each and 1 costs 13 p, find (a) the mean, median and modal prices, (b) the angles at the centre of a pie chart representing this data.

14 The sector angles in a pie chart are 90°, 120° and 150°. If the whole chart represents 600 items, how many items are represented by each of the three sectors?

15 A pie chart is drawn to display the favourite sports of 90 children. How many choose football if the angle representing this sport is 140°?

16 If the areas of the sectors in a pie chart are in the ratio 1:2:4:5, what are the angles at the centre?

17 Find the mean, median and modal values of x for each of the following three frequency distributions:

(a)

x	1	2	3	4	5
f	12	10	8	11	9

(b)

x	0.5	1	1.5	2
f	2	5	4	4

(c)

x	10	15	20	25	30
f	24	36	40	52	48

18 If the data in question 17(b) is represented in a pie chart, what will be the angles at the centre?

19 A pie chart is drawn to show the percentages of the population who vote for various political parties at an election. What percentage vote Conservative if the angle representing this is 162°?

20 Four quantities are represented on a bar chart by rectangles with heights of 1 cm, 2 cm, 2.5 cm and 3.5 cm. If this data is displayed in a pie chart what will be the angles at the centre?

21 Some darts players are each given 20 shots at the bull, and the following results are recorded:

Hits	0	1	2	3	4	5
Frequency	2	5	4	4	3	2

Find (a) the number of players and the mean, median and modal number of hits, (b) the sector angles representing 1, 2 and 4 hits in a pie chart.

22 After paying his rent, a man divides his income between housekeeping, saving and pocket-money in the ratio 9:3:2. If the amount he saves is represented by a sector angle of 54° in a pie chart, what percentage of his income is used (a) for housekeeping, (b) for rent?

23 A pie chart consists of 4 sectors. Two of the sector angles are 70° and 90°, and the areas of the remaining sectors are in the ratio 2:3. If the smallest sector corresponds to a rectangle of height 3.5 cm on a bar chart, what are the heights of the other rectangles?

Discrete and continuous variables

The variables in the examples given so far have all been *discrete*, which means that they can take only particular, separated values such as 0, 1, 2, etc. The goals scored by a football team is clearly a discrete variable since this quantity can only have positive integral values.

Most variables, however, are not limited in this way. Although a person's height or weight cannot take *any* values — they cannot be negative or very large, for example — there are no restrictions on these quantities within a certain range of possible values. A height of 5.832 feet is no less possible than one of 6 feet exactly. Variables of this kind, which can take *all values within a certain range*, are called *continuous* variables.

Grouping data into classes

It is convenient to group raw data into classes whenever we have to deal with a large number of different values. This is always likely in the case of a continuous variable — since, for example, people seldom have exactly the same height — and it can sometimes occur when the variable is discrete. To see how the grouping is done consider the following 20 numbers and suppose that they represent the lengths of a set of articles, measured to the nearest centimetre:

$$17, 12, 9, 27, 18, 16, 20, 22, 14, 19,$$
$$11, 21, 23, 18, 23, 20, 23, 24, 22, 21.$$

This data can be presented as a grouped frequency distribution in various ways, one of which is the following:

Length (cm)	8–10	11–13	14–16	17–19	20–22	23–25	26–28
Frequency	1	2	2	4	6	4	1

It should be noted that this table gives less actual information than the original list of raw data. The information is more organised, however, and thus easier for a reader to absorb. If we have more classes, of smaller size, the table contains more information but is larger and more complex; while if we have fewer classes the opposite effects are achieved.

The size of each class is measured by the *width of the class interval.* This is not 2 cm, as it might at first appear, but 3 cm. The reason is that the lengths are given to the nearest centimetre, which means that the interval marked 8–10 really contains all the lengths between 7.5 cm and 10.5 cm.

Mid-interval values; calculation of mean

The exact value of the mean length cannot be obtained from the above grouped frequency distribution because the table does not give the exact lengths from which it was constructed. We can, however, calculate an approximation to the mean by using *mid-interval values.* To do this we assume that the lengths of all the articles in each class are equal to the value at the centre of the class interval. For example, we assume that all lengths in the 8–10 class are 9 cm. The calculation is then carried out in the usual way:

$$\text{Total length} \approx (1 \times 9) + (2 \times 12) + (2 \times 15) + (4 \times 18)$$
$$+ (6 \times 21) + (4 \times 24) + (1 \times 17)$$
$$= 374 \text{ cm.}$$

$$\text{Hence mean length} \approx \frac{374}{20} = 18.7 \text{ cm.}$$

$$\text{(Using the raw data the mean length is } \frac{380}{20} = 19 \text{ cm.)}$$

The modal class of a grouped frequency distribution

The modal class is the class containing the greatest number of items, e.g. the class marked 20–22 in the last example. The modal class should be carefully distinguished from the mode itself, which cannot be deduced from the grouped frequency table and is only obtainable from the raw data. In the above example the mode is 23 cm, which does not even lie inside the modal class.

The modal class is often a more appropriate measurement than the mode, particularly for dealing with a continuous variable. To say that 'the most common height of English men is 175 cm' is not really correct because very few if any men are *exactly* 175 cm in height. What is meant is something like 'more men's heights lie between 174.9 cm and 175.1 cm than in any other interval of equal size.'

Histograms

Histograms are used to represent frequency distributions in which there is sufficient raw data to justify division into classes. They are often confused with bar charts since, like the latter, they consist of sets of vertical rectangles. The two kinds of diagrams differ, however, in the following two important ways:

(1) The horizontal axis of a histogram is graduated numerically, like an *x*-axis or number line.

(2) In a histogram, frequencies are represented not by the heights but by the *areas* of the rectangles.

Fig. 38.4 gives an example of a histogram showing a distribution of weights. It is not essential in histograms (though it is usual) to use equal class intervals, and in this case the intervals have deliberately not been made all equal.

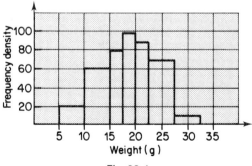

Fig. 38.4

By calculating the areas of the rectangles we can tell from this histogram that $5 \times 20 = 100$ articles have weights between 5 g and 10 g, that 300 have weights between 10 g and 15 g, that 200 have weights between 15 g and 17.5 g, and so on. It is essential to use area and not height to measure frequency in this kind of diagram, since otherwise the height of each bar depends on the width of the class interval chosen. There will clearly be more items (in general) in a large class interval than a small one, so using height as a measure of frequency would make wide bars tall and narrow bars short irrespective of the concentrations of items at the different regions. If we use area to measure frequency, however, the height of each bar measures the *frequency density,* that is the number of items in a class represented by 1 unit on the horizontal axis. The heights of the bars thus measure the *concentration* or *density of cluster* of the items at the various regions, and the overall shape of the diagram shows the distribution of the items irrespective of the sizes of the class intervals.

Frequency polygons, frequency curves

The general shape of a histogram can be obtained by joining the mid-points of the tops of the rectangles by straight lines. When this is done the resulting figure is called a *frequency polygon.* The more classes that are taken, and thus the smaller the corresponding class intervals, the nearer the polygon approaches to a curve called a *frequency curve* (Fig. 38.5).

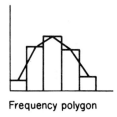
Frequency polygon

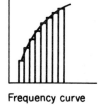
Frequency curve

Fig. 38.5

Cumulative frequency

In a cumulative frequency table we record the number of items *below* each value or *up to and including* each value. It is always possible to construct a cumulative frequency table from an ordinary frequency distribution. Consider, for example, the following distribution, which shows the marks obtained by a class of 35 children at a test consisting of 5 questions:

Mark	0	1	2	3	4	5
Frequency	3	5	8	9	7	3

From this data we can construct the following cumulative frequency table:

Mark	≤ 0	≤ 1	≤ 2	≤ 3	≤ 4	≤ 5
Cumulative frequency	3	8	16	25	32	35

Cumulative frequency curves, percentiles, quartiles

When we have a grouped frequency distribution dealing with a large number of items, it is often possible to obtain a smooth graph by plotting cumulative frequency against the variable. Such a graph is called a *cumulative frequency curve.*

Consider, for example, the following grouped frequency distribution, which gives the weights to the nearest gram of 500 articles:

Weight (g)	0–5	6–10	11–15	16–20	21–25	26–30	31–40	41–50
Frequency	0	30	70	140	110	60	60	30

From this we can construct a cumulative frequency table:

Weight (g)	≤5	≤10	≤15	≤20	≤25	≤30	≤40	≤50
Cumulative frequency	0	30	100	240	350	410	470	500

Now we can draw a graph of cumulative frequency against weight as shown in Fig. 38.6.

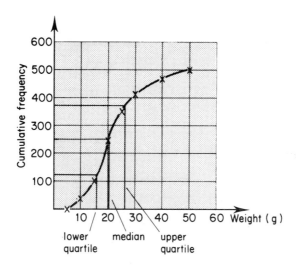

Fig. 38.6

The shape of the graph in Fig. 38.6 is typical of cumulative frequency curves and should be carefully noted. Notice particularly that the gradient (steepness) is a maximum at a point near the centre of the graph. This is in fact the point at which the frequency density is greatest, that is the point around which the items are most densely clustered.

Percentiles, quartiles

Cumulative frequency curves are particularly useful for estimating the quantities known as *percentiles*, one example of which we have already met in the *median*. To obtain the percentiles of a set of values we begin, as in the case of the median, by arranging the values in ascending order. Then the 10th percentile, for example, is the value which is 10% of the way along the list, the 70th percentile is 70% of the way along, and so on. It follows that the median is the 50th percentile; and two other percentiles with special names are the 25th and 75th, which are known as the *lower quartile* and the *upper quartile,* respectively. It is important to remember that in defining percentiles we work in *ascending* order, so that, for example, the 5th percentile is one of the lowest values and the 95th percentile is one of the highest.

Now from the first table above giving the grouped distribution of frequencies against weights, the values of the median weight and the various percentiles are not easy to estimate. The median is the weight of the 250th article (roughly), but all we can tell from the table is that this lies in the 21–25 interval and is thus somewhere between 20.5 g and 25.5 g. The cumulative frequency curve enables us to make a better estimate. The point on the graph at which the cumulative frequency is 250 is the point which divides the complete set of 500 articles into two equal parts, and thus the weight at this point will be the median weight. From the reading on the horizontal axis we find that the median weight is in fact 20.5 g approximately.

Similarly, the lower and upper quartiles are given by the readings on the horizontal axis at which the cumulative frequencies are 125 and 375, respectively; that is approximately 16 g and 26.5 g.

Dispersion, semi-interquartile range

The dispersion of a set of values is the extent to which they are *spread out* rather than clustered around the central values. For example, the two sets of values 9, 9, 10, 11, 11 and 1, 5, 10, 14, 20 both have 10 as mean and median, but the second set is more dispersed than the first. A very crude measurement of dispersion is the *range*, which is simply the difference between the highest and lowest values. This is unsatisfactory because it is entirely dependent on the two extreme values, and these may give no indication of the general extent of the dispersion. A measurement which is better because it takes into account half of the values is the *semi-interquartile range*. (The interquartile range itself can also be used.) This is defined to be *half the difference between the lower and upper quartiles.* In the example we have just considered, the interquartile range is 26.5 g − 16 g = 10.5 g, and the semi-interquartile range is therefore 5.25 g.

EXERCISE 38d

1 Say whether each of the following variables is discrete or continuous:
(a) a cricket team's scores, (b) temperature, (c) speed, (d) shoe sizes,
(e) the number of A-Level maths passes per year, (f) wages, (g) weight.
2 The following table gives the heights of 25 men, to the nearest centimetre:

Height (cm)	164–167	168–171	172–175	176–179	180–183
Frequency	2	3	8	9	3

State the width of the class interval and the modal class. Also estimate the
mean height, using mid-interval values.
3 Use the given table to construct a cumulative frequency table, taking
intervals $\leqslant 5, \leqslant 10$, etc.

x	5	10	15	20	25
f	2	7	12	10	8

4 The following table gives the cumulative frequencies of a set of scores. The
scores can take only integral values.

Score	<1	<2	<3	<6	<10
Cumulative frequency	2	5	10	20	50

Find (a) the number of scores of 1 and the number of scores of 2, (b) the
maximum possible number of scores of 5, (c) the minimum possible number
of scores of 6, (d) the number of scores of 3 or over.
5 The following table gives a grouped frequency distribution of a set of
weights:

Weight (kg)	100–105	105–110	110–115	115–120	120–125
Frequency	12	20	25	17	14

Draw a histogram to represent this data and state the frequency density when
the weight is (a) 113 kg, (b) 116 kg.
6 The table gives the cumulative frequencies of a variable x which can only
take integral values from -4 to $+4$ inclusive. Construct an ordinary frequency
table and use it to find the mean, median and mode values of x.

x	$\leqslant -4$	$\leqslant -3$	$\leqslant -2$	$\leqslant -1$	$\leqslant 0$	$\leqslant 1$	$\leqslant 2$	$\leqslant 3$	$\leqslant 4$
Cumulative frequency	2	5	10	18	25	30	35	38	40

7 A golfer's scores in 20 rounds were as follows: 72, 69, 74, 78, 71, 72, 74, 79,
76, 71, 82, 76, 74, 77, 74, 68, 75, 77, 80, 73. Make a grouped frequency table,
taking classes of 68–70 inclusive, 71–73 inclusive etc., and find (a) the mean
score using mid-interval values and the mean score using the raw data,
(b) the modal class and the mode.

8 The temperature at a certain place is recorded on 50 successive days, with the following results:

Temperature (°C)	12–14	14–16	16–17	17–18	18–19	19–20	20–22	22–25
Frequency	3	7	5	8	9	6	7	5

(a) Draw a histogram to represent this data and state the frequency densities at temperatures of 15°C, 18.4°C and 23°C.
(b) Estimate the mean temperature for the 50 days.

9 Using the data given in question 8, make a cumulative frequency table and draw a cumulative frequency curve. Use the curve to estimate the median temperature, the lower and upper quartiles, the 10th percentile and the semi-interquartile range.

10 The following table records a cricketer's scores in 100 innings:

Score	0–19	20–29	30–39	40–49	50–59	60–79	80–99	100–120
Frequency	12	13	18	20	13	13	8	3

Make a cumulative frequency table and draw a cumulative frequency curve. Use the curve to estimate the median score, the lower and upper quartiles, the 85th percentile and the semi-interquartile range.

11 The following cumulative frequency table gives the percentage marks of 200 candidates in an examination:

Mark	≤10	≤20	≤30	≤40	≤50	≤60	≤70	≤80	≤90	≤100
Cumulative frequency	4	16	32	56	92	144	174	188	196	200

(a) Draw a cumulative frequency curve and use it to estimate the median mark and the lower and upper quartiles. (b) If the pass mark is 44%, estimate the number of candidates who pass. (c) If 96 candidates fail, estimate the pass mark.

12 Use the data given in question 11 to construct a grouped frequency distribution and draw a histogram. Estimate the mean mark.

39 Probability

Definition of probability

Suppose a game is played with a die in which a throw of a 5 or a 6 counts as a win. Can we get a measurement of the likelihood or *probability* of a win on any single throw?

Every throw has six possible outcomes, each of which is clearly equally likely if the die is 'fair' (properly constructed). There are $\frac{2}{6}$ or $\frac{1}{3}$ of these outcomes which count as a win, and it is easy to see that this fraction in fact measures the probability of a win. If we take a more probable event, such as 'getting a 1, 2, 3, 4 or 5', the fraction becomes greater ($\frac{5}{6}$), while if we take a less probable event, such as 'getting a 2', the fraction becomes smaller ($\frac{1}{6}$). So it is clear that the fraction

$$\frac{\text{number of successful outcomes}}{\text{total number of outcomes}}$$

provides a means of measuring the probability of an event. One point should however be noted. It is very important to realise that *all the outcomes must be equally likely* (or 'equiprobable') if the above definition is to be valid. An example will demonstrate this. We *could* describe the experiment with the die as having just three outcomes, namely 'getting a 1', 'getting a 2, 3 or 4' and 'getting a 5 or 6'. It would clearly be incorrect, however, to say that since there are three outcomes and one of them is 'getting a 1', the probability of this event is $\frac{1}{3}$. The correct probability is of course $\frac{1}{6}$. It is only when three outcomes are *equiprobable* that the probability of each is $\frac{1}{3}$.

Two immediate consequences of the above definition of probability are the following:

(1) All probabilities lie between 0 and 1, and a probability of 0 indicates that an event is *impossible*, while a probability of 1 indicates that an event is *certain*.

(2) The sum of the probabilities of all possible outcomes is 1.

Some terminology

Possibility space

The language of set theory is often useful in work on probability. It will be remembered that a universal set $\mathscr{E}$ is a set containing all the elements under consideration. In probability theory we regard a set of *all possible outcomes* as a universal set and describe such a set as a *possibility space*. Thus the possibility space for the die experiment is

$$\mathscr{E} = \{1, 2, 3, 4, 5, 6\}$$

Events

An event is an occurrence which is associated with a subset of a possibility space. For example, the event 'getting a 5 or a 6' is associated with the subset A of the above possibility space, where $A = \{5, 6\}$. In practice the same capital letter is used to denote the event and the subset associated with it, so we can have both

$$A = \text{the event 'getting a 5 or a 6'},$$
$$\text{and} \quad A = \text{the subset } \{5, 6\}.$$

The definition of probability given above can now be expressed in the language of sets. Denoting the probability of the event A by $p(A)$, and remembering that the number of elements in the set A is denoted by $n(A)$, we have

$$p(A) = \frac{n(A)}{n(\mathscr{E})},$$

provided that all the events in the possibility space $\mathscr{E}$ are equiprobable.

Experimental methods of obtaining probabilities

In the examples given so far we have considered a die which is properly constructed, and this has meant that all the outcomes in the possibility space are equally likely. Suppose, however, that we have a biased die; how can we then discover the probabilities of the different outcomes?

To answer this question, consider what would happen if we threw a fair die a large number of times. Common sense would suggest that any given number such as a 2 would occur on about $\frac{1}{6}$ of the throws, and that this fraction would get nearer and nearer to $\frac{1}{6}$ as the number of throws increased. It can in fact be proved that this, in general, is what does occur. Consequently a method of *estimating* the probability of each outcome with the biased die would be to throw the die a large number of times and record the fraction of successes for the outcome. Thus if we threw the die 500 times and a 2 occurred on 125 occasions, our estimate of the probability of a 2 would be $\frac{125}{500}$ or $\frac{1}{4}$. This is called an *experimental* method of finding probabilities, and while it does not give exact results, it is often the only method by which probabilities can be obtained at all.

A very common application of the experimental approach is the use of statistics to estimate probabilities such as that of living to be eighty, or being burgled or struck by lightning. If an insurance company knows, say, that $\frac{1}{5}$ of men in Britain live to be eighty, it is likely to take this fraction as the probability that a man chosen at random will live to be eighty. Of course, extra knowledge about a particular man may change this estimate. If a man has had a heart attack at the age of fifty, the insurance company will need to know not what fraction of all men live to be eighty, but what fraction of those who have had heart attacks at about fifty live to be eighty. And even then, more special knowledge about this particular man may modify the estimate further.

When studying the theory of probability, we usually limit our attention to simple experiments with dice, coins, cards, etc. in which the probabilities can be calculated exactly. It was from the investigation of games of chance that the theory of probability was originally developed. Nevertheless it should not be forgotten that in most practical applications of the theory — and nowadays there are a great many — exact values of probabilities are seldom available and the experimental approach is essential.

▷ Example 1

A card is drawn at random from an ordinary pack. Find the probability of (a) getting a spade, (b) not getting a heart, (c) getting an Ace, King or Queen, (d) getting a heart, club, diamond or spade.

(a) The possibility space contains 52 elements and 13 of these are spades. Hence

$$p(\text{spade}) = \frac{13}{52} = \frac{1}{4}.$$

(b) There are 39 non-hearts. Hence

$$p(\text{non-heart}) = \frac{39}{52} = \frac{3}{4}.$$

(c) There are 4 Aces, 4 Kings and 4 Queens. Hence

$$p(\text{Ace or King or Queen}) = \frac{12}{52} = \frac{3}{13}.$$

(d) It is certain that one of the suits will be obtained, so the probability of this event is 1. ◁

▷ Example 2

A point is chosen at random from the part of a number line between 0 and 5. Find the probability that it lies between 0.8 and 2.

The possibility space is infinite here since there is an infinite number of points on any part of a line. However, the probability that a point lies in any region is clearly proportional to the length of that region, so the required probability is $\frac{1.2}{5} = \frac{12}{50} = \frac{6}{25}.$ ◁

▷ Example 3

A penny is thrown three times. List the elements of the possibility space and hence find the probability of getting (a) 3 heads, (b) 2 heads and 1 tail.

The possibility space is $\{HHH, HHT, HTH, HTT, TTT, TTH, THT, THH\}$. Hence

$$\text{(a)}\quad p(HHH) = \frac{1}{8},$$

$$\text{(b)}\quad p(2\ H\text{'s and } 1\ T) = \frac{3}{8}. \qquad \blacktriangleleft$$

▷ Example 4

The table below shows the distribution of children's ages in a certain school. Find the probability that a child chosen at random is (a) six years old, (b) at least seven.

Age	5	6	7	8	9
Frequency	35	40	40	48	37

(a) There are 200 children altogether, and 40 of them are six years old. Hence the probability is $\frac{40}{200} = \frac{1}{5}$.

(b) The number who are at least seven is $40 + 48 + 37 = 125$. Hence the probability is $\frac{125}{200} = \frac{5}{8}$. $\qquad \blacktriangleleft$

EXERCISE 39a

(In all the exercises in this chapter, assume that coins and dice are properly constructed.)

1 A die is thrown. Find the probability of (a) an odd number, (b) a number more than 2, (c) a prime number, (d) a number that is prime, even or both.

2 A ball is drawn at random from a bag containing 2 red balls, 3 blue balls and 5 green balls. Find the probability of (a) a red ball, (b) a ball that is not blue, (c) a ball that is either red, blue or green.

3 A point is chosen at random from the part of a number line between 10 and 20. Find the probability that it lies between 12.3 and 17.1.

4 Two coins are thrown. List the elements of the possibility space and hence find the probability of (a) 2 heads, (b) both a head and a tail.

5 A number is selected at random from the set {integers from 1 to 20 inclusive}. Find the probability that it is (a) odd, (b) prime, (c) a square number, (d) a multiple of 3, (e) a factor of 12, (f) a square number, a multiple of 2, or both.

6 A card is drawn at random from an ordinary pack. Find the probability that it is (a) black, (b) a red Queen, (c) not the Jack of clubs, (d) red or an Ace or both, (e) a club or a King but not both.

7 A circle is inscribed in a square (to touch all the sides) and a point inside the square is chosen at random. Find to 2 d.p. the probability that the point is inside the circle.

8 The amount of time that each of a group of 100 men spends on a certain job is measured to the nearest minute, with the following results:

Time (min)	3	4	5	6	7	8
Frequency	8	14	30	28	16	4

Find the probability that a man chosen at random takes (a) 6 minutes, (b) less than 6 minutes, (c) at least 5 minutes, (d) longer than the median time.

9 In a game of cards the first card dealt to a man is an Ace. Find the probability that the next card he receives is also an Ace if (a) no one else's cards can be seen, (b) it can be seen that one other Ace and 2 non-Aces have already been dealt.

10 One of the ten letters in the word *APPEARANCE* is chosen at random. Find the probability that it is (a) a vowel, (b) next to a vowel, (c) in the first half of the alphabet, (d) between two vowels, (e) immediately followed by a later letter in the alphabet.

11 In a class of 30 children every child has to study French or German or both. Given that 18 study French and 15 study German, draw a Venn diagram and use it to find the probability that a child chosen at random studies (a) French but not German, (b) both subjects, (c) one of the two but not both.

12 A penny and a die are thrown. List the elements of the possibility space and hence find the probability of (a) a 6 and a head, (b) an even number and a tail, (c) neither a 6 nor a head, (d) a number greater than 4 or a tail or both.

13 The results of measuring the heights of 60 men are shown in the following grouped frequency table:

Height (cm)	155–165	165–170	170–175	175–180	180–190
Frequency	8	12	15	13	12

Find the probability that the height of a man chosen from the group at random is (a) more than 175 cm, (b) between 165 cm and 180 cm, (c) less than 170 cm, (d) not in the modal class.

14 Two dice are thrown. State the number of elements in the possibility space and list all those in which the sum of the scores on the two dice is (a) 5, (b) 6, (c) 7, (d) 8, (e) more than 8. Hence find the probabilities of these events.

15 In a group of 50 boys, 20 like both cricket and football, 15 like football only and 5 like neither. Draw a Venn diagram and use it to find the probability that a boy chosen from the group at random (a) likes cricket, (b) likes cricket but not football, (c) dislikes football.

The event 'A and B'

Suppose that a die and a penny are thrown in succession, and let A be the event 'getting a 2' and B the event 'getting a head'. Then the compound event 'A and B' is the event 'getting *both* a 2 and a head'. We have already seen that the probability of this event can be obtained from the complete possibility space, which here contains the 12 elements $1H$, $1T$, $2H$, $2T$, etc. This is rather a crude procedure, however, and clearly impracticable when the possibility space is very large. Can we therefore obtain a general method of calculating the probability of the compound event 'A and B' from the probability of A alone and the probability of B alone? One approach to this problem is the following.

If we throw a die and a penny a large enough number of times, a 2 will occur on $\frac{1}{6}$ of the throws. On half of these occasions a head will also occur, so both events will occur on $\frac{1}{12}$ of the throws. It follows that the probability of both events occurring is $\frac{1}{12}$, or *the product of the probabilities of the individual events*.

An important point to note is that the events 'getting a 2' and 'getting a head' are *independent*. This means that the occurrence of one of them does not affect the probability that the other occurs. To see how the above reasoning must be modified when the two events are not independent, let us suppose that the die has a magnetic effect upon the penny, so that when a 2 occurs the probability of a head is no longer $\frac{1}{2}$ but $\frac{3}{4}$. Now if the die and the penny are thrown a large number of times a 2 still occurs on $\frac{1}{6}$ of the throws, but it will be accompanied by a head on $\frac{3}{4}$ rather than $\frac{1}{2}$ of these occasions. Hence a 2 and a head both occur on $\frac{1}{2} \times \frac{3}{4} = \frac{3}{8}$ of the throws, and this is the new value of the probability of the event 'A and B'.

The probability of an event B, *given that the event A definitely occurs*, is called a *conditional* probability and written $p(B|A)$. (This is usually read: 'The probability of B, given A'.) Thus in the above example we have $p(H|2) = \frac{3}{4}$. The reasoning given shows that $p(2 \text{ and } H) = p(2) \times p(H|2)$ and illustrates the second of the following two general results.

(1) *If A and B are independent events,*

$$p(A \text{ and } B) = p(A) \times p(B).$$

(2) *If the probability of B is affected by the occurrence of A,*

$$p(A \text{ and } B) = p(A) \times p(B|A).$$

As the Venn diagram in Fig. 39.1 illustrates, the event 'A and B' can be expressed in set language by $A \cap B$.

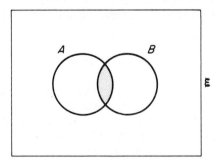

Fig. 39.1

The complete possibility space is represented by the rectangle, and the events A and B are associated with subsets of the possibility space. The shaded region representing $A \cap B$ contains all the elements which are in both subsets, and which thus make up the event called 'A and B'.

▷ Example 5

A penny is thrown 5 times. Find the probability that 5 heads are obtained.

The throws are clearly independent and the probability of a head is $\frac{1}{2}$ on each throw. Hence the probability of 5 heads is

$$\frac{1}{2} \times \frac{1}{2} \times \frac{1}{2} \times \frac{1}{2} \times \frac{1}{2} = \left(\frac{1}{2}\right)^5 = \frac{1}{32}.$$ ◁

▷ Example 6

Two cards are drawn at random from an ordinary pack. Find the probability that both are hearts.

The probability that the first card is a heart is $\frac{1}{4}$. Now in this case the second event is not independent of the first, since if the first card is a heart there are fewer hearts left in the pack than there are if the first is not a heart. In fact there are 12 hearts left if the first is a heart, and 51 cards left altogether. So the probability that the second is a heart, *given that the first is a heart*, is $\frac{12}{51}$. The probability of the compound event is therefore

$$\frac{1}{4} \times \frac{12}{51} = \frac{1}{17}.$$

(If the first card were *replaced* before the second draw, the two draws would be independent and the probability of two hearts would be $\frac{1}{4} \times \frac{1}{4} = \frac{1}{16}$.) ◁

Complementary events

Given any event A, associated with a subset of a possibility space, we can define the event 'not-A' which is associated with the *complement* of the set A'. For example, the event 'getting a 1 or a 2' for a throw of a die has as complement the event 'getting a 3, 4, 5 or 6'. Pairs of events such as these are called *complementary events*. Now since the sum of the probabilities of all possible outcomes of an experiment is 1, we have $p(A) + p(A') = 1$ and thus

$$p(A') = 1 - p(A).$$

This result is often useful in solving problems since it frequently happens that the probability of the complement of an event is easier to calculate than the probability of the event itself. In particular, whenever the term 'at least' is used in describing an event, it is usually best to begin by finding the probability of the complementary event. This technique is illustrated by the first of the following examples.

▷ Example 7

A coin is thrown 4 times. Find the probability that at least one head is obtained.

'At least one head' is a complicated event because it includes the cases in which 1 head, 2 heads, 3 heads and 4 heads occur. To calculate its probability directly is therefore quite difficult. The complementary event, on the other hand, is the simple event 'no heads' or 'all tails', whose probability is easily found by the method explained in example 5.

$$p(\text{all tails}) = \left(\frac{1}{2}\right)^4 = \frac{1}{16}$$

$$\therefore \quad p(\text{at least 1 head}) = 1 - \frac{1}{16}$$

$$= \frac{15}{16}.$$

◀

▷ Example 8

Two dice are thrown. Find the probability that (a) the total score is more than 4, (b) neither die gives a 6, (c) at least one 6 occurs.

(a) The complement of the event 'more than 4' is '4 or less', and the probability of this is much the easier of the two to calculate. The combinations which give a score of 4 or less are shown in the following table.

1st die	2nd die
1	1
1	2
1	3
2	1
2	2
3	1

The table shows that there are 6 outcomes in which the total score is 4 or less. Also, since the throw with the first die has 6 outcomes altogether, and each of these can be combined with each of the 6 outcomes with the second die, there are 36 outcomes in the complete possibility space. Hence

$$p(4 \text{ or less}) = \frac{6}{36} = \frac{1}{6},$$

$$\therefore \quad p(\text{more than 4}) = 1 - \frac{1}{6},$$

$$= \frac{5}{6}.$$

(b) 'Neither die gives a 6' means that *both dice do not* give 6's. This is an event of the type 'A and B', and its probability can therefore be calculated by the multiplication method.

$$p(\text{1st die does not give a 6}) = \frac{5}{6}$$

$$\therefore \quad p(\text{both dice do not give 6's}) = \left(\frac{5}{6}\right)^2 = \frac{25}{36}.$$

(c) 'At least one die gives a 6' is the complement of the event 'neither die gives a 6'. Hence

$$p(\text{at least one 6}) = 1 - \frac{25}{36},$$

$$= \frac{11}{36}.$$

◀

EXERCISE 39b

1 A coin and a die are thrown. Find the probability of (a) a head and a 4, (b) a tail and a prime number.

2 A die is thrown 3 times. Find the probability of (a) 3 sixes, (b) 3 numbers of more than 4, (c) 3 odd numbers.

3 A penny is thrown 3 times. Find the probability of (a) *HHH,* (b) *THT,* (c) at least one tail.

4 Two balls are drawn at random, without replacement, from a bag containing 4 red and 2 blue balls. Find the probability that (a) both are red, (b) the first is blue and the second is red, (c) at least one is blue.

5 A committee of 2 is chosen at random from 6 men and 4 women. Find the probability that (a) both are men, (b) there is at least one woman.

6 Statistics show that in a certain country 3 men in every 5 drive cars. If two men are chosen at random, calculate the probability that (a) both drive, (b) neither does, (c) at least one does.

7 Jane and Mary enter a competition in which there are 10 equally matched contestants altogether. Find the probability that Jane wins and Mary is second.

8 Four equally matched boys, Peter, John, Harry and James, play against each other in a competition. Find the probability that (a) John wins and James is second, (b) Peter does not win, (c) neither James nor Harry wins.

9 Two numbers, not necessarily different, are selected at random from the set {integers from 11 to 20 inclusive}. Find the probability that (a) both are prime, (b) neither is over 18, (c) at least one is odd.

10 When a biased coin is thrown 2000 times, 1500 heads are obtained. Estimate the probability that in 3 throws the coin gives (a) 3 heads, (b) no heads, (c) at least one head.

11 Two different cards are drawn at random from a reduced pack consisting of only the Aces and Kings. Find the probability that (a) both are Aces, (b) both are of the same suit, (c) neither is a heart, (d) at least one is a heart.

12 A man's chance of beating a certain opponent at chess, in any single game, is $\frac{1}{8}$. Calculate the probability, to 2 d.p., that he does not achieve a single win in (a) 4 games, (b) 5 games, (c) 6 games. Deduce (d) the number of games he needs to play to make it more likely than not that he will achieve at least one win.

13 Statistics show that 2 people in every 5 are brown-eyed. Out of 5000 married couples, estimate the number in which both partners are brown-eyed.

14 Three balls are drawn at random, without replacement, from a bag containing 3 red balls, 4 white balls and 5 black balls. Find the probability that (a) all are black, (b) none are red, (c) at least one is white.

15 Three cards are drawn at random from an ordinary pack, each being replaced in the pack before the next draw is made. Find the probability that (a) all are of the same suit, (b) at least one is red, (c) at least one is a spade.

16 Two cards are drawn at random, without replacement, from a reduced pack consisting of only the Aces, Kings and Queens. Find the probability that (a) both are Aces, (b) neither is a King, (c) the first is a King and the second is not, (d) at least one is a Queen.

17 Balls are drawn at random, without replacement, from a bag containing 9 black balls and 1 white ball. (a) Calculate the probability that the first three balls drawn are all black. (b) How many draws must be made in order for it to be more likely than not that the white ball has been drawn?

18 All days are classed as 'fine' or 'wet'. If it is fine on one day the probability that the next day is fine is $\frac{3}{4}$, while if it is wet the probability that the next day is wet is $\frac{2}{3}$. Given that a certain day is fine, calculate the probability that (a) on the next 3 days the sequence is wet, fine, fine, (b) at least one of the next 2 days is fine, (c) on the next 4 days the sequence is fine, wet, wet, fine.

The event 'A or B'

Suppose that a ball is drawn from a bag containing 2 red balls, 3 blue balls and 4 green balls, and we require the probability of the event 'getting a red ball or a blue ball'. This is an example of an event of the type 'A or B', and it is easy to see that since there are 2 ways of getting a red ball, 3 ways of getting a blue ball and 9 possible outcomes altogether, the probability of the event is $\dfrac{2+3}{9}$ or $p(A) + p(B)$. The Venn diagram shown in Fig. 39.2 illustrates this result.

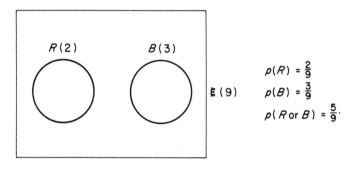

$$p(R) = \tfrac{2}{9}$$
$$p(B) = \tfrac{3}{9}$$
$$p(R \text{ or } B) = \tfrac{5}{9}.$$

Fig. 39.2

When the event 'getting a red or a blue' occurs, the outcome is one of the 5 in the *union* of the two sets. Thus just as the event 'A *and* B' was found to be associated with the set $A \cap B$, we now see that the event 'A or B' is associated with the set $A \cup B$.

In the example given the result is $p(A \text{ or } B) = p(A) + p(B)$. Now is this a general formula, which applies in all cases, or is there anything special about the example we have used? In fact the example does have one special feature, and this means that although the formula applies to a large class of cases, it does not apply to all. The special feature is that the two events 'getting a red' and 'getting a blue' are *mutually exclusive*; that is, they cannot both occur together. To see how the reasoning must be modified when the events are not mutually exclusive, let us take another example.

Suppose that a card is drawn from a reduced pack consisting of only the Aces and Kings, and we require the probability of the event 'getting an Ace or a heart'. These two events are not mutually exclusive since if the Ace of hearts is obtained they both occur together:

Hearts	Clubs	Diamonds	Spades
Ⓐ	Ⓐ	Ⓐ	Ⓐ
Ⓚ	K	K	K

In the table above the cases which count as 'getting an Ace or a heart' are ringed, and the case in which both events occur has a double ring. We can now construct the Venn diagram shown in Fig. 39.3.

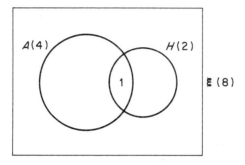

Fig. 39.3

It can be seen from Fig. 39.3 that the number of outcomes in the union of the two sets is not 4 + 2 (the sum of the numbers in the individual sets) but 4 + 2 − 1. Hence we have

$$p(A \text{ or } H) = \frac{4+2-1}{8}$$
$$= \frac{4}{8} + \frac{2}{8} - \frac{1}{8}$$
$$= p(A) + p(H) - p(A \text{ and } H).$$

In other words, when the two events are not mutually exclusive, we add their probabilities as before, but then *subtract the probability that both events occur.*

It should be noted that in everyday life there is a slight ambiguity in the expression 'A or B'. Sometimes this means 'A or B or both' — as we have interpreted the expression in the example just given — and sometimes it means 'A or B but not both'. If a child is asked whether he will have ice-cream or chocolate he has to make a choice and cannot normally opt for both! In probability theory 'A or B' is in fact always taken to mean 'A or B or both', though there is no harm in writing this out in full to remove any possible misunderstanding.

Summing up, we have the following two results:

(1) *If A and B are mutually exclusive events,*

$$p(A \text{ or } B) = p(A) + p(B).$$

(2) *If A and B can both occur together,*

$$p(A \text{ or } B \text{ or both}) = p(A) + p(B) - p(A \text{ and } B).$$

(In set language, the second formula can be expressed

$$p(A \cup B) = p(A) + p(B) - p(A \cap B).)$$

Note: There is an alternative to the use of the second formula since the complement of the event 'A or B or both' is 'neither A nor B'. The probability of an event of the latter kind can be obtained by the multiplication principle, as illustrated in the first of the following examples.

▷Example 9

A coin and a die are thrown. Find the probability of a head or a 6 or both.

Method (a) We have $p(H) = \frac{1}{2}$, $p(6) = \frac{1}{6}$, and since the events are independent, $p(H \text{ and } 6) = \frac{1}{2} \times \frac{1}{6} = \frac{1}{12}$. Hence, applying the standard formula for $p(A \text{ or } B \text{ or both})$, we obtain

$$p(H \text{ or } 6 \text{ or both}) = p(H) + p(6) - p(H \text{ and } 6)$$
$$= \frac{1}{2} + \frac{1}{6} - \frac{1}{12}$$
$$= \frac{7}{12}.$$

Method (b) The complement of 'a head or a 6 or both' is 'neither a head nor a 6', that is, 'not a head and not a 6'. Since $p(\text{not } H) = \frac{1}{2}$ and $p(\text{not } 6) = \frac{5}{6}$, we have

$$p(\text{not } H \text{ and not } 6) = \frac{1}{2} \times \frac{5}{6} = \frac{5}{12}$$
$$\therefore \ p(H \text{ or } 6 \text{ or both}) = 1 - \frac{5}{12}$$
$$= \frac{7}{12}. \quad \triangleleft$$

▷Example 10

A penny is thrown 3 times. Find the probability that one and only one tail is obtained.

There are three ways of obtaining exactly one tail, namely *THH, HTH, HHT*. We require the probability that any one of these outcomes occurs, and since the outcomes are clearly mutually exclusive, we simply add their individual probabilities. By the multiplication principle the probability of each is $\frac{1}{8}$; hence the probability of any one of them is $\frac{1}{8} + \frac{1}{8} + \frac{1}{8} = \frac{3}{8}$. $\triangleleft$

▷Example 11

Two balls are drawn at random from a bag containing 3 white and 5 coloured balls. Find the probability that exactly one of them is white.

This event can occur in two mutually exclusive ways, namely

$$A = \text{White, Non-White,}$$
$$B = \text{Non-White, White.}$$

The probability of A is $\frac{3}{8} \times \frac{5}{7} = \frac{15}{56}$, and that of B is $\frac{5}{8} \times \frac{3}{7} = \frac{15}{56}$.

Hence $p(A \text{ or } B) = \frac{15}{56} + \frac{15}{56} = \frac{30}{56} = \frac{15}{28}.$ $\triangleleft$

▷**Example 12**

$p(A \cup B) = \frac{5}{12}$, $p(A') = \frac{2}{3}$ and $p(B) = \frac{1}{4}$. (a) Find $p(A \cap B)$ and say whether or not A and B are independent events. (b) Find $p(A' \cap B')$.

(a) Expressed in set language, the formula for $p(A$ or B or both) is

$$p(A \cup B) = p(A) + p(B) - p(A \cap B).$$

Since $p(A') = \frac{2}{3}$, $p(A) = 1 - \frac{2}{3} = \frac{1}{3}$. Hence, applying the formula, we have

$$\frac{5}{12} = \frac{1}{3} + \frac{1}{4} - p(A \cap B)$$
$$\therefore \ p(A \cap B) = \frac{1}{3} + \frac{1}{4} - \frac{5}{12}$$
$$= \frac{1}{6}.$$

To decide whether A and B are independent events, we simply see whether $p(A \cap B) = p(A) \times p(B)$. Here this is not so, and it follows that A and B are not independent.

(b) The set $A' \cap B'$ contains all the elements which are neither in A nor in B. This set is therefore equal to $(A \cup B)'$, and the required probability is $1 - p(A \cup B) = 1 - \frac{5}{12} = \frac{7}{12}$.   ◀

EXERCISE 39c

1 A card is drawn at random from an ordinary pack, and a die is thrown. Find the probability of (a) a heart or a 6 or both, (b) a red card or an odd number or both.

2 A and B are mutually exclusive events. Given that $p(A) = \frac{1}{4}$ and $p(B') = \frac{1}{3}$, find the probability of $p(A$ or $B)$.

3 A penny is thrown twice. Find the probability that exactly one head is obtained.

4 John and James are in the same class. The probability that John does not come top is $\frac{5}{6}$ and the probability that James does not come top is $\frac{2}{3}$. Find the probability that either John or James comes top.

5 $p(A) = \frac{1}{4}$, $p(B) = \frac{1}{6}$ and $p(A \cup B) = \frac{1}{3}$. Find $p(A \cap B)$ and say whether or not A and B are independent.

6 Find the probability that a family of 3 children contains exactly 2 boys.

7 Peter and Paul each fire at a target, their probabilities of a hit being respectively $\frac{1}{3}$ and $\frac{1}{4}$. Find the probability that (a) Peter hits and Paul misses, (b) Peter misses and Paul hits, (c) one and only one of them hits.

8 A and B are independent events. Given that $p(A) = \frac{2}{3}$ and $p(B) = \frac{1}{2}$, find $p(A \cup B)$.

9 A ball is drawn at random from a bag containing 2 white and 3 black balls, then it is replaced and another draw is made. Find the probability that a white ball is obtained (a) on either or both of the draws, (b) on exactly one of the draws.

10 $p(A) = \frac{1}{2}$, $p(B') = \frac{1}{3}$ and $p(A \cup B) = \frac{5}{6}$. Find $p(A \cap B)$ and say whether or not A and B are independent.

11 The probability that John is late for school on any given day is $\frac{1}{3}$. Find the probability (a) that he is late on Monday, then on time on Tuesday and Wednesday, (b) that he is late on eactly one of these three days.

12 A man plays his friend at chess and then at darts, with winning chances of $\frac{4}{5}$ and $\frac{3}{10}$, respectively. Find the probability that he wins (a) at either or both games, (b) at chess but not at darts, (c) at exactly one of the games.

13 In a certain country 1 in 4 people are left-handed, 1 in 3 are left-footed and 1 in 2 are either left-handed, left-footed or both. Find the probability that a person chosen at random is both left-handed and left-footed, and say whether or not left-handedness and left-footedness are independent.

14 The probability of getting a head with a biased coin is $\frac{3}{4}$. Find the probability that one and only one head is obtained when the coin is thrown (a) twice, (b) 3 times.

15 $p(A) = \frac{3}{4}, p(A \cap B) = \frac{1}{2}$ and $p(A' \cap B') = \frac{1}{8}$. Find $p(B)$ and say whether or not A and B are independent.

Tree diagrams

Tree diagrams are useful for dealing with the more complicated experiments in which several different combinations of outcomes are possible. Suppose, for example, that 2 cards are drawn at random from a set of 4 Aces and 4 Kings. The tree diagram in Fig. 39.4 shows the possible outcomes and their probabilities.

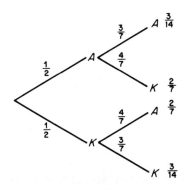

Fig. 39.4

The following points should be noted:

(1) The branches leading away from any 'node' represent mutually exclusive events and their probabilities add up to 1.

(2) Each fraction on the extreme right is the probability of the complete branch leading to it, and is obtained by multiplying the probabilities on the individual branches. For example the first fraction, $\frac{3}{14}$, is the probability of an Ace followed by an Ace, and is obtained by multiplying $\frac{1}{2}$ by $\frac{3}{7}$.

(3) The fractions on the right are probabilities of mutually exclusive events, and they add up to 1. This provides a check on the correctness of the tree diagram.

Tree diagrams are particularly helpful when the event whose probability is required can occur in several different ways, so that several different branches of the tree diagram contribute to the event. This is illustrated by the following example.

▷ Example 13

Three balls are drawn at random, without replacement, from a bag containing 4 white and 3 black balls. Draw a tree diagram and use it to find the probabilities that (a) more than one black ball is drawn, (b) 2 white balls and 2 black balls are left in the bag.

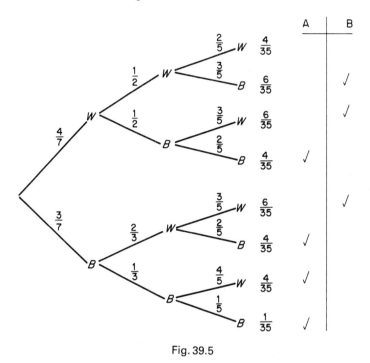

Fig. 39.5

(a) The ticks in column A of Fig. 39.5 show the branches which contribute to the given event. Since the branches represent mutually exclusive events, the probability that one of them occurs is obtained by adding the probabilities of each branch.

$$p(\text{more than 1 black is drawn}) = \frac{4}{35} + \frac{4}{35} + \frac{4}{35} + \frac{1}{35} = \frac{13}{35}.$$

(b) If 2 white balls and 2 black balls are left in the bag, 2 white balls and 1 black ball must have been drawn. Column B shows the branches which represent this event, and proceeding as in (a) we have

$$p(\text{2 white balls and 2 black balls are left}) = \frac{6}{35} + \frac{6}{35} + \frac{6}{35} = \frac{18}{35}. \quad ◁$$

EXERCISE 39d

1 A man with two 50 p pieces and three 10 p pieces in his pocket takes out two coins at random. Draw a tree diagram and find the probability that (a) he takes out two coins of the same kind, (b) he is left with 70 p in his pocket.

2 When Peter plays John at chess, the probability of a draw is $\frac{1}{2}$ and the probability that Peter wins is $\frac{1}{6}$. Draw a tree diagram for two games and find the probability that (a) the same result occurs in both games, (b) both a win and a draw occur.

3 A bag contains 3 red balls, 2 white balls and 1 blue ball. Two random draws are made, without replacement. Draw a tree diagram and find the probability that (a) exactly one white is obtained, (b) both a red and a blue are obtained, (c) the blue ball remains in the bag.

4 Three balls are drawn at random, without replacement, from a bag containing 4 red and 4 white balls. Draw a tree diagram and find the probability that (a) the third ball drawn is red, (b) 2 red balls and 1 white ball are drawn, (c) alternating colours are drawn.

5 Two random cards are drawn, without replacement, from a set of 4 hearts, 3 clubs, 2 diamonds and 1 spade. Draw a tree diagram and find the probability that (a) the spade is drawn, (b) 2 cards of the same suit are drawn, (c) 1 red card and 1 black are drawn, (d) no hearts are drawn.

6 All days are classed as 'fine' or 'wet'. If one day is fine the probability that the next is fine is $\frac{4}{5}$, while if one day is wet the probability that the next is wet is $\frac{3}{5}$. Today (Monday) is fine. Draw a tree diagram for the next three days and find the probability that (a) Thursday is wet, (b) exactly 2 of the 3 days are fine, (c) Thursday's weather differs from Tuesday's.

7 John and Paul play a game with a die. John throws first, and then if a player gets a 5 or a 6 he throws again; otherwise the other player throws. Draw a tree diagram for the first 4 throws, and find the probability that (a) both players throw twice, (b) John has more throws than Paul, (c) Paul throws last.

8 Balls are drawn at random from a box which initially contains 1 white and 1 black ball. After a draw, the ball itself is replaced together with one of the other colour. Draw a tree diagram for the first three draws and find the probability that (a) exactly 1 black ball is drawn, (b) the first ball drawn is black or the last is white or both of these occur, (c) 2 or more successive white balls are drawn.

9 Tom and Harry play three points at table-tennis. They are equally likely to win the first point, but when Tom wins a point his confidence increases and his probability of winning the next point rises to $\frac{2}{3}$, while when Harry wins a point his probability of winning the next point remains at $\frac{1}{2}$. Draw a tree diagram for the three points and find the probability that (a) Harry wins exactly 2 points, (b) the wins alternate, (c) the winner of the first point loses the third point.

10 When a certain man does not drive to work, he tosses a coin to decide whether to go by bus or by train. After he has driven on one day the probability that he drives the next day is $\frac{1}{5}$, while if he does not drive the probability that he drives the next day is $\frac{1}{2}$. Given that he drives on Monday, draw a tree diagram up to and including Wednesday and find the probability that (a) he goes by bus exactly once, (b) his method of transport is the same on Tuesday and Wednesday.

EXERCISE 39e (miscellaneous questions)

1 A card is drawn at random from the Ace, King and Queen of clubs, the Ace of spades and the King of diamonds. Find the probability that it is (a) a club, (b) an Ace, (c) a heart, (d) not a King, (e) a spade or a King.

2 James and John both fire one shot at a target. If their probabilities of a hit are x and y, respectively, find the probability that (a) both score hits, (b) James misses and John hits, (c) at least one of them hits.

3 George is in a class of 20 boys and Jane is in a class of 10 girls. Assuming that the children in the classes are of similar ability find the probability that in the summer examination (a) George is top and Jane is not in the top three, (b) at least one of the two is top, (c) neither is in the bottom four, (d) at least one of them is in the bottom two.

4 P, Q, R, S are the mid-points of the sides AB, BC, CD, DA of a square $ABCD$. If a point inside the square $ABCD$ is chosen at random, find the probability that it is inside (a) square $PQRS$, (b) triangle PQS, (c) triangle PCS.

5 In a certain country 40% of the population have blue eyes, 36% have fair hair and 48% have neither. Draw a Venn diagram and use it to find the probability that a person chosen at random has both blue eyes and fair hair.

6 Two hikers reach a road junction and each makes a random choice between three roads, only one of which leads to the required destination. What is the probability that the correct road is chosen by (a) at least one hiker, (b) exactly one of them?

7 Two independent events have probabilities of $\frac{3}{8}$ and $\frac{5}{6}$. Find the probability of either or both.

8 Two independent events each have a probability of p. Write down an expression for the probability of either or both, and find the value of p if the probability of either or both is $\frac{8}{9}$.

9 Two cards are drawn at random, without replacement, from a reduced pack consisting of the Aces, Kings, Queens and Jacks of each suit. Find the probability that (a) both are hearts, (b) both are of the same suit, (c) the first is an Ace and the second a King, (d) an Ace and a King are drawn, (e) at least one Ace is drawn, (f) exactly one Ace is drawn.

10 Balls are drawn at random from a bag which initially contains 2 red balls, 1 white ball and 1 blue ball. After each draw of a white or blue ball the ball is replaced in the bag, but red balls are not replaced. Draw a tree diagram for two draws and find the probability that (a) the blue ball is drawn just once, (b) a red and a white ball are drawn, (c) two balls of the same colour are drawn.

11 The probability of obtaining a head with a biased coin is 0.9. Find to 2 d.p. the probability of getting no tails in (a) 3 throws, (b) 4 throws, (c) 5 throws. Find also (d) the number of throws needed to make it more likely than not that a tail will occur.

12 Balls are drawn at random, without replacement, from a bag containing 5 white balls and 1 black ball. Find the probability that (a) the first three balls drawn are all white, (b) the black ball is drawn last, (c) the black ball is one of the first two balls drawn.

13 All of a class of 20 sixth-formers study at least one of the subjects Physics, Chemistry and Biology. Equal numbers study Physics and Biology but none study both. Given that 10 study Chemistry, 2 Chemistry only and 5 Chemistry and Biology, draw a Venn diagram and use it to find the probability that a student chosen at random studies (a) Physics, (b) Chemistry, Biology or both of these subjects.

14 In each of the following cases say whether or not the events A and B are independent: (a) $p(A) = \frac{1}{4}$, $p(B) = \frac{2}{5}$, $p(A \text{ and } B) = \frac{1}{10}$;
(b) $p(A) = \frac{2}{5}$, $p(B) = \frac{1}{2}$, $p(A \cup B) = \frac{7}{10}$; (c) $p(A') = \frac{1}{4}$, $p(B') = \frac{7}{9}$, $p(A \cap B) = \frac{7}{36}$;
(d) $p(A) = \frac{1}{3}$, $p(A \cap B) = \frac{5}{18}$, $p(A \cup B) = \frac{8}{9}$.

15 In a certain country 3 out of 4 of the women are married, 7 out of 16 are married and drive cars, and 13 out of 16 either are married or drive cars or both. Find the probability that a woman chosen at random drives a car, and say whether or not being married and driving a car are independent.

16 When a certain man takes a taxi followed by a fast train his journey takes 4 hours. Using a bus instead of a taxi adds 30 minutes to the journey, and taking a slow train instead of a fast one adds 1 hour. If he takes a taxi once in every 3 journeys and a fast train 3 times in every 4 journeys, find the probability that any given journey takes (a) $4\frac{1}{2}$ hours, (b) 5 hours, (c) $5\frac{1}{2}$ hours. Find also (d) the probability that in two journeys there is just one which takes 4 hours.

17 A man has four 2 p pieces and three 10 p pieces in his pocket. He takes out three coins in succession, at random, without replacement. Draw a tree diagram and find the probability that (a) the third coin drawn has the same value as the first, (b) more 2 p's than 10 p's are drawn, (c) the man is left with 16 p in his pocket.

18 In a game with a die a throw of 5 or 6 is counted as a win. Find the probability that in two throws the number of wins is (a) 0, (b) 1, (c) 2.

19 A girl and a boy both throw dice. Find the probability that after two throws each the girl has more scores of 5 or 6 than the boy.

20 A runner in an 8-man race rates his probability of winning to be $\frac{1}{2}$ if he is drawn in lanes 1–3, and $\frac{2}{5}$ if he is drawn in lanes 5–8. Find his overall probability of winning.

21 A circle is inscribed in an equilateral triangle, and a point inside the triangle is chosen at random. Find to 3 d.p. the probability that the point is inside the circle.

22 In a certain competition the players are divided into three sections on the basis of ability. After each round the winners move up a section unless they are already in the top section, and the losers move down a section unless they are already in the bottom section. (No games are drawn.) One particular player's chances of winning, in the three sections, are $\frac{3}{4}$, $\frac{1}{2}$ and $\frac{1}{4}$. Given that he starts in the middle section, draw a tree diagram for the first three rounds he plays, and find the probability that (a) he wins exactly twice, (b) his results alternate, (c) his results include two consecutive losses.

40 Matrices

In everyday life we often find information presented in the form of rectangular arrays of numbers. Examples are the sets of numbers in price catalogues, calendars, bus and railway timetables, and cricket and football league tables. The following is the top of the cricket County Championship table of 1978.

	Played	Won	Lost	Drawn	Points
Kent	22	13	3	6	292
Essex	22	12	1	9	273
Middlesex	22	11	5	5	255

It is possible to think of this array of numbers, without the headings or other explanatory words, as a single entity. When this is done the array is called a *matrix,* enclosed in brackets and denoted by a capital letter:

$$\mathbf{A} = \begin{pmatrix} 22 & 13 & 3 & 6 & 292 \\ 22 & 12 & 1 & 9 & 273 \\ 22 & 11 & 5 & 5 & 255 \end{pmatrix}$$

Points to note

(1) Each number in the array is called an *entry* or an *element.*
(2) Commas are not used in matrices, so a small gap is left between adjacent numbers.
(3) Matrices always consist of *pure numbers* only and not numbers together with units. Thus the set of prices

$$\begin{array}{ccc} £1.20 & 80\,p & £1.50 \\ 50\,p & £2 & £1 \end{array}$$

can be represented either as a 'pence' matrix or a 'pounds' matrix, but it cannot be enclosed in brackets and regarded as a matrix as it stands:

$$\begin{pmatrix} 120 & 80 & 150 \\ 50 & 200 & 100 \end{pmatrix} \qquad \begin{pmatrix} 1.2 & 0.8 & 1.5 \\ 0.5 & 2 & 1 \end{pmatrix}$$
$$\text{'pence' matrix} \qquad\qquad \text{'pounds' matrix}$$

The order of a matrix

The matrix formed above from the cricket league table has 3 rows and 5 columns. This matrix is said to have an *order of 3 × 5* (read '3 by 5') and the general definition is as follows.

The order of a matrix with *m* rows and *n* columns is *m* × *n*.

(To obtain the order of a matrix, *count down and then count across.*)

Row, column and square matrices

A matrix with a single row only is called a *row matrix*, one with just a single column is called a *column matrix,* and one with equal numbers of rows and columns is called a *square matrix:*

$$\begin{pmatrix} 2 & 0 & -4 & 3 \end{pmatrix} \qquad \begin{pmatrix} 1 \\ 5 \\ -7 \end{pmatrix} \qquad \begin{pmatrix} 10 & -2 \\ 0 & 25 \end{pmatrix}$$

row matrix   column matrix   square matrix
(order 1 × 4)   (order 3 × 1)   (order 2 × 2)

Matrix algebra

In ordinary algebra letters represent numbers and the rules for operating with the letters are those which apply to numbers. Matrices provide an example of a different algebra in which rectangular arrays of numbers are considered as single entities and operations are defined which enable these arrays to be combined together. For convenience the main operations are known as 'addition', 'subtraction' and 'multiplication', and there are certainly similarities between these operations and those with the same names which apply to ordinary numbers. It must be realised, however, that the new operations apply to different kinds of things and therefore are really different operations to those by which numbers are combined.

It is not easy to understand why the rules for operating with matrices are defined as they are. In particular, the rule for multiplying matrices will seem complicated and unnatural at first. Some kind of explanation of the rules, in terms for example of combining lists of prices, is attempted in many textbooks, but since no one in fact ever uses the algebra of matrices for everyday life operations like this, such explanations are rather unconvincing and will be omitted here. The real reason why the rules are defined as they are is that mathematicians have found these rules useful in solving problems, and the best way to come to appreciate the rules is to learn the mathematics in which they are applied. In this book we shall consider the application of matrices to transformation geometry and to the solution of simultaneous equations. There are many other applications, but mainly at a more advanced level.

We begin the algebra of matrices by defining *equal matrices,* and the operations *addition, subtraction,* and *multiplication by a real number.*

Equal matrices

Matrices are defined to be equal when they are *identical*; that is, they have the same order and their corresponding elements are equal. For example,

$$(1 \quad 3 \quad 5) = (1 \quad 3 \quad 5)$$
$$\text{but} \quad (3 \quad 5 \quad 1) \neq (1 \quad 3 \quad 5)$$
$$\text{and} \quad \begin{pmatrix} 2 \\ 7 \\ 0 \end{pmatrix} \neq \begin{pmatrix} 2 \\ 7 \end{pmatrix}.$$

If we know that two matrices are equal, it follows from the definition of equality that their corresponding elements are equal. Thus for example the matrix equation

$$\begin{pmatrix} 2x \\ x - y \end{pmatrix} = \begin{pmatrix} 6 \\ 1 \end{pmatrix}$$

is equivalent to the two equations

$$2x = 6,$$
$$x - y = 1,$$

from which it follows that $x = 3$ and $y = 2$.

Addition and subtraction of matrices

Matrices can only be added or subtracted if they have the same order. The rule is simply to add or subtract corresponding elements. E.g.

$$\begin{pmatrix} 5 \\ 2 \end{pmatrix} - \begin{pmatrix} -2 \\ 3 \end{pmatrix} = \begin{pmatrix} 7 \\ -1 \end{pmatrix}.$$

Multiplication by a number

To multiply a matrix by a number we simply multiply each element by the number. E.g.

$$-2 \begin{pmatrix} 3 & -1 \\ 4 & 2 \end{pmatrix} = \begin{pmatrix} -6 & 2 \\ -8 & -4 \end{pmatrix}.$$

Zero or null matrices

A zero or null matrix is one whose elements are all zero. Such a matrix is denoted by $\mathbf{0}$, or, if it is necessary to make the order explicit, $\mathbf{0}_{2 \times 3}$, etc. E.g.

$$\mathbf{0}_{2 \times 1} = \begin{pmatrix} 0 \\ 0 \end{pmatrix}.$$

▷ Example 1

Simplify $3y \begin{pmatrix} 2xy \\ -x \end{pmatrix} - x \begin{pmatrix} -2y^2 \\ 4y \end{pmatrix}$.

First we perform the multiplications:

$$\begin{pmatrix} 6xy^2 \\ -3xy \end{pmatrix} - \begin{pmatrix} -2xy^2 \\ 4xy \end{pmatrix}$$

Now since the corresponding elements consist of like terms, we can proceed to

$$\begin{pmatrix} 6xy^2 + 2xy^2 \\ -3xy - 4xy \end{pmatrix}$$

$$= \begin{pmatrix} 8xy^2 \\ -7xy \end{pmatrix} \text{ or } xy \begin{pmatrix} 8y \\ -7 \end{pmatrix} . \qquad ◁$$

▷ Example 2

Find a 2×1 *matrix* **X** *such that* $2\mathbf{X} - \begin{pmatrix} 2 \\ -1 \end{pmatrix} = \begin{pmatrix} 7 \\ 4 \end{pmatrix} - \mathbf{X}.$

This type of equation, in which the unknown quantity is a matrix, can be solved in the same way as an ordinary equation in which the unknown is a number. We *do the same to both sides* until the matrix **X** is isolated on one side of the equation.

Add $\begin{pmatrix} 2 \\ -1 \end{pmatrix}$ and **X** to both sides:

$$3\mathbf{X} = \begin{pmatrix} 9 \\ 3 \end{pmatrix}.$$

Divide both sides by 3:

$$\mathbf{X} = \begin{pmatrix} 3 \\ 1 \end{pmatrix}. \qquad ◁$$

▷ Example 3

Find x and y, given that $\begin{pmatrix} 2x \\ y \end{pmatrix} - \begin{pmatrix} 5y \\ 1 \end{pmatrix} = x \begin{pmatrix} 3 \\ 1 \end{pmatrix}.$

This matrix equation is equivalent to the following two simultaneous equations.

$$2x - 5y = 3x \quad (1)$$
$$y - 1 = x \quad (2)$$

From (1) we have $x = -5y$, and (2) gives $x = y - 1$. Hence x can be eliminated immediately:

$$-5y = y - 1$$
$$\therefore y = \frac{1}{6}.$$

Substitution of this value into (2) gives $x = -\frac{5}{6}.$ ◁

EXERCISE 40a

1 State the order of each of the following matrices:

(a) $\begin{pmatrix} 2 \\ 3 \end{pmatrix}$, (b) $\begin{pmatrix} 1 & -3 \\ 2 & 5 \end{pmatrix}$, (c) $(4 \ \ 1 \ \ 2)$, (d) $\begin{pmatrix} x^2 & x-y \\ y & 0 \\ x+y & x \end{pmatrix}$.

2 With reference to the matrix shown below, name the elements in (a) the 2nd row and 3rd column, (b) the 1st row and 4th column, (c) the 3rd row and 3rd column.

$$\begin{pmatrix} 3 & 7 & 0 & 4 \\ 2 & -5 & -1 & 9 \\ -4 & 6 & -3 & 8 \end{pmatrix}$$

3 Complete the subtraction table shown below, and taking the matrix formed by the results of the subtraction, name the elements in (a) the 2nd row and 4th column, (b) the 3rd column and 2nd row, (c) the 1st column and 4th row.

$-$	0	1	2	3
0	0	-1		
1	1	0		
2				
3				

4 Say whether or not the following pairs of matrices are equal:

(a) $\begin{pmatrix} 6 \div 3 \\ 2^4 \end{pmatrix}$ and $\begin{pmatrix} \sqrt{4} \\ 4^2 \end{pmatrix}$ (b) $(5 \ \ 7)$ and (12) (c) $\begin{pmatrix} \sqrt{36} & 2\frac{1}{2} \\ 5 & -\frac{1}{3} \end{pmatrix}$ and $\begin{pmatrix} 6 & \frac{5}{2} \\ \sqrt{25} & \frac{-2}{-6} \end{pmatrix}$

(d) $\begin{pmatrix} 2\times0 & -5\div-5 & 3\div-6 \\ 27 & 4\times12 & 0 \end{pmatrix}$ and $\begin{pmatrix} 0 & 1 & 1\div-2 \\ 3^3 & 6\times8 & 3\times0 \end{pmatrix}$

(e) $\begin{pmatrix} a-b \\ a+b \end{pmatrix}$ and $\begin{pmatrix} -b+a \\ b+a \end{pmatrix}$.

5 Given that $\mathbf{A} = (3 \ \ 2)$, $\mathbf{B} = \begin{pmatrix} 1 \\ 4 \end{pmatrix}$, $\mathbf{C} = \begin{pmatrix} 2 & 3 \\ 4 & -1 \end{pmatrix}$, $\mathbf{D} = \begin{pmatrix} -5 \\ 2 \end{pmatrix}$,

$\mathbf{E} = (-2 \ \ 1)$, $\mathbf{F} = \begin{pmatrix} 0 & 1 \\ 5 & 7 \end{pmatrix}$,

say whether or not each of the following combinations of matrices can be formed, and evaluate those which can: (a) $\mathbf{A} + \mathbf{B}$, (b) $\mathbf{B} + \mathbf{D}$, (c) $\mathbf{C} - \mathbf{F}$, (d) $\mathbf{F} - \mathbf{D} - \mathbf{D}$, (e) $\mathbf{E} - \mathbf{A}$, (f) $\mathbf{F} + \mathbf{F} - \mathbf{C}$, (g) $\mathbf{A} + \mathbf{E} + \mathbf{C}$.

6 Work out

(a) $\begin{pmatrix} 2 & -3 \\ 1\frac{1}{2} & -1 \end{pmatrix} + \begin{pmatrix} -1 & -2 \\ 2\frac{1}{2} & -3 \end{pmatrix}$, (b) $\begin{pmatrix} 1 & 2 & 2 \\ 2 & 3 & 5 \end{pmatrix} + \begin{pmatrix} 1 & 2 & 1 \\ 4 & 1\frac{2}{3} & \frac{1}{10} \end{pmatrix}$,

(c) $\begin{pmatrix} 2\frac{1}{4} \\ -3 \end{pmatrix} - \begin{pmatrix} 1\frac{5}{8} \\ -5 \end{pmatrix}$, (d) $\begin{pmatrix} 0 & -3 \\ 4 & -1 \end{pmatrix} - \begin{pmatrix} -2 & 1 \\ 6 & -2 \end{pmatrix}$.

7 Given that $\mathbf{A} = \begin{pmatrix} -2 & 3 \\ 0 & -1 \end{pmatrix}$ and $\mathbf{B} = \begin{pmatrix} 1 & -2 \\ 4 & 0 \end{pmatrix}$, work out (a) $3\mathbf{A}$, (b) $2\mathbf{B}$, (c) $2\mathbf{A} + \mathbf{B}$, (d) $3\mathbf{A} - 2\mathbf{B}$, (e) $-\mathbf{A} - 4\mathbf{B}$, (f) $-3(\mathbf{A} - 2\mathbf{B})$.

8 Is it true that the operation of addition is (a) commutative, (b) associative, for matrices of the same order? (See chapter 22 for the meanings of these terms.)

9 Is it always true that $k(\mathbf{A} + \mathbf{B}) = k\mathbf{A} + k\mathbf{B}$ when k is a real number and $\mathbf{A}$ and $\mathbf{B}$ are matrices of the same order?

10 Work out

(a) $(2x \quad y) + (x \quad y + 1)$, (b) $\begin{pmatrix} m \\ n \end{pmatrix} - \begin{pmatrix} 2 \\ n-2 \end{pmatrix}$, (c) $\begin{pmatrix} a & -2 \\ b-1 & a-b \end{pmatrix} + \begin{pmatrix} a & -1 \\ 3 & -a \end{pmatrix}$,

(d) $a(2 \quad a) - 2(a \quad a^2)$, (e) $2x \begin{pmatrix} xy \\ -y \end{pmatrix} - y \begin{pmatrix} 3x^2 \\ x \end{pmatrix}$, (f) $x - 1 \begin{pmatrix} x+1 \\ x-1 \end{pmatrix} - \begin{pmatrix} 1+x^2 \\ 1-2x \end{pmatrix}$.

11 Given that $\mathbf{A} = \begin{pmatrix} x-1 \\ 3x \end{pmatrix}$ and $\mathbf{B} = \begin{pmatrix} x+2 \\ 2x-3 \end{pmatrix}$, work out (a) $\mathbf{A} + \mathbf{B}$,

(b) $\mathbf{A} - \mathbf{B}$, (c) $2\mathbf{A} + \mathbf{B}$, (d) $3\mathbf{B} - 2\mathbf{A}$.

12 Complete the following matrix equations:

(a) $\begin{pmatrix} 48 \\ 84 \end{pmatrix} = 6 \begin{pmatrix} \quad \end{pmatrix}$, (b) $(3 \quad 0 \quad 6 \quad -15) = -3 (\qquad)$,

(c) $\begin{pmatrix} 2x & 8xy \\ 4x^3 & 0 \end{pmatrix} = 2x \begin{pmatrix} \quad \end{pmatrix}$, (d) $\begin{pmatrix} a^2 - b^2 \\ (a-b)^2 \\ a-b \end{pmatrix} = a - b \begin{pmatrix} \quad \end{pmatrix}$,

(e) $\begin{pmatrix} \frac{1}{x} & 1 \\ x & \frac{1}{x^2} \end{pmatrix} = \frac{1}{x} \begin{pmatrix} \quad \end{pmatrix}$.

13 Find a 2×1 matrix $\mathbf{X}$ which satisfies the following equations:

(a) $\mathbf{X} + \begin{pmatrix} 3 \\ 1 \end{pmatrix} = \begin{pmatrix} 5 \\ -2 \end{pmatrix}$, (b) $2\mathbf{X} = \begin{pmatrix} 1\frac{1}{3} \\ \frac{1}{4} \end{pmatrix}$, (c) $3\mathbf{X} - \begin{pmatrix} 2 \\ 3 \end{pmatrix} = \begin{pmatrix} -8 \\ 6 \end{pmatrix}$,

(d) $2\mathbf{X} - \begin{pmatrix} 4 \\ -1 \end{pmatrix} = \mathbf{0}$, (e) $\begin{pmatrix} 5 \\ -2 \end{pmatrix} - \mathbf{X} = \begin{pmatrix} -2 \\ -3 \end{pmatrix}$, (f) $\mathbf{X} - \begin{pmatrix} -6 \\ 12 \end{pmatrix} = 4\mathbf{X}$.

14 Find x and y from the following matrix equations:

(a) $(2x \quad 4) = (8 \quad 6y)$, (b) $\begin{pmatrix} x-y \\ x+y \end{pmatrix} = \begin{pmatrix} 2 \\ 10 \end{pmatrix}$, (c) $3 \begin{pmatrix} x \\ y \end{pmatrix} = \begin{pmatrix} y \\ 6 \end{pmatrix}$,

(d) $x(2 \quad y) = (\frac{1}{2} \quad 1)$, (e) $\begin{pmatrix} 2x-3 \\ x+1 \end{pmatrix} = y \begin{pmatrix} 1 \\ 3 \end{pmatrix}$, (f) $\begin{pmatrix} 2x-3y \\ 5x-2y \end{pmatrix} = \begin{pmatrix} -5 \\ 4 \end{pmatrix}$,

(g) $\begin{pmatrix} 2x \\ x \end{pmatrix} - \begin{pmatrix} y \\ 2y \end{pmatrix} = \begin{pmatrix} 14 \\ 13 \end{pmatrix}$, (h) $x \begin{pmatrix} 3 \\ 1 \end{pmatrix} + 2y \begin{pmatrix} 1 \\ 3 \end{pmatrix} = \begin{pmatrix} -8 \\ 0 \end{pmatrix}$.

15 Say whether each of the following statements is true (T) or false (F). ($\mathbf{A}$ and $\mathbf{B}$ are matrices.)

(a) The matrices $\mathbf{A}$ and $k\mathbf{A}$ always have the same order.

(b) $\mathbf{A} - \mathbf{B} = \mathbf{0} \quad \Leftrightarrow \quad \mathbf{A} = \mathbf{B}$.

(c) All column matrices have order $1 \times n$.

(d) $\begin{pmatrix} a \\ b \end{pmatrix} = \begin{pmatrix} b \\ c \end{pmatrix} \Rightarrow a = c$.

(e) Adding three matrices of order 3×1 gives a matrix of order 3×3.

(f) $\begin{pmatrix} 2x \\ y \end{pmatrix} = \begin{pmatrix} x^2 \\ x \end{pmatrix} \Rightarrow y = 2$.

(g) $3\mathbf{A} = \mathbf{A} \Rightarrow \mathbf{A} = \mathbf{0}$.

(h) $k\mathbf{A} = \mathbf{A} \Rightarrow \mathbf{A} = \mathbf{0}$.

Multiplication of a matrix by a matrix

The simplest way to illustrate the multiplication of two matrices is to take the product of a row matrix and a column matrix. For example,

$$(2 \quad 1 \quad 4) \begin{pmatrix} 10 \\ 30 \\ 20 \end{pmatrix}.$$

This product is defined to equal a matrix with just one element, which is obtained by the following rule.

Multiply each element of the row by the corresponding element of the column, and add the numbers which result.

Applying this rule to the above example, we have

$$(2 \times 10) + (1 \times 30) + (4 \times 20) = 130,$$

and it follows that

$$(2 \quad 1 \quad 4) \begin{pmatrix} 10 \\ 30 \\ 20 \end{pmatrix} = (130).$$

Here are two similar examples:

$$(3 \quad 2) \begin{pmatrix} 100 \\ 200 \end{pmatrix} = (700), \qquad (1 \quad 2 \quad 0 \quad 4) \begin{pmatrix} 3 \\ 1 \\ 2 \\ 1 \end{pmatrix} = (9).$$

When this idea of 'multiplying a row by a column' has been mastered, it is easy to extend the definition to apply to more complicated cases. The first point to note is that *the product of a row and a column can only be formed at all if the row and the column have the same number of elements.* With more complicated matrices the same condition holds, but now it is *all* the rows of the first matrix and all the columns of the second which must have the same numbers of elements. Thus for example the first of the following products can be formed, while the second cannot.

$$\begin{pmatrix} 1 & 3 & 5 \\ 4 & 0 & 2 \end{pmatrix} \begin{pmatrix} 2 & 7 \\ 1 & 2 \\ 4 & 3 \end{pmatrix} \qquad \qquad \begin{pmatrix} 4 & 2 \\ 3 & 5 \end{pmatrix} \begin{pmatrix} 3 & 4 \\ 1 & 7 \\ 2 & 6 \end{pmatrix}$$

multiplication possible 　　　　　 multiplication impossible

When the multiplication can be performed, the elements of the product matrix are obtained by applying the following rule.

To obtain the element in row *m* and column *n* of the product matrix, multiply row *m* of the first matrix by column *n* of the second.

For example, to obtain the element in row 2 and column 3 of the following product, we multiply row 2 by column 3:

$$\begin{pmatrix} 2 & 0 & 1 & 4 \\ \boxed{1 \ \ 3 \ \ 2 \ \ 1} \\ 4 & 0 & 3 & 2 \end{pmatrix} \begin{pmatrix} 1 & 3 & \boxed{2} \\ 4 & 1 & \boxed{0} \\ 2 & 1 & \boxed{5} \\ 0 & 3 & \boxed{2} \end{pmatrix} = \begin{pmatrix} \cdot & \cdot & \cdot \\ \cdot & \cdot & 14 \\ \cdot & \cdot & \cdot \end{pmatrix}.$$

The complete product of these two matrices is

$$\begin{pmatrix} 4 & 19 & 17 \\ 17 & 11 & 14 \\ 10 & 21 & 27 \end{pmatrix}.$$

Here are two more examples:

$$\begin{pmatrix} 1 & 2 & 3 \\ 2 & 1 & 3 \end{pmatrix} \begin{pmatrix} 20 \\ 40 \\ 30 \end{pmatrix} = \begin{pmatrix} 190 \\ 170 \end{pmatrix},$$

$$\begin{pmatrix} 4 & 2 \\ 5 & 0 \\ 3 & 1 \end{pmatrix} \begin{pmatrix} 1 & 0 & 2 & 4 \\ 3 & 1 & 0 & 2 \end{pmatrix} = \begin{pmatrix} 10 & 2 & 8 & 20 \\ 5 & 0 & 10 & 20 \\ 6 & 1 & 6 & 14 \end{pmatrix}.$$

It should be noted that the product matrix has the same number of rows as the first matrix and the same number of columns as the second. In general, the rule relating the orders of the matrices is as follows.

If the orders of the matrices being multiplied are ($m \times n$) and ($n \times p$), the order of the product matrix is ($m \times p$).

When the order of a matrix needs to be made explicit, we express the matrix in the form $A_{m \times n}$. Thus, for example, $A_{3 \times 2}$ denotes a matrix with 3 rows and 2 columns. The rule for obtaining the order of a product matrix is illustrated by the following examples.

$$A_{3 \times 2} \times B_{2 \times 5} = (AB)_{3 \times 5},$$
$$P_{1 \times 4} \times Q_{4 \times 2} = (PQ)_{1 \times 2}.$$

These examples show why the rule relating orders is sometimes called the *domino rule*. A brief way of expressing it is the following:

$$(m \times n)(n \times p) = m \times p.$$

Some terminology

When it is possible to form the product **AB**, we say that the matrices **A** and **B** are *conformable* for multiplication. In this product, **B** is said to be *pre-multiplied* by **A**, and **A** is said to be *post-multiplied* by **B**. The order in which the multiplication is performed clearly matters since it often happens that the product **AB** is possible while the product **BA** is not.

The product of a matrix **A** with itself, when this is possible, is denoted by A^2. A matrix can only be multiplied by itself if its rows and columns contain the same numbers of elements; hence *only a square matrix can be multiplied by itself.*

EXERCISE 40b

1 Work out

(a) $(2 \quad 3)\begin{pmatrix} 4 \\ 5 \end{pmatrix}$, (b) $(2 \quad 1 \quad 4)\begin{pmatrix} 20 \\ 30 \\ 10 \end{pmatrix}$, (c) $(3 \quad 0^- 2 \quad 5)\begin{pmatrix} 100 \\ 200 \\ 300 \\ 100 \end{pmatrix}$,

(d) $(-5 \quad 2)\begin{pmatrix} -3 \\ -1 \end{pmatrix}$, (e) $(7 \quad -2 \quad 6)\begin{pmatrix} -1 \\ 4 \\ -3 \end{pmatrix}$, (f) $(-1 \quad 4 \quad -3 \quad 7)\begin{pmatrix} 20 \\ -10 \\ -15 \\ 5 \end{pmatrix}$.

2 Work out

(a) $(x \quad y)\begin{pmatrix} 2y \\ x \end{pmatrix}$, (b) $(3x \quad 2)\begin{pmatrix} -1 \\ 4x \end{pmatrix}$, (c) $(y \quad 3)\begin{pmatrix} 2 \\ x \end{pmatrix}$,

(d) $(x \quad 2 \quad 3x)\begin{pmatrix} -4 \\ x \\ 2 \end{pmatrix}$, (e) $(p^2 \quad 2 \quad p \quad -4)\begin{pmatrix} 4 \\ p^2 \\ 3 - 2p \\ p^2 + 2p \end{pmatrix}$.

3 Work out

(a) $\begin{pmatrix} 1 & 2 \\ 2 & 3 \end{pmatrix}\begin{pmatrix} 5 \\ 3 \end{pmatrix}$, (b) $\begin{pmatrix} 2 & -3 \\ 0 & 5 \end{pmatrix}\begin{pmatrix} 1 \\ -2 \end{pmatrix}$, (c) $\begin{pmatrix} 1 & 0 & 2 \\ 0 & 3 & -4 \\ 2 & -1 & 3 \end{pmatrix}\begin{pmatrix} 2 \\ 1 \\ 3 \end{pmatrix}$,

(d) $(10 \quad 20)\begin{pmatrix} 3 & 4 \\ 2 & 1 \end{pmatrix}$, (e) $(-2 \quad 6)\begin{pmatrix} 1 & 4 & -3 & 5 \\ 0 & 2 & 1 & -3 \end{pmatrix}$, (f) $\begin{pmatrix} 2 \\ 3 \\ 1 \end{pmatrix}(4 \quad 2)$.

4 Given that $A = (2 \quad 5 \quad 1)$, $B = \begin{pmatrix} -2 \\ 1 \end{pmatrix}$, $C = \begin{pmatrix} 4 & -3 & 0 \\ 1 & 2 & -5 \end{pmatrix}$, $D = \begin{pmatrix} 1 & 0 \\ 0 & 2 \end{pmatrix}$,

$E = \begin{pmatrix} 1 \\ 4 \\ 3 \end{pmatrix}$,

say whether each of the following products can be formed and evaluate those which can: (a) **AE**, (b) **CB**, (c) **DC**, (d) **CD**, (e) **BA**, (f) **AC**, (g) B^2, (h) D^2.

5 Work out

(a) $\begin{pmatrix} p & 3 \\ 0 & p \end{pmatrix}\begin{pmatrix} 2 \\ p \end{pmatrix}$, (b) $(x - 2 \quad 1 - x)\begin{pmatrix} 2 & 1 \\ 1 & 3 \end{pmatrix}$, (c) $\begin{pmatrix} x & -2 \\ -1 & 2x \end{pmatrix}\begin{pmatrix} 3 & x \\ x & -1 \end{pmatrix}$.

6 Given that $A = \begin{pmatrix} 2 & 5 \\ 1 & 3 \end{pmatrix}$ and $B = \begin{pmatrix} 1 & 4 \\ 3 & 2 \end{pmatrix}$, work out (a) A^2, (b) B^2, (c) **AB**,

(d) **AB** − **BA**, (e) $2A^2 - 3B^2$.

7 Find $\mathbf{A}^2$ if (a) $\mathbf{A} = \begin{pmatrix} 2 & 0 & -1 \\ 0 & -3 & 2 \\ 4 & 1 & -2 \end{pmatrix}$ (b) $\mathbf{A} = \begin{pmatrix} x & 0 & x \\ 0 & x & 0 \\ x & x & x \end{pmatrix}$.

8 State the order of the product matrix in each of the following cases:
(a) $\mathbf{A}_{2 \times 5} \times \mathbf{B}_{5 \times 4}$, (b) $\mathbf{B}_{3 \times 1} \times \mathbf{A}_{1 \times 4}$, (c) $\mathbf{A}_{p \times q} \times \mathbf{B}_{q \times r}$.

9 Find x from the following matrix equations:

(a) $(2 \quad x)\begin{pmatrix} 1 \\ 3 \end{pmatrix} = (11)$, (b) $(x \quad 4)\begin{pmatrix} -2 \\ x \end{pmatrix} = (8)$, (c) $(-x \quad 5)\begin{pmatrix} 3 \\ x-1 \end{pmatrix} = (-1)$,

(d) $(x \quad -1)\begin{pmatrix} x \\ 2x \end{pmatrix} = (3)$, (e) $(x \quad 3)\begin{pmatrix} x \\ x-2 \end{pmatrix} = (4)$.

10 The orders of matrices **A, B, C, D** are 2×3, 2×1, 3×2 and 1×3, respectively. Say whether each of the following is possible: (a) premultiplying **C** by **A**, (b) post-multiplying **B** by **C**, (c) post-multiplying **D** by **C**, (d) pre-multiplying **D** by **B**, (e) pre-multiplying **A** by **B**.

11 Find x and y from the following matrix equations:

(a) $\begin{pmatrix} 2 & 1 \\ 1 & 0 \end{pmatrix}\begin{pmatrix} x \\ y \end{pmatrix} = \begin{pmatrix} 7 \\ 3 \end{pmatrix}$, (b) $(-3 \quad x)\begin{pmatrix} y & x \\ 2 & 0 \end{pmatrix} = (-16 \quad 6)$,

(c) $\begin{pmatrix} x & 3 \\ 1 & 2 \end{pmatrix}\begin{pmatrix} 2 \\ y \end{pmatrix} = \begin{pmatrix} x \\ 1 \end{pmatrix}$, (d) $(2x \quad -y)\begin{pmatrix} 1 & 2 \\ -1 & 3 \end{pmatrix} = (0 \quad 10)$.

12 Find p, q, r, s from the following matrix equations:

(a) $\begin{pmatrix} 2 & 1 \\ 0 & 3 \end{pmatrix}\begin{pmatrix} p & q \\ 1 & s \end{pmatrix} = \begin{pmatrix} 3 & 8 \\ r & 6 \end{pmatrix}$,

(b) $\begin{pmatrix} \frac{1}{2} & 2r \\ 1\frac{1}{2} & p \end{pmatrix}\begin{pmatrix} 4 & 2q \\ 1 & -1 \end{pmatrix} = \begin{pmatrix} s & 2 \\ 8 & 1 \end{pmatrix}$.

Identity matrices for multiplication

The square matrices

$$(1), \begin{pmatrix} 1 & 0 \\ 0 & 1 \end{pmatrix}, \begin{pmatrix} 1 & 0 & 0 \\ 0 & 1 & 0 \\ 0 & 0 & 1 \end{pmatrix}, \begin{pmatrix} 1 & 0 & 0 & 0 \\ 0 & 1 & 0 & 0 \\ 0 & 0 & 1 & 0 \\ 0 & 0 & 0 & 1 \end{pmatrix}, \text{etc.}$$

are identity matrices for the operation of matrix multiplication. When premultiplying or post-multiplying any matrix of appropriate order, they leave the matrix unchanged. E.g.

$$(3 \quad 4)\begin{pmatrix} 1 & 0 \\ 0 & 1 \end{pmatrix} = (3 \quad 4), \begin{pmatrix} 1 & 0 & 0 \\ 0 & 1 & 0 \\ 0 & 0 & 1 \end{pmatrix}\begin{pmatrix} 2 \\ 5 \\ 7 \end{pmatrix} = \begin{pmatrix} 2 \\ 5 \\ 7 \end{pmatrix},$$

$$\begin{pmatrix} a & b \\ c & d \end{pmatrix}\begin{pmatrix} 1 & 0 \\ 0 & 1 \end{pmatrix} = \begin{pmatrix} 1 & 0 \\ 0 & 1 \end{pmatrix}\begin{pmatrix} a & b \\ c & d \end{pmatrix} = \begin{pmatrix} a & b \\ c & d \end{pmatrix}.$$

The identity matrices for multiplication clearly play a similar role to the number 1 in ordinary arithmetic.

All the identity matrices are denoted by **I**, or, if it is necessary to make the order explicit, I_2, I_3, etc.

Is matrix multiplication commutative?

We have already seen that **AB** cannot equal **BA** for all matrices **A** and **B**, because these products cannot be formed for all matrices. But is it perhaps true that **AB** = **BA** whenever both the products can be formed?

In fact it is *not* generally true that **AB** = **BA** when these products are possible, and to show this we need only find one case in which the products are unequal. It is important to see that just *one counter-example* disproves any general statement, because a general statement claims to be true for *all* cases. (A single example in favour of a general statement does not of course prove the statement!)

Counter-example 1

Let $A = \begin{pmatrix} 2 & 1 \\ 1 & 3 \end{pmatrix}$ and $B = \begin{pmatrix} 1 & 5 \\ 4 & 2 \end{pmatrix}$. Then

$$AB = \begin{pmatrix} 2 & 1 \\ 1 & 3 \end{pmatrix}\begin{pmatrix} 1 & 5 \\ 4 & 2 \end{pmatrix} = \begin{pmatrix} 6 & 12 \\ 13 & 11 \end{pmatrix},$$

$$BA = \begin{pmatrix} 1 & 5 \\ 4 & 2 \end{pmatrix}\begin{pmatrix} 2 & 1 \\ 1 & 3 \end{pmatrix} = \begin{pmatrix} 7 & 16 \\ 10 & 10 \end{pmatrix}.$$

Hence **AB** ≠ **BA**.

Counter-example 2

Let **A** be any matrix with order 2 × 3 and let **B** be any matrix with order 3 × 2. Then both the products **AB** and **BA** can be formed, but **AB** has order 2 × 2 and **BA** has order 3 × 3. Hence **AB** ≠ **BA**.

Note: It is not being claimed that **AB** is *never* equal to **BA**, and there are in fact many cases in which the two products are equal. We have just seen, for example, that **AI** = **IA** = **A** for any square matrix **A** and the identity matrix **I** of the same order. Since the property is not present in all cases, however, matrix multiplication cannot be called a commutative operation.

Is matrix multiplication associative?

If matrix multiplication is associative, then **(AB)C** = **A(BC)** for any three matrices whose orders allow these products to be formed, and it will be possible to write **ABC** without ambiguity. In fact the operation *is* associative, though this is not easy to prove and we shall not give a proof here. We shall *illustrate* the presence of the property by an example, but it must be stressed that this is not a proof.

Let $A = \begin{pmatrix} 2 & 0 \\ 0 & 1 \end{pmatrix}$, $B = \begin{pmatrix} 1 & 3 \\ 0 & 4 \end{pmatrix}$ and $C = \begin{pmatrix} 0 & 2 \\ 1 & 3 \end{pmatrix}$. Then we have

$$AB = \begin{pmatrix} 2 & 0 \\ 0 & 1 \end{pmatrix}\begin{pmatrix} 1 & 3 \\ 0 & 4 \end{pmatrix} = \begin{pmatrix} 2 & 6 \\ 0 & 4 \end{pmatrix}$$

$$\therefore (AB)C = \begin{pmatrix} 2 & 6 \\ 0 & 4 \end{pmatrix}\begin{pmatrix} 0 & 2 \\ 1 & 3 \end{pmatrix} = \begin{pmatrix} 6 & 22 \\ 4 & 12 \end{pmatrix}.$$

Also

$$BC = \begin{pmatrix} 1 & 3 \\ 0 & 4 \end{pmatrix}\begin{pmatrix} 0 & 2 \\ 1 & 3 \end{pmatrix} = \begin{pmatrix} 3 & 11 \\ 4 & 12 \end{pmatrix}$$

$$\therefore A(BC) = \begin{pmatrix} 2 & 0 \\ 0 & 1 \end{pmatrix}\begin{pmatrix} 3 & 11 \\ 4 & 12 \end{pmatrix} = \begin{pmatrix} 6 & 22 \\ 4 & 12 \end{pmatrix}.$$

Hence $(AB)C = A(BC)$.

It follows from the presence of the associative property that expressions denoting powers, such as A^3 and A^4, are meaningful for any square matrix A. If matrix multiplication were not associative, A^2A would not necessarily equal AA^2, and the expression A^3 would therefore be ambiguous.

Removal of brackets (the 'distributive' laws)

It can be shown, though once again the proof will be omitted here, that for matrices of appropriate orders,

$$A(B + C) = AB + AC$$
$$\text{and} \quad (B + C)A = BA + CA.$$

(These are called *distributive* laws: we say that 'matrix multiplication is distributive over matrix addition'.)

Note that since matrix multiplication is not commutative, $A(B + C)$ is not in general equal to $(B + C)A$.

Manipulation of matrix expressions

In ordinary algebra, letters stand for numbers and many manipulations of algebraic expressions are possible because the commutative, associative and distributive properties are present. For example,

$$(x + y)(x - y) = x^2 - xy + yx - y^2 \text{ (distributive properties)},$$
$$\text{but } xy = yx \text{ (commutative property)},$$
$$\therefore (x + y)(x - y) = x^2 - y^2.$$

In matrix algebra we can perform any manipulations depending on the associative or distributive properties, but the absence of the commutative property for multiplication often means that expressions cannot be simplified to the same extent as in ordinary algebra. Given for example two square matrices **A** and **B** of the same order, we have

$$(\mathbf{A} + \mathbf{B})(\mathbf{A} - \mathbf{B}) = \mathbf{A}^2 - \mathbf{AB} + \mathbf{BA} - \mathbf{B}^2 \text{ (distributive properties),}$$

but since **AB** $\ne$ **BA** the expression cannot be simplified further and we do not therefore obtain the 'difference of two squares' result of ordinary algebra.

There are of course some cases in which the multiplication of two matrices is commutative, and when this is so we can proceed very much as in ordinary algebra. Consider for example the expression

$$(\mathbf{A} - 2\mathbf{I})(\mathbf{A} + 3\mathbf{I}),$$

where **A** is a square matrix and **I** is the identity matrix of the same order. We have

$$\begin{aligned}
(\mathbf{A} - 2\mathbf{I})(\mathbf{A} + 3\mathbf{I}) &= \mathbf{A}^2 + 3\mathbf{AI} - 2\mathbf{IA} - 6\mathbf{I}^2 \text{ (distributive properties)} \\
&= \mathbf{A}^2 + \mathbf{AI} - 6\mathbf{I}^2 \text{ (since } \mathbf{AI} = \mathbf{IA}) \\
&= \mathbf{A}^2 + \mathbf{A} - 6\mathbf{I}.
\end{aligned}$$

This is clearly very similar to the following 'removal of brackets' procedure from ordinary algebra:

$$\begin{aligned}
(x - 2)(x + 3) &= x^2 + 3x - 2x - 6 \\
&= x^2 + x - 6.
\end{aligned}$$

EXERCISE 40c

1 $\mathbf{A} = \begin{pmatrix} 1 & 2 \\ 3 & 0 \end{pmatrix}$, $\mathbf{B} = \begin{pmatrix} 0 & 2 \\ 1 & 3 \end{pmatrix}$, $\mathbf{C} = \begin{pmatrix} 2 & 3 \\ 0 & 1 \end{pmatrix}$.

(a) Find **AB** and **BA**. Does the result prove that matrix multiplication is not a commutative operation?
(b) Find **A(BC)** and **(AB)C**. Does the result prove that matrix multiplication is an associative operation?
(c) Find **A(B + C)** and **AB + AC**. Does the result prove that matrix multiplication is distributive over addition?

2 $\mathbf{A} = \begin{pmatrix} 1 & 2 \\ 2 & 1 \end{pmatrix}$, $\mathbf{B} = \begin{pmatrix} 0 & 2 \\ 1 & 1 \end{pmatrix}$, $\mathbf{C} = \begin{pmatrix} 3 & 1 \\ 1 & 3 \end{pmatrix}$. Say whether the following are

true (T) or false (F): (a) **AB = BA**, (b) **AC = CA**, (c) **BC = CB**.

3 $\mathbf{P} = \begin{pmatrix} a & b \\ b & a \end{pmatrix}$ and $\mathbf{Q} = \begin{pmatrix} c & d \\ d & c \end{pmatrix}$. Prove that **PQ = QP**.

4 In each of the following cases say whether it is possible to form the product **ABC** and, if so, work out this product.

(a) $\mathbf{A} = (-2 \quad 5)$, $\mathbf{B} = \begin{pmatrix} 1 & 2 \\ 0 & 1 \end{pmatrix}$, $\mathbf{C} = \begin{pmatrix} 3 \\ 1 \end{pmatrix}$.

(b) $\mathbf{A} = \begin{pmatrix} 2 \\ 3 \end{pmatrix}$, $\mathbf{B} = (4 \quad 0)$, $\mathbf{C} = (5)$.

(c) $\mathbf{A} = \begin{pmatrix} 2 & 1 \\ 1 & 0 \end{pmatrix}$, $\mathbf{B} = \begin{pmatrix} 0 & 1 & 0 \\ 2 & 1 & 3 \end{pmatrix}$, $\mathbf{C} = \begin{pmatrix} -1 \\ 0 \\ 2 \end{pmatrix}$.

5 $\mathbf{A} = \begin{pmatrix} 3 & -1 \\ 1 & 2 \end{pmatrix}$ and $\mathbf{B} = \begin{pmatrix} 1 & 2 \\ 0 & 3 \end{pmatrix}$. Show that $\mathbf{A}^2 - \mathbf{AB} = \mathbf{A}(\mathbf{A} - \mathbf{B})$ and that $\mathbf{A}^2 - \mathbf{BA} = (\mathbf{A} - \mathbf{B})\mathbf{A}$.

6 $\mathbf{A} = (2 \quad 3)$. Write down identity matrices $\mathbf{I}$ such that (a) $\mathbf{AI} = \mathbf{A}$, (b) $\mathbf{IA} = \mathbf{A}$.

7 $\mathbf{B} = \begin{pmatrix} 1 & 2 & 3 \\ 3 & 2 & 1 \end{pmatrix}$. What are the orders of the identity matrices $\mathbf{I}$ such that

(a) $\mathbf{BI} = \mathbf{B}$, (b) $\mathbf{IB} = \mathbf{B}$?

8 Simplify (a) $\mathbf{AI}$, (b) $\mathbf{I}^4$, (c) $\mathbf{IAIBIC}$, (d) $\mathbf{I_3}^2 + \mathbf{I_3}^4$, (e) $2\mathbf{I_5}^7 - 5\mathbf{I_5}^9$.

9 $\mathbf{P} = \begin{pmatrix} 2 & 0 \\ 0 & 2 \end{pmatrix}$. Work out $\mathbf{P}^2$, $\mathbf{P}^3$ and $\mathbf{P}^4$ (a) by repeated multiplication,

(b) by first expressing $\mathbf{P}$ in terms of $\mathbf{I}$.

10 $\mathbf{S} = \begin{pmatrix} 0 & 1 \\ 1 & 0 \end{pmatrix}$. Work out $\mathbf{S}^2$ and hence simplify $\mathbf{S}^6$ and $\mathbf{S}^9$.

11 $\mathbf{T} = \begin{pmatrix} 0 & 2 \\ 2 & 0 \end{pmatrix}$. Express $\mathbf{T}^6$ in terms of $\mathbf{I}$.

12 $\mathbf{X} = \begin{pmatrix} 1 & 2 \\ 3 & 1 \end{pmatrix}$. Work out $\mathbf{X}^4$ and $(\mathbf{X}^2)^2$. Is it true that if $\mathbf{X}$ is any square matrix,

$(\mathbf{X}^m)^n = \mathbf{X}^{mn}$?

13 $\mathbf{X} = (4 \quad 1)$, $\mathbf{Y} = \begin{pmatrix} 1 \\ 2 \end{pmatrix}$, $\mathbf{Z} = \begin{pmatrix} 2 \\ -2 \end{pmatrix}$. Show that $\mathbf{XY} = \mathbf{XZ}$. What follows from

the equation $xy = xz$ if x, y and z are numbers? Does a similar result hold for matrices?

14 $\mathbf{P} = (3 \quad 2)$ and $\mathbf{Q} = \begin{pmatrix} 4 & -8 \\ -6 & 12 \end{pmatrix}$. Show that $\mathbf{PQ} = \mathbf{0}$. What follows from the

equation $pq = 0$ if p and q are numbers? Does a similar result hold for matrices?

15 $\mathbf{X} = \begin{pmatrix} a & b \\ c & d \end{pmatrix}$ and $\mathbf{I} = \begin{pmatrix} 1 & 0 \\ 0 & 1 \end{pmatrix}$. Show that $(\mathbf{X} + \mathbf{I})(\mathbf{X} - 2\mathbf{I}) = \mathbf{X}^2 - \mathbf{X} - 2\mathbf{I}$.

16 $\mathbf{A}$ and $\mathbf{B}$ are 2×2 matrices and $\mathbf{0}$, $\mathbf{I}$ are the zero and identity matrices of order 2×2. Say whether or not each of the following statements is always true.
(a) $\mathbf{A0} = \mathbf{0}$. (b) $(\mathbf{A} + \mathbf{B})^2 = \mathbf{A}^2 + 2\mathbf{AB} + \mathbf{B}^2$. (c) $\mathbf{AB} = \mathbf{0} \Rightarrow \mathbf{A} = \mathbf{0}$ or $\mathbf{B} = \mathbf{0}$.
(d) $(\mathbf{A}^3)^4 = \mathbf{A}^{12}$. (e) $(\mathbf{A} - 2\mathbf{I})^2 = \mathbf{A}^2 - 4\mathbf{A} + 4\mathbf{I}$. (f) $(\mathbf{AB})^2 = \mathbf{A}^2\mathbf{B}^2$.
(g) $\mathbf{A}^3 \times \mathbf{A}^4 = \mathbf{A}^7$. (h) $\mathbf{A}^2\mathbf{B}^3 \times \mathbf{A}^4\mathbf{B} = \mathbf{A}^6\mathbf{B}^4$.

The determinant of a 2 × 2 matrix

The determinant of the matrix $\mathbf{A} = \begin{pmatrix} a & b \\ c & d \end{pmatrix}$ is the number $ad - bc$.

It is denoted by $|A|$ or $\begin{vmatrix} a & b \\ c & d \end{vmatrix}$. For example, if $P = \begin{pmatrix} 4 & 1 \\ 3 & 2 \end{pmatrix}$ and

$Q = \begin{pmatrix} 2 & 3 \\ -1 & -7 \end{pmatrix}$, we have

$$|P| = 8 - 3 = 5, \text{ and } |Q| = -14 - (-3) = -11.$$

The multiplicative inverse of a matrix

The multiplicative inverse of a matrix P is defined to be a matrix P^{-1} such that

$$PP^{-1} = P^{-1}P = I,$$

where I is the identity matrix of appropriate order. It can be shown that only square matrices can have multiplicative inverses, and in this book we shall limit our attention to the inverses of 2×2 matrices. Those of matrices with higher orders are considerably more difficult to calculate.

The multiplicative inverse of a matrix is usually called simply its *inverse*, partly because the additive inverse can be described as the *negative* of the matrix.

The inverse of a 2 × 2 matrix

It can be shown that the inverse of a 2×2 matrix is obtained by applying the following rule.

Interchange the elements of the leading diagonal, change the signs of the other two elements, and divide by the determinant.

▶**Example 4**

Given the matrix $M = \begin{pmatrix} 4 & 2 \\ 5 & 3 \end{pmatrix}$, *find* M^{-1} *and show that* $MM^{-1} = M^{-1}M = I$.

Since $|M| = 12 - 10 = 2$, $M^{-1} = \frac{1}{2}\begin{pmatrix} 3 & -2 \\ -5 & 4 \end{pmatrix}$ or $\begin{pmatrix} 1\frac{1}{2} & -1 \\ -2\frac{1}{2} & 2 \end{pmatrix}$. When this

matrix either pre-multiplies or post-multiplies M, the result is the identity matrix I:

$$MM^{-1} = \begin{pmatrix} 4 & 2 \\ 5 & 3 \end{pmatrix}\begin{pmatrix} 1\frac{1}{2} & -1 \\ -2\frac{1}{2} & 2 \end{pmatrix} = \begin{pmatrix} 1 & 0 \\ 0 & 1 \end{pmatrix},$$

$$\text{and } M^{-1}M = \begin{pmatrix} 1\frac{1}{2} & -1 \\ -2\frac{1}{2} & 2 \end{pmatrix}\begin{pmatrix} 4 & 2 \\ 5 & 3 \end{pmatrix} = \begin{pmatrix} 1 & 0 \\ 0 & 1 \end{pmatrix}.$$

Inverse matrices should normally be expressed as simply as possible. Suppose for example that

$$P = \begin{pmatrix} -10 & 4 \\ 6 & -2 \end{pmatrix}, \text{ so that } P^{-1} = -\frac{1}{4}\begin{pmatrix} -2 & -4 \\ -6 & -10 \end{pmatrix}.$$

This can be simplified by taking the factor -2 outside the matrix, to give

$$\mathbf{P}^{-1} = \tfrac{1}{2}\begin{pmatrix} 1 & 2 \\ 3 & 5 \end{pmatrix} \quad \text{or} \quad \begin{pmatrix} \tfrac{1}{2} & 1 \\ 1\tfrac{1}{2} & 2\tfrac{1}{2} \end{pmatrix}. \qquad \triangleleft$$

Singular matrices

If $ad = bc$ the determinant of the matrix $\begin{pmatrix} a & b \\ c & d \end{pmatrix}$ is zero, and since division by zero is impossible it follows that the matrix has no inverse. Matrices of this kind are called *singular* matrices. For example, the following matrices are all singular and have no inverses:

$$\begin{pmatrix} 4 & 6 \\ 2 & 3 \end{pmatrix}, \begin{pmatrix} 1 & 2 \\ 3 & 6 \end{pmatrix}, \begin{pmatrix} -8 & 4 \\ -6 & 3 \end{pmatrix}, \begin{pmatrix} 3 & -9 \\ -\tfrac{1}{2} & 1\tfrac{1}{2} \end{pmatrix}.$$

Exercise 40d

In questions 1–19 find the inverses of the given matrices if they exist. If they do not, give the answer 'singular'.

1 $\begin{pmatrix} 2 & 3 \\ 3 & 5 \end{pmatrix}$, **2** $\begin{pmatrix} 4 & 3 \\ 5 & 4 \end{pmatrix}$, **3** $\begin{pmatrix} 2 & 8 \\ 2 & 9 \end{pmatrix}$, **4** $\begin{pmatrix} 6 & 2 \\ 9 & 3 \end{pmatrix}$, **5** $\begin{pmatrix} 7 & 3 \\ 8 & 4 \end{pmatrix}$, **6** $\begin{pmatrix} 2 & -1 \\ 3 & 1 \end{pmatrix}$,

7 $\begin{pmatrix} 8 & 2 \\ -4 & -1 \end{pmatrix}$, **8** $\begin{pmatrix} -3 & -2 \\ 5 & 4 \end{pmatrix}$, **9** $\begin{pmatrix} 1\tfrac{1}{4} & 3 \\ 1 & 2 \end{pmatrix}$, **10** $\begin{pmatrix} \tfrac{1}{3} & 1\tfrac{1}{3} \\ 1\tfrac{1}{5} & 6 \end{pmatrix}$, **11** $\begin{pmatrix} -12 & 8 \\ 8 & -6 \end{pmatrix}$,

12 $\begin{pmatrix} \tfrac{2}{3} & \tfrac{1}{2} \\ 4 & -3 \end{pmatrix}$, **13** $\begin{pmatrix} 1\tfrac{1}{2} & -\tfrac{1}{6} \\ 2 & \tfrac{4}{9} \end{pmatrix}$, **14** $\begin{pmatrix} 8 & -6 \\ 24 & -18 \end{pmatrix}$, **15** $\begin{pmatrix} 1\tfrac{1}{2} & -\tfrac{3}{4} \\ -3\tfrac{1}{3} & 2 \end{pmatrix}$, **16** $\begin{pmatrix} a & b \\ a & b \end{pmatrix}$,

17 $\begin{pmatrix} 2x & 5 \\ x & 3 \end{pmatrix}$, **18** $\begin{pmatrix} a & -2b \\ a & -b \end{pmatrix}$, **19** $\begin{pmatrix} x+5 & x+4 \\ x+4 & x+3 \end{pmatrix}$.

In questions 20–26 find the values of x for which the given matrices are singular.

20 $\begin{pmatrix} x & 3 \\ 4 & 2 \end{pmatrix}$, **21** $\begin{pmatrix} 2 & x-1 \\ 3 & x \end{pmatrix}$, **22** $\begin{pmatrix} -3 & 1-x \\ 5 & x \end{pmatrix}$, **23** $\begin{pmatrix} x & 2 \\ 8 & x \end{pmatrix}$, **24** $\begin{pmatrix} x-1 & 2 \\ 3 & x \end{pmatrix}$,

25 $\begin{pmatrix} -3 & 3-2x \\ x+1 & 11 \end{pmatrix}$, **26** $\begin{pmatrix} x-2 & 4-x^2 \\ -1 & x+2 \end{pmatrix}$.

Matrix equations

The solution of equations in which the unknown quantities are matrices provides a simple example of the use of inverse matrices.

Let $\mathbf{A} = \begin{pmatrix} 2 & 1 \\ 1 & 3 \end{pmatrix}$ and $\mathbf{B} = \begin{pmatrix} 3 & 7 \\ -1 & 6 \end{pmatrix}$, and suppose we require a matrix $\mathbf{X}$ such that $\mathbf{AX} = \mathbf{B}$. If we pre-multiply both sides of this equation by $\mathbf{A}^{-1}$, we have

$$A^{-1}AX = A^{-1}B$$
$$\text{i.e. } X = A^{-1}B \text{ (since } A^{-1}A = I).$$

It follows that

$$X = \frac{1}{5}\begin{pmatrix} 3 & -1 \\ -1 & 2 \end{pmatrix}\begin{pmatrix} 3 & 7 \\ -1 & 6 \end{pmatrix}$$

$$= \frac{1}{5}\begin{pmatrix} 10 & 15 \\ -5 & 5 \end{pmatrix}$$

$$= \begin{pmatrix} 2 & 3 \\ -1 & 1 \end{pmatrix}.$$

Note: It is essential to *pre*-multiply both sides of the equation $AX = B$ by A^{-1}. If we needed to solve the equation $XA = B$, we should *post*-multiply both sides by A^{-1}.

The use of matrices to solve simultaneous equations

Consider the pair of simultaneous equations

$$3x - 2y = 5,$$
$$4x + y = 14.$$

This pair of equations can be expressed as a single matrix equation as follows:

$$\begin{pmatrix} 3 & -2 \\ 4 & 1 \end{pmatrix}\begin{pmatrix} x \\ y \end{pmatrix} = \begin{pmatrix} 5 \\ 14 \end{pmatrix}.$$

We can obtain the values of x and y from this equation by pre-multiplying both sides by the inverse of the 'coefficients matrix' $\begin{pmatrix} 3 & -2 \\ 4 & 1 \end{pmatrix}$:

$$\frac{1}{11}\begin{pmatrix} 1 & 2 \\ -4 & 3 \end{pmatrix}\begin{pmatrix} 3 & -2 \\ 4 & 1 \end{pmatrix}\begin{pmatrix} x \\ y \end{pmatrix} = \frac{1}{11}\begin{pmatrix} 1 & 2 \\ -4 & 3 \end{pmatrix}\begin{pmatrix} 5 \\ 14 \end{pmatrix}$$

$$\therefore \begin{pmatrix} 1 & 0 \\ 0 & 1 \end{pmatrix}\begin{pmatrix} x \\ y \end{pmatrix} = \frac{1}{11}\begin{pmatrix} 33 \\ 22 \end{pmatrix}$$

$$\therefore \begin{pmatrix} x \\ y \end{pmatrix} = \begin{pmatrix} 3 \\ 2 \end{pmatrix}$$

$$\therefore x = 3 \text{ and } y = 2.$$

This method of solving pairs of simultaneous equations is not as quick as the usual methods based on equalising the coefficients or substitution, but the matrix method is more systematic than these, and therefore more suitable when a computer is being programmed to solve large numbers of simultaneous equations.

If the coefficients matrix is singular, the pair of equations has no unique solutions. Consider, for example, the following pair of equations, which could be represented graphically by two parallel lines.

$$y = 2x - 1,$$
$$3y = 6x + 4.$$

Since the graphs of the equations do not meet, there can be no pair of x and y values which satisfy both equations simultaneously. Writing the equations in the usual way we have

$$2x - y = 1,$$
$$6x - 3y = -4,$$

and it can be seen that the coefficients matrix $\begin{pmatrix} 2 & -1 \\ 6 & -3 \end{pmatrix}$ is singular and has no inverse.

Pairs of equations representing the same straight line, e.g.

$$2y - 3x = 4,$$
$$4y - 6x = 8,$$

have infinite numbers of solutions (represented by all the points on the line), but no *unique* solutions. The coefficients matrix is again singular.

EXERCISE 40e

1 $A = \begin{pmatrix} 2 & 3 \\ 1 & 2 \end{pmatrix}$ and $B = \begin{pmatrix} 1 & 4 \\ 3 & 2 \end{pmatrix}$. Find matrices X and Y such that $AX = B$ and $YA = B$.

2 $A = \begin{pmatrix} 2 & 4 \\ 1 & 3 \end{pmatrix}$ and $B = \begin{pmatrix} 16 \\ 13 \end{pmatrix}$. Solve the equation $AX = B$.

3 $A = \begin{pmatrix} 2 & 5 \\ 3 & 8 \end{pmatrix}$ and $B = (1 \quad 4)$. Solve the equation $XA = B$.

4 $A = \begin{pmatrix} 2 & -2 \\ 1 & 1 \end{pmatrix}$ and $B = \begin{pmatrix} 1 & 0 & 2 \\ 0 & 3 & 1 \end{pmatrix}$. Solve the equation $AX = B$.

5 $A = \begin{pmatrix} 3 & 1 \\ 2 & 1 \end{pmatrix}$ and $B = \begin{pmatrix} 2 & 5 \\ -1 & -3 \end{pmatrix}$. Solve the equations $AX = B$, $XA = B$, $BX = A$, $XB = A$.

Where possible, solve the following pairs of simultaneous equations by the matrix method. When no unique solutions can be obtained, say whether the equations represent parallel or coincident lines.

6 $2x + y = 5$ **7** $x + 2y = 5$ **8** $2x - 3y = 11$ **9** $2x + 5y = 6$
       $x + y = 3$ $x + 3y = 6$ $x - y = 5$ $4x + 10y = 3$

10 $4x + 5y = 3$ **11** $6x - 5y = -2$ **12** $2x + 3y = 4$ **13** $2y = 4 - 3x$
        $2x + 3y = 1$ $3x - 2y = 1$ $3x + 4y = 5$ $y + 1\frac{1}{2}x = 2$

14 $-3x + 2y = 9$ **15** $4y - 3x = -6$ **16** $-4x + 9y = 8$ **17** $0.6y = 0.4x + 0.3$
     $5x - 2y = -13$ $3y - x = -7$ $2x + 5 = 5y$ $2x - 3y = 1\frac{1}{2}$

18 $x = 2y - 1$ **19** $2x + y + 13 = 0$ **20** $4x - 5y = -2$
     $y = 2x$ $-4x + 3y + 9 = 0$ $8y - 6x = 5$

21 $y = 1\frac{1}{2}x - 8 = 3 - 4x$ **22** $3y - 6x + 11 = 0$
                                  $y + 2x - 5 = 0$

41 Vectors

A vector is a quantity having both magnitude (or size) and direction. For example *force* is a vector because to describe a force completely we must give both its size and the direction in which it acts. On the other hand *temperature* is not a vector because a temperature is completely described by a single value such as 40°C. Quantities such as temperature, which have magnitude only, are called *scalars*. Some other examples of vectors are displacement, velocity, momentum and acceleration, and some other scalar quantities are mass, length, time and energy. In this book we shall consider only the vectors *displacement* and *velocity*, but the rules which apply to these quantities apply to all vectors.

Displacement

Suppose that a body starts at a point *P* and moves in a horizontal straight line to a point *Q*. To fix the journey completely *two* pieces of information are required, namely the *distance PQ* and the *direction* of the line *PQ*. This information might be expressed diagrammatically as in Fig. 41.1.

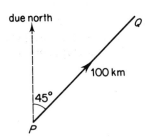

Fig. 41.1

Fig. 41.1 shows that the body moves 100 km north-east, and this *directed distance* is an example of a displacement. It is important to realise that a displacement is considered to be a *single* quantity, even though *two* values (at least) are required to specify it. This is a characteristic feature of all vector quantities.

416

Definition

**A displacement is a movement through a definite distance
in a definite direction.**

(The magnitude of the displacement is the distance moved.)

Velocity

In everyday life the words *velocity* and *speed* have virtually the same
meaning, but in mathematics we use the terms more strictly. Velocity is a
speed *in a definite direction*, such as 10 km h^{-1} due north or 20 m s $^{-1}$
vertically upwards. Velocity is therefore a vector quantity, while speed (the
magnitude of velocity) is a scalar. Velocity is in fact related to speed just
as displacement is related to distance.

Definition

A velocity is definite speed in a definite direction.

(The magnitude of the velocity is the speed.)

The representation of vectors

Fig. 41.1 shows one way of representing a displacement on paper. The
length of the line represents the magnitude of the displacement (that is,
the distance moved), while the direction of the line indicates the direction
of the displacement (north-east). A line of this kind is called a *directed line
segment*.

Fig. 41.2 shows a more general method of labelling a directed line
segment. This line segment (and the vector it represents) can be denoted
either by $\overrightarrow{AB}$ or by the single small letter **a**. In textbooks, single small letters
denoting vectors are printed in bold type, and when ordinary handwriting
is used they should be underlined.

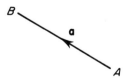

Fig. 41.2

The *magnitude* of a vector – also called its *modulus* – can be denoted
by placing a pair of vertical lines around the symbol for the vector. Thus
the magnitude of the vector above is denoted by $|\overrightarrow{AB}|$ or $|\mathbf{a}|$. It can also
be denoted simply by *AB.*

Free and localised vectors

A vector is normally considered to be completely specified by its magnitude and direction, and we do not consider its value to be affected by a change in position. Thus the vectors shown in Fig. 41.3 are all regarded as equal:

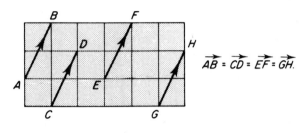

$$\overrightarrow{AB} = \overrightarrow{CD} = \overrightarrow{EF} = \overrightarrow{GH}.$$

Fig. 41.3

Sometimes, however, we do want to say that a change in the position of a vector alters its value, and then the vector is described as *localised*. For example, forces are localised vectors because a change in the line of action of a force changes its effect upon a body. Non-localised vectors are called *free* vectors, and it can normally be assumed that vectors are free unless otherwise stated.

Multiplication by a real number; the negative of a vector.

The vector $k\mathbf{a}$, where k is a real number, is defined to be a vector having the same direction as $\mathbf{a}$ but with k times the magnitude. The vector $-\mathbf{a}$ is defined to be a vector which is equal in magnitude to $\mathbf{a}$ but with the opposite direction. Fig. 41.4 illustrates these definitions.

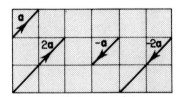

Fig. 41.4

The zero or null vector

A vector of magnitude zero is called a zero or null vector and denoted by **0**. It clearly has no direction.

Addition of vectors

The rules for adding and subtracting vectors will be explained by considering displacements, but they apply to all vectors.

Suppose that a displacement from A to B is followed by one from B to C (Fig. 41.5):

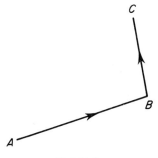

Fig. 41.5

It is natural to say that the *sum* of the two displacements is the single displacement which achieves the same effect as the two together. This is clearly the displacement $\overrightarrow{AC}$, and we therefore define $\overrightarrow{AC}$ to equal the vector sum $\overrightarrow{AB} + \overrightarrow{BC}$, thus obtaining the *triangle law* of vector addition (Fig. 41.6).

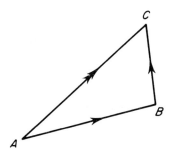

Fig. 41.6

The triangle law states that

$$\overrightarrow{AB} + \overrightarrow{BC} = \overrightarrow{AC}.$$

It should be noted that the two vectors with the same direction around the triangle (i.e. clockwise or anticlockwise) are added to give the vector with the opposite direction. The vector $\overrightarrow{AC}$ is called the *vector sum* or the *resultant* of the other two vectors, and is sometimes, as in Fig. 41.6, indicated in diagrams by the use of a double arrow-head.

Vectors can also be added by the *parallelogram law*, which is equivalent to the triangle law and illustrated by Fig. 41.7:

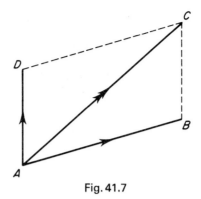

Fig. 41.7

The parallelogram law states that

$$\overrightarrow{AB} + \overrightarrow{AD} = \overrightarrow{AC}.$$

The two laws are equivalent since $\overrightarrow{AD} = \overrightarrow{BC}$.

Subtraction

Subtraction is defined as the *addition of the negative*, and we thus have $\mathbf{a} - \mathbf{b} = \mathbf{a} + (-\mathbf{b})$. The operation can be performed by using either the triangle law (as illustrated in Fig. 41.8) or the parallelogram law.

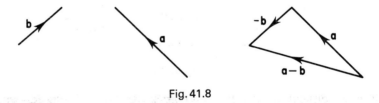

Fig. 41.8

The polygon law

It is easy to see by considering displacements that more than two vectors can be added by constructing a polygon. We thus obtain an extension of the triangle law called the *polygon law* (Fig. 41.9).

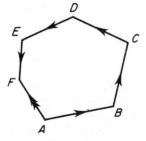

Fig. 41.9

With reference to Fig. 41.9 the polygon law states that

$$\overrightarrow{AB} + \overrightarrow{BC} + \overrightarrow{CD} + \overrightarrow{DE} + \overrightarrow{EF} = \overrightarrow{AF}.$$

The vectors represented by *all* the sides of a polygon, the directions around the polygon all being the same, clearly have a sum of zero (Fig. 41.10).

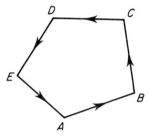

Fig. 41.10

$$\overrightarrow{AB} + \overrightarrow{BC} + \overrightarrow{CD} + \overrightarrow{DE} + \overrightarrow{EA} = \mathbf{0}.$$

The addition of velocities

Suppose that a man walks at 3 m s^{-1} across a train which is itself moving at 4 m s^{-1} (Fig. 41.11).

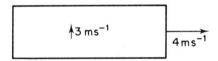

Fig. 41.11

It is not difficult to see that the man's resultant velocity (his velocity relative to the ground) is given by adding these two velocities vectorially (Fig. 41.12).

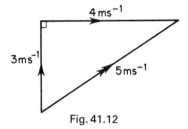

Fig. 41.12

In one second the man travels 3 m across the train, and he is also carried 4 m in the direction of the train's movement. His resultant displacement is therefore 5 m in the direction shown, and it follows that his true velocity is 5 m s^{-1} in this direction. The example thus shows that the triangle law applies to velocities as well as to displacements.

▷ Example 1

*In Fig. 41.13 ABDE is a parallelogram and BC = ½AB. Letting $\vec{AB}$ = **p** and $\vec{AE}$ = **q**, as shown, express the following in terms of **p** and **q**: (a) $\vec{AD}$, (b) $\vec{DE}$, (c) $\vec{AC}$, (d) $\vec{BE}$, (e) $\vec{CD}$.*

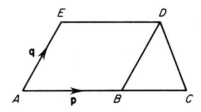

Fig. 41.13

(a) By the parallelogram law, $\vec{AD}$ = **p** + **q**.
(b) Since $AB = ED$ and AB is parallel to ED (properties of a parallelogram), $\vec{DE}$ = −**p**.
(c) Since $AC = 1\frac{1}{2}AB$, $\vec{AC} = 1\frac{1}{2}$**p**.
(d) By the triangle law, $\vec{BE} = \vec{BA} + \vec{AE} = $ −**p** + **q** or **q** − **p**.
(e) By the polygon law, $\vec{CD} = \vec{CA} + \vec{AE} + \vec{ED} = $ −$1\frac{1}{2}$**p** + **q** + **p** = **q** − $\frac{1}{2}$**p**.   ◁

▷ Example 2

$|$**a**$| = 4$, $|$**b**$| = 3$ and the angle between **a** and **b** is 60°. Find $|$**a** + **b**$|$ and $|$**a** − **b**$|$.

Since the magnitude of a vector is equal to the length of the line segment representing it, we can construct the diagram shown in Fig. 41.14.

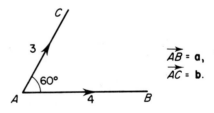

Fig. 41.14

(a) By the parallelogram law, **a** + **b** is represented by $\vec{AP}$, where $ABPC$ is a parallelogram (Fig. 41.15). We require the length of AP.

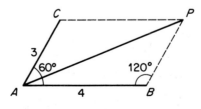

Fig. 41.15

By the cosine formula we have

$$AP^2 = 4^2 + 3^2 - 2 \times 4 \times 3 \cos 120°$$
$$= 37$$
$$\therefore \quad AP = 6.08 \text{ to 3 s.f.}$$
$$\therefore \quad |\mathbf{a} + \mathbf{b}| = 6.08 \text{ to 3 s.f.}$$

(b) One way of obtaining $\mathbf{a} - \mathbf{b}$ is to add the negative of $\mathbf{b}$ to $\mathbf{a}$ by constructing another parallelogram. It is simpler here, however, to note that $\overrightarrow{CB}$ represents $\mathbf{a} - \mathbf{b}$ since $\overrightarrow{CB} = \overrightarrow{CA} + \overrightarrow{AB}$. We therefore require the length of CB, and this again can be obtained by the cosine formula:

$$CB^2 = 4^2 + 3^2 - 2 \times 4 \times 3 \cos 60°$$
$$= 13$$
$$\therefore \quad CB = 3.61 \text{ to 3 s.f.}$$
$$\therefore \quad |\mathbf{a} - \mathbf{b}| = 3.61 \text{ to 3 s.f.} \qquad \blacktriangleleft$$

▷ Example 3

A man who can swim at 4 km h^{-1} wishes to swim directly across a river flowing at 3 km h^{-1}. In which direction should he aim, and what will be his true speed?

The man swims at 4 km h^{-1} relative to the water, and as he swims the movement of the water carries him downstream. He must therefore aim against the flow of the water, at an angle indicated by the triangle of velocities shown in Fig. 41.16.

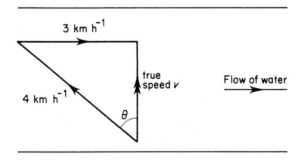

Fig. 41.16

Clearly we have

$$\sin \theta = \tfrac{3}{4}$$
$$\therefore \quad \theta = 48.6° \text{ to 3 s.f.}$$

Also the true speed v is given by

$$v^2 = 4^2 - 3^2$$
$$\therefore \quad v = 2.65 \text{ m s}^{-1} \text{ to 3 s.f.} \qquad \blacktriangleleft$$

EXERCISE 41a

1 $ABCD$ is a parallelogram and E is the mid-point of CD. Letting $\overrightarrow{AB} = \mathbf{p}$ and $\overrightarrow{AD} = \mathbf{q}$, express the following vectors in terms of $\mathbf{p}$ and $\mathbf{q}$: (a) $\overrightarrow{DC}$, (b) $\overrightarrow{CB}$, (c) $\overrightarrow{DE}$, (d) $\overrightarrow{AE}$, (e) $\overrightarrow{CA}$, (f) BE.

2 ABC is a triangle. Simplify (a) $\overrightarrow{AB} + \overrightarrow{BC}$, (b) $\overrightarrow{CA} + \overrightarrow{AB}$, (c) $\overrightarrow{CB} + \overrightarrow{AC}$, (d) $\overrightarrow{AB} - \overrightarrow{AC}$ (remember that $-\overrightarrow{AC} = + \overrightarrow{CA}$), (e) $\overrightarrow{BC} - \overrightarrow{BA}$, (f) $\overrightarrow{CA} - \overrightarrow{CB}$.

3 $ABCD$ is a quadrilateral whose diagonals meet at E. Simplify (a) $\overrightarrow{AB} + \overrightarrow{BC}$, (b) $\overrightarrow{AE} + \overrightarrow{ED}$, (c) $\overrightarrow{AE} + \overrightarrow{EC}$, (d) $\overrightarrow{DE} - \overrightarrow{DC}$, (e) $\overrightarrow{BC} - \overrightarrow{DC}$, (f) $\overrightarrow{BC} + \overrightarrow{CD} + \overrightarrow{DA}$, (g) $\overrightarrow{EC} + \overrightarrow{CB} + \overrightarrow{BE}$, (h) $\overrightarrow{BE} + \overrightarrow{EC} - \overrightarrow{BA}$.

4 A displacement of 2 km north-east is followed by one of 2 km south-east. Find the magnitude and bearing of the resultant displacement.

5 $\mathbf{a}$ and $\mathbf{b}$ are perpendicular vectors. Given that $|\mathbf{a}| = 12$ and $|\mathbf{b}| = 16$, find $|\mathbf{a} + \mathbf{b}|$ and $|\mathbf{a} - \mathbf{b}|$.

6 A displacement of 10 km due east is followed by one of 12 km due north and then by one of 5 km due west. Find the magnitude and bearing of the resultant displacement.

7 With reference to Fig. 41.17, simplify (a) $\mathbf{a} + \mathbf{d} + \mathbf{e}$, (b) $\mathbf{a} + \mathbf{f} + \mathbf{e}$, (c) $\mathbf{f} - \mathbf{g}$, (d) $\mathbf{c} - \mathbf{g}$, (e) $\mathbf{d} - \mathbf{f} + \mathbf{b}$, (f) $\mathbf{g} - \mathbf{d} - \mathbf{b} - \mathbf{c}$.

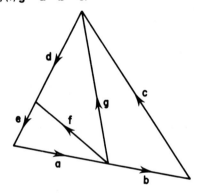

Fig. 41.17

8 A man who can swim at 3 km h^{-1} tries to swim straight across a river. Since the river is flowing at 2 km h^{-1} he is carried downstream. Find the magnitude of his true velocity and the angle between his direction of motion and the banks.

9 ABC is a triangle in which $AB = AC = 8$ and angle $A = 60°$. Find $|\overrightarrow{AB} + \overrightarrow{AC}|$ and $|\overrightarrow{AB} - \overrightarrow{AC}|$.

10 Given that $AB = BC$ in Fig. 41.18, express in terms of $\mathbf{p}$ and $\mathbf{q}$ (a) $\overrightarrow{AD}$, (b) $\overrightarrow{CD}$.

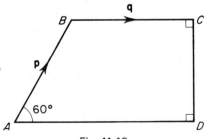

Fig. 41.18

11 While a goldfish in a bowl is swimming horizontally at 30 cm s^{-1} the bowl is suddenly raised vertically. When the bowl is moving upwards at 60 cm s^{-1} what is the resultant speed of the goldfish and the angle between the direction of its motion and the horizontal?

12 Two vectors **a** and **b** are inclined to each other at 40°. If $|\mathbf{a}| = 5$ and $|\mathbf{b}| = 6$, find $|\mathbf{a} + \mathbf{b}|$ and $|\mathbf{a} - \mathbf{b}|$.

13 A man runs at 8 m s^{-1} across the deck of a boat which is sailing due north at 5 m s^{-1}. If his true velocity is due east find his true speed and the bearing on which he is aiming to run.

14 An aeroplane which can fly at 500 km h^{-1} needs to fly due west. If a wind of 150 km h^{-1} is blowing from due north, what course must the pilot set?

15 Say whether the following statements are true (T) or false (F):

(a) $\mathbf{p} = \mathbf{q} \Rightarrow |\mathbf{p}| = |\mathbf{q}|$.

(b) $\mathbf{p} + \mathbf{q} = \mathbf{r} \Rightarrow |\mathbf{p}| + |\mathbf{q}| = |\mathbf{r}|$.

(c) $\mathbf{p} = k\mathbf{q} \Rightarrow \mathbf{p}$ and $\mathbf{q}$ are parallel or zero vectors.

(d) $\mathbf{p}$ and $\mathbf{q}$ are perpendicular vectors $\Rightarrow |\mathbf{p} + \mathbf{q}| = |\mathbf{p} - \mathbf{q}|$.

The components of a vector

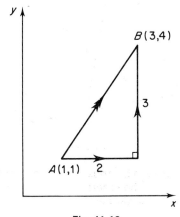

Fig. 41.19

Consider the displacement vector from $A(1,1)$ to $B(3,4)$ (Fig. 41.19). It is possible but slightly awkward to calculate the magnitude and direction of this vector, and the vector is much more simply described as the resultant or sum of a horizontal displacement of 2 and a vertical displacement of 3. These two numbers are called the *components* of the vector, and it is clear that when the components are given the vector is completely described. The usual way of stating the components is by writing the vector as a *column matrix,* with the x component above the y component:

$$\overrightarrow{AB} = \begin{pmatrix} 2 \\ 3 \end{pmatrix}.$$

A vector expressed in this way is sometimes called a *column vector.*

▷Example 4

Express as column vectors the displacements from (a) P(3,1) to Q(0,2), (b) S(2,4) to T(0,3).

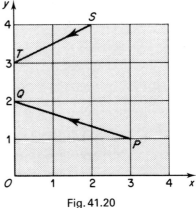

Fig. 41.20

(a) The displacement from *P* to *Q* could be described as 'move 3 to the left and 1 up' (Fig. 41.20). The components are therefore −3 and 1, and we have

$$\overrightarrow{PQ} = \begin{pmatrix} -3 \\ 1 \end{pmatrix}.$$

(b) The displacement from *S* to *T* could be described as 'move 2 to the left and 1 down'. The components are therefore −2 and −1, and we have

$$\overrightarrow{ST} = \begin{pmatrix} -2 \\ -1 \end{pmatrix}. \qquad \blacktriangleleft$$

Position vectors

Any displacement vector $\overrightarrow{OP}$ which starts at the origin *O* clearly has as components the co-ordinates of **P**. E.g:

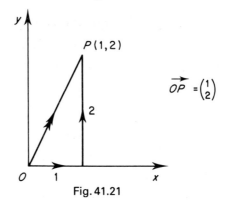

Fig. 41.21

Fig. 41.21 shows that the vector $\overrightarrow{OP}$, or $\begin{pmatrix} 1 \\ 2 \end{pmatrix}$, specifies the position of the point *P* just as the pair of co-ordinates (1,2) specifies this point.

Consequently the vector $\overrightarrow{OP}$ is called the *position vector* of P and denoted by **p**.

We can use the idea of a position vector to obtain a quicker method of answering the type of question considered in example 4. Let the position vectors of the points A and B be **a** and **b**, respectively (Fig. 41.22).

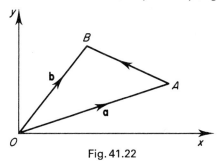

Fig. 41.22

By the triangle law we have

$$\mathbf{a} + \overrightarrow{AB} = \mathbf{b}$$
$$\therefore \; \overrightarrow{AB} = \mathbf{b} - \mathbf{a}.$$

This is an important result which should be learned by heart. It enables us to find vectors such as $\overrightarrow{PQ}$ and $\overrightarrow{ST}$ of example 4 without drawing a diagram. E.g:

$$\overrightarrow{PQ} = \mathbf{q} - \mathbf{p}$$

$$= \begin{pmatrix} 0 \\ 2 \end{pmatrix} - \begin{pmatrix} 3 \\ 1 \end{pmatrix}$$

$$= \begin{pmatrix} -3 \\ 1 \end{pmatrix}.$$

The magnitude and direction of a column vector

These are easily obtained by using Pythagoras' theorem and trigonometry, respectively. Consider the vector $\overrightarrow{PQ} = \begin{pmatrix} a \\ b \end{pmatrix}$ (Fig. 41.23).

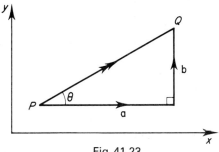

Fig. 41.23

We have

$$|\overrightarrow{PQ}| = \sqrt{(a^2 + b^2)}$$

and also

$$\tan \theta = \frac{b}{a} \quad .$$

▷ Example 5

A is the point (6,8) and B is the point (1,−4). Find (a) $|\overrightarrow{OA}|$, (b) $|\overrightarrow{AB}|$.

(a)
$$\overrightarrow{OA} = \mathbf{a} = \begin{pmatrix} 6 \\ 8 \end{pmatrix}$$

$$\therefore \; |\overrightarrow{OA}| = \sqrt{(6^2 + 8^2)} = 10.$$

(b)
$$\overrightarrow{AB} = \mathbf{b} - \mathbf{a}$$

$$= \begin{pmatrix} 1 \\ -4 \end{pmatrix} - \begin{pmatrix} 6 \\ 8 \end{pmatrix}$$

$$= \begin{pmatrix} -5 \\ -12 \end{pmatrix}$$

$$\therefore \; |\overrightarrow{AB}| = \sqrt{(5^2 + 12^2)} = 13. \quad ◁$$

▷ Example 6

Find the angle between the vector $\begin{pmatrix} 3 \\ 2 \end{pmatrix}$ and the vector $\begin{pmatrix} -1 \\ 4 \end{pmatrix}$.

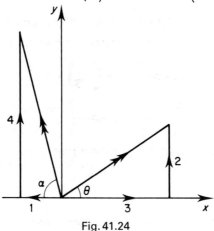

Fig. 41.24

We have (Fig. 41.24):

$$\tan \theta = \frac{2}{3} \qquad \therefore \; \theta = 33.69°,$$
$$\tan \alpha = 4 \qquad \therefore \; \alpha = 75.96°.$$

Hence the angle between the vectors is $180° - 33.69° - 75.96° = 70.3°$ to 3 s.f. ◁

The mid-point of a line

Consider two points A and B, with position vectors $\mathbf{a}$ and $\mathbf{b}$, and let the mid-point of AB be P. Complete the parallelogram $OACB$ (Fig. 41.25).

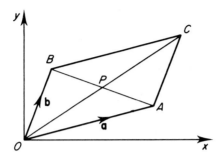

Fig. 41.25

By the parallelogram law we have $\overrightarrow{OC} = \mathbf{a} + \mathbf{b}$, and since the diagonals of a parallelogram bisect each other,

$$\overrightarrow{OP} = \tfrac{1}{2}(\mathbf{a} + \mathbf{b}).$$

Thus *the position vector of the mid-point of AB is the 'average' of the position vectors of A and B.*

▷ Example 7

Find the position vector of the mid-point of PQ, where P is (3,5) and Q is (−7,3).

Letting the position vector of the mid-point be $\mathbf{r}$, we have

$$\mathbf{p} + \mathbf{q} = \begin{pmatrix} 3 \\ 5 \end{pmatrix} + \begin{pmatrix} -7 \\ 3 \end{pmatrix} = \begin{pmatrix} -4 \\ 8 \end{pmatrix}$$

$$\therefore \; \mathbf{r} = \tfrac{1}{2}(\mathbf{p} + \mathbf{q}) = \begin{pmatrix} -2 \\ 4 \end{pmatrix}.$$

(It follows that the co-ordinates of the mid-point are (−2,4), or (average of x's, average of y's). This is a well-known result in co-ordinate geometry — see chapter 23.) ◀

The addition and subtraction of column vectors

The real advantage of the component representation of vectors is that it makes addition and subtraction very easy. (Adding vectors by constructing a polygon of vectors is obviously tedious and inaccurate.) Vectors represented as column matrices in fact obey the same rules as matrices: we add and subtract them by adding and subtracting corresponding elements. An example will demonstrate that this rule is equivalent to the parallelogram or triangle law for adding vectors.

Consider the vectors **a** and **b**, where

$$\mathbf{a} = \begin{pmatrix} 2 \\ 1 \end{pmatrix} \text{ and } \mathbf{b} = \begin{pmatrix} 1 \\ 3 \end{pmatrix}.$$

Fig. 41.26 shows how the sum of these vectors can be obtained by the triangle law.

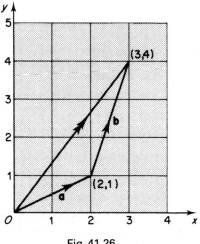

Fig. 41.26

The triangle law clearly gives $\mathbf{a} + \mathbf{b} = \begin{pmatrix} 3 \\ 4 \end{pmatrix}$, which is the result obtained by simply adding corresponding components:

$$\begin{pmatrix} 2 \\ 1 \end{pmatrix} + \begin{pmatrix} 1 \\ 3 \end{pmatrix} = \begin{pmatrix} 3 \\ 4 \end{pmatrix}.$$

Thus the triangle law is equivalent to the rule by which matrices are added. Since subtraction is defined as the addition of the negative, it follows that the subtraction of vectors also obeys the rule for subtracting matrices.

These results are particularly useful when a large number of vectors have to be added or subtracted. E.g:

$$\begin{pmatrix} 4 \\ -2 \end{pmatrix} + \begin{pmatrix} -3 \\ 1 \end{pmatrix} - \begin{pmatrix} 5 \\ 3 \end{pmatrix} + \begin{pmatrix} 1 \\ 4 \end{pmatrix} + \begin{pmatrix} 6 \\ 2 \end{pmatrix} = \begin{pmatrix} 3 \\ 2 \end{pmatrix}.$$

To add these vectors by constructing an accurate polygon would clearly be impracticable.

Multiplication by a real number

It is easily shown that the multiplication of a vector by a real number (or scalar) also obeys the rule which applies to matrices. To multiply a column vector by a real number we multiply each component by that number. E.g:

$$4\begin{pmatrix} -1 \\ 2 \end{pmatrix} - 3\begin{pmatrix} 2 \\ 1 \end{pmatrix} = \begin{pmatrix} -4 \\ 8 \end{pmatrix} - \begin{pmatrix} 6 \\ 3 \end{pmatrix} = \begin{pmatrix} -10 \\ 5 \end{pmatrix}.$$

Parallel vectors

We know that if a vector **p** is multiplied by a real number k, the product vector $k\mathbf{p}$ is parallel to **p** and has k times the magnitude. This indicates that *two vectors are parallel if one is a scalar multiple of the other.* For example, the vectors

$$\begin{pmatrix} 3 \\ 1 \end{pmatrix} \text{ and } \begin{pmatrix} 6 \\ 2 \end{pmatrix}$$

are parallel.

It can also be seen that these two vectors are parallel by considering their gradients. These are $\frac{1}{3}$ and $\frac{2}{6}$, respectively, and therefore equal. It follows that the condition can be expressed in another way, namely *two vectors are parallel if the ratios of their components are equal.*

It should be noted that two vectors çan be parallel yet opposite in direction. Two vectors of this kind are

$$\begin{pmatrix} 2 \\ 3 \end{pmatrix} \text{ and } \begin{pmatrix} -4 \\ -6 \end{pmatrix}.$$

For two vectors to have the same direction, one of them must be a *positive* scalar multiple of the other.

▷**Example 8**

Find the values of k for which the vectors $\begin{pmatrix} k \\ 2 \end{pmatrix}$ *and* $\begin{pmatrix} 8 \\ k \end{pmatrix}$ *(a) are parallel, (b) have the same direction.*

(a) Equating ratios of components, we have

$$\frac{k}{2} = \frac{8}{k}$$

$$\therefore k^2 = 16$$
$$\therefore k = \pm 4.$$

(b) If $k = +4$, the two vectors are $\begin{pmatrix} 4 \\ 2 \end{pmatrix}$ and $\begin{pmatrix} 8 \\ 4 \end{pmatrix}$. The second vector is a *positive* multiple of the first, so the vectors have the same direction. When $k = -4$, however, the vectors are $\begin{pmatrix} -4 \\ 2 \end{pmatrix}$ and $\begin{pmatrix} 8 \\ -4 \end{pmatrix}$, and the second is a *negative* multiple of the first. The vectors therefore have the same direction only when $k = +4$. ◁

EXERCISE 41b

1 A is the point $(1,3)$, B is $(2,5)$ and C is $(3,-1)$. Express as column vectors $\overrightarrow{OA}$, $\overrightarrow{OB}$, $\overrightarrow{CO}$, $\overrightarrow{AB}$, $\overrightarrow{CA}$, $\overrightarrow{BC}$.

2 $p = \begin{pmatrix} 2 \\ -3 \end{pmatrix}$ and $q = \begin{pmatrix} -1 \\ 4 \end{pmatrix}$. Find (a) $p + q$, (b) $-3p$, (c) $2p + 3q$, (d) $2q - 4p$.

3 The position vectors of A, B, C are $\begin{pmatrix} 0 \\ 2 \end{pmatrix}$, $\begin{pmatrix} 4 \\ 0 \end{pmatrix}$ and $\begin{pmatrix} -2 \\ 6 \end{pmatrix}$, respectively. Find the position vectors of the mid-points of OA, AB, AC and BC.

4 $\overrightarrow{OP} = \begin{pmatrix} 1 \\ 2 \end{pmatrix}$, $\overrightarrow{OQ} = \begin{pmatrix} 3 \\ -4 \end{pmatrix}$ and R is the mid-point of PQ. Find (a) $p - q + r$,

(b) $p + q - 3r$, (c) $2p - 3q + 5r$.

5 $OABC$ is a parallelogram in which A is the point $(5,2)$, C is $(3,4)$ and D is the mid-point of BC. Express as column vectors $\overrightarrow{OB}$, $\overrightarrow{BC}$, $\overrightarrow{OD}$, $\overrightarrow{DA}$.

6 Find the magnitudes of the following vectors, leaving the answers in square root form where appropriate:

(a) $\begin{pmatrix} 3 \\ 4 \end{pmatrix}$, (b) $\begin{pmatrix} 2 \\ 3 \end{pmatrix}$, (c) $\begin{pmatrix} 5 \\ 7 \end{pmatrix}$, (d) $\begin{pmatrix} 10 \\ 24 \end{pmatrix}$, (e) $\begin{pmatrix} 12 \\ 16 \end{pmatrix}$, (f) $\begin{pmatrix} 4 \\ 12 \end{pmatrix}$.

7 $p = \begin{pmatrix} 4 \\ 1 \end{pmatrix}$ and $q = \begin{pmatrix} -3 \\ 2 \end{pmatrix}$. Find (a) $|p + q|$, (b) $|p - q|$, (c) $|3p + 4q|$.

8 A is the point $(2,3)$, B is $(5,7)$ and C is $(-2,0)$. Find $|b - a|$ and $|c - a|$. What kind of triangle is ABC?

9 Find the angles between the following pairs of vectors, giving the answers to the nearest degree where appropriate:

(a) $\begin{pmatrix} 2 \\ 1 \end{pmatrix}$ and $\begin{pmatrix} 1 \\ 0 \end{pmatrix}$, (b) $\begin{pmatrix} 2 \\ 3 \end{pmatrix}$ and $\begin{pmatrix} 0 \\ -1 \end{pmatrix}$, (c) $\begin{pmatrix} -1 \\ 2 \end{pmatrix}$ and $\begin{pmatrix} 1 \\ 3 \end{pmatrix}$,

(d) $\begin{pmatrix} -3 \\ -2 \end{pmatrix}$ and $\begin{pmatrix} 6 \\ 4 \end{pmatrix}$, (e) $\begin{pmatrix} 2 \\ 5 \end{pmatrix}$ and $\begin{pmatrix} 5 \\ -2 \end{pmatrix}$, (f) $\begin{pmatrix} -3 \\ -2 \end{pmatrix}$ and $\begin{pmatrix} 5 \\ -4 \end{pmatrix}$.

10 $OABC$ is a parallelogram in which A is the point $(4,1)$ and B is $(5,3)$. Find $\overrightarrow{AC}$. If D is a point such that $\overrightarrow{BD} = \overrightarrow{AC}$, find the co-ordinates of D. What kind of figure is $ABDC$?

11 In each of the following cases, find the value or values of k for which the given two vectors are parallel:

(a) $\begin{pmatrix} 3 \\ 4 \end{pmatrix}$ and $\begin{pmatrix} k \\ 12 \end{pmatrix}$, (b) $\begin{pmatrix} 5 \\ k \end{pmatrix}$ and $\begin{pmatrix} 25 \\ 10 \end{pmatrix}$, (c) $\begin{pmatrix} -2 \\ 3 \end{pmatrix}$ and $\begin{pmatrix} 4 \\ k \end{pmatrix}$,

(d) $\begin{pmatrix} k \\ 2\frac{1}{2} \end{pmatrix}$ and $\begin{pmatrix} 28 \\ 3\frac{1}{2} \end{pmatrix}$, (e) $\begin{pmatrix} k \\ 1 \end{pmatrix}$ and $\begin{pmatrix} 4 \\ k \end{pmatrix}$, (f) $\begin{pmatrix} k-1 \\ k+1 \end{pmatrix}$ and $\begin{pmatrix} 2 \\ 3 \end{pmatrix}$,

(g) $\begin{pmatrix} k+2 \\ 12 \end{pmatrix}$ and $\begin{pmatrix} 3 \\ k+2 \end{pmatrix}$.

12 P is the point $(a,-3)$ and Q is the point $(0,a)$. Find the value of a if $\overrightarrow{PQ}$ is parallel to the vector $\begin{pmatrix} 2 \\ 1 \end{pmatrix}$.

13 $p = \begin{pmatrix} 2 \\ 3 \end{pmatrix}$. Find a vector q such that $p + q$ is parallel to the x-axis and $p - q$ is parallel to the y-axis.

14 Find the column vector which

(a) is in the same direction as the vector $\begin{pmatrix} 0 \\ 1 \end{pmatrix}$ and has a magnitude of 5,

(b) is opposite in direction to the vector $\begin{pmatrix} 2 \\ 0 \end{pmatrix}$ and has a magnitude of 8,

(c) is in the same direction as the vector $\begin{pmatrix} 3 \\ 4 \end{pmatrix}$ and has a magnitude of 20,

(d) is opposite in direction to the vector $\begin{pmatrix} 7 \\ 24 \end{pmatrix}$ and has a magnitude of 100.

15 Find in each of the following cases the vector **v** which satisfies the given vector equation:

(a) $\mathbf{v} + \begin{pmatrix} -2 \\ 5 \end{pmatrix} = \begin{pmatrix} 1 \\ -2 \end{pmatrix}$, (b) $2\begin{pmatrix} 1 \\ 4 \end{pmatrix} - \mathbf{v} = \begin{pmatrix} 3 \\ -2 \end{pmatrix}$, (c) $2\mathbf{v} - \begin{pmatrix} 5 \\ -3 \end{pmatrix} = \begin{pmatrix} 1 \\ 7 \end{pmatrix}$,

(d) $\begin{pmatrix} 1 \\ 2 \end{pmatrix} + \mathbf{v} = \begin{pmatrix} 7 \\ 5 \end{pmatrix} - 2\mathbf{v}$.

Vector geometry

It is often possible to use vector theory to obtain geometrical results. The theorems which are used most frequently for this purpose are the following.

(1) If A, B, C are points such that any one of the vectors $\overrightarrow{AB}$, $\overrightarrow{AC}$, $\overrightarrow{BC}$ is a scalar multiple of any other, the three points are collinear (lie on a straight line).
(2) If $\overrightarrow{AB} = \overrightarrow{PQ}$, then

(i) the line segments AB and PQ are parallel to each other,
(ii) $AB = PQ$.

Similarly, if $\overrightarrow{AB} = k\overrightarrow{PQ}$, it follows that

(i) AB is parallel to PQ,
(ii) $AB = kPQ$.

(3) If **p** and **q** are non-parallel, non-zero vectors and we have an equation of the form

$$a\mathbf{p} + b\mathbf{q} = m\mathbf{p} + n\mathbf{q},$$

we can equate the coefficients of **p** and **q** to obtain $a = m$ and $b = n$.

Proof of theorem (3)

The equation to be proved is equivalent to

$$(a - m)\mathbf{p} = (n - b)\mathbf{q}.$$

The equation now states that a scalar multiple of **p** is equal to a scalar multiple of **q**, and since **p** and **q** are neither parallel nor zero, this is impossible unless both $a - m$ and $n - b$ are zero. Hence $a = m$ and $b = n$.

▷ Example 9

*The points A, B, P have position vectors of **a**, **b** and 2**b** − **a**. Prove that A, B, P are collinear and show the position of P relative to A and B in a diagram.*

Using the main theorem on position vectors, we have

$$\overrightarrow{BA} = \mathbf{a} - \mathbf{b}$$
$$\text{and } \overrightarrow{PA} = \mathbf{a} - (2\mathbf{b} - \mathbf{a})$$
$$= 2\mathbf{a} - 2\mathbf{b}$$
$$= 2(\mathbf{a} - \mathbf{b}).$$

Hence $\overrightarrow{PA} = 2\overrightarrow{BA}$, and it follows that the three points are collinear with P positioned as follows: ◁

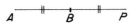

▷ Example 10

ABCD is a quadrilateral in which AB is equal and parallel to DC. Prove (a) that AD is equal and parallel to BC (and thus that ABCD is a parallelogram), (b) that the diagonals AC and BD bisect each other (Fig. 41.27).

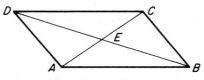

Fig. 41.27

(a) By the triangle law we have

$$\overrightarrow{AD} = \overrightarrow{AB} + \overrightarrow{BD},$$
$$\overrightarrow{BC} = \overrightarrow{BD} + \overrightarrow{DC}.$$

Since AB is equal and parallel to DC, it follows that $\overrightarrow{AB} = \overrightarrow{DC}$ and thus that the right-hand sides of these equations are equal. Hence $\overrightarrow{AD} = \overrightarrow{BC}$ and it follows that AD is equal and parallel to BC.

(b) Let $DE = mEB$ and $CE = nEA$. We have to show that $m = n = 1$. By the triangle law,

$$\overrightarrow{AB} = \overrightarrow{AE} + \overrightarrow{EB},$$
$$\overrightarrow{DC} = \overrightarrow{DE} + \overrightarrow{EC}$$
$$= m\overrightarrow{EB} + n\overrightarrow{AE}.$$
$$\text{But } \overrightarrow{AB} = \overrightarrow{DC} \text{ (given)}$$
$$\therefore \ \overrightarrow{AE} + \overrightarrow{EB} = m\overrightarrow{EB} + n\overrightarrow{AE}$$
$$\therefore \ \overrightarrow{AE}(1 - n) = \overrightarrow{EB}(m - 1).$$

Now since $\overrightarrow{AE}$ and $\overrightarrow{EB}$ are neither zero nor parallel, it follows that $1 - n = m - 1 = 0$ and thus that $m = n = 1$.

(Both of these results can also of course be proved by congruent triangles.) ◀

▷Example 11

OAB is a triangle, and P, Q are points on OA, OB, respectively such that PQ is parallel to AB (Fig. 41.28). Prove that $\dfrac{OA}{OP} = \dfrac{OB}{OQ}$.

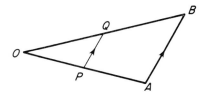

Fig. 41.28

Let $\overrightarrow{OP} = \mathbf{p}$, $\overrightarrow{OQ} = \mathbf{q}$, $\overrightarrow{OA} = m\mathbf{p}$ and $\overrightarrow{OB} = n\mathbf{q}$. Then $\overrightarrow{PQ} = \mathbf{q} - \mathbf{p}$ and $\overrightarrow{AB} = n\mathbf{q} - m\mathbf{p}$. Since PQ is parallel to AB, however, we have $\overrightarrow{PQ} = k\overrightarrow{AB}$, that is

$$\mathbf{q} - \mathbf{p} = k(n\mathbf{q} - m\mathbf{p}).$$

Equating the coefficients of $\mathbf{q}$ and $\mathbf{p}$ gives

$$1 = kn,$$
$$-1 = -km,$$

from which it follows that $m = n$ and thus that $\dfrac{OA}{OP} = \dfrac{OB}{OQ}$. ◀

▷Example 12 (harder)

In a triangle OAB (Fig. 41.29), P is the point on OA such that $OP = \frac{2}{3}OA$, and Q is the mid-point of AB. OQ and BP meet at R, and $OR = mOQ$, $BR = nBP$. Let $\overrightarrow{OA} = \mathbf{a}$ and $\overrightarrow{OB} = \mathbf{b}$, and by expressing $\overrightarrow{OR}$ in terms of $\mathbf{a}$ and $\mathbf{b}$ in two different ways, find m and n.

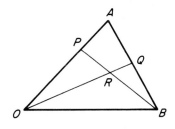

Fig. 41.29

$$\text{Since } \overrightarrow{OQ} = \tfrac{1}{2}(\mathbf{a} + \mathbf{b}),$$
$$\overrightarrow{OR} = \frac{m}{2}\,(\mathbf{a} + \mathbf{b}). \qquad (1)$$
$$\text{Also } \overrightarrow{BP} = \overrightarrow{BO} + \overrightarrow{OP}$$
$$= -\mathbf{b} + \frac{2\mathbf{a}}{3}$$
$$\therefore \ \overrightarrow{BR} = n(-\mathbf{b} + \frac{2\mathbf{a}}{3})$$
$$\therefore \ \overrightarrow{OR} = \overrightarrow{OB} + \overrightarrow{BR}$$
$$= \mathbf{b} + n(-\mathbf{b} + \frac{2\mathbf{a}}{3}). \qquad (2)$$

Taking the expressions for $\overrightarrow{OR}$ from (1) and (2) and equating the coefficients of **a** and **b**, we have

$$\frac{m}{2} = \frac{2n}{3}$$

$$\text{and } \frac{m}{2} = 1 - n.$$

Solving these simultaneous equations gives $m = \dfrac{4}{5}$ and $n = \dfrac{3}{5}$. ◁

EXERCISE 41c

In this exercise do not use similar or congruent triangles, and use no theorems other than those concerning vectors.

1 $ABCD$ is a quadrilateral in which $\overrightarrow{DB} - \overrightarrow{DA} = 2\overrightarrow{DC}$. Prove that AB is parallel to DC and find $\dfrac{AB}{DC}$.

2 Given that the position vectors of A, B, C with respect to O are **a**, **b** and $2\mathbf{a} + \mathbf{b}$, prove that BC is parallel to OA and that $BC = 2OA$.

3 Points A, B, C have position vectors **a**, **b** and $4\mathbf{a} - 3\mathbf{b}$. Prove that A, B, C are collinear.

4 Points A, B, C, D have position vectors **a**, **b**, $3\mathbf{a} - \mathbf{b}$ and $4\mathbf{a} - \mathbf{b}$. Prove that AC is parallel to BD and find $\dfrac{AC}{BD}$.

5 $ABCD$ is a quadrilateral in which $\overrightarrow{AB} = 2\overrightarrow{DC}$, and E is a point on AC such that $AE = 2EC$. Prove that B, E, D are collinear.

6 Points A, B, C have position vectors **a**, **b**, **c**, and $2\mathbf{a} + 3\mathbf{b} = 5\mathbf{c}$. Prove that A, B, C are collinear.

7 A, B, C, D are points such that $\overrightarrow{AD} + 2\overrightarrow{DC} = \overrightarrow{DB}$. Prove that A, B, C are collinear.

8 P and Q are points on the sides OA, OB of a triangle OAB such that $OP = 2PA$ and $OQ = 2QB$. Let $\overrightarrow{OA} = \mathbf{a}$ and $\overrightarrow{OB} = \mathbf{b}$, and express $\overrightarrow{AB}$ and $\overrightarrow{PQ}$ in terms of **a, b**. Hence prove that PQ is parallel to AB and find $\dfrac{PQ}{AB}$.

9 $ABCD$ is a quadrilateral in which P, Q, R, S are the mid-points of AB, BC, CD, DA, respectively. By expressing both $\overrightarrow{SP}$ and $\overrightarrow{RQ}$ in terms of $\overrightarrow{DB}$, prove that SP is equal and parallel to RQ. What kind of quadrilateral is $PQRS$?

10 OAB is a triangle in which P is the mid-point of OA and Q is the point on OA such that $OQ = \frac{1}{3}OA$. Also R is the point on OB such that $OR = 2RB$. Let $\overrightarrow{OA} = \mathbf{a}$ and $\overrightarrow{OB} = \mathbf{b}$, and by expressing $\overrightarrow{BP}$ and $\overrightarrow{RQ}$ in terms of $\mathbf{a}$ and $\mathbf{b}$, prove that BP is parallel to RQ and find $\dfrac{BP}{RQ}$.

11 $OACB$ is a rectangle, P and Q being the mid-points of OA and AC, respectively. OQ and BP meet at R, and $OR = mOQ$, $BR = nBP$. Let $\overrightarrow{OA} = \mathbf{a}$ and $\overrightarrow{OB} = \mathbf{b}$, and express $\overrightarrow{OR}$ in terms of $\mathbf{a}$, $\mathbf{b}$ in two different ways. Hence find m and n.

12 ABC is a triangle in which D and E are points on BC, AC respectively such that $BD = DC$ and $AE = 2EC$. F is the point on AD produced such that AB is parallel to EF. Prove that $AF = \dfrac{4AD}{3}$.

13 OAB is a triangle in which P and Q are the mid-points of AB and OB respectively. OP, AQ meet at G, and $AG = mAQ$, $OG = nOP$. Let $\overrightarrow{OA} = \mathbf{a}$ and $OB = \mathbf{b}$, and by expressing $\overrightarrow{OG}$ in two different ways, prove that $m = n = \dfrac{2}{3}$.

42 Further Transformation Geometry

Transformation geometry was introduced in chapter 27, where we considered the two important transformations *reflection* and *rotation*. The continuation of the subject has been left until this stage in order that matrices and vectors can be used in the representation of transformations.

Both reflection and rotation are *isometries* (they map object figures to *congruent* image figures), and we continue by considering one more transformation of this kind, which is best represented by a vector.

Translation

The idea of translation follows easily from that of *displacement*, which was dealt with in the last chapter. *A translation gives every point an equal displacement*, that is *it shifts or displaces every point by the same distance in the same direction*. This means that all lines are mapped to parallel lines, and geometrical figures are mapped *without rotation* to congruent figures (Fig. 42.1).

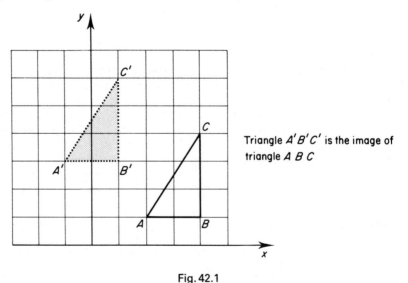

Triangle $A'B'C'$ is the image of triangle ABC

Fig. 42.1

Since a piece of cardboard fitting exactly over triangle *ABC* could be shifted *without being turned over* to the position *A'B'C'*, the transformation is a *direct* and not an opposite isometry.

The translation is completely described by any of the three directed line segments $\overrightarrow{AA'}$, $\overrightarrow{BB'}$, $\overrightarrow{CC'}$, or by any of an infinite number of equivalent directed line segments. All of these represent the same displacement vector, and it is this vector which describes the translation in the most convenient way. The vector itself is most conveniently specified by giving its components. In the above example the triangle moves 3 units to the left and 2 units upwards, so the vector is $\begin{pmatrix} -3 \\ 2 \end{pmatrix}$. The transformation is therefore described either as 'a translation represented by the vector $\begin{pmatrix} -3 \\ 2 \end{pmatrix}$', or, more briefly, simply as 'a translation of $\begin{pmatrix} -3 \\ 2 \end{pmatrix}$'.

There are clearly no invariant points under a (non-zero) translation.

Successive translations

We saw in chapter 27 that combinations of transformations are normally represented as 'products'. For example, a half-turn followed by a reflection in the x-axis is represented as XH. Translations however are combined in the same way as displacements, and we have seen that this is done by *adding* the displacements according to the general laws for the addition of vectors. Thus for example to add the displacements (or translations) represented by $\begin{pmatrix} 2 \\ 1 \end{pmatrix}$ and $\begin{pmatrix} 1 \\ 3 \end{pmatrix}$ we either use the triangle law or add corresponding components:

$$\begin{pmatrix} 2 \\ 1 \end{pmatrix} + \begin{pmatrix} 1 \\ 3 \end{pmatrix} = \begin{pmatrix} 3 \\ 4 \end{pmatrix}.$$

It is important to remember, therefore, that the 'products' ST and TS of two translations S and T are obtained by *adding* the vectors representing S and T.

Since addition is a *commutative* operation it clearly follows that translation, considered as an operation, is also commutative. Thus for any two translations S and T, we have ST = TS. It is not of course true in general that combinations of transformations are commutative.

The inverse of a translation

The identity translation, which leaves all points unchanged, is the translation represented by the zero vector $\begin{pmatrix} 0 \\ 0 \end{pmatrix}$, and the inverse of the translation $\begin{pmatrix} a \\ b \end{pmatrix}$ is therefore the translation which must be added to $\begin{pmatrix} a \\ b \end{pmatrix}$ to give $\begin{pmatrix} 0 \\ 0 \end{pmatrix}$. This is clearly the negative of $\begin{pmatrix} a \\ b \end{pmatrix}$, namely $\begin{pmatrix} -a \\ -b \end{pmatrix}$.

▷ Example 1

The translation S maps (0,1) to (3,0), and the translation T maps (1,1) to (3,4). Express S, T, ST and (ST)⁻¹ as column vectors and find the image of the point (−2,3) under (ST)⁻¹.

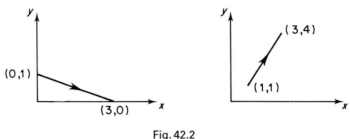

Fig. 42.2

Fig. 42.2 shows that S translates a point 3 units to the right and 1 unit downwards, while T translates a point 2 units to the right and 3 units upwards. Hence S is the translation $\begin{pmatrix} 3 \\ -1 \end{pmatrix}$ and T is the translation $\begin{pmatrix} 2 \\ 3 \end{pmatrix}$.

The product ST (and also TS) is obtained by adding the components of S and T, so ST is the translation $\begin{pmatrix} 5 \\ 2 \end{pmatrix}$. Also the inverse of ST is the negative of $\begin{pmatrix} 5 \\ 2 \end{pmatrix}$, so (ST)⁻¹ is the translation $\begin{pmatrix} -5 \\ -2 \end{pmatrix}$.

To obtain the image of a point under the translation $\begin{pmatrix} -5 \\ -2 \end{pmatrix}$ we simply add −5 to the x co-ordinate of the point and add −2 to the y co-ordinate. Hence (ST)⁻¹(−2,3) = (−7,1). This procedure can also be expressed as a vector addition. The position vector of the point (−2,3) is $\begin{pmatrix} -2 \\ 3 \end{pmatrix}$, and if we add to this the vector $\begin{pmatrix} -5 \\ -2 \end{pmatrix}$ which represents the translation, we obtain the position vector of the image point:

$$\begin{pmatrix} -2 \\ 3 \end{pmatrix} + \begin{pmatrix} -5 \\ -2 \end{pmatrix} = \begin{pmatrix} -7 \\ 1 \end{pmatrix}.$$

◀

▷ Example 2

*Fig. 42.3 shows an equilateral triangle which is divided into 9 congruent equilateral triangles. Express in terms of the vectors **u** and **v** the translations which map (a) triangle ABG to triangle HJK, (b) triangle CDE to triangle FEJ, (c) triangle FEJ to triangle ABG, (d) triangle BCF to triangle HJK.*

(a) A translation is completely described by the vector linking one object point to its image point, so this translation is specified by the vector $\overrightarrow{AH}$ or 2**v**.

(b) Here we need the value of the vector $\overrightarrow{CF}$ (or $\overrightarrow{DE}$ or $\overrightarrow{EJ}$). Since $\overrightarrow{CF} = \overrightarrow{BG} = \overrightarrow{BA} + \overrightarrow{AG}$ by the triangle law, the required vector is **v** − **u**.

(c) The required vector is $\overrightarrow{FA}$, which is equal to −(**u** + **v**) by the parallelogram law.

(d) Taking the vector $\overrightarrow{BH}$ and using the triangle law, we have $\overrightarrow{BH} = \overrightarrow{BA} + \overrightarrow{AH}$. Hence the required vector is 2**v** − **u**. ◀

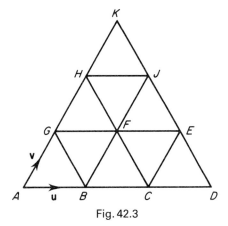

Fig. 42.3

Combinations of isometries

In chapter 27 we considered some combinations of the isometries reflection and rotation, and found that a product of two of these is often equivalent to a single reflection or rotation. With the introduction of translation this topic can be developed further. All isometries are describable in terms of reflection, rotation and translation, and products of these three basic isometries can always be expressed in different ways, some simpler than others. When dealing with combinations of isometries it is useful to remember the following rules, which most students will find self-evident:

(1) A product of isometries is always equivalent to another isometry.
(2) A product of direct isometries is equivalent to a direct isometry.
(3) A product involving opposite isometries is direct or indirect according to whether the number of opposite isometries is even or odd.

▷ Example 3

The triangle formed by the points A(−1,1), B(−2,1) and C(−1,3) is reflected in the y-axis, and then the image A′B′C′ is reflected in the line x = 3 to give a second image A″B″C″. Find the co-ordinates of all the image points and describe the single transformation which is equivalent to the combination of the two reflections.

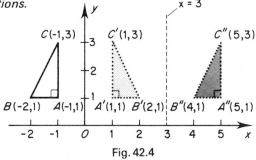

Fig. 42.4

Fig. 42.4 is self-explanatory and shows that the two reflections are equivalent to a translation of 6 units to the right, or $\begin{pmatrix} 6 \\ 0 \end{pmatrix}$. (Note that a product of two opposite isometries has resulted in a direct isometry.)   ◀

Example 3 in fact illustrates the following general theorem:

Two successive reflections in parallel lines a distance *d* apart are equivalent to a translation of 2*d* perpendicular to the lines.

(Reversing the order of the reflections causes the direction of the translation to be reversed.)

The examples given in chapter 27 illustrate the corresponding theorem for non-parallel lines:

Two successive reflections in lines meeting at a point *O* and inclined to each other at an angle of *θ* are equivalent to a rotation about *O* of 2*θ*.

(It is not necessary to learn these theorems by heart, but students should be aware that they exist.)   ◄

▶ **Example 4**

The triangle ABC of Example 3 is given a half-turn about the origin and then the image A'B'C' is given a half-turn about the point (3,1). Find the co-ordinates of all the image points and describe the single transformation which is equivalent to the two rotations.

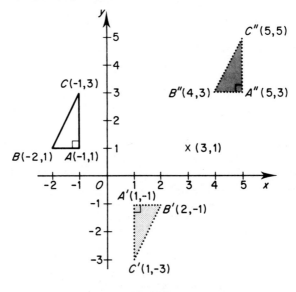

Fig. 42.5

Under a half-turn each image point is the reflection of its object point in the centre of rotation, and thus the centre of rotation is the mid-point of the line joining each object point and its image. For example, the centre of rotation (3,1) is the mid-point of the line joining $B'(2,-1)$ to $B''(4,3)$ (Fig. 42.5). This explains how the co-ordinates of the image points are calculated.

The combination of the two transformations is again equivalent to a translation, in this case of $\begin{pmatrix} 6 \\ 2 \end{pmatrix}$. Clearly successive half-turns about any two points must cause the sides of a figure to regain their original directions, so *any product of two half-turns is equivalent to a translation.*   ◄

EXERCISE 42a

1 Draw on graph paper the triangle formed by the points $A(1,0)$, $B(2,0)$ and $C(1,3)$. Draw also the images of the triangle under the translations (a) $\begin{pmatrix} -3 \\ 0 \end{pmatrix}$, (b) $\begin{pmatrix} 2 \\ 1 \end{pmatrix}$, (c) $\begin{pmatrix} -2 \\ -4 \end{pmatrix}$, stating the co-ordinates of the image points in each case.

2 Draw on graph paper the triangle formed by the points $A(-2,3)$, $B(2,3)$ and $C(0,4)$. Draw also the images of the triangle under the translations (a) $\begin{pmatrix} 0 \\ -3 \end{pmatrix}$, (b) $\begin{pmatrix} -2 \\ -1 \end{pmatrix}$, stating the co-ordinates of the image points in each case.

3 Draw on graph paper the triangle formed by the points $A(-2,-2)$, $B(-3,-2)$ and $C(-2,0)$. Draw its image $A'B'C'$ under the translation $\begin{pmatrix} 4 \\ 1 \end{pmatrix}$ and also the image $A''B''C''$ obtained when $A'B'C'$ is translated by $\begin{pmatrix} -1 \\ 3 \end{pmatrix}$. State the translations which map (a) triangle ABC to triangle $A''B''C''$, (b) triangle $A''B''C''$ to triangle $A'B'C'$.

4 Fig. 42.6 shows a set of congruent parallelograms. Express in terms of the vectors **u** and **v** the translations which map (a) 1 to 3, (b) 5 to 10, (c) 12 to 4, (d) 9 to 6.

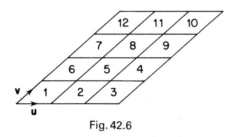

Fig. 42.6

5 Fig. 42.7 shows a rectangle which is divided into congruent right-angled triangles. Name the triangle or triangles onto which it is possible to map by translation (a) triangle ABH, (b) triangle HJF. Express the translations in terms of the vectors **u** and **v** in each case.

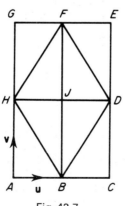

Fig. 42.7

6 S is the translation $\begin{pmatrix} -2 \\ 1 \end{pmatrix}$ and T is the translation $\begin{pmatrix} 5 \\ -2 \end{pmatrix}$. Find the images of the point $(3,-2)$ under S, T, ST and $(ST)^{-1}$.

7 Express as column vectors the translations which map (a) $(-2,0)$ to $(0,3)$, (b) $(4,0)$ to $(5,2)$, (c) $(3,0)$ to $(-5,0)$ (d) $(0,-1)$ to $(-4,0)$, (e) $(-2,-3)$ to $(-5,2)$.

8 S is the translation which maps $(2,0)$ to $(0,3)$ and T is the translation which maps $(-1,3)$ to $(-2,4)$. Find the images of the point $(-1,2)$ under S, T^{-1} and ST.

9 Find the point which (a) is mapped to $(4,5)$ under the translation $\begin{pmatrix} 2 \\ 1 \end{pmatrix}$, (b) is mapped to $(0,3)$ under the translation $\begin{pmatrix} -7 \\ 5 \end{pmatrix}$, (c) is mapped to $(-5,-9)$ under the translation $\begin{pmatrix} 3 \\ -4 \end{pmatrix}$.

10 S and T are translations. If S is $\begin{pmatrix} 2 \\ 3 \end{pmatrix}$ find T given that (a) ST $= \begin{pmatrix} 4 \\ -1 \end{pmatrix}$, (b) $TS^{-1} = \begin{pmatrix} 5 \\ 0 \end{pmatrix}$, (c) $ST^{-1} = \begin{pmatrix} 0 \\ -3 \end{pmatrix}$, (d) $(ST)^{-1} = \begin{pmatrix} 1 \\ 2 \end{pmatrix}$.

11 X = reflection in the x-axis, Q is a positive quarter-turn about the origin and T is the translation $\begin{pmatrix} -2 \\ 3 \end{pmatrix}$. Find (a) XT(1,2), (b) TX(1,2), (c) QT(-1,-2), (d) $TQ^{-1}(3,1)$.

12 Using the diagram given in question 5 name all the triangles onto which it is possible to map triangle *ABH* by direct isometries.

13 Using the diagram given in question 5 name the triangle or triangles onto which it is possible to map triangle *ABH* by reflection in *AH* followed by a translation. Express the translation(s) in terms of **u** and **v**.

14 Draw on graph paper the triangle formed by the points $A(0,-1)$, $B(0,-2)$ and $C(2,-1)$. Draw its image under reflection in the x-axis and the image of this image under reflection in the line $y = 3$. State (a) the co-ordinates of the final images of A, B, C, (b) the single transformation which is equivalent to the product of the two reflections.

15 Draw on graph paper the triangle *ABC* of question 14 together with its image under a half-turn about the origin and the image of this image under a half-turn about the point $(1,1)$. State (a) the co-ordinates of the final images of A, B, C, (b) the single transformation which is equivalent to the product of the two half-turns.

16 Fig. 42.8 shows a parallelogram which is divided into congruent right-angled triangles. Name the triangle or triangles onto which it is possible to map triangle *ABF* (a) by a translation, (b) by a half-turn about F followed by a translation, (c) by a reflection in the line *FE* followed by a translation. Express the translations in terms of **u** and **v** in each case.

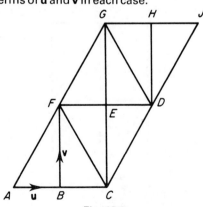

Fig. 42.8

17 With reference to the diagram given in question 16, name a single transformation which will map (a) triangle *FEG* to triangle *FEC*, (b) triangle *GED* to triangle *FBC*, (c) triangle *ABF* to triangle *JHD*.

18 Draw on graph paper the triangle formed by the points $A(1,1)$, $B(2,-1)$ and $C(2,3)$, and draw also its image under a positive quarter-turn about the point $(1,-1)$. Show that the same effect is achieved by a quarter-turn about A, B or C followed by an appropriate translation, and state the value of the translation in each case.

19 The triangle formed by the points $A(1,0)$, $B(3,0)$ and $C(1,1)$ is given a positive quarter-turn about O and then its image is given a negative quarter-turn about the point $(-2,1)$. State (a) the co-ordinates of the final images of A, B, C, (b) the single transformation which is equivalent to the product of the quarter-turns.

20 The triangle formed by the points $A(0,1)$, $B(0,2)$ and $C(1,2)$ is given a negative quarter-turn about A and then its image is given a negative quarter-turn about the point $(1,0)$. Let the final images of A, B, C be P, Q, R, respectively, and state (a) the co-ordinates of P, Q, R. Describe also (b) a single transformation in which $A \rightarrow P$, $B \rightarrow Q$ and $C \rightarrow R$, (c) a single transformation in which $A \rightarrow R$, $B \rightarrow Q$ and $C \rightarrow P$.

21 $OABC$ is a rectangle formed by the origin and the points $A(1,0)$, $B(1,2)$ and $C(0,2)$, and $APQR$ is a rectangle formed by the points A, $P(1,1)$, $Q(-1,1)$ and $R(-1,0)$. The second rectangle can be mapped onto the first by (a) a downward translation followed by a clockwise rotation, (b) a translation to the right followed by a reflection, (c) a clockwise rotation about O followed by a translation, (d) reflection in the line $y = 1$ followed by an anticlockwise rotation. Describe these transformations fully.

22 State the single transformations which are equivalent to the following: (a) reflection in the line $y = -1$ followed by reflection in the line $y = 2$, (b) a half-turn about $(2,0)$ followed by a half-turn about $(-1,0)$, (c) reflection in the line $x = 2$ followed by a translation of $\begin{pmatrix} -2 \\ 0 \end{pmatrix}$, (d) a translation of $\begin{pmatrix} 0 \\ 4 \end{pmatrix}$ followed by reflection in the line $y = 6$.

Non-isometric transformations

Enlargement

To define an enlargement it is necessary to specify one point — the *centre of enlargement* — and a number called the *scale factor* of the enlargement.

Suppose for example that we have an enlargement of centre O and scale factor 2. What this means is that any point A is mapped to an image A' which is positioned such that $\overrightarrow{OA'} = 2\overrightarrow{OA}$.

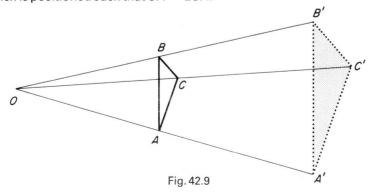

Fig. 42.9

Fig. 42.9 shows that every point is mapped to a point which is twice as far from O, and this results in an image figure which is *similar* to the object figure. The sides of the image figure are parallel to the corresponding sides of the object figure, and their lengths have been increased in the ration 2:1. The centre of enlargement O is the only invariant point.

An enlargement may have a negative scale factor, in which case the directions of the vectors $\overrightarrow{OA}$, $\overrightarrow{OB}$, etc. are reversed. The image therefore appears on the opposite side of O and is inverted.

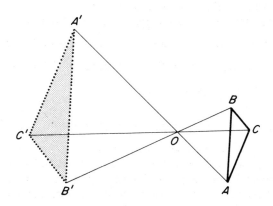

Fig. 42.10

Fig. 42.10 shows an enlargement with scale factor -2. An enlargement with scale factor -1 is equivalent to a half-turn.

If the scale factor of an enlargement is fractional, the image figure is smaller than the object figure and nearer to the centre (Fig. 42.11).

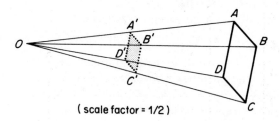

(scale factor = 1/2)

Fig. 42.11

(The name 'enlargement' might seem inappropriate here, and sometimes the word 'compression' is preferred. It is convenient, however, to use a single name for all transformations of the same type.)

The effect of an enlargement on area

In chapter 26 it was explained that the ratio of the areas of similar figures is equal to the square of the ratio of corresponding sides. Thus *under an enlargement of scale factor k, the area of a figure is increased by a factor k^2*.

Successive enlargements, the inverse of an enlargement

Suppose that a figure is subjected to an enlargement of scale factor 2 followed by an enlargement of scale factor 3. Both enlargements leave the shape and orientation of the figure unaltered, and affect only the size. The final image will therefore be an enlargement of the object figure with scale factor 6, and it follows that in general *two successive enlargements are equivalent to a single enlargement whose scale factor is equal to the product of the original scale factors*. The position of the final image depends on the positions of the two centres.

Clearly, two successive enlargements with the same centre and scale factors of k and $\dfrac{1}{k}$ are equivalent to the identity transformation. Hence *the inverse of an enlargement with a scale factor of k is an enlargement with the same centre and scale factor of $\dfrac{1}{k}$.*

The location of the centre of an enlargement

The examples given show that all lines AA', BB', etc. joining object and image points pass through the centre of the enlargement. Hence if an object figure and its image are given the centre can be located by taking any two of these lines and finding their point of intersection.

▷ Example 5

Draw the images of (a) the triangle formed by the points $A(2,2)$, $B(4,2)$, $C(2,6)$ under an enlargement of centre O and scale factor $-\frac{1}{2}$, (b) the triangle formed by the points $P(0,1)$, $Q(2,1)$, $R(2,2)$ under an enlargement of centre $E(1,0)$ and scale factor 3.

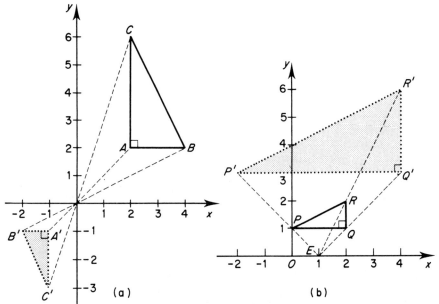

Fig. 42.12

The co-ordinates of the image points in case (b) can be calculated quite easily by using vector components. For example, to locate R' we note that $\overrightarrow{ER} = \begin{pmatrix} 1 \\ 2 \end{pmatrix}$ and hence $\overrightarrow{ER'} = 3\begin{pmatrix} 1 \\ 2 \end{pmatrix} = \begin{pmatrix} 3 \\ 6 \end{pmatrix}$. Since E is the point $(1,0)$ it follows that R' is $(4,6)$. Similarly P' is $(-2,3)$ and Q' is $(4,3)$.   ◀

▷ Example 6

In Fig. 42.13 the rectangle $A'B'C'D'$ is an enlargement with scale factor 2 of the rectangle ABCD. The sides of the smaller rectangle are 1 cm and 2 cm, and the distance AB' is 3 cm. Locate the centre of enlargement E.

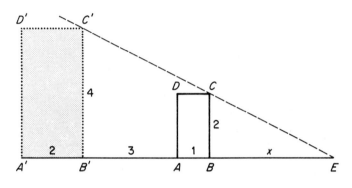

Fig. 42.13

E lies on the point of intersection of AA' and CC', as shown in Fig. 42.13. Letting $EB = x$ cm and using the similar triangles EBC, $EB'C'$, we have

$$\frac{x}{x+4} = \frac{2}{4},$$

from which it follows that $x = 4$ and hence that $EB = 4$ cm.   ◀

One-way stretches

A one-way stretch can be thought of as **an enlargement in one direction only**. To define a one-way stretch we need to specify an invariant *line* and a scale factor: for example, if the scale factor is 2, each point moves at right angles to the invariant line to an image point which is twice as far from the line (Fig. 42.14).

The lengths of lines parallel to the invariant line are unchanged, and the lengths of lines perpendicular to the invariant line are multiplied by the scale factor. Hence *with a scale factor of k, the area of an image figure is k times that of the object figure.*

Note: The lines perpendicular to the invariant line of a one-way stretch can themselves be described as invariant, but these lines are not *point* invariant. When we speak of 'the invariant line' in defining a one-way stretch, it is understood that we refer to the line whose points are all individually invariant. There is only one line of this kind.

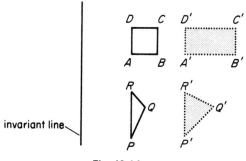

Fig. 42.14

Shears

We have a simple example of a shear when a pack of cards is pushed sideways so that the side view changes from a rectangle to a parallelogram (Fig. 42.15).

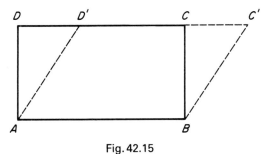

Fig. 42.15

There is one (point) invariant line (*AB*) and all other points move parallel to this line in such a way that straight lines are mapped to straight lines and parallel lines remain parallel. This means that the amount each point is displaced is proportional to its distance from the invariant line: for example, if a point which is 10 cm from the line is displaced 3 cm, a point which is 20 cm from the line will be displaced 6 cm (Fig. 42.16).

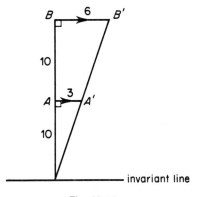

Fig. 42.16

It also follows from the fact that straight lines are mapped to straight lines that points on opposite sides of the invariant line move in opposite directions (Fig. 42.17).

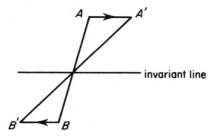

Fig. 42.17

It was shown above that an enlargement preserves shape but not size; a shear has the opposite effects. The shape of a figure is obviously distorted, but *area is preserved under a shear*. For example, the rectangle *ABCD* and the parallelogram *ABC'D'* in Fig. 42.15 are equal in area because both have the same base (*AB*) and the same height (*AD*).

The simplest way to specify a shear is to give the invariant line and the image of one point which is not on the line. As the following example illustrates, this enables all other images to be located.

▷ **Example 7**

A shear has the line y = 1 as invariant line and the point (1,2) is mapped to (3,2). Find the image of the triangle formed by the points A(1,3), B(2,3) and C(1,4).

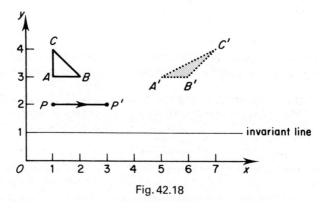

Fig. 42.18

Since $P(1,2)$ is mapped to $P'(3,2)$, all points distant 1 unit from the invariant line move 2 units horizontally (Fig. 42.18). Hence A, which is 2 units from the line, moves 4 units horizontally, and C, which is 3 units from the line, moves 6 units horizontally. This means that A' is the point (5,3), B' is (6,3) and C' is (7,4).   ◁

▷ **Example 8**

Under a certain shear the point (1, −1) is mapped to (1,2) and the point (3, −1) is mapped to (3,3). Find the equation of the invariant line.

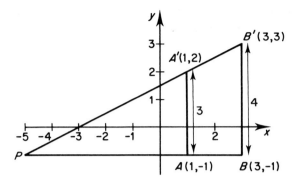

Fig. 42.19

Let the lines BA and $B'A'$ meet at P (Fig. 42.19); then since straight lines are mapped to straight lines, PAB is mapped to $PA'B'$ and it follows that P is an invariant point. Also since A and B move vertically the invariant line is vertical, and we therefore require the vertical line through P. By similar triangles we have

$$\frac{PA}{PA+2} = \frac{3}{4}$$

$$\therefore \quad 4PA = 3PA + 6$$
$$\therefore \quad PA = 6.$$

It follows that the value of x at P is -5 and thus that the equation of the invariant line is $x = -5$.   ◀

EXERCISE 42b

1 Draw on graph paper the triangle with vertices $(1,1)$, $(2,1)$ and $(1,3)$. Draw also its images under the enlargements with (a) centre O and scale factor 2, (b) centre O and scale factor $-\frac{1}{2}$, (c) centre $(4,0)$ and scale factor 2. State the co-ordinates of the image points in each case.

2 Draw on graph paper the triangle with vertices $(-1,0)$, $(-\frac{1}{2},1)$ and $(-1,2)$. Draw also its images under the enlargements with (a) centre O and scale factor 3, (b) centre $(1,0)$ and scale factor -2, (c) centre $(-1,2)$ and scale factor -1. State the co-ordinates of the image points in each case.

3 Find the images of the following points under an enlargement of centre O and scale factor 3: (a) $(2,1)$, (b) $(-4,5)$, (c) (a,b).

4 Find the images of the following points under an enlargement of centre O and scale factor $-\frac{1}{2}$: (a) $(4,2)$, (b) $(6,-10)$.

5 Find the images of the following points under an enlargement of centre $(2,0)$ and scale factor 3: (a) $(2,1)$, (b) $(1,0)$, (c) $(3,2)$, (d) $(0,-2)$, (e) $(-3,-4)$.

6 Find the images of the following points under an enlargement of centre $(2,3)$ and scale factor 2: (a) $(2,4)$, (b) $(4,3)$, (c) $(3,5)$, (d) $(0,0)$, (e) $(-2,-1)$.

7 Find the images of the following points under an enlargement of centre $(1,3)$ and scale factor $-\frac{1}{2}$: (a) $(1,7)$, (b) $(-1,3)$, (c) $(-5,5)$, (d) $(7,-9)$.

8 Under an enlargement of centre O and scale factor 2, the vertices of the triangle ABC are mapped to $A'(4,2)$, $B'(4,6)$ and $C'(2,4)$. Find the points A, B, C.

9 Under an enlargement of centre O and scale factor $-\frac{1}{2}$, find the points which are mapped to (a) $(-1,-3)$, (b) $(2,1)$, (c) $(-4,1\frac{1}{2})$.

10 Under an enlargement of centre $(2,1)$ and scale factor 3, find the points which are mapped to (a) $(5,7)$, (b) $(-7,4)$.

11 Under an enlargement of centre O and scale factor 4, the point $(3,p)$ is mapped to $(q,20)$. Find p and q.

12 Under an enlargement of centre $(2,1)$ and scale factor 3, the point $(5,p)$ is mapped to $(q,10)$. Find p and q.

13 Under an enlargement of centre $(3,5)$ and scale factor -1, the point $(p,7)$ is mapped to $(0,q)$. Find p and q.

14 Find the centres and scale factors of the enlargements under which (a) $(2,3) \rightarrow (2,5)$ and $(1,1) \rightarrow (0,1)$, (b) $(2,2) \rightarrow (4,4)$ and $(3,1) \rightarrow (7,1)$, (c) $(-4,3) \rightarrow (0,3)$ and $(4,5) \rightarrow (4,4)$, (d) $(-3,2) \rightarrow (0,2)$ and $O \rightarrow (-6,6)$.

15 Draw on graph paper the square with vertices $(1,1)$, $(2,1)$, $(2,2)$, $(1,2)$, and the rectangle with vertices $(3,-2)$, $(5,-2)$, $(5,-3)$, $(3,-3)$. Draw also the image of the square under an enlargement of centre O and scale factor 2, and the image of the rectangle under an enlargement of centre O and scale factor $\frac{1}{2}$. By what factors have the areas of the square and the rectangle been multiplied?

16 A triangle is formed by the points $(0,1)$, $(4,1)$ and $(2,3)$. Find its area and the area of its images under enlargements with scale factors 2, 3 and $-\frac{1}{2}$.

17 Draw on graph paper the triangle with vertices $(1,1)$, $(2,1)$ and $(1,3)$. Draw its image under an enlargement of centre O and scale factor 2, and the image of this image under an enlargement of centre $(4,0)$ and scale factor $\frac{1}{2}$. State (a) the co-ordinates of the final image points, (b) the single transformation which is equivalent to the product of the two enlargements.

18 Draw on graph paper the triangle formed by the points $(1,0)$, $(3,0)$ and $(2,1)$, and also its images under the following one-way stretches: (a) invariant line the y-axis, scale factor 2; (b) invariant line $y = -1$, scale factor -3; (c) invariant line $x = -3$, scale factor $\frac{1}{2}$. State the co-ordinates of the image points in each case.

19 What single transformation is equivalent to a one-way stretch of scale factor 3 with invariant line $y = 1$, followed by a one-way stretch of scale factor 3 with invariant line $x = -2$?

20 The triangle with vertices $(1,-2)$, $(1,4)$ and $(5,0)$ is subjected to a one-way stretch whose invariant line is the y-axis. If the stretch maps the point $(4,0)$ to $(6,0)$, what is the area of the image triangle?

21 Find the equation of the invariant line of a one-way stretch with scale factor $2\frac{1}{2}$ which maps $(2,0)$ to $(11,0)$.

22 Draw on graph paper the triangle with vertices $(0,1)$, $(1,1)$ and $(0,2)$. Draw also its images under (a) the shear with the x-axis as invariant line which maps $(2,1)$ to $(4,1)$, (b) the shear with invariant line $x = 1$ which maps $(3,0)$ to $(3,6)$. State the co-ordinates of the image points in each case.

23 A shear with invariant line $y = 1$ maps $(-1,2)$ to $(1,2)$. Find the images of the following points under the shear: (a) $(0,3)$, (b) $(4,5)$, (c) $(1,0)$, (d) $(4,-2)$.

24 Find the equations of the invariant lines of the shears which map (a) $(3,2)$ to $(5,2)$ and $(3,4)$ to $(6,4)$ (b) $(3,0)$ to $(2,1)$ and $(4,0)$ to $(2,2)$.

25 A shear whose invariant line is the x-axis maps the line $y = -x$ to the line $y = x$. Find the equations of the lines to which it maps (a) the y-axis, (b) the line $y = x$, (c) the line $y = 2x$. Find also (d) the equation of the line which is mapped to the y-axis.

26 In Fig. 42.20, *ABCD* and *PQRS* are squares with sides of 6 cm and 3 cm, respectively, and *AP* = 1 cm. Regarding the larger square as an enlargement of the smaller, locate the centre of enlargement.

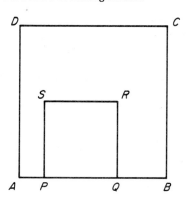

Fig. 42.20

27 The distances shown in Fig. 42.21 are in centimetres, and triangle *BCD* is an enlargement of triangle *ABE*. Locate the centre of enlargement.

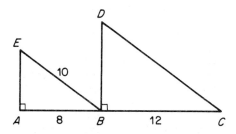

Fig. 42.21

28 In Fig. 42.22, *ABCD* and *PQRS* are squares. Use the theory of enlargements to prove that the lines *BQ* and *CR* meet on *AS* produced.

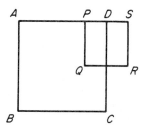

Fig. 42.22

29 By describing two shears prove that the rectangle *ABFH* and the parallelogram *ECHG* (Fig. 42.23) are equal in area.

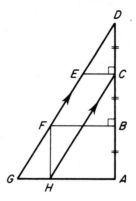

Fig. 42.23

30 *ABCD* and *DRWT* are rectangles (Fig. 42.24). By describing three shears prove that these rectangles are equal in area.

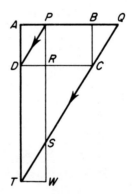

Fig. 42.24

43 The Representation of Transformations by Matrices

A geometrical transformation is a rule or procedure which tells us how to obtain an image point P' from an object point P. A particular transformation can be described in various ways; for example two ways of describing the transformation denoted by Y are 'reflect the object point in the y-axis' and 'change the sign of x and leave y unaltered'.

We are now going to look at another way of describing transformations, which involves matrix multiplication. The point (x,y) can be represented by the column matrix $\begin{pmatrix} x \\ y \end{pmatrix}$, and if this column matrix is pre-multiplied by any 2×2 matrix, the result is another column matrix which represents, in general, a different point. E.g.

$$\begin{pmatrix} -1 & 0 \\ 0 & 1 \end{pmatrix} \begin{pmatrix} x \\ y \end{pmatrix} = \begin{pmatrix} -x \\ y \end{pmatrix}.$$

We can think of the 2×2 matrix in this equation as transforming or mapping the point (x,y) to the point $(-x,y)$, and consequently the whole operation represented by the equation is known as a *matrix transformation*. Also, since the transformation which maps (x,y) to $(-x,y)$ is *reflection in the y-axis* or Y, the matrix $\begin{pmatrix} -1 & 0 \\ 0 & 1 \end{pmatrix}$ is said to represent this particular transformation. Clearly it is possible to regard any 2×2 matrix as representing a transformation, and we therefore have the following general principle.

Any 2×2 matrix can be considered to represent a geometrical transformation. It performs the transformation by pre-multiplying the column matrix which represents the object point.

The effect of a matrix transformation on the origin

If we operate with any 2×2 matrix on the column matrix $\begin{pmatrix} 0 \\ 0 \end{pmatrix}$ representing the origin, we have

$$\begin{pmatrix} a & b \\ c & d \end{pmatrix} \begin{pmatrix} 0 \\ 0 \end{pmatrix} = \begin{pmatrix} 0 \\ 0 \end{pmatrix}.$$

It follows that *the origin is always invariant* under a matrix transformation, and this imposes a limit on the transformations which can be represented by 2×2 matrices. It means that a transformation with a single invariant point, such as a rotation or an enlargement, can only be represented by a 2×2 matrix if the origin is the invariant point; and it also means that a transformation with an invariant line, such as a reflection, stretch or shear, can only be represented in this way if the invariant line passes through the origin. Transformations which have no invariant points, such as translations, cannot be represented by 2×2 matrices at all.

Finding the transformation represented by a given matrix

The easiest way to find the transformation represented by a given matrix is to apply the transformation to a simple figure such as a rectangle or triangle. (The simplest figure of all is the *unit square*, which will be considered shortly.) Any standard transformation such as a reflection or rotation can usually be recognised if the object figure and its image are drawn together on graph paper.

▷ Example 1

Apply the transformation represented by $\begin{pmatrix} 0 & 1 \\ 1 & 0 \end{pmatrix}$ to the triangle whose vertices are A(3,1), B(5,1) and C(5,2). Hence describe the transformation.

To transform a set of points by a 2×2 matrix, the simplest method is to represent the points by a single matrix in which each column stands for one point. Then the corresponding columns in the product matrix represent the images of the points:

$$\begin{pmatrix} 0 & 1 \\ 1 & 0 \end{pmatrix} \begin{matrix} A & B & C \\ \begin{pmatrix} 3 & 5 & 5 \\ 1 & 1 & 2 \end{pmatrix} \end{matrix} = \begin{matrix} A' & B' & C' \\ \begin{pmatrix} 1 & 1 & 2 \\ 3 & 5 & 5 \end{pmatrix} \end{matrix}.$$

The object and image figures are therefore positioned as shown in Fig. 43.1.

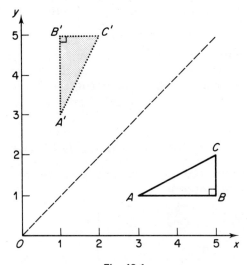

Fig. 43.1

It can now be seen that the transformation represented by the matrix $\begin{pmatrix} 0 & 1 \\ 1 & 0 \end{pmatrix}$ is *reflection in the line y = x* (the dotted line in Fig. 43.1).   ◁

Inverse transformations, combinations of transformations

One of the main advantages of the matrix method of representing transformations is that this enables matrix algebra to be applied to transformation geometry. It can be shown that (a) the inverse of a transformation is represented by the inverse of the transformation matrix, (b) a combination or product of transformations is represented by the product of the transformation matrices. It is of course important to take into account the *order* in which a product of matrices is written. If **M** and **N** are matrices, the product **MN** gives the single transformation which is equivalent to applying **N** *and then* **M** to a point.

▷ **Example 2**

Apply the transformation represented by $\mathbf{Q} = \begin{pmatrix} 0 & -1 \\ 1 & 0 \end{pmatrix}$ *to the triangle t whose vertices are (1,0), (1,2) and (0,2). Hence describe the transformation. Work out also* $\mathbf{Q}^2$ *and* $\mathbf{Q}^{-1}$*, describe the transformations they represent, and illustrate these transformations by applying them to the triangle t.*
We have

$$\mathbf{Q}(t) = \begin{pmatrix} 0 & -1 \\ 1 & 0 \end{pmatrix} \begin{pmatrix} 1 & 1 & 0 \\ 0 & 2 & 2 \end{pmatrix} = \begin{pmatrix} 0 & -2 & -2 \\ 1 & 1 & 0 \end{pmatrix}.$$

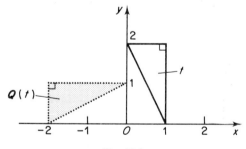

Fig. 43.2

It can be seen from Fig. 43.2 that **Q** represents a *positive quarter-turn about O*.
  To find $\mathbf{Q}^2$ we multiply **Q** by itself, and to find $\mathbf{Q}^{-1}$ we use the rule given in chapter 40, namely *interchange the elements of the leading diagonal, change the signs of the other two elements and divde by the determinant.* Here the determinant is 1, and we have

$$\mathbf{Q}^2 = \begin{pmatrix} 0 & -1 \\ 1 & 0 \end{pmatrix} \begin{pmatrix} 0 & -1 \\ 1 & 0 \end{pmatrix} = \begin{pmatrix} -1 & 0 \\ 0 & -1 \end{pmatrix},$$

$$\mathbf{Q}^{-1} = \begin{pmatrix} 0 & 1 \\ -1 & 0 \end{pmatrix}.$$

The transformation represented by $\mathbf{Q}^2$ means 'apply $\mathbf{Q}$ twice', and $\mathbf{Q}^{-1}$ denotes the inverse or 'opposite' of $\mathbf{Q}$. We should therefore expect to find that the matrices for $\mathbf{Q}^2$ and $\mathbf{Q}^{-1}$ represent, respectively, a *half-turn* (or rotation of 180°) about O, and a *negative quarter-turn* (or rotation of 90° clockwise). Applying the transformations to the triangle t, we have

$$\mathbf{Q}^2(t) = \begin{pmatrix} -1 & 0 \\ 0 & -1 \end{pmatrix} \begin{pmatrix} 1 & 1 & 0 \\ 0 & 2 & 2 \end{pmatrix} = \begin{pmatrix} -1 & -1 & 0 \\ 0 & -2 & -2 \end{pmatrix},$$

$$\mathbf{Q}^{-1}(t) = \begin{pmatrix} 0 & 1 \\ -1 & 0 \end{pmatrix} \begin{pmatrix} 1 & 1 & 0 \\ 0 & 2 & 2 \end{pmatrix} = \begin{pmatrix} 0 & 2 & 2 \\ -1 & -1 & 0 \end{pmatrix}.$$

The triangle and its images under $\mathbf{Q}$, $\mathbf{Q}^2$ and $\mathbf{Q}^{-1}$ are therefore as shown in Fig. 43.3.

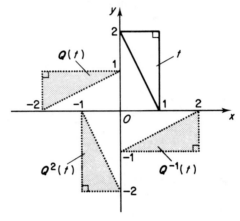

Fig. 43.3

It can now be seen that $\mathbf{Q}^2$ and $\mathbf{Q}^{-1}$ do represent a half-turn and a negative quarter-turn about O. ◀

A transformation as a pair of linear equations

Suppose that the point (x,y) is mapped by the matrix $\begin{pmatrix} 2 & 3 \\ 1 & 4 \end{pmatrix}$ to the point (x',y'):

$$\begin{pmatrix} x' \\ y' \end{pmatrix} = \begin{pmatrix} 2 & 3 \\ 1 & 4 \end{pmatrix} \begin{pmatrix} x \\ y \end{pmatrix}.$$

If we carry out the matrix multiplication and equate corresponding elements, we obtain the following two linear equations:

$$x' = 2x + 3y$$
$$y' = x + 4y.$$

These two equations are clearly equivalent to the single matrix equation, and they therefore provide an alternative method of describing the transformation represented by the matrix $\begin{pmatrix} 2 & 3 \\ 1 & 4 \end{pmatrix}$. It follows that one way to find the matrix representing a particular transformation is to express the transformation as a pair of linear equations and then form the matrix from the coefficients of x and y. For example, the equations representing reflection in the y-axis (Y) are

$$x' = -x + 0y,$$
$$y' = 0x + y,$$

and it therefore follows that the matrix representing Y is $\begin{pmatrix} -1 & 0 \\ 0 & 1 \end{pmatrix}$.

EXERCISE 43a

(Graph paper should be used when appropriate.)

1 Find the images of the points $(1,0)$, $(2,3)$, $(-2,5)$ and $(-3,-4)$ under the transformation whose matrix is $\begin{pmatrix} 2 & 1 \\ 3 & 5 \end{pmatrix}$.

2 Find the images of the points $(0,2)$, $(-4,0)$, $(-6,1)$ and $(2,-3)$ under the transformation whose matrix is $\begin{pmatrix} -2 & 0 \\ \frac{1}{2} & -1 \end{pmatrix}$.

3 Write down the inverse matrices of $\begin{pmatrix} 2 & 1 \\ 1 & 1 \end{pmatrix}$, $\begin{pmatrix} 8 & 5 \\ 3 & 2 \end{pmatrix}$, $\begin{pmatrix} 4 & 2 \\ 5 & 3 \end{pmatrix}$, $\begin{pmatrix} -4 & 3 \\ 7 & -6 \end{pmatrix}$ and $\begin{pmatrix} 4 & -2 \\ 3 & -4 \end{pmatrix}$.

4 Apply the transformation represented by $\mathbf{P} = \begin{pmatrix} 1 & 0 \\ 0 & -1 \end{pmatrix}$ to the triangle whose vertices are $A(2,1)$, $B(4,1)$ and $C(4,2)$, and hence describe the transformation. State also the matrix which maps the image triangle $A'B'C'$ back to triangle ABC.

5 Apply the transformation represented by $\mathbf{T} = \begin{pmatrix} 0 & 1 \\ -1 & 0 \end{pmatrix}$ to the triangle ABC of question 4, and hence describe the transformation. Work out also the matrices $\mathbf{T}^2$ and $\mathbf{T}^{-1}$, and describe the transformations they represent.

6 Draw the triangle whose vertices are $(4,2)$, $(6,2)$ and $(6,6)$, and apply to it the transformations represented by the following matrices: (a) $\begin{pmatrix} -1 & 0 \\ 0 & -1 \end{pmatrix}$, (b) $\begin{pmatrix} 0 & -1 \\ -1 & 0 \end{pmatrix}$,   (c) $\begin{pmatrix} \frac{1}{2} & 0 \\ 0 & \frac{1}{2} \end{pmatrix}$,   (d) $\begin{pmatrix} -\frac{1}{2} & 0 \\ 0 & -\frac{1}{2} \end{pmatrix}$.   Hence   describe   the transformations.

7 Write down the matrix of the transformation represented by the equations $x' = 2x + 5y$, $y' = x + 3y$. Find also the matrix which maps (x',y') to (x,y).

8 Write down the matrix of the transformation represented by the equations $x' = 2x - y$, $y' = 3x + y$. Find also the matrix representing two successive applications of this transformation.

9 Apply the transformation represented by $\mathbf{M} = \begin{pmatrix} 2 & 0 \\ 0 & 2 \end{pmatrix}$ to any point (x,y), and hence describe the transformation. Work out also $\mathbf{M}^2$ and $\mathbf{M}^{-1}$ and describe the transformations they represent.

10 If a matrix $\mathbf{N}$ represents a reflection, what is the matrix $\mathbf{N}^2$?

11 Work out the products **PT** and **TP,** where **P** and **T** are the matrices given in questions 4 and 5. By considering the geometrical meanings of **P** and **T,** describe the transformations represented by these products.

12 Apply the transformation represented by $\begin{pmatrix} 0 & -2 \\ 2 & 0 \end{pmatrix}$ to the triangle whose vertices are (0,0), (2,0) and (2,1). Given that this transformation is the product of a rotation and an enlargement, find the angle of the rotation and the scale factor of the enlargement.

13 Apply the transformation represented by $\begin{pmatrix} -3 & 0 \\ 0 & 3 \end{pmatrix}$ to the triangle with vertices $(\frac{1}{2},1)$, (1,1) and (1,2). Given that this transformation is the product of a reflection and an enlargement, find the axis of reflection and the scale factor of the enlargement.

14 Apply the transformation represented by $\begin{pmatrix} 1 & -1 \\ 1 & 1 \end{pmatrix}$ to the square with vertices (0,0), (1,0), (1,1), (0,1). Given that this transformation is the product of an enlargement and another transformation, find the scale factor (in square-root form) and describe the other transformation.

15 By considering its effect on some convenient figure, verify that the matrix $\begin{pmatrix} 1 & -3 \\ 3 & 1 \end{pmatrix}$ represents the product of an enlargement and a rotation. State in square root form the scale factor of the enlargement, and give the tangent of the angle of rotation.

16 **T** is the matrix $\begin{pmatrix} 0.8 & 0.6 \\ 0.6 & -0.8 \end{pmatrix}$. Work out $\mathbf{T}^{-1}$ and $\mathbf{T}^2$, and say what kind of transformation these results suggest that **T** represents.

17 By applying the transformation represented by $\begin{pmatrix} -0.6 & 0.8 \\ 0.8 & 0.6 \end{pmatrix}$ to the triangle whose vertices are (5,10), (10,10) and (10,20), show that the transformation is a reflection and state the equation of the axis of reflection.

18 Apply the transformation represented by $\begin{pmatrix} 2 & 0 \\ 0 & 1 \end{pmatrix}$ to the rectangle with vertices (0,1), (1,1), (1,3), (0,3), and hence describe the transformation.

19 Apply the transformation represented by $\begin{pmatrix} 1 & 3 \\ 0 & 1 \end{pmatrix}$ to the rectangle represented by $\begin{pmatrix} 0 & 1 & 1 & 0 \\ 0 & 0 & 2 & 2 \end{pmatrix}$, and hence describe the transformation.

20 Letting the matrix $\begin{pmatrix} 2 & 0 \\ 0 & 1 \end{pmatrix}$ of question 18 be **S,** work out $\mathbf{S}^{-1}$, $\mathbf{S}^2$ and $\mathbf{S}^3$, and describe the transformations they represent.

21 Express the transformation 'reflection in the x-axis' as a pair of linear equations, and hence obtain the matrix representing this transformation.

22 Repeat question 21 for the transformations (a) a positive quarter-turn about the origin, (b) reflection in the line $y = -x$.

The unit square

The square with vertices $O(0,0)$, $A(1,0)$, $B(0,1)$ and $C(1,1)$ is called the *unit square* (Fig. 43.4).

The unit square is important because the effect on it of a matrix transformation gives us the effect of the transformation on the whole

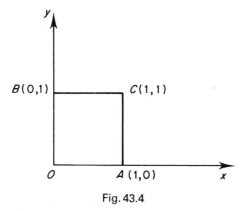

Fig. 43.4

plane. Applying the general 2 × 2 matrix to each of the vertices of the square, we have

$$\begin{pmatrix} a & b \\ c & d \end{pmatrix} \begin{array}{cccc} O & A & B & C \\ \begin{pmatrix} 0 & 1 & 0 & 1 \\ 0 & 0 & 1 & 1 \end{pmatrix} \end{array} = \begin{array}{cccc} O & A' & B' & C' \\ \begin{pmatrix} 0 & a & b & a+b \\ 0 & c & d & c+d \end{pmatrix} \end{array}.$$

The square is therefore mapped to a *parallelogram* (Fig. 43.5).

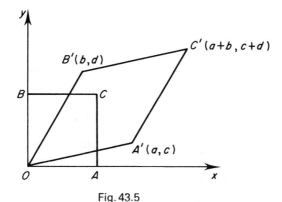

Fig. 43.5

Now it can be shown quite easily that if the whole plane is divided into identical squares, each square is mapped to an identical parallelogram. Hence the effect of a transformation on the whole plane is determined by its effect on the unit square.

The effect of a transformation on area

The area of the unit square is clearly 1 square unit, and it can be shown that the area of the parallelogram to which the square is mapped is $|ad - bc|$ or *the numerical value of the determinant of the transformation matrix.* Since the whole plane behaves in a similar way to the unit square we have the following general result.

The area of the image figure under a matrix transformation is equal to the area of the object figure multiplied by the numerical value of the determinant of the matrix.

For example the transformation represented by the matrix $\begin{pmatrix} 2 & -1 \\ -4 & 3 \end{pmatrix}$ causes the areas of all figures to be doubled.

The matrices representing particular transformations

Since the unit square is transformed by a 2×2 matrix to a parallelogram with the origin invariant, it follows that a transformation is completely determined by its effects on the two points $(1,0)$ and $(0,1)$. Now we saw above that the transformation represented by $\begin{pmatrix} a & b \\ c & d \end{pmatrix}$ maps $\begin{pmatrix} 1 \\ 0 \end{pmatrix}$ to $\begin{pmatrix} a \\ c \end{pmatrix}$ and $\begin{pmatrix} 0 \\ 1 \end{pmatrix}$ to $\begin{pmatrix} b \\ d \end{pmatrix}$. This gives the following general result.

The first and second columns of a transformation matrix represent the images of the points (1,0) and (0,1), respectively.

Consequently the matrix representing any particular transformation can be obtained simply by calculating the images of the points $(1,0)$ and $(0,1)$.

▷**Example 3**

Find the matrices which map (a) (1,0) to (−2,3) and (0,1) to (5,7), (b) (2,0) to (6,8) and (0,−3) to (−6,9), (c) (1,0) to (2,1) and (1,1) to (3,4).

(a) Since $\begin{pmatrix} 1 \\ 0 \end{pmatrix} \to \begin{pmatrix} -2 \\ 3 \end{pmatrix}$ and $\begin{pmatrix} 0 \\ 1 \end{pmatrix} \to \begin{pmatrix} 5 \\ 7 \end{pmatrix}$, the matrix is $\begin{pmatrix} -2 & 5 \\ 3 & 7 \end{pmatrix}$.

(b) Since $\begin{pmatrix} 2 \\ 0 \end{pmatrix} = 2\begin{pmatrix} 1 \\ 0 \end{pmatrix}$, it follows that $\begin{pmatrix} 1 \\ 0 \end{pmatrix} \to \begin{pmatrix} 3 \\ 4 \end{pmatrix}$. Similarly $\begin{pmatrix} 0 \\ 1 \end{pmatrix} \to \begin{pmatrix} 2 \\ -3 \end{pmatrix}$, and the matrix is therefore $\begin{pmatrix} 3 & 2 \\ 4 & -3 \end{pmatrix}$.

(c) We know (see above) that under the transformation represented by $\begin{pmatrix} a & b \\ c & d \end{pmatrix}$, $\begin{pmatrix} 1 \\ 0 \end{pmatrix} \to \begin{pmatrix} a \\ c \end{pmatrix}$, $\begin{pmatrix} 0 \\ 1 \end{pmatrix} \to \begin{pmatrix} b \\ d \end{pmatrix}$ and $\begin{pmatrix} 1 \\ 1 \end{pmatrix} \to \begin{pmatrix} a+b \\ c+d \end{pmatrix}$.

In this case we are told that $\begin{pmatrix} 1 \\ 0 \end{pmatrix} \to \begin{pmatrix} 2 \\ 1 \end{pmatrix}$, giving us the first column of the transformation matrix, and that $\begin{pmatrix} 1 \\ 1 \end{pmatrix} \to \begin{pmatrix} 3 \\ 4 \end{pmatrix}$, which gives us the results of adding the elements in the two columns. It follows that $\begin{pmatrix} 0 \\ 1 \end{pmatrix} \to \begin{pmatrix} 1 \\ 3 \end{pmatrix}$, and that the transformation matrix is $\begin{pmatrix} 2 & 1 \\ 1 & 3 \end{pmatrix}$. ◁

The next example shows how the unit square method can be used to find the matrices representing some of the main types of transformations considered earlier. It must be remembered of course that 2×2 matrices can only represent transformations in which the origin is invariant.

▷Example 4

Use the unit square method to obtain the matrices representing (a) a positive (anticlockwise) quarter-turn about the origin, (b) an enlargement of centre the origin and scale factor k.

(a) The unit square and its image are shown in Fig. 43.6.

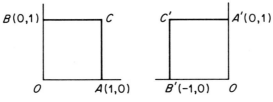

Fig. 43.6

Since $\begin{pmatrix} 1 \\ 0 \end{pmatrix} \rightarrow \begin{pmatrix} 0 \\ 1 \end{pmatrix}$ and $\begin{pmatrix} 0 \\ 1 \end{pmatrix} \rightarrow \begin{pmatrix} -1 \\ 0 \end{pmatrix}$, the matrix representing a positive quarter-turn is $\begin{pmatrix} 0 & -1 \\ 1 & 0 \end{pmatrix}$.

(b) The unit square and its image are shown in Fig. 43.7.

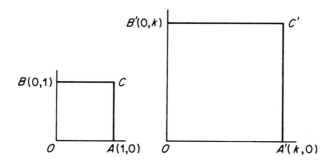

Fig. 43.7

Since $\begin{pmatrix} 1 \\ 0 \end{pmatrix} \rightarrow \begin{pmatrix} k \\ 0 \end{pmatrix}$ and $\begin{pmatrix} 0 \\ 1 \end{pmatrix} \rightarrow \begin{pmatrix} 0 \\ k \end{pmatrix}$, the matrix representing an enlargement of centre O and scale factor k is $\begin{pmatrix} k & 0 \\ 0 & k \end{pmatrix}$.   ◀

This example should make the method clear. It is not, of course, necessary to learn the results by heart, but students should know how to derive them. For convenience, the matrices of all the simple transformations with O invariant are tabulated below.

1 Identity matrix	$\begin{pmatrix} 1 & 0 \\ 0 & 1 \end{pmatrix}$	2 Reflection in x-axis	$\begin{pmatrix} 1 & 0 \\ 0 & -1 \end{pmatrix}$
3 Reflection in y-axis	$\begin{pmatrix} -1 & 0 \\ 0 & 1 \end{pmatrix}$	4 Reflection in line $y = x$	$\begin{pmatrix} 0 & 1 \\ 1 & 0 \end{pmatrix}$
5 Reflection in line $y = -x$	$\begin{pmatrix} 0 & -1 \\ -1 & 0 \end{pmatrix}$	6 Half-turn about O	$\begin{pmatrix} -1 & 0 \\ 0 & -1 \end{pmatrix}$

7	Positive quarter-turn about O	$\begin{pmatrix} 0 & -1 \\ 1 & 0 \end{pmatrix}$	8	Negative quarter-turn about O	$\begin{pmatrix} 0 & 1 \\ -1 & 0 \end{pmatrix}$
9	Enlargement, centre O, scale factor k	$\begin{pmatrix} k & 0 \\ 0 & k \end{pmatrix}$	10	Shear with x-axis invariant	$\begin{pmatrix} 1 & k \\ 0 & 1 \end{pmatrix}$
11	Shear with y-axis invariant	$\begin{pmatrix} 1 & 0 \\ k & 1 \end{pmatrix}$	12	One-way stretch, x-axis invariant	$\begin{pmatrix} 1 & 0 \\ 0 & k \end{pmatrix}$
13	One-way stretch, y-axis invariant	$\begin{pmatrix} k & 0 \\ 0 & 1 \end{pmatrix}$			

Powers of the standard transformation matrices

The geometrical meanings of the above matrices are useful if powers of these matrices are required. Suppose, for example, that $\mathbf{M} = \begin{pmatrix} 1 & 3 \\ 0 & 1 \end{pmatrix}$ and we require $\mathbf{M}^5$. The matrix represents a shear in which the x-axis is invariant and points 1 unit above the x-axis move 3 units to the right. $\mathbf{M}^5$ is the matrix representing 5 successive applications of this shear, which is equivalent to a shear in which the same points move 15 units to the right. Hence $\mathbf{M}^5 = \begin{pmatrix} 1 & 15 \\ 0 & 1 \end{pmatrix}$.

Enlargement, and multiplication of a matrix by a scalar

It is noteworthy that the matrix representing an enlargement, $\begin{pmatrix} k & 0 \\ 0 & k \end{pmatrix}$, is closely related to the identity matrix $\mathbf{I}$. We can in fact take out the common factor k from the enlargement matrix and obtain a scalar multiple of $\mathbf{I}$:

$$\begin{pmatrix} k & 0 \\ 0 & k \end{pmatrix} = k\begin{pmatrix} 1 & 0 \\ 0 & 1 \end{pmatrix} = k\mathbf{I}.$$

This indicates that multiplication by a matrix of the form $\begin{pmatrix} k & 0 \\ 0 & k \end{pmatrix}$ is equivalent to multiplication by the number k; and since multiplication by a number is commutative, it follows that the operation of enlargement commutes with any of the other operations represented by 2 × 2 matrices. Thus for example an enlargement followed by a rotation (both with centre O) is equivalent to the rotation followed by the enlargement.

The equivalence of the enlargement matrix and the scalar multiplier k also means that any transformation represented by a 2 × 2 matrix can be regarded as the product of an enlargement of any magnitude and another transformation. This sometimes enables a matrix to be re-expressed in terms of one of the above standard matrices. Consider for example the matrices $\mathbf{A} = \begin{pmatrix} -2 & 0 \\ 0 & 2 \end{pmatrix}$ and $\mathbf{B} = \begin{pmatrix} 3 & 6 \\ 0 & 3 \end{pmatrix}$. We have

$$\mathbf{A} = 2\begin{pmatrix} -1 & 0 \\ 0 & 1 \end{pmatrix} \text{ and } \mathbf{B} = 3\begin{pmatrix} 1 & 2 \\ 0 & 1 \end{pmatrix},$$

and it follows that **A** represents an enlargement of scale factor 2 together with a reflection in the y-axis, while **B** represents an enlargement of scale factor 3 together with a shear whose invariant line is the x-axis.

The transformation represented by a singular matrix

The determinant of a singular matrix equals zero, which suggests that the unit square is mapped to a parallelogram with an area of zero! In fact this is essentially true, since it can be shown that the vertices of the square are all mapped to points on a straight line. An infinite number of other points are also mapped to each of the points on this line, so there can be no inverse transformation.

EXERCISE 43b

1 Use the unit square method to find the matrices which map (a) (1,0) to (2,3) and (0,1) to (1,5), (b) (1,0) to (−5,2) and (0,1) to (3,−4), (c) (2,0) to (8,2) and (0,4) to (12,0), (d) (−3,0) to (6,0) and (0,2) to (−8,4).

2 $M = \begin{pmatrix} 1 & 0 \\ 0 & -1 \end{pmatrix}$ and $N = \begin{pmatrix} -1 & 0 \\ 0 & -1 \end{pmatrix}$. By using the unit square (and without consulting the table of standard matrices) describe the transformations represented by **M, N** and **MN**. Does **MN** = **NM**?

3 Find the matrices which map (a) (1,0) to (3,2) and (1,1) to (5,3), (b) (0,1) to (4,2) and (1,1) to (9,5), (c) (2,0) to (−2,6) and (1,1) to (1,−2), (d) (0,3) to (0,6) and (2,2) to (−3,−6).

4 $S = \begin{pmatrix} 0 & -1 \\ 1 & 0 \end{pmatrix}$ and $T = \begin{pmatrix} 0 & 1 \\ 1 & 0 \end{pmatrix}$. Describe the transformations represented by **S, T, ST** and **TS**.

5 $P = \begin{pmatrix} 0 & 1 \\ -1 & 0 \end{pmatrix}$. Describe the transformations represented by **P, P²** and **P⁻¹**.

6 $A = \begin{pmatrix} 3 & 0 \\ 0 & 1 \end{pmatrix}$ and $B = \begin{pmatrix} 1 & 0 \\ 0 & 3 \end{pmatrix}$. Describe the transformations represented by **A, B** and **AB**. Does **AB** = **BA**?

7 Use the unit square method to obtain the matrix **V** representing reflection in the line $y = -x$. Work out V^2, V^3 and V^{-1}, and describe the transformations they represent.

8 Draw on graph paper the images of the unit square under the transformations whose matrices are $\begin{pmatrix} 4 & 0 \\ 0 & 1 \end{pmatrix}$ and $\begin{pmatrix} 0 & -1 \\ 4 & 0 \end{pmatrix}$. Find the matrices which map (a) the first image to the second, (b) the second image to the first.

9 Work out the matrices representing the following products, and describe the transformations they represent: (a)YQ, (b) QY, (c) X², (d) HX, (e) YXQ, (f) Q⁻¹ XH. (See chapter 27 for the meanings of these symbols.)

10 The following matrices all represent products of positive enlargements with other simple transformations. In each case state the scale factor and the other transformation: (a) $\begin{pmatrix} -2 & 0 \\ 0 & 2 \end{pmatrix}$, (b) $\begin{pmatrix} 0 & 4 \\ 4 & 0 \end{pmatrix}$, (c) $\begin{pmatrix} 0 & -\frac{1}{2} \\ \frac{1}{2} & 0 \end{pmatrix}$.

11 Write down the matrices representing the products of (a) an enlargement of scale factor 3 with Q⁻¹, (b) an enlargement of scale factor $\frac{1}{3}$ with H. Multiply the two matrices together and name (c) the transformation represented by the product.

12 The matrix $\begin{pmatrix} 1 & 1 \\ -1 & 1 \end{pmatrix}$ represents the product of an enlargement and a rotation. By considering the unit square and using Pythagoras' theorem, find the scale factor (in square-root form) and the angle of rotation.

13 Draw the image of the unit square under each of the following transformations, and use the formula $A = bh$ for the area of a parallelogram to find the area of each image: (a) $\begin{pmatrix} 3 & 0 \\ 0 & 3 \end{pmatrix}$, (b) $\begin{pmatrix} 1 & 4 \\ 0 & 1 \end{pmatrix}$, (c) $\begin{pmatrix} 2 & 0 \\ 0 & 1 \end{pmatrix}$, (d) $\begin{pmatrix} 4 & 0 \\ 2 & 1 \end{pmatrix}$, (e) $\begin{pmatrix} 8 & -3 \\ 6 & 4 \end{pmatrix}$. Check that in each case the area is given by the determinant of the matrix.

14 The area of a figure is 3. Find its area after transformation by the following matrices: (a) $\begin{pmatrix} 2 & 4 \\ 2 & 5 \end{pmatrix}$, (b) $\begin{pmatrix} -2 & 1 \\ 1 & -3 \end{pmatrix}$, (c) $\begin{pmatrix} -2\frac{1}{2} & -2 \\ 3\frac{1}{2} & 3 \end{pmatrix}$, (d) $\begin{pmatrix} 7 & -6 \\ -8 & 4 \end{pmatrix}$.

15 In each of the following cases find the two values of k for which the given transformation leaves area unchanged: (a) $\begin{pmatrix} k & 3 \\ 1 & 2 \end{pmatrix}$, (b) $\begin{pmatrix} 1 & -1 \\ k & 4 \end{pmatrix}$, (c) $\begin{pmatrix} 1 & 1 \\ -3 & -2k \end{pmatrix}$.

16 Draw the image of the quadrilateral with vertices (2,0), (6,1), (0,4) and (0,1) under the transformation whose matrix is $\begin{pmatrix} 2 & 4 \\ 3 & 6 \end{pmatrix}$. What kind of matrix is this?

17 $Q = \begin{pmatrix} 0 & -1 \\ 1 & 0 \end{pmatrix}$. Use the geometrical meaning of Q to work out (a) Q^8, (b) Q^{14}, (c) $(Q^{17})^{-1}$.

18 $M = \begin{pmatrix} 2 & 0 \\ 0 & 1 \end{pmatrix}$. Work out M^6.

19 $T = \begin{pmatrix} 0 & 1 \\ 1 & 0 \end{pmatrix}$. Work out (a) T^{10}, (b) T^{13}.

20 $P = \begin{pmatrix} 1 & 0 \\ 3 & 1 \end{pmatrix}$. Work out (a) P^7, (b) P^{12}.

21 $S = \begin{pmatrix} 0 & 2 \\ 2 & 0 \end{pmatrix}$. By regarding S as the product of an enlargement and another transformation, work out (a) S^4, (b) S^7.

22 Use the method of question 21 to work out N^7 when N is (a) $\begin{pmatrix} 0 & -2 \\ 2 & 0 \end{pmatrix}$, (b) $\begin{pmatrix} 2 & 0 \\ 4 & 2 \end{pmatrix}$.

23 State the theorem regarding the product of two reflections in intersecting lines. If A is reflection in the line $y = 2x$ and B is reflection in the line $y = -\frac{1}{2}x$, what single transformation is equivalent to AB?

24 The matrices $P = \begin{pmatrix} -1 & 0 \\ 0 & 1 \end{pmatrix}$ and $S = \begin{pmatrix} -0.6 & 0.8 \\ 0.8 & 0.6 \end{pmatrix}$ both represent reflections. Work out PS and, by considering the unit square, show that this represents a rotation. Measure the angle of rotation to the nearest degree.

25 The matrices $M = \begin{pmatrix} -0.8 & 0.6 \\ 0.6 & 0.8 \end{pmatrix}$ and $N = \begin{pmatrix} 0.6 & 0.8 \\ 0.8 & -0.6 \end{pmatrix}$ both represent reflections. Work out MN and NM and state the transformations they represent. Use the theorem regarding the product of two reflections to find the angle between the axes of reflection of M and N.

26 $M = \begin{pmatrix} 0 & -1 \\ 1 & 0 \end{pmatrix}$, $N = \begin{pmatrix} 0 & 1 \\ -1 & 0 \end{pmatrix}$, $P = \begin{pmatrix} -1 & 0 \\ 0 & -1 \end{pmatrix}$ and $R = \begin{pmatrix} 1 & 0 \\ 0 & 1 \end{pmatrix}$.

Construct a combination table (see chapter 22) for the set $\{M, N, P, R\}$ under the operation of matrix multiplication. Say whether or not (a) the set is closed under the operation, (b) the operation, defined on this set, is commutative. Name (c) the identity element, and also the elements equal to (d) the inverse of **N**, (e) $\mathbf{M}^7$, (f) $\mathbf{P}^6$. State (g) whether or not the set is a group under the operation.

27 Repeat question 26 with $\mathbf{M} = \begin{pmatrix} -1 & 0 \\ 0 & 1 \end{pmatrix}$, $\mathbf{N} = \begin{pmatrix} 1 & 0 \\ 0 & -1 \end{pmatrix}$, $\mathbf{P} = \begin{pmatrix} 1 & 0 \\ 0 & 1 \end{pmatrix}$, $\mathbf{R} = \begin{pmatrix} -1 & 0 \\ 0 & -1 \end{pmatrix}$.

28 Show that when the point $(1,0)$ is rotated through $+120°$ about O its image is $\left(-\frac{1}{2}, \frac{\sqrt{3}}{2} \right)$, and find the image of the point $(0,1)$ under the same rotation. Hence find the matrix **M** representing the rotation.

Verify that $\mathbf{M}^3 = \mathbf{I}$ and let $\mathbf{M}^2 = \mathbf{P}$. Show that **M, P** and **I** form a group under the operation of matrix multiplication and find the elements equal to (a) $\mathbf{P}^{-1}$, (b) $\mathbf{M}^9$, (c) $\mathbf{P}^8$.

The invariant lines of a matrix transformation

We have already seen that the invariant lines of transformations are of two types. If every point of a line is individually invariant, the line is said to be *point invariant;* while if the points on a line are in general mapped to different points on the same line, the line is described as *invariant but not point invariant.* The following example deals with both kinds of invariant line, though we limit our attention to lines passing through the origin.

▶ Example 5

Show that the transformation whose matrix is $\begin{pmatrix} 2 & -1 \\ 5 & -4 \end{pmatrix}$ has a point invariant line passing through the origin, and also a line which is invariant but not point invariant. Find the equations of both lines.

Letting the image of the point (x, y) be (x', y'), we have

$$\begin{pmatrix} x' \\ y' \end{pmatrix} = \begin{pmatrix} 2 & -1 \\ 5 & -4 \end{pmatrix} \begin{pmatrix} x \\ y \end{pmatrix},$$

and hence

$$x' = 2x - y,$$
$$y' = 5x - 4y.$$

Now if (x, y) and (x', y') are points on the same line through O, so that the line is invariant but not necessarily point invariant, we have

$$\frac{x}{y} = \frac{x'}{y'}$$
$$\therefore \; \frac{x}{y} = \frac{2x - y}{5x - 4y}$$
$$\therefore \; 5x^2 - 4xy = 2xy - y^2$$
$$\therefore \; y^2 - 6xy + 5x^2 = 0$$
$$\therefore \; (y - x)(y - 5x) = 0$$
$$\therefore \; y = x \text{ or } y = 5x.$$

It follows that the lines with equations $y = x$ and $y = 5x$ are both invariant.

The two lines can be tested for point invariance as follows. Any point on the line $y = x$ can be represented by the column vector $\begin{pmatrix} x \\ x \end{pmatrix}$, and any point on the line $y = 5x$ can be represented by $\begin{pmatrix} x \\ 5x \end{pmatrix}$. Hence the image of any point (x,x) on the line $y = x$ is given by

$$\begin{pmatrix} 2 & -1 \\ 5 & -4 \end{pmatrix} \begin{pmatrix} x \\ x \end{pmatrix},$$

and the image of any point $(x, 5x)$ on the line $y = 5x$ is given by

$$\begin{pmatrix} 2 & -1 \\ 5 & -4 \end{pmatrix} \begin{pmatrix} x \\ 5x \end{pmatrix}.$$

When the matrices are multiplied out in the first case we obtain

$$\begin{pmatrix} 2x - x \\ 5x - 4x \end{pmatrix} \text{ or } \begin{pmatrix} x \\ x \end{pmatrix},$$

and in the second case we have

$$\begin{pmatrix} 2x - 5x \\ 5x - 20x \end{pmatrix} \text{ or } \begin{pmatrix} -3x \\ -15x \end{pmatrix}.$$

Hence since the image point is the same as the object point for the line $y = x$, but not for the line $y = 5x$, it follows that the first line is point invariant but the second is not.   ◀

The image of a non-invariant line

Transformations represented by 2 × 2 matrices are *linear,* which means that they map straight lines to straight lines. The method for finding the image of a non-invariant line through the origin is illustrated in the following example.

▶ Example 6

Find the image of the line $y = 3x$ under the transformation represented by $\begin{pmatrix} 5 & -1 \\ 2 & 1 \end{pmatrix}$.

Any point on the line $y = 3x$ can be represented as $(x, 3x)$. Letting the image of the point $(x, 3x)$ be (x', y'), we have

$$\begin{pmatrix} x' \\ y' \end{pmatrix} = \begin{pmatrix} 5 & -1 \\ 2 & 1 \end{pmatrix} \begin{pmatrix} x \\ 3x \end{pmatrix} = \begin{pmatrix} 5x - 3x \\ 2x + 3x \end{pmatrix} = \begin{pmatrix} 2x \\ 5x \end{pmatrix}.$$

It follows that $x' = 2x$ and $y' = 5x$. Now the equation of the image line is simply an equation relating x' and y', and by eliminating x from the two equations obtained we get $2y' = 5x'$. Hence the equation of the image line expressed in the more usual way is $2y = 5x$.   ◀

EXERCISE 43c

1 For the transformations represented by the following matrices find the equations of the lines through O which are (i) point invariant, (ii) invariant but not point invariant: (a) $\begin{pmatrix} 3 & 1 \\ 4 & 3 \end{pmatrix}$, (b) $\begin{pmatrix} 2 & -3 \\ 2 & -5 \end{pmatrix}$, (c) $\begin{pmatrix} -1 & 5 \\ 2 & -4 \end{pmatrix}$.

2 By considering the image of the point $(x, 3x)$, prove that the line $y = 3x$ is point invariant under the transformation whose matrix is $\begin{pmatrix} 4 & -1 \\ 0 & 1 \end{pmatrix}$. Also by considering the image of the point $(x, 2x)$ under the same transformation, prove that the image of the line $y = 2x$ is $y = x$.

3 Find the equations of the images of the line $y = 2x$ under the transformations represented by the following matrices: (a) $\begin{pmatrix} 2 & 3 \\ 2 & 1 \end{pmatrix}$, (b) $\begin{pmatrix} -1 & 2 \\ 3 & -2 \end{pmatrix}$, (c) $\begin{pmatrix} 8 & -5 \\ -3 & 4 \end{pmatrix}$.

4 Show that the transformation represented by $\begin{pmatrix} 3 & -1 \\ 4 & -1 \end{pmatrix}$ has just one invariant line through O, and that this line is point invariant. Draw on graph paper the square whose vertices are O, $(2, -1)$, $(3, 1)$, $(1, 2)$, and draw also its image under the transformation. Hence show that the transformation is a shear with invariant line $y = 2x$.

5 Show that the transformation whose matrix is $\begin{pmatrix} 0.8 & 0.6 \\ 0.6 & -0.8 \end{pmatrix}$ has two perpendicular invariant lines through O, one of them being point invariant. By considering its effect on the square whose vertices are O, $(3, 1)$, $(2, 4)$, $(-1, 3)$, show that the transformation represents a reflection and state the equation of the axis of reflection.

6 Show that the transformation whose matrix is $\begin{pmatrix} 0.5 & 0.5 \\ -0.5 & 1.5 \end{pmatrix}$ has just one invariant line through O, and that this line is point invariant. Consider the effect of the transformation on the square whose vertices are O, $(1, 1)$, $(0, 2)$, $(-1, 1)$, and hence describe the transformation.

7 The matrix $\begin{pmatrix} 6 & 8 \\ 8 & -6 \end{pmatrix}$ represents the product of an enlargement and a reflection. By considering the effect of the transformation on the vector $\begin{pmatrix} 1 \\ 0 \end{pmatrix}$, show that the scale factor of the enlargement is 10, and obtain the equation of the axis of reflection by finding the point invariant line of the transformation $\begin{pmatrix} 0.6 & 0.8 \\ 0.8 & -0.6 \end{pmatrix}$.

8 The matrix $\begin{pmatrix} -5 & 12 \\ 12 & 5 \end{pmatrix}$ represents the product of an enlargement and a reflection. Use the method of question 7 to obtain the scale factor and the equation of the axis.

9 Show that the transformation whose matrix is $\begin{pmatrix} 5 & 2 \\ 2 & 2 \end{pmatrix}$ has two perpendicular invariant lines through O. Consider the effect of the transformation on the rectangle whose vertices are O, $(2, 1)$, $(0, 5)$, $(-2, 4)$, and hence describe the transformation.

10 Show that the transformation whose matrix is $\begin{pmatrix} 12 & 9 \\ -9 & 12 \end{pmatrix}$ has no invariant lines through O. Given that transformation is the product of an enlargement and a rotation, find the scale factor of the enlargement and the tangent of the angle of rotation.

44 Introduction to Calculus; Differentiation

Gradient

We saw in chapter 23 that the gradient of a straight line graph measures the graph's *steepness,* and is defined as

$$\frac{\text{increase in } y}{\text{increase in } x} \left(\text{or} \frac{\text{vertical distance}}{\text{horizontal distance}} \right).$$

When the graph slopes to the right the gradient is positive and when the graph slopes to the left the gradient is negative (Fig. 44.1).

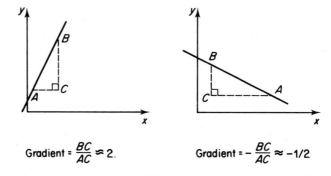

Gradient $= \dfrac{BC}{AC} \approx 2$.　　　　Gradient $= -\dfrac{BC}{AC} \approx -1/2$

Fig. 44.1

The gradient of a curved graph varies from point to point on the graph. At any particular point it is defined to be the gradient of the *tangent* to the graph at that point (Fig. 44.2).

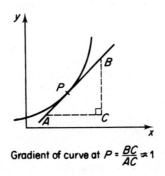

Gradient of curve at $P = \dfrac{BC}{AC} \approx 1$

Fig. 44.2

470

Differentiation

It is clear that drawing tangents and measuring their gradients is a slow and inaccurate method of obtaining the gradient of a graph at various points. We begin the study of *calculus* by showing how it is possible to obtain a *formula* for the gradient at any point on a graph by performing certain operations on the equation of the graph. This process is called *differentiation*, and the expression for the gradient which it provides is called the *differential coefficient* or *derivative* of y with respect to x. The differential coefficient is denoted by $\frac{dy}{dx}$, where dy and dx are single symbols which cannot be split up (dy does not mean 'd multiplied by y'). In this book we shall only give the rules by which the expressions for $\frac{dy}{dx}$ are obtained, and shall not prove the rules: the proofs require further algebra which is normally covered in the first year of an A-level course.

Differentiation of simple powers of x

The general method for differentiating powers of x can be expressed in words by the following rule.

Multiply by the power and subtract 1 from the power.

The following examples illustrate the rule.

$$y = x^3, \qquad y = x^8, \qquad y = x^2, \qquad y = x,$$
$$\frac{dy}{dx} = 3x^2. \qquad \frac{dy}{dx} = 8x^7. \qquad \frac{dy}{dx} = 2x. \qquad \frac{dy}{dx} = 1.$$

Note that the rule works for the special case of $y = x$, since if we subtract 1 from the power in this case we obtain x^0, which is 1. An alternative way to express the differentiation rule is by an algebraic formula:

$$y = x^n,$$
$$\frac{dy}{dx} = nx^{n-1}.$$

To see how the differentiation rule is used in practice, consider the graph of $y = x^3$. We have seen that in this case $dy/dx = 3x^2$, and this means that the gradient at all points on the graph is $3x^2$. For example the gradient at the point where $x = 2$ is $3 \times 2^2 = 12$, and the gradient at the point $(-4, -64)$ is $3(-4)^2 = 48$. It should be noted that only the value of x is required for the calculation of the gradient. To find the gradient at the point $(-4, -64)$ we do not use the value of y, namely -64, at all.

The differentiation rule still applies when a power of x is multiplied by a constant. We have, for example

$$y = 5x^4, \qquad y = 7x, \qquad y = \frac{x^3}{9}, \qquad y = \frac{3x}{4},$$

$$\frac{dy}{dx} = 20x^3. \qquad \frac{dy}{dx} = 7. \qquad \frac{dy}{dx} = \frac{3x^2}{9} = \frac{x^2}{3}. \qquad \frac{dy}{dx} = \frac{3}{4}.$$

A *constant standing alone* has a differential coefficient of zero. E.g:

$$y = 6,$$

$$\frac{dy}{dx} = 0.$$

(This case does obey the general differentiation rule since 6 can be expressed as $6x^0$.)

Expressions with more than one term

When an expression consists of several different powers of x added together, the rule is simply to differentiate term-by-term. E.g:

$$y = 8x^4 - 7x^3 + \frac{x^2}{4} - \frac{x}{3} + 5,$$

$$\frac{dy}{dx} = 32x^3 - 21x^2 + \frac{x}{2} - \frac{1}{3}.$$

Products and quotients

If two functions form a product or quotient (one expression divided by another), *it is incorrect to differentiate each individual function.* The correct procedure is to multiply or divide first, and then differentiate.

Examples

(a) $y = (2x^2 - 1)(x - 3)$. Removing the brackets, we have
$y = 2x^3 - 6x^2 - x + 3$, and now we can differentiate term-by-term:

$$\frac{dy}{dx} = 6x^2 - 12x - 1.$$

(b) $y = \frac{6x^5 - x^4}{2x^2}$. Here we begin by dividing the top line by the bottom:

$$y = \frac{6x^5}{2x^2} - \frac{x^4}{2x^2} = 3x^3 - \frac{x^2}{2}.$$

Now differentiating term-by-term gives

$$\frac{dy}{dx} = 9x^2 - x.$$

Negative indices

Suppose we require $\dfrac{dy}{dx}$ when $y = \dfrac{1}{6x^3}$. The first point to note is that it is quite wrong to differentiate the $6x^3$ as it stands, obtaining $\dfrac{1}{18x^2}$. The differentiation rule applies only to a power of x multiplied by a constant, which means in effect that the power of x must always be placed on the top line of a fraction. The first step is therefore to write

$$y = \frac{x^{-3}}{6}.$$

It should be noted that the 6 remains on the bottom line, since the power 3 applies only to the x and not to the 6.

Now we apply the differentiation rule to x^{-3}:

$$\frac{dy}{dx} = \frac{-3x^{-4}}{6}.$$

Finally $\dfrac{3}{6}$ is cancelled to $\dfrac{1}{2}$, and x^{-4} is written in the usual way as $\dfrac{1}{x^4}$.

$$\frac{dy}{dx} = -\frac{1}{2x^4}.$$

EXERCISE 44a

Obtain expressions for $\dfrac{dy}{dx}$:

1 $y = x^9$ **2** $y = x^{12}$ **3** $y = 2x^5$ **4** $y = 6x^7$ **5** $y = kx^9$ **6** $y = 4x$

7 $y = 3$ **8** $y = x^2 + x$ **9** $y = 3x - 2$ **10** $y = ax + b$ **11** $y = k$ **12** $y = \dfrac{x^4}{2}$

13 $y = \dfrac{x^3}{6}$ **14** $y = \dfrac{3x^2}{2}$ **15** $y = \dfrac{3x^5}{10}$ **16** $y = \dfrac{5x^6}{4}$ **17** $y = \dfrac{kx^4}{8}$ **18** $y = \dfrac{x^k}{k}$

19 $y = 4x^3 - 5x^2 + 7x - 6$ **20** $y = 5 + 2x - 3x^2 - x^3$

21 $y = 2 - 6x - 5x^3 + 8x^5$ **22** $y = ax^2 + bx + c$ **23** $y = \dfrac{2x^3}{9} + \dfrac{x^2}{4} - \dfrac{x}{3}$

24 $y = (x - 4)(x + 3)$ **25** $y = (2x - 1)(3x - 1)$ **26** $y = (3 - 2x)(5 + 4x)$

27 $y = (3x^2 - x)(2x - 5)$ **28** $y = (2x - 3)^2(x - 1)$

29 $y = (ax + b)(px + q)$ **30** $y = \dfrac{x^2 + x}{x}$ **31** $y = \dfrac{2x^3 - 6x^2}{2x}$ **32** $y = \dfrac{8x^4 - x^3}{4x}$

33 $y = \dfrac{9x^6 + 8x^4}{6x^2}$ **34** $y = \dfrac{5x^4 - 3x^5 + x^8}{10x^3}$ **35** $y = \dfrac{1}{x}$ **36** $y = \dfrac{1}{2x^2}$ **37** $y = \dfrac{3}{x^2}$

38 $y = -\dfrac{1}{9x^3}$ **39** $y = -\dfrac{2}{x^5}$ **40** $y = \dfrac{5}{6x^4}$ **41** $y = 2x + \dfrac{1}{4x^2}$ **42** $y = \dfrac{x^5 - 4}{x^2}$

43 $y = \dfrac{x^2 + 6x^5}{2x^3}$ **44** $y = \dfrac{7x^4 - 8x}{6x^4}$ **45** $y = (x + \dfrac{1}{x})^2$ **46** $y = (x - \dfrac{1}{x})(2 + \dfrac{1}{4x})$.

Gradients at particular points on graphs

Expressions for $\dfrac{dy}{dx}$ are normally in terms of x, and it follows that in order to find the gradient at a particular point on a graph we must know the value of x at that point. Sometimes the value of x is given directly, and sometimes it has to be calculated.

▷ **Example 1**

Find the gradient of the graph of $y = x^2 + 3x$ at (a) the point (2, 10), (b) the point where $x = -6$, (c) the two points where $y = 4$.

$$\text{Since } y = x^2 + 3x,$$
$$\frac{dy}{dx} = 2x + 3.$$

The expression for the gradient is thus $2x + 3$, and to find the gradient at a particular point we substitute the value of x at the point into this expression.

(a) We are given that $x = 2$ and $y = 10$, but only need the first of these values.

$$\text{When } x = 2, \quad \frac{dy}{dx} = 2(2) + 3 = 7.$$

(b) $$\text{When } x = -6, \quad \frac{dy}{dx} = 2(-6) + 3 = -9.$$

(c) Here we are not given the values of x directly, and must therefore begin by calculating these values. Since we are given the value of y, we use the equation of the graph itself, which relates x and y.

Substituting $y = 4$ into the equation $y = x^2 + 3x$, we have

$$x^2 + 3x = 4$$
$$\therefore \ x^2 + 3x - 4 = 0$$
$$\therefore \ (x - 1)(x + 4) = 0$$
$$\therefore \ x = 1 \text{ or } -4.$$

Now we use the formula for $\dfrac{dy}{dx}$, namely $\dfrac{dy}{dx} = 2x + 3$, to obtain the gradients.

$$\text{When } x = 1, \quad \frac{dy}{dx} = 2(1) + 3 = 5.$$
$$\text{When } x = -4, \quad \frac{dy}{dx} = 2(-4) + 3 = -5. \qquad \triangleleft$$

▷ **Example 2**

Find the gradient of the graph of $y = 3 + 2x - x^2$ at the points where it meets the axes. Sketch the graph.

We must begin by finding the values of x at the points where the graph meets the axes. Now *all graphs meet the y-axis when $x = 0$ and the x-axis when $y = 0$*; hence $x = 0$ is one of the required values, and we can obtain the others be letting $y = 0$ in the equation of the graph:

$$0 = 3 + 2x - x^2$$
$$\therefore \ x^2 - 2x - 3 = 0$$
$$\therefore \ (x - 3)(x + 1) = 0$$
$$\therefore \ x = 3 \text{ or } -1.$$

Now we differentiate to obtain the formula for the gradient:

$$y = 3 + 2x - x^2,$$
$$\therefore \frac{dy}{dx} = 2 - 2x.$$

Finally we substitute the values of x at the points where the gradient is required.

When $x = 0$, $\dfrac{dy}{dx} = 2$.

When $x = 3$, $\dfrac{dy}{dx} = 2 - 6 = -4$.

When $x = -1$, $\dfrac{dy}{dx} = 2 + 2 = 4$.

To sketch the graph (Fig. 44.3) we note that since the expression for y is a quadratic function of x in which the term in x^2 is negative, the graph is a *parabola with a maximum* (see chapter 23).

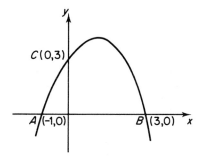

Fig. 44.3

It can be seen from the symmetry of the graph that the gradient is numerically the same at A and at B. This provides a check on the calculation, which gave 4 and -4 for the gradients at these points.   ◀

In the next example we have to find the co-ordinates of a point (x and y values) at which the gradient has a given value.

▷ **Example 3**

Find the point on the graph of $y = 3x - \dfrac{x^2}{4}$ *at which the gradient is 2.*

Since $y = 3x - \dfrac{x^2}{4}$,

$$\frac{dy}{dx} = 3 - \frac{2x}{4}$$
$$= 3 - \frac{x}{2}.$$

Hence when $\frac{dy}{dx} = 2$, we have

$$2 = 3 - \frac{x}{2}$$
$$\therefore \frac{x}{2} = 1$$
$$\therefore x = 2.$$

To specify a point completely we need the values of both x and y, so we substitute this value of x into the equation of the graph.

$$\text{When } x = 2, \quad y = 6 - \frac{4}{4} = 5.$$

It follows that the point at which the gradient is 2 is (2,5). ◀

EXERCISE 44b

In the following questions, calculate the gradients of the given graphs at the given points.

1 $y = x^2 - 3x + 5$, at the points where x is $2, 4, -1, -1\frac{1}{2}$.

2 $y = 1 + x - 2x^2$, at the points where x is $1, \frac{1}{2}, -2, -2\frac{1}{2}$.

3 $y = \frac{x^3}{6}$, at the points where x is $4, -3, \frac{1}{2}$.

4 $y = 3x^2 - 2x$, at the points $(1,1)$, $(0,0)$, $(2,8)$, $(-1,5)$.

5 $y = 2x^3 - x^2$, at the points $(2,12)$, $(-1,-3)$, $(\frac{1}{2},0)$.

6 $y = x - \frac{x^2}{4}$, at the points $(4,0)$, $(-2,-3)$, $(-4,-8)$.

7 $y = (2x - 1)(x - 3)$, at the points $(0,3)$, $(\frac{1}{2},0)$, $(2,-3)$, $(-1,12)$.

8 $y = x^2$, at the points where $y = 4$.

9 $y = x^2 - 6x$, at the points where $y = 0$.

10 $y = 2x - x^2$, at the points where $y = 0$.

11 $y = x^2 - x$, at the ponts where $y = 2$.

12 $y = x^2 - 5x$, at the points where $y = -4$.

13 $y = 2x^2 + x$, at the points where $y = 3$.

14 $y = \frac{x^2}{6} - \frac{x}{3}$, at the points where $y = 2\frac{1}{2}$.

15 $y = \frac{x^3}{2}$, at the point where $y = 4$.

16 $y = x^3 + 7$, at the point where $y = -20$.

17 $y = \frac{2}{x}$, at the points $(2,1)$ and $(\frac{1}{2},4)$.

18 $y = \frac{1}{4x^2}$, at the point where $x = \frac{1}{2}$.

19 $y = x - \frac{3}{x}$, at the points where $y = 2$.

20 $y = \frac{1}{2x} - 2x$, at the points where $y = 1\frac{1}{2}$.

Sketch the graphs of the following equations, and find the gradients at the points where they meet the axes:

21 $y = x^2 - 2x$ **22** $y = 4x - x^2$ **23** $y = x^2 - 9$ **24** $y = 3 + 5x - 2x^2$
25 $y = 2x^2 - 11x + 12$

In the following questions, find the co-ordinates of the point or points on the given graph at which the gradient has the given value.

26 $y = x^2$, gradient 6.   **27** $y = x^2 - x$, gradient 3.

28 $y = 2x^2$, gradient -8.   **29** $y = 8x - x^2$, gradient 0.

30 $y = 1 + x - \dfrac{3x^2}{4}$, gradient 4.   **31** $y = x^3$, gradient 12.

32 $y = x^3 + x^2$, gradient 1.   **33** $y = 12x - 3x^2 - x^3$, gradient 3.

34 $y = \dfrac{x^3}{12} - \dfrac{x^2}{4}$, gradient 2.   **35** $y = \dfrac{1}{x}$, gradient $-\dfrac{1}{4}$.

36 $y = \dfrac{2}{x^2}$, gradient 4.   **37** $y = 3 + \dfrac{9}{x^2}$, gradient $-\dfrac{2}{3}$.

38 $y = 2x - \dfrac{1}{2x^2}$, gradient 10.

Maxima and minima

Consider the graph of y against x shown in Fig. 44.4.

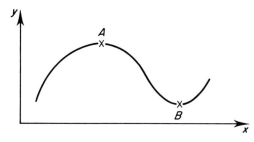

Fig. 44.4

A point such as A is called a *maximum* point, and one such as B is called a *minimum* point. Both kinds of points are known as *turning points.*

It should be noted that although the *points* are called maxima and minima, it is really y (and not x) which has a maximum or minimum value at such points. Thus if $y = f(x)$ is the equation of the graph, the function $f(x)$ has a maximum or minimum value at the graph's turning points.

It should also be noted that the values of y at turning points are *local* and not *absolute* maxima and minima. The value of y at A is greater than the value of y at the points surrounding A, but the graph may rise above the level of A elsewhere.

We can discover the positions of turning points by using the fact that the tangents to the graph are horizontal at these points. This gives the following important rule.

$$\text{At turning points, } \frac{dy}{dx} = 0.$$

Turning points are not the only points at which the gradient is equal to zero. The possibilities shown in Fig. 44.5 should also be noted.

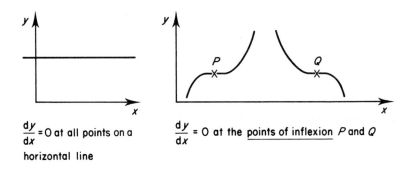

$\dfrac{dy}{dx} = 0$ at all points on a

horizontal line

$\dfrac{dy}{dx} = 0$ at the points of inflexion P and Q

Fig. 44.5

(A point of inflexion is a point at which a graph changes from 'concave-up' to 'concave-down' or vice-versa. It is possible, but not essential, for the tangent to be horizontal at a point of inflexion.)

Tests for turning points, higher differential coefficients

If we differentiate an expression for $\dfrac{dy}{dx}$ we obtain an expression called the *second differential coefficient* of y with respect to x, which is written $\dfrac{d^2y}{dx^2}$ (pronounce 'd two y by dx squared'). Similarly we can define $\dfrac{d^3y}{dx^3}, \dfrac{d^4y}{dx^4}$, etc. For example,

$$\text{if } y = x^4,$$
$$\text{we have } \frac{dy}{dx} = 4x^3,$$
$$\frac{d^2y}{dx^2} = 12x^2, \text{ etc.}$$

Now it can be shown that the second differential coefficient provides a test for the existence of a turning point (given that $\dfrac{dy}{dx} = 0$), and a method of distinguishing between maxima and minima. The rules are as follows.

If $\dfrac{dy}{dx} = 0$ and $\dfrac{d^2y}{dx^2}$ is negative, the point is a maximum.

If $\dfrac{dy}{dx} = 0$ and $\dfrac{d^2y}{dx^2}$ is positive, the point is a minimum.

If $\dfrac{d^2y}{dx^2} = 0$ the test fails and we could have a maximum, a minimum, or some other kind of point such as a point of inflexion. In this case a longer test has to be used, consisting of an examination of the gradient on either side of the point. We shall not deal with any cases of this kind here.

▷**Example 4**

Find the turning point on the graph of $y = x^2 - 4x$ and determine its nature.

$$\text{Since } y = x^2 - 4x,$$
$$\frac{dy}{dx} = 2x - 4.$$

At a turning point $\frac{dy}{dx} = 0$; hence

$$2x - 4 = 0$$
$$\therefore \ x = 2.$$

Now we substitute this value of x into the equation of the graph to find y:

$$\text{When } x = 2, y = 2^2 - 4(2)$$
$$= -4.$$

It follows that there is a possible turning point at $(2, -4)$. To determine its nature more fully we examine $\frac{d^2y}{dx^2}$.

$$\text{Since } \frac{dy}{dx} = 2x - 4,$$
$$\frac{d^2y}{dx^2} = 2.$$

This is positive at all points, so the point $(2, -4)$ is a *minimum*.   ◁

▷**Example 5**

Find the turning points on the graph of $y = 2x^3 - 3x^2 - 12x + 5$ and determine their nature. Sketch the graph.

$$\text{Since } y = 2x^3 - 3x^2 - 12x + 5,$$
$$\frac{dy}{dx} = 6x^2 - 6x - 12.$$

At turning points $\frac{dy}{dy} = 0$; hence we have

$$6x^2 - 6x - 12 = 0$$
$$\therefore \ x^2 - x - 2 = 0$$
$$\therefore \ (x - 2)(x + 1) = 0$$
$$\therefore \ x = 2 \text{ or } -1.$$

Now we find the corresponding values of y.

$$\text{When } x = 2, \ y = 2(2)^3 - 3(2)^2 - 12(2) + 5$$
$$= 16 - 12 - 24 + 5$$
$$= -15.$$

$$\text{When } x = -1, \ y = 2(-1)^3 - 3(-1)^2 - 12(-1) + 5$$
$$= -2 - 3 + 12 + 5$$
$$= 12.$$

It follows that there are possible turning points at $(2,-15)$ and $(-1,12)$. To determine their nature more fully we examine $\dfrac{d^2y}{dx^2}$.

$$\text{Since } \dfrac{dy}{dx} = 6x^2 - 6x - 12,$$
$$\dfrac{d^2y}{dx^2} = 12x - 6.$$

When $x = 2$ this is positive, and when $x = -1$ it is negative. It follows that the point $(2,-15)$ is a minimum, and the point $(-1,12)$ is a maximum. The graph has the form shown in Fig. 44.6.

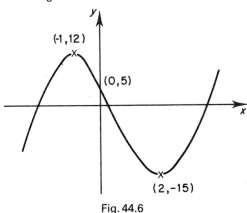

Fig. 44.6

Note: Graphs of cubics in general have two turning points, and thus are of one of the two forms shown in Fig. 44.7.

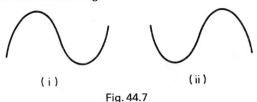

(i)   (ii)

Fig. 44.7

The first form (Fig. 44.7(i)) occurs when the term in x^3 is positive, and the second (Fig. 44.7(ii)) when the term in x^3 is negative.   ◄

EXERCISE 44c

Find the turning points on the graphs of the following equations and determine their nature. Sketch the graphs of questions 1–15.

1 $y = x^2 - 2x$ **2** $y = 4x - x^2$ **3** $y = x^2 + x$ **4** $y = 4 - x^2$

5 $y = 8 - 2x - x^2$ **6** $y = 4x^2 - 4x + 1$ **7** $y = (9 + 2x)(1 - 2x)$

8 $y = x^3 - 3x^2 + 2$ **9** $y = 4 + 3x - x^3$ **10** $y = 10 - 6x^2 - x^3$

11 $y = x^3 - 3x^2 - 9x + 12$ **12** $y = 2x^3 + 3x^2 - 12x - 4$

13 $y = 2 + 6x - 3x^2 - 4x^3$ **14** $y = (1 - x)(1 + 4x + 4x^2)$

15 $y = 2x^3 - 15x^2 + 36x - 20$ **16** $y = x + \dfrac{9}{x}$ **17** $y = \dfrac{x}{4} + \dfrac{1}{x}$

18 $y = 2x - \dfrac{1}{x^2}$ **19** $y = \dfrac{x^2}{8} + \dfrac{2}{x}$ **20** $y = \dfrac{1}{x} - \dfrac{1}{x^2}$.

Practical problems on maxima and minima

The theory of maxima and minima developed above by considering turning points can often be applied to practical problems in which a maximum or minimum value is required. The main difficulty in such problems is the setting up of an equation in the form required for the application of calculus. In the problems considered above, the graphs represented equations of the form $y = f(x)$, and the turning points, located by letting $\frac{dy}{dx} = 0$, indicated maximum or minimum values of the subject of the equation, y. It follows that *if we require the maximum or minimum values of any quantity we must set up an equation in which this quantity is the subject and the other side of the equation consists of a function of one other variable.* If, for example, the equation $A = 2x - x^2$ gives the area of a figure in terms of the length of one of its sides, we can find the maximum area in just the same way as we should find the maximum point on the graph of $y = 2x - x^2$. The maximum area occurs when $\frac{dA}{dx} = 0$ and $\frac{d^2A}{dx^2}$ is negative.

The following series of steps provides a systematic summary of the procedure to be adopted in all maxima and minima problems.

(1) Introduce a letter (if one does not already exist) to denote the quantity whose maximum or minimum value is required.
(2) Set up an equation in which this letter is the subject and the other side of the equation consists of a function of one variable.
(3) Proceed in the same way as when finding turning points on the graph of $y = f(x)$: find the value of y (or the subject of the equation) at which $\frac{dy}{dx} = 0$, and test for a maximum or minimum value of y by examining the sign of $\frac{d^2y}{dx^2}$.

▷ **Example 6**

The velocity of a moving body after t seconds is $(6t^2 - t^3)$ m s^{-1}. Find the maximum velocity.

$$\text{Let } v = 6t^2 - t^3;$$
$$\text{then } \frac{dv}{dt} = 12t - 3t^2.$$

Now v is a maximum or minimum when $\frac{dv}{dt} = 0$, that is when

$$12t - 3t^2 = 0$$
$$\therefore \ 3t(4 - t) = 0$$
$$\therefore \ t = 0 \text{ or } 4.$$

Also $\frac{d^2v}{dt^2} = 12 - 6t$, which is negative when $t = 4$; hence v is a maximum when $t = 4$.

Substituting this value of t into the equation for v, we have

$$v = 6(4)^2 - 4^3$$
$$= 96 - 64$$
$$= 32.$$

It follows that the maximum velocity is 32 m s^{-1}.   ◁

▷ Example 7

Find the maximum area of a rectangle whose perimeter is 20 m.

First we must introduce a letter to denote the area; so let $A = xy$, where x and y are the length and breadth of the rectangle in metres. Now we express A in terms of one variable only. Since the perimeter is 20 m, we have

$$2x + 2y = 20$$
$$\therefore \ x + y = 10$$
$$\therefore \ y = 10 - x$$
$$\therefore \ A = x(10 - x)$$
i.e. $A = 10x - x^2$.

The equation is now in the required form, and we differentiate.

$$\frac{dA}{dx} = 10 - 2x$$
$$= 0 \text{ when } x = 5.$$

Also $\dfrac{d^2A}{dx^2} = -2$, which is negative; hence A is a maximum when $x = 5$.
Substituting $x = 5$ into the equation for A, we have

$$A = 10(5) - 5^2$$
$$= 25,$$

and it follows that the maximum area is 25 m^2. (The maximum area occurs when the rectangle is a square.)   ◁

EXERCISE 44d

1 The distance travelled by a moving body in t seconds is $(6t - t^2)$ m. Find the maximum distance travelled.
2 Find the minimum value of the function $2w^2 + 10w + 15$.
3 The sum of two numbers is 20. Find the maximum value of their product.
4 Find the maximum value of xy, given that $2x + y = 60$.
5 $ABCD$ is a rectangle in which $AB + BC + CD = 12$ m. Letting $AB = x$ metres, show that the area of the rectangle is $(12x - 2x^2)$ m^2, and hence find the maximum area.
6 The velocity of a moving body after t seconds is $(2t^3 - 12t^2)$ m s^{-1}. Find the body's minimum velocity.
7 Find the maximum area of a right-angled triangle, given that the sum of the two short sides is 8 cm.
8 If the sum of two numbers is 20, what is the minimum value of the sum of their squares?

9 The perimeter of a rectangle is 60 cm. Find the minimum area of the square on its diagonal.

10 A rectangular block (cuboid) has a square base of side x cm and a height of h cm. If $x + h = 30$, show that the volume of the block is $(30x^2 - x^3)$ cm^3, and hence find the maximum volume.

11 A square piece of cardboard has sides of 6 cm. Equal squares of side x cm are cut from each of the corners, and the sides of the remainder are folded up to form an open box with a square base. Show that the volume of the box is $(4x^3 - 24x^2 + 36x)$ cm^3, and hence find the maximum volume.

12 Given that the perimeter of the figure shown in Fig. 44.8 is 20 cm, show that the area is $(20x - 5x^2)$ cm^2, and hence find the maximum area.

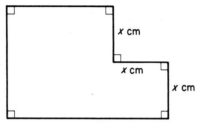

Fig. 44.8

13 The sum of the radius and height of a cylinder is 12 cm. Prove that its maximum volume is 256π cm^3.

14 The radius and height of a cylinder are r cm and h cm, respectively, and $h + 2r = 16$. Prove that the maximum curved surface area is 64π cm^2.

15 The roof of a house forms the surface of a prism whose cross-section is a right-angled isosceles triangle. If the perimeter of each of the sloping faces is 36 m, find the maximum volume enclosed by the roof.

Rate of increase

As well as giving the gradient of the graph of y against x, the function $\dfrac{dy}{dx}$ can be considered to represent a quantity called the *rate of increase of y with respect to x.* To illustrate this idea we will take a practical example. Let h metres be the height of a growing plant and t years the plant's age, and suppose that the plant grows in accordance with the table and graph shown in Fig. 44.9.

t	h
0	0
0.5	1.5
1	2.2
2	3.0
3	3.5
4	3.8
5	4.0

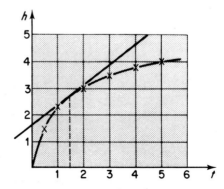

Fig. 44.9

It is not difficult to see that the *steeper* the curve is, the faster the plant is growing. In fact the gradient of the graph at any point represents the *rate of growth,* in metres per year, at that point. For example, at the age of $1\frac{1}{2}$ years, the tangent in Fig. 44.9 indicates a rate of growth of about 1 metre per year. As the plant gets older it grows more slowly, until at the age of about 6 years it stops growing altogether and the graph becomes horizontal.

If a quantity y *decreases* as another quantity x increases, we say that the rate of increase of y with respect to x is negative. Clearly the gradient of the graph will be negative in this case and thus $\frac{dy}{dx}$ will still give the correct rate of increase.

▷ Example 8

While an ink blot is increasing in area, its area is given by the formula $A = 7 + 6t - t^2$, *where A is in cm² and t in seconds. Find (a) the initial area of the blot and the initial rate of increase of the area, (b) the time at which the blot stops growing and its area at that time, (c) the area of the blot when it is increasing at 2 cm² s⁻¹.*

(a) The initial area is the area when $t = 0$, that is 7 cm². To obtain the initial rate of increase of the area, we differentiate the equation for A and then let $t = 0$.

$$\text{Since } A = 7 + 6t - t^2,$$
$$\frac{dA}{dt} = 6 - 2t.$$

Hence, when $t = 0$ we have $\frac{dA}{dt} = 6$, and it follows that the initial rate of increase is 6 cm² s⁻¹.

(b) When the blot stops growing we have $\frac{dA}{dt} = 0$; hence

$$6 - 2t = 0$$
$$\therefore t = 3.$$

It follows that the blot stops growing after 3 s. The area of the blot at this time (which is its maximum area) is obtained by substituting $t = 3$ into the formula for A:

$$A = 7 + 6(3) - 3^2$$
$$= 16,$$

and the area of the blot when it stops growing is therefore 16 cm².

(c) When the rate of increase of the blot is 2 cm² s⁻¹ we have $\frac{dA}{dt} = 2$; hence

$$6 - 2t = 2$$
$$\therefore t = 2.$$

Substitution of this value into the formula for A gives

$$A = 7 + 6(2) - 2^2$$
$$= 15,$$

and it follows that the area of the blot when it is increasing at 2 cm² s⁻¹ is 15 cm².   ◁

EXERCISE 44e

1 The height of a growing tree after t years is $(5t - \frac{1}{4}t^2)$ m. Find (a) its initial rate of growth and its rate of growth after 4 years, (b) the age of the tree when it stops growing and its height at this time.

2 Find (a) the rate of increase of the function $2r^2 - 8r$ with respect to r when $r = 1, 2$ and 3, (b) the value of the function when the rate of increase is 2.

3 The distance x cm travelled by a moving body in t seconds is given by the formula $x = 2t^2 - t$. Find the rate of increase of x with respect to t (i.e. the velocity) after 2 s, and the value of x at which the rate of increase is 19 cm s^{-1}.

4 Liquid is poured into a vessel in such a way that the height after t seconds is $\left(\frac{3t^2}{10} - \frac{t^3}{100}\right)$ cm. Find (a) the rate of increase of the height after 5 s, 10 s and 15 s, (b) the time at which the height stops increasing, (c) the maximum height.

5 The height of a balloon after t seconds is $(10t - \frac{1}{8}t^2)$ m. Find (a) its height value of the greatest height, (c) the rate at which it is rising when it first reaches a height of 150 m.

6 While it is growing, the population of an island after t years is given by the formula $N = 100(125 + 20t - t^2)$. Find (a) the initial population and its initial rate of increase, (b) the time at which the population stops growing and its value at this time, (c) the rate of growth when the population is 20 000, (d) the population when the rate of growth is 400 people per year.

7 The height of a certain object after t seconds is $(2t^2 - 3t + 2)$ m. Find (a) the initial height of the object and the rate at which it is decreasing, (b) the time for which the object is descending, (c) its minimum height, (d) its height when the height is increasing at 1 m s^{-1}.

8 While an ink blot is increasing in area, its area after t seconds is $(2 + 4t - \frac{1}{3}t^3)$cm^2. Find (a) the initial area of the blot and the initial rate of increase of the area, (b) the area when the rate of increase is 3 cm^2 s^{-1}, (c) the maximum area.

9 Liquid is released from a vessel in such a way that the height of liquid in the vessel after t seconds is $(60 - 4t - t^2)$ cm. Find (a) how long the vessel takes to empty, (b) the rate at which the level is falling after 2 s, (c) the rate at which the level is falling when the height is 28 cm, (d) the height when the level is falling at 10 cm s^{-1}.

10 The population of a seaside town, x weeks after July 1, is given by the formula $N = \frac{1}{3}x^3 - 15x^2 + 20\,000$. Show that the population is a maximum on July 1 and falls to a minimum 30 weeks later, and find (a) the minimum population, (b) the rate at which the population is falling after 10 weeks, (c) the size of the population when it is falling at 225 people per week.

45 Integration; Areas and Volumes

Integration is the inverse or 'opposite' operation of differentiation, and it therefore enables us to deduce an expression for y when we are given an expression for $\dfrac{dy}{dx}$. The method for integrating powers of x can be derived as follows. Suppose we have $\dfrac{dy}{dx} = x^5$. We know that differentiation reduces the power by 1, so it is reasonable to start by adding 1 to the power, obtaining x^6. If, however, we differentiate x^6 itself we get $6x^5$, which indicates that we must divide x^6 by 6. We thus obtain $\dfrac{x^6}{6}$ as the required function whose differential coefficient is x^5.

In fact it is not only $\dfrac{x^6}{6}$ which gives x^5 when differentiated. Any function of the form $\dfrac{x^6}{6} + c$, where c is any constant, has the same differential coefficient as $\dfrac{x^6}{6}$ since the differential coefficient of a constant standing alone is zero. The final result is thus

$$\frac{dy}{dx} = x^5,$$

$$y = \frac{x^6}{6} + c.$$

The function $\dfrac{x^6}{6} + c$ is called the *integral* of x^5 with respect to x. The result can be generalised to give the following standard rule.

$$\frac{dy}{dx} = x^n,$$

$$y = \frac{x^{n+1}}{n+1} + c.$$

In words, the rule for integrating can be expressed as follows.

Add 1 to the power and divide by the new power.

The following points should be noted regarding the integration rule:

(1) The integral of a constant k is $kx + c$. Here the original power is 0 and the new power is 1.

(2) The function $\dfrac{1}{x}$ cannot be integrated by the standard rule, since this gives the meaningless expression $\dfrac{x^0}{0}$. The integration of the function $\dfrac{1}{x}$ is an A-Level topic.

▷ **Example 1**

Obtain expressions for y, given (a) $\dfrac{dy}{dx} = 6x^2 - \dfrac{x}{3} + 5$,

(b) $\dfrac{dy}{dx} = (2x - 1)(2x + 1)$, *(c)* $\dfrac{dy}{dx} = \dfrac{6}{x^3}$.

(a) Applying the integration rule to each term, we have

$$y = \frac{6x^3}{3} - \frac{x^2}{2 \times 3} + 5x + c,$$

i.e. $y = 2x^3 - \dfrac{x^2}{6} + 5x + c.$

(b) As in the case of differentiation, we begin by removing the brackets:

$$\frac{dy}{dx} = 4x^2 - 1.$$

Now we integrate term-by-term, obtaining

$$y = \frac{4x^3}{3} - x + c.$$

(c) Again we start in the same way as when differentiating: the power of x is placed on the top line of the fraction.

$$\frac{dy}{dx} = 6x^{-3}.$$

Now the integration rule can be applied:

$$y = \frac{6x^{-2}}{-2} + c,$$

i.e. $y = -\dfrac{3}{x^2} + c.$ ◁

EXERCISE 45a

Obtain expressions for y (integrate):

1 $\dfrac{dy}{dx} = x^7$ **2** $\dfrac{dy}{dx} = x^{11}$ **3** $\dfrac{dy}{dx} = x$ **4** $\dfrac{dy}{dx} = 5$ **5** $\dfrac{dy}{dx} = 9x^2$ **6** $\dfrac{dy}{dx} = 0$

7 $\dfrac{dy}{dx} = \dfrac{x^3}{2}$ **8** $\dfrac{dy}{dx} = \dfrac{6x^2}{5}$ **9** $\dfrac{dy}{dx} = 1\frac{1}{3}x^3$ **10** $\dfrac{dy}{dx} = 1\frac{1}{2}x^5$ **11** $\dfrac{dy}{dx} = 2x - 1$

12 $\dfrac{dy}{dx} = 3x^2 - 4x + 7$ **13** $\dfrac{dy}{dx} = 2x(4x - 1)$ **14** $\dfrac{dy}{dx} = 1\frac{1}{2}x(3x - 1)$

15 $\dfrac{dy}{dx} = 2 - \dfrac{x}{5} - \dfrac{3x^2}{4}$ **16** $\dfrac{dy}{dx} = \dfrac{4x^2 - x}{x}$ **17** $\dfrac{dy}{dx} = \dfrac{9x^3 - 2x}{3x}$

18 $\dfrac{dy}{dx} = \dfrac{(3x-1)(x^2-x)}{2x}$　**19** $\dfrac{dy}{dx} = \dfrac{1}{x^2}$　**20** $\dfrac{dy}{dx} = -\dfrac{4}{x^3}$　**21** $\dfrac{dy}{dx} = \dfrac{1}{2x^4}$

22 $\dfrac{dy}{dx} = -\dfrac{2}{5x^3}$　**23** $\dfrac{dy}{dx} = \dfrac{2x^5-6}{x^4}$　**24** $\dfrac{dy}{dx} = \left(x^2 - \dfrac{3}{x^2}\right)^2$

The geometrical meaning of the constant c

Suppose we have $\dfrac{dy}{dx} = 2$, which states that the gradient of a graph is constant and equal to 2. The graph is clearly a straight line, since only straight line graphs have gradients which are independent of x, but no *particular* straight line is specified by the information given: all we know is that the line is one of the family of parallel lines with gradient 2 (Fig. 45.1).

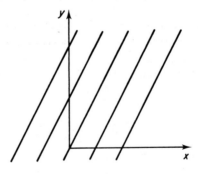

Fig. 45.1

We would expect, therefore, that when the expression for $\dfrac{dy}{dx}$ is integrated to give an equation for y in terms of x, we shall not get a completely definite result. In fact we obtain $y = 2x + c$, which again represents the family of lines with gradient 2. The constant c has a definite value for each individual member of the family, but changes when we move from one line to another.

　　The value of c becomes definite when we are given some further piece of information, such as the fact that the graph passes through a fixed point. The following example shows how c can then be calculated.

▷**Example 2**

A certain graph passes through the point $(-1,2)$, and its gradient at all points is given by the expression $6x^2 - 2x + 1$. Find the equation of the graph.

We have

$$\frac{dy}{dx} = 6x^2 - 2x + 1.$$

Hence, integrating,

$$y = 2x^3 - x^2 + x + c.$$

Now since the graph passes through the point $(-1,2)$, we know that when $x = -1$, $y = 2$. Hence, substituting these values into the equation for y, we have

$$2 = 2(-1)^3 - (-1)^2 - 1 + c$$
$$\therefore \ 2 = -2 - 1 - 1 + c$$
$$\therefore \ c = 6.$$

It follows that the equation of the graph is

$$y = 2x^3 - x^2 + x + 6.$$

◁

EXERCISE 45b

Find the equations of the graphs with the given properties. In each case the expression for $\dfrac{dy}{dx}$ represents the gradient at all points.

1 $\dfrac{dy}{dx} = 2$, graph passes through (1,5).

2 $\dfrac{dy}{dx} = 3$, graph passes through $(-1,4)$.

3 $\dfrac{dy}{dx} = -1$, graph passes through (2,1).

4 $\dfrac{dy}{dx} = \dfrac{1}{2}$, graph passes through $(-2,5)$.

5 $\dfrac{dy}{dx} = \dfrac{2}{3}$, graph passes through $(3,4\frac{1}{3})$.

6 $\dfrac{dy}{dx} = -1\frac{1}{2}$, graph passes through $(-4,6)$.

7 $\dfrac{dy}{dx} = 2x - 1$, graph passes through (2,4).

8 $\dfrac{dy}{dx} = 4x + 3$, graph passes through $(-1,-1)$.

9 $\dfrac{dy}{dx} = 2 - x$, graph passes through (2,3).

10 $\dfrac{dy}{dx} = \dfrac{1-x}{3}$, graph passes through $(3,\frac{1}{2})$.

11 $\dfrac{dy}{dx} = 6x^2 - 2x$, graph passes through $(-1,-6)$.

12 $\dfrac{dy}{dx} = (3x - 1)(x + 1)$, graph passes through (2,11).

13 $\dfrac{dy}{dx} = \dfrac{9x^3 - 4x^2 - x}{2x}$, graph passes through (1,1).

14 $\dfrac{dy}{dx} = \dfrac{(3x^2 - 2x)(3x + 4)}{x}$, graph passes through $(-2,9)$.

15 $\dfrac{dy}{dx} = -\dfrac{8}{x^3}$, graph passes through (2,3).

16 $\dfrac{dy}{dx} = 2 + \dfrac{1}{3x^2}$, graph passes through $\left(\dfrac{1}{3}, -\dfrac{1}{3}\right)$.

Definite and indefinite integrals

The symbol for the integral of a function f(x) with respect to x is $\int f(x)dx$.
Thus, for example, we have

$$\int x^2 dx = \frac{x^3}{3} + c, \quad \text{and} \quad \int (2x - 1)dx = x^2 - x + c.$$

The symbol $\int (\quad)dx$ must be thought of as a *single* symbol which tells
us to integrate with respect to x whatever function is placed between the
integral sign $\int$ and the dx. Brackets are needed when the function to be
integrated contains more than one term.

Because of the presence of the constant c after the integration has been
performed, an expression such as $\int x^2 dx$ is called an *indefinite* integral. On
the other hand an expression such as

$$\int_1^4 xdx$$

is called a *definite* integral. Unlike indefinite integrals, this expression has
a *numerical value*, which is obtained as follows. First we integrate the
function x, *omitting the constant c* and obtaining $\frac{x^2}{2}$. Then we substitute
the values 4 and 1 into this function, and finally subtract the second result
from the first. The working is set out as follows:

$$\int_1^4 xdx = \left[\frac{x^2}{2}\right]_1^4 = \frac{16}{2} - \frac{1}{2} = 7\frac{1}{2}.$$

The numbers 4 and 1 are called the *limits* of the integral.

Here is a more difficult example.

$$\int_{-2}^3 (8x^3 + 2x^2 - 1)dx = \left[2x^4 + \frac{2x^3}{3} - x\right]_{-2}^3$$

$$= (162 + \frac{54}{3} - 3) - (32 - \frac{16}{3} + 2)$$

$$= 177 - 28\frac{2}{3} = 148\frac{1}{3}.$$

EXERCISE 45c

Evaluate the following definite integrals.

1 $\int_2^4 xdx$ **2** $\int_0^3 x^2 dx$ **3** $\int_1^2 4xdx$ **4** $\int_{-1}^1 6x^2 dx$ **5** $\int_{-2}^3 2dx$ **6** $\int_0^2 2x^3 dx$

7 $\int_{-2}^2 8x^3 dx$ **8** $\int_3^6 \frac{x^2}{2}dx$ **9** $\int_{-1}^2 (2x - 1)dx$ **10** $\int_{-2}^4 (3 - x)dx$

11 $\int_{-1}^3 (6x - 5)dx$ **12** $\int_3^{12} (1 - \frac{x}{3})dx$ **13** $\int_0^4 (3x^2 - 2x + 4)dx$

14 $\int_{1}^{2} (x^3 - \frac{3x}{4}) dx$ **15** $\int_{2}^{3} (x^2 + x + 3) dx$ **16** $\int_{-1}^{1} (2x + 1)(3x - 4) dx$

17 $\int_{1}^{2} \frac{2x^3 - 3x^2 - x}{x} dx$ **18** $\int_{-1}^{2} (1 - x)(2x + 3x^2) dx$ **19** $\int_{1/2}^{1} \frac{1}{4x^3} dx$

20 $\int_{1}^{2} \frac{12}{x^4} dx$ **21** $\int_{2}^{4} (2 - \frac{8}{x^3}) dx$ **22** $\int_{1/3}^{1} \frac{x^2 - 1}{x^4} dx.$

The area 'under' a curve

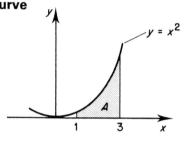

Fig. 45.2

Fig. 45.2 shows a sketch of the graph of $y = x^2$. The shaded area A is called the area 'under' the graph between the lines $x = 1$ and $x = 3$, and its value is given by the definitive integral

$$\int_{1}^{3} x^2 dx.$$

In general, the area under a graph is the area between the graph, the x-axis and a pair of vertical lines. Fig. 45.3 and the accompanying standard formula refer to the case in which the lines have equations $x = a$ and $x = b$.

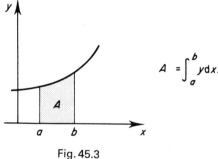

$$A = \int_{a}^{b} y dx.$$

Fig. 45.3

Points to note

(1) The y in the formula stands for the function of x which is equated to y in the equation of the graph. Thus if the equation of the graph is $y = x^2$, any area under the graph is given by $\int x^2 dx$ with appropriate limits.

(2) The lower value of x is always placed at the bottom of the integral, and the higher value is placed at the top. Note that the limits must be values of x, and not y.

(3) When the area being found is *below* the x-axis (as in example 3, below), the standard formula gives a *negative* result for the area. Usually however we only require the numerical value of the area, so the minus is ignored.

▷ **Example 3**

Find the area between the graph of y = x² − 2x and the x-axis.

The graph is a parabola with a minimum, as shown in Fig. 45.4.

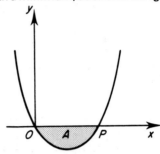

Fig. 45.4

In this case the vertical lines defining the area are of zero length. We begin by finding the value of x at P.

At O and P the value of y is zero; hence

$$x^2 - 2x = 0$$
$$\therefore \quad x(x - 2) = 0$$
$$\therefore \quad x = 0 \text{ or } 2.$$

Now using the standard formula $A = \int y dx$, we have

$$A = \int_0^2 (x^2 - 2x)dx$$
$$= \left[\frac{x^3}{3} - x^2\right]_0^2$$
$$= \frac{8}{3} - 4$$
$$= -1\tfrac{1}{3}.$$

The minus appears because the area is *below* the x-axis, and it can be ignored. The required area is therefore $1\tfrac{1}{3}$ square units.   ◀

The difference between two areas

Sometimes an area is required which is not itself bounded by the x-axis but which can be regarded as the difference between two areas of this kind.

▷ **Example 4**

Sketch the graphs of y = 5 + 4x − x² and y = 5, and find the area between these two graphs.

Solution of the quadratic equation $5 + 4x - x^2 = 0$ gives $x = -1$ or 5, so the first graph cuts the x-axis at $(-1,0)$ and $(5,0)$. Also this graph cuts the y-axis at $(0,5)$. The graph of $y = 5$ is a horizontal line through the point $(0,5)$, so the two graphs are as shown in Fig. 45.5.

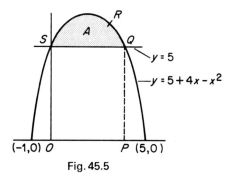

Fig. 45.5

To find the shaded area A we drop the perpendicular QP, as shown, and calculate the difference between the area under the curve $(OPQRS)$ and the area of the rectangle $OPQS$. For both of these areas we need the value of x at Q, which (together with S) is a point at which the equations $y = 5$ and $y = 5 + 4x - x^2$ are simultaneously true.

At S and Q we have

$$5 = 5 + 4x - x^2$$
$$\therefore \quad x^2 - 4x = 0$$
$$\therefore \quad x(x - 4) = 0$$
$$\therefore \quad x = 0 \text{ or } 4.$$

Clearly S is the point $(0,5)$ and Q is the point $(4,5)$. Now we find the areas between the two graphs and the x-axis.

$$\text{Area of region } OPQRS = \int_0^4 (5 + 4x - x^2)dx$$
$$= \left[5x + 2x^2 - \frac{x^3}{3} \right]_0^4$$
$$= (20 + 32 - \frac{64}{3}) - 0$$
$$= 30\frac{2}{3} .$$

$$\text{Area of rectangle } OPQS = \text{length} \times \text{breadth}$$
$$= 4 \times 5$$
$$= 20.$$

$$\text{Hence required area } A = 30\frac{2}{3} - 20 = 10\frac{2}{3} \text{ square units.} \quad \triangleleft$$

EXERCISE 45d

Find the areas between the given graphs, lines and points. Sketch the required region in each case.

1 $y = 2x$, the lines $x = 1$, $x = 3$ and the x-axis.

2 $y = 6x^2$, the lines $x = 1$, $x = 2$ and the x-axis.
3 $y = x^3$, the line $x = 2$ and the x-axis.
4 $y = 4x + 3$, the lines $x = 1$, $x = 3$ and the x-axis.
5 $y = \frac{x}{2} + 1$, the lines $x = 2$, $x = 4$ and the x-axis.
6 $y = x^2 + 1$, the line $x = 3$, the x-axis and the y-axis.
7 $y = x^2 - 4x$ and the x-axis.
8 $y = 3x - x^2$ and the x-axis.
9 $y = 6 + x - x^2$, the line $x = 1$, the x-axis and the y-axis.
10 $y = x^3 + 8$, the lines $x = -1$, $x = 2$ and the x-axis.
11 $y = 4 - x^2$, the point $(-2,0)$, the line $x = 1$ and the x-axis.
12 $y = x^2 - x - 2$ and the x-axis.
13 $y = (2 + x)(4 - x)$ and the x-axis.
14 $y = x^2$ and $y = 2x$.
15 $y = x^2$, the line $y = 4$ and the y-axis.
16 $y = x(x^2 - 5x + 6)$, the points $(0,0)$, $(2,0)$ and the x-axis.
17 $y = \frac{5}{4} + 2x - x^2$, the x-axis, the y-axis and the line $x = 2$.
18 $y = 4x - x^2$, the line $y = 4$ and the y-axis.
19 $y = \frac{3}{2} + \frac{5x}{2} - x^2$, the x-axis, the y-axis and the point at which the curve meets the positive x-axis.
20 $y = \frac{x^2}{2}$ and the line $y = 8$.
21 $y = 16x - x^3$, the lines $x = 1$, $x = 3$ and the x-axis.
22 $y = 4x - x^2$ and the line $y = 3$.
23 $y = 6 - 5x - x^2$ and the line $y = 6$.
24 $y = 8x - x^2$ and $y = 4x$.
25 $y = x^3$, the origin, the line $y = 5x$ and the line $x = 2$.
26 $y = 12 - 3x^2$, the horizontal line through the maximum point of this curve, and the line $x = 2$.
27 $y = 7x - x^2$, $y = 2x$ and the lines $x = 1$, $x = 3$.
28 $y = x^2 - 6x$, the y-axis and the lines $x = 3$, $y = 4$.
29 $y = 6 + 5x - x^2$ and $y + x = 6$.
30 $y = 9 + 16x - 4x^2$, the horizontal line through the maximum point of this curve, and the y-axis.

Volumes of revolution

When every point on a section of a graph is rotated through 360° about the x-axis, the resulting figure is called a *volume of revolution* or a *solid of revolution*. For example, when a straight line through the origin is rotated we get a *cone*, and when the graph of $y = x^2$ is rotated a *horn-shaped* figure results (Fig. 45.6).

It can be shown that when the section of a graph between $x = a$ and $x = b$ is rotated about the x-axis, the volume of the resulting figure is given by the following formula.

$$V = \int_b^a \pi y^2 dx.$$

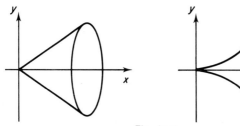

Fig. 45.6

Points to note

(1) As in the case of areas, if $y = f(x)$ is the equation of the graph, the y in the volume formula stands for $f(x)$.
(2) When a volume is calculated, the constant π comes through every step in the integration unchanged, and is therefore best kept outside the integration sign. The final answer is usually left as a multiple of π.
(3) Volumes of revolution are always positive.

▷ **Example 5**

Find the volume of the solid formed when the region between the graph of $y = 2x - x^2$ and the x-axis is rotated about the x-axis.

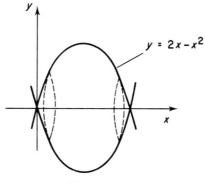

Fig. 45.7

Solution of the quadratic equation $2x - x^2 = 0$ gives $x = 0$ or 2; hence the graph (Fig. 45.7) cuts the x-axis at (0,0) and (2,0). The volume of revolution is therefore given by

$$V = \pi \int_0^2 (2x - x^2)^2 \, dx$$

$$= \pi \int_0^2 (4x^2 - 4x^3 + x^4) \, dx$$

$$= \pi \left[\frac{4x^3}{3} - x^4 + \frac{x^5}{5} \right]_0^2$$

$$= \pi \left(\frac{32}{3} - 16 + \frac{32}{5} \right)$$

$$= 1\frac{1}{15} \pi \text{ cubic units.}$$

◀

▷ **Example 6**

Find the volume of the solid formed when the region between the graph of $y^2 = 8x$, the line $y = 4$ and the y-axis is rotated about the x-axis.

Since the graph of the equation $y = ax^2 + bx + c$ is a vertical parabola, that of $x = ay^2 + by + c$ is a horizontal parabola. The equation $y^2 = 8x$ in fact represents a horizontal parabola through the origin with the x-axis as axis of symmetry, and the region to be rotated is as shown in Fig. 45.8.

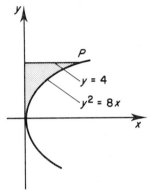

Fig. 45.8

We begin by finding the value of x at P, by treating the equations $y^2 = 8x$ and $y = 4$ as simultaneous.

$$\text{At } P, \quad 4^2 = 8x$$
$$\therefore \quad x = 2$$

Now the required volume of revolution is the difference between the volume of revolution of the line $y = 4$ and that of the curve $y^2 = 8x$.

$$\text{Volume of revolution of line} = \pi \int_0^2 16dx$$

$$= \pi \left[16x \right]_0^2$$

$$= 32\,\pi.$$

$$\text{Volume of revolution of curve} = \pi \int_0^2 8xdx$$

$$= \pi \left[4x^2 \right]_0^2$$

$$= 16\,\pi.$$

It follows that the required volume is $32\,\pi - 16\,\pi = 16\,\pi$ cubic units.   ◁

EXERCISE 45e

Find the volumes of the solids formed when the regions between the following graphs and lines are rotated about the x-axis. Leave the answers as multiples of π.

1 $y = 3x$, the lines $x = 1$, $x = 2$ and the x-axis.
2 $y = \sqrt{x}$, the lines $x = 2$, $x = 4$ and the x-axis.
3 $y = x^2$, the line $x = 2$ and the x-axis.
4 $y^2 = 2x$, the lines $x = 5$, $x = 3$ and the x-axis.
5 $y^2 = 3x + 1$, the line $x = 4$, the x-axis and the y-axis.
6 $y = 3x + 1$, the line $x = 2$, the x-axis and the y-axis.
7 $y = 3x - 2$, the lines $x = 1$, $x = 2$ and the x-axis.
8 $y = 6 - 3x$, the x-axis and the y-axis.
9 $y^2 = x + 4$, the x-axis and the y-axis.
10 $y = \frac{x}{2} + 1$, the lines $x = -1$, $x = 2$ and the x-axis.
11 $y = x^2 - x$ and the x-axis.
12 $y = 3x - x^2$ and the x-axis.
13 $y^2 = 2x$ and $y = x$.
14 $y = x^2$ and $y = 3x$.
15 $y^2 = x$, the line $y = 2$ and the y-axis.
16 $y = x^2$, the line $y = 4$ and the y-axis.
17 The lines $y = \frac{3x}{2}$, $y = 3x$ and $x = 4$.
18 $y^2 = 2x + 5$, the line $y = 3$ and the y-axis.
19 $y = 2x - x^2$, the line $y = 1$ and the y-axis.
20 $y^2 = 3x + 4$, $y = x$ and the y-axis.
21 $y = 3x - x^2$ and the line $y = 2$.
22 $y = 6x - x^2$ and $y = 3x$.
23 $y = \frac{1}{x}$, the lines $x = 1$, $x = 2$ and the x-axis.
24 $y = \frac{3}{x^2}$, the lines $x = \frac{1}{2}$, $x = 1$ and the x-axis.

Approximations to definite integrals, the trapezium rule

An area under a graph cannot always be obtained by integration. Sometimes the graph cannot be represented by an equation of the form $y = f(x)$ at all, and even when this can be done it is not always possible to integrate the function of x. We therefore require methods of approximating areas under graphs, and here we consider one of the simplest of these, called the *trapezium rule*.

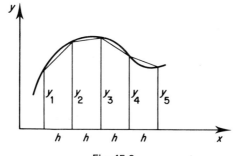

Fig. 45.9

The trapezium rule is based on the idea of dividing up the required area into regions of equal width, and approximating each region to a trapezium. In other words, we regard each section of the graph as a straight line. In Fig. 45.9 the required area is divided into 4 regions, but any number can be taken and the approximation improves as the number of regions is increased.

Since the area of a trapezium is given by the expression *average of parallel sides x height*, the area shown is approximately

$$\left(\frac{y_1 + y_2}{2}\right)h + \left(\frac{y_2 + y_3}{2}\right)h + \left(\frac{y_3 + y_4}{2}\right)h + \left(\frac{y_4 + y_5}{2}\right)h,$$

which reduces to

$$h\left[\frac{y_1 + y_5}{2} + y_2 + y_3 + y_4\right].$$

In words, the general trapezium rule can be expressed as follows.

Take the average of the first and last values of y, add all the other values, and multiply by the width of each region, h.

The trapezium rule is not limited to finding areas under graphs: since it is possible to regard any definite integral as representing such an area, any definite integral can be approximated by the use of the trapezium rule.

The integral in the following example would not in practice be evaluated by the trapezium rule, but the example is designed to show how the value given by this method approaches the exact value more and more closely as the number of values of y is increased.

▶ **Example 7**

Evaluate the integral $\int_1^5 x^2 dx$ *(a) by ordinary integration, (b) by using the trapezium rule with 5 values of y, (c) by using the trapezium rule with 9 values of y.*

(a) We have

$$\int_1^5 x^2 \, dx = \left[\frac{x^3}{3}\right]_1^5 = \frac{125}{3} - \frac{1}{3} = 41\tfrac{1}{3}.$$

This is of course the exact value of the integral.

(b) To use the trapezium rule we first let y denote the function being integrated (x^2), and then make a table of values of y against values of x:

x	1	2	3	4	5
y	1	4	9	16	25

Now the trapezium rule gives

$$\int_1^5 x^2 dx \approx 1\left[\frac{1+25}{2} + 4 + 9 + 16\right]$$
$$= 13 + 4 + 9 + 16$$
$$= 42.$$

(c) If we let the width of each region be $\frac{1}{2}$ instead of 1, we obtain 9 values of y:

x	1	1.5	2	2.5	3	3.5	4	4.5	5
y	1	2.25	4	6.25	9	12.25	16	20.25	25

Now the trapezium rule gives

$$\int_1^5 x^2 dx \approx \frac{1}{2}\left[\frac{1+25}{2} + 2.25 + 4 + 6.25 + 9 + 12.25 + 16 + 20.25\right]$$

$$= 41.5.$$

The second approximation is quite near to the correct value of $41\frac{1}{3}$.   ◀

EXERCISE 45f

1 Evaluate the integral $\int_1^5 (2x + 1)dx$ by using the trapezium rule with 5 values of y. Check by ordinary integration that in this case the trapezium rule gives the exact value of the integral. Why is this?

2 Some of the points on a graph of y against x are $(2,7)$, $(2\frac{1}{2},8)$, $(3,10)$ and $(3\frac{1}{2},13)$. Use the trapezium rule with $h = \frac{1}{2}$ to estimate the value of the integral

$$\int_2^{3\,1/2} y\,dx.$$

3 Evaluate the integral $\int_0^2 (4 - x^2)dx$ (a) by ordinary integration, (b) by the trapezium rule with $h = 1$, (c) by the trapezium rule with $h = \frac{1}{2}$.

4 Sketch the graph of $y = x^2 + 1$ for the range $0 \leqslant x \leqslant 4$, and use the trapezium rule with 9 values of y to obtain an approximation to $\int_0^4 (x^2 + 1)dx$.

By considering the shape of the graph, say whether the approximate answer is more or less than the exact answer.

5 Use the trapezium rule with $h = 0.2$ to estimate the value of $\int_4^5 \sqrt{x - 2}\,dx$.

Work to 4 significant figures in the calculation and give the final answer to 3 significant figures.

6 Sketch the graph of $y = 6x - x^2$ for the range $0 \leqslant x \leqslant 6$. Use the trapezium rule with $h = \frac{1}{2}$ to estimate the value of $\int_0^3 (6x - x^2)dx$. Is the approximate answer more or less than the exact answer?

7 A graph of y against x is drawn from the following data:

x	0	0.2	0.4	0.6	0.8	1
y	12	15.4	17.6	18.3	18.8	19.2

Use the trapezium rule to estimate the area under the graph (a) between the y-axis and the line $x = 0.6$, (b) between the lines $x = 0.2$ and $x = 1$.

8 Use the trapezium rule with $h = 0.2$ to estimate the value of $\int_0^1 \dfrac{1}{2x + 3}\, dx$.

Work to 4 significant figures in the calculation and give the final answer to 3 significant figures.

9 It can be shown that the distance travelled by a moving body is given by $\int v\, dt$, where v is the body's velocity. Use the trapezium rule to estimate the distance travelled in 3 seconds by a body whose velocity varies as follows:

t (seconds)	0	0.5	1	1.5	2	2.5	3
v (m s^{-1})	8	9.6	11	12.3	13.5	14.6	15.5

10 Use the trapezium rule with $h = 0.1$ to estimate the value of $\int_1^2 \dfrac{2x + 1}{2x - 1}\, dx$.

Work to 4 significant figures in the calculation and give the final answer to 3 significant figures.

46 Kinematics

Kinematics is the mathematical study of moving bodies. We started the topic in chapter 5, where we considered motion with constant speed. This is the simplest type of motion, and it is dealt with by the single formula

$$\text{speed} = \frac{\text{distance}}{\text{time}}.$$

When the speed is not constant this formula no longer holds, and the analysis of the motion requires the use of calculus.

The general relationship between distance and velocity

Suppose a body is moving in a straight line with a constant velocity of 2 m s^{-1}. Letting s metres be the total distance covered in a time of t seconds, we can draw up the following table for values of s against values of t:

t	0	1	2	3
s	0	2	4	6

From this table it is clear that the graph of s against t is a straight line (Fig. 46.1).

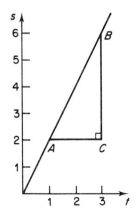

Fig. 46.1

Consider now what feature of this graph represents the velocity of the body, that is the quantity $\dfrac{\text{distance travelled}}{\text{time taken}}$. When the body moves from the point represented by A to that represented by B, the distance travelled is given by BC and the time taken by AC. It follows that the velocity is given by the *gradient* of the graph, $\dfrac{BC}{AC}$. In this case the gradient is 2 and the velocity is $2\,\text{m s}^{-1}$.

When the velocity is not constant the graph of s against t is no longer a straight line. It is not difficult to see, however, that the velocity at any particular point will now be represented by the gradient of the *tangent* to the graph at that point. One way to justify this reasoning is to regard a curved graph as made up of many short lines (Fig. 46.2).

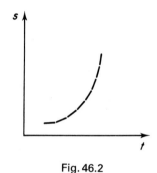

Fig. 46.2

The body represented in Fig. 46.2 is moving with a succession of speeds which are constant for very short periods, each speed being given by the gradient of one of the small straight lines. Since the gradients are increasing as time increases, the body is accelerating. Clearly as the lines are made smaller and smaller, the graph approximates more and more closely to a smooth curve in which the gradient of the tangent represents the velocity at any particular point.

Since the gradient of a graph of s against t is given by $\dfrac{ds}{dt}$, it follows that velocity is given by this quantity. Hence, denoting the velocity by $v\,\text{m s}^{-1}$, we have the following important result:

$$v = \frac{ds}{dt}.$$

In words, the velocity of a body can be defined as the *rate of increase of distance with respect to time*.

The signs of s, v, t

The quantities, s, v, t are all *signed* quantities; that is they can all be positive or negative. When a body is moving in a straight line one of the directions of the line is taken as positive and the other as negative, just as in the case of an x-axis or number line:

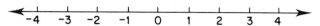

In the above diagram the positive direction is 'to the right' and the negative direction is 'to the left'. Thus, for example, if a body is positioned 3 units to the left of 0 the value of s is -3, and if it is moving at 4 units per second to the right its velocity is $+4$. The quantities *distance* and *velocity* are quite independent of each other, and the sign of one of them has no influence on that of the other. The sign of s depends only on the body's *position* (relative to 0), and the sign of v depends only upon its *direction of motion*.

The quantity *speed*, which is virtually synonymous with *velocity* in everyday usage, is used in mathematics and science to mean the *numerical value* of velocity, that is the value of the velocity without its sign. Thus if a body is moving at 2 m s^{-1} in the negative direction, its velocity is -2 m s^{-1} and its speed is 2 m s^{-1}.

The sign of t does not depend on direction; this quantity is positive or negative according to whether the moment in question is before or after the starting point of the motion — the point from which t is measured. In many problems negative values of t can be discarded as they correspond to times before the motion started.

▷ Example 1

A body starts at a point P, and moves according to the equation
$s = 4t + 2t^2 - t^3$, *where s metres is the distance of the body from P after t seconds. Find (a) the distance from P after 3 seconds, (b) the velocity at this time, (c) the initial velocity, (d) the time at which the velocity is zero, (e) the distance from P at this time.*

(a)
$$\text{When } t = 3, \quad s = 4(3) + 2(3)^2 - 3^3$$
$$= 12 + 18 - 27$$
$$= 3.$$

Hence, after 3 s, the body is 3 m from P in the positive direction.

(b)
$$\text{Since } s = 4t + 2t^2 - t^3,$$
$$v = \frac{ds}{dt} = 4 + 4t - 3t^2.$$
$$\text{Hence, when } t = 3, \quad v = 4 + 4(3) - 3(3)^2$$
$$= 4 + 12 - 27$$
$$= -11.$$

It follows that after 3 s, the body is moving at 11 m s^{-1} in the negative direction.

(c) The initial velocity is the velocity when $t = 0$. At this time we have $v = 4$, and it follows that the initial velocity is 4 m s^{-1} in the positive direction.

(d) When $v = 0$ we have

$$4 + 4t - 3t^2 = 0$$
$$\therefore \quad (2 + 3t)(2 - t) = 0$$
$$\therefore \quad t = -\frac{2}{3} \text{ or } 2.$$

The negative solution corresponds to a time before the motion started, and can be discarded. Hence the velocity is zero 2 s after the starting point.

(e) When $t = 2$ we have

$$s = 4(2) + 2(2)^2 - 2^3$$
$$= 8 + 8 - 8$$
$$= 8.$$

It follows that the body is 8 m from P when its velocity is zero.   ◀

Acceleration

The following table shows values of velocity against those of time for a body which is gaining velocity at a steady rate.

t(s)	0	1	2	3
v(m s^{-1})	0	5	10	15

The body is clearly gaining 5 m s^{-1} every second, and we say that its acceleration is *5 metres per second per second*, or *5 m s^{-2}*. The graph of velocity against time is a straight line, with a gradient of 5 (Fig. 46.3).

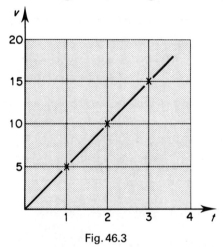

Fig. 46.3

When the graph is not a straight line the acceleration is no longer constant, but we still consider the gradient at any point to represent the acceleration at that point. (The reasoning is the same as that given for the distance–time graph.) In other words we define acceleration (a) to be the *rate of increase of velocity with respect to time*, and thus have

$$a = \frac{dv}{dt}.$$

Like s and v, a is a signed quantity, being positive or negative according to the direction in which velocity is being gained.

We can sum up the relationships between the quantities s, v, a and t as follows:

$$s = \text{distance, measured in m,}$$

$$v = \frac{ds}{dt} = \text{velocity, measured in m s}^{-1},$$

$$a = \frac{dv}{dt} = \text{acceleration, measured in m s}^{-2}.$$

▷ Example 2

A body moves according to the equation $v = 8t - t^2$, v metres per second being the velocity after t seconds. Find (a) the velocity when the acceleration is $2\,m\,s^{-2}$, (b) the acceleration when the velocity is $12\,m\,s^{-1}$.

(a) Since $v = 8t - t^2$,

$$a = \frac{dv}{dt} = 8 - 2t.$$

Hence when $a = 2$, we have

$$8 - 2t = 2$$
$$\therefore \quad 2t = 6$$
$$\therefore \quad t = 3.$$

Now we substitute this value into the formula for v. When $t = 3$ we have

$$v = 8(3) - 3^2$$
$$= 24 - 9$$
$$= 15.$$

It follows that when the acceleration is $2\,m\,s^{-2}$ the velocity is $15\,m\,s^{-1}$.
(b) When the velocity is $12\,m\,s^{-1}$, we have

$$12 = 8t - t^2$$
$$\therefore \quad t^2 - 8t + 12 = 0$$
$$\therefore \quad (t - 2)(t - 6) = 0$$
$$\therefore \quad t = 2 \text{ or } 6.$$

Now we substitute these values into the formula for a:

$$\text{When } t = 2, \quad a = 8 - 2(2)$$
$$= 4.$$
$$\text{When } t = 6, \quad a = 8 - 2(6)$$
$$= -4.$$

It follows that when the velocity is $12\,m\,s^{-1}$ the acceleration is $\pm 4\,m\,s^{-2}$.   ◁

▷ Example 3

A body thrown vertically upwards moves according to the equation $h = 15 + 10t - 5t^2$, where h metres is the height of the body above ground level after t seconds. Find (a) the initial height of the body, (b) the greatest height it reaches, (c) the acceleration, (d) the total time the body takes to return to its starting point, (e) the total time it takes to reach the ground.

(a) The word 'initial' means 'at the beginning' and always implies that $t = 0$. Substituting $t = 0$ into the formula for h we get $h = 15$; hence the initial height is 15 m.

(b) It can be seen in two ways that the greatest height occurs when $v = 0$. Firstly, if we think about a body thrown upwards, it is clear that its velocity steadily decreases as it rises, *becomes instantaneously zero at the highest point*, and then becomes negative as the body starts to descend. (We are taking the upward direction as positive.) Secondly, we know from the theory of maxima and minima (see chapter 43) that if y is a function of x, y has its maximum or minimum values when $\frac{dy}{dx} = 0$. It follows by similar reasoning that if h is a function of t, h has its maximum or minimum values when $\frac{dh}{dt}$, that is the velocity, is zero.

$$\text{Since } h = 15 + 10t - 5t^2,$$
$$v = \frac{dh}{dt} = 10 - 10t$$
$$= 0 \text{ when } t = 1.$$

Now substituting $t = 1$ into the formula for h, we have

$$h = 15 + 10 - 5$$
$$= 20,$$

and it follows that the greatest height is 20 m.

(c)
$$\text{Since } v = 10 - 10t$$
$$a = -10.$$

It follows that the body moves with a constant downward acceleration of $10\,\text{m s}^{-2}$.

(d) The body starts at a height of 15 m, so to find the time it takes to return to this height we substitute $h = 15$ into the formula for h:

$$15 = 15 + 10t - 5t^2$$
$$\therefore \quad 5t^2 - 10t = 0$$
$$\therefore \quad 5t(t - 2) = 0$$
$$\therefore \quad t = 0 \text{ or } 2.$$

Clearly $t = 0$ is the time at the start of the motion, so $t = 2$ must give the time the body takes to return. It follows that the total time the body takes to return to its starting point is 2 s.

(e) Since h metres is the height of the body above ground level, the body is at ground level when $h = 0$. Hence we have

$$15 + 10t - 5t^2 = 0$$
$$\therefore \quad t^2 - 2t - 3 = 0$$
$$\therefore \quad (t - 3)(t + 1) = 0$$
$$\therefore \quad t = 3 \text{ or } -1.$$

The negative solution represents a time before the motion started, and can be discarded. It follows that the time the body takes to reach the gound is 3 s.   ◀

EXERCISE 46a

All the motion is in a straight line and starts when $t = 0$. The units are metres and seconds throughout.

1 A body moves according to the equation $s = 4t - t^2$. Find the distance from the starting point after $1\,s, 2\,s, 3\,s$, and the velocities at these times.
2 A body moves according to the equation $s = 4t^2$. Find the distance from the starting point after $\frac{1}{2}s, 1\,s, 1\frac{1}{2}s$, and the velocities at these times.
3 The velocity of a body is given by the equation $v = t^2 + t - 1$. Find the velocity after $1\,s, 2\,s, 3\,s$, and the accelerations at these times.
4 A body moves according to the equation $v = t^2 - 3t$. Find the times at which (a) the velocity is $4\,m\,s^{-1}$, (b) the acceleration is $7\,m\,s^{-2}$.
5 The velocity of a body is given by the equation $v = 2t^2 - 5t$. Find the time at which the acceleration is $3\,m\,s^{-2}$ and the velocity at this time.
6 A body's velocity is given by $v = t^2 - t$. Find (a) the velocity when the acceleration is $5\,m\,s^{-2}$, (b) the acceleration when the velocity is $2\,m\,s^{-1}$, (c) the acceleration when the body is instantaneously stationary.
7 A body moves according to the equation $v = 5 - 4t - t^2$. Find (a) the initial velocity, (b) the initial acceleration, (c) the time at which the body is instantaneously stationary, (d) the acceleration at this time.
8 A stone is dropped from the top of a building 20 m high, and moves such that $s = 5t^2$. How long does it take to reach the ground and what is its speed when it strikes the ground?
9 A body moves such that $s = 2t^2 + 3t$. Find (a) the distance from the starting point after 3 s, (b) the inital velocity, (c) the velocity after 3 s, (d) the acceleration, (e) the distance when the velocity is $11\ m\ s^{-1}$, (f) the velocity when the distance is 2 m.
10 A body moves according to the equation $v = 3t^2 - 9t$. Find (a) the velocity when the acceleration is $9\ m\ s^{-2}$, (b) the acceleration when the velocity is $12\,m\,s^{-1}$.
11 A body moves such that $v = 8t - t^2$. Find its maximum velocity.
12 A body thrown vertically upwards moves such that $h = 20t - 5t^2$, where h metres is the height above the starting point. Find (a) the height and speed after 1 s, (b) the acceleration, (c) the greatest height, (d) the total time the body takes to return to its starting point.
13 A body moves such that $s = 2t^3 - 3t^2 - 6t$. Find the distance from the starting point and the acceleration when the velocity is $6\,m\,s^{-1}$.
14 A particle moves along an x-axis in accordance with the equation $x = 5 + 4t - t^2$. Find (a) the initial position, (b) the initial velocity, (c) the position at which the particle changes direction, (d) the position when the particle is moving in the negative direction at $2\ m\ s^{-1}$, (e) the time at which the particle reaches the origin, (f) the velocity at the origin.
15 A body moves such that $s = 15t^2 - 2t^3$. Find its maximum velocity.
16 A stone is thrown downwards from the top of a building 40 m high, and moves such that $s = 10t + 5t^2$. Find (a) the speed with which it is thrown, (b) the time it takes to reach the ground, (c) its speed after falling 15 m, (d) the distance it has fallen when its speed is $15\,m\,s^{-1}$.
17 A body moves such that $s = 5t + 2t^2 - t^3$. Find the distance from the starting point and the velocity when the acceleration is $1\,m\,s^{-2}$.
18 A particle starts at the origin and moves along the x-axis according to the equation $x = 6t - t^2$. Find (a) the time it takes to return to the origin, (b) the value of x when it is moving in the positive direction at $4\ m\ s^{-1}$, (c) the value of x when it is moving in the negative direction at $10\ m\ s^{-1}$, (d) its velocity when $x = -7$.

19 A ball thrown vertically upwards moves such that $h = 8t - 5t^2$. Find (a) its maximum height, (b) its velocity when it reaches a point 13 m below the starting point.

20 A particle moves along an x-axis in such a way that $x = 3 + 2t - t^2$. Find (a) the maximum value of x, (b) the time the particle takes to return to its starting point, (c) the time it takes to reach the origin, (d) its velocity at the origin.

21 A body moves such that $v = 24t + 3t^2 - t^3$. Find (a) the velocity when the acceleration is zero, (b) the maximum acceleration.

22 A ball thrown vertically upwards moves such that $h = 6t - 5t^2$. Find (a) the time during which it is more than 1 m above its starting point, (b) the time it takes to reach a point 8 m below the starting point, (c) its speed when 27 m below the starting point.

23 A ball thrown vertically upwards moves such that $h = 25 + 20t - 5t^2$, where h metres is the height of the ball above the ground. Find (a) the initial height and initial speed, (b) the maximum height, (c) the total time the ball takes to return to its starting point, (d) the total time it takes to reach the ground.

24 A ball is thrown vertically upwards from the top of a building 32 m high, and moves according to the equation $h = 12t - 5t^2$, where h metres is the height of the ball above the top of the building. Find the speed with which it hits the ground.

Kinematics problems involving integration

Since we differentiate to obtain a formula for v from a formula for s or a formula for a from a formula for v, it follows that we must integrate to perform the inverse procedures. In brief,

we differentiate to proceed $s \rightarrow v \rightarrow a$;
we integrate to proceed $a \rightarrow v \rightarrow s$.

The main difference between problems involving integration and ones involving differentiation is that an *arbitrary constant* has to be put into the formula after integration. Usually information is given which enables the constant to be evaluated, as the following examples illustrate.

▷ Example 4

A particle starts at a point P with a velocity of 16 m s^{-1}, and moves such that its acceleration is $(4 - 12t)$ m s^{-2} after t seconds. Obtain formulae for the particle's velocity and distance from P, and hence find its maximum distance from P.

First we integrate the formula for a to obtain a formula for v containing an unknown constant:

$$a = 4 - 12t$$
$$\therefore \quad v = 4t - 6t^2 + A.$$

We are told that the velocity is 16 m s^{-1} at P, which means that $v = 16$ when $t = 0$. Hence, substituting these values, we obtain $A = 16$ and thus

$$v = 16 + 4t - 6t^2.$$

Now we integrate again to obtain a formula for the distance from P:

$$s = 16t + 2t^2 - 2t^3 + B.$$

To find the constant B we note that when the particle starts its motion at P, both t and s are equal to zero. Substituting these values gives $B = 0$, and we thus have

$$s = 16t + 2t^2 - 2t^3.$$

We now have formulae for s, v and a, and can solve any numerical problems by the methods given earlier. Thus the maximum value of s occurs when $\frac{ds}{dt} = 0$ or $v = 0$; that is when

$$16 + 4t - 6t^2 = 0$$
$$\therefore \quad 3t^2 - 2t - 8 = 0$$
$$\therefore \quad (3t + 4)(t - 2) = 0$$
$$\therefore \quad t = -1\tfrac{1}{3} \text{ or } 2.$$

Since the motion starts when $t = 0$, we discard the negative value of t and substitute $t = 2$ into the formula for s:

$$s = 16(2) + 2(2)^2 - 2(2)^3$$
$$= 32 + 8 - 16$$
$$= 24.$$

We can check that this is a maximum and not a minimum value of s by finding the sign of the quantity $\frac{d^2s}{dt^2}$, which is simply a:

$$\frac{d^2s}{dt^2} = a = 4 - 12t$$
$$= 4 - 24 \text{ when } t = 2.$$

This is negative, so s is a maximum when $t = 2$ and it follows that the particle's maximum distance from P is 24 m.   ◁

The constant which appears in the formula for s is usually zero because time and distance are usually zero together at the start of the motion. Even so, *the constant should always be put in the formula initially*, and *shown to be zero*.

We conclude with a less common type of example in which the constant in the formula for distance is not zero.

▷ Example 5

A particle starts at the point (5,0) on an x-axis graduated in metres, and moves along the axis with a constant acceleration towards the origin of 2 m s⁻². After 1 second its velocity is 2 m s⁻¹ in the positive direction. Obtain formulae for v and x, and use them to find the particle's velocity when it reaches the origin.

In this question care is needed in dealing with the *signs* of the quantities. An x-axis is positive 'to the right', and this means that each of the quantities x, v and a is positive when directed to the right and negative when directed to the left. Since the particle starts at (5,0) with an acceleration directed towards the origin, the acceleration is negative until the particle reaches the origin. We therefore have

$$a = -2.$$

Despite its appearance, this equation is a *formula* for a, giving the value of a at all points, and it can therefore be integrated. We cannot differentiate or integrate an equation such as '$a = 2$ when $t = 3$', which gives a *particular* value of a, because it does not make sense to speak of the graph of $a = 2$ in this case. We could, however, draw a graph of a against t for the given equation $a = -2$, since this equation states that $a = -2$ for *all* values of t (within a certain range). The graph is a horizontal straight line.

Integrating with respect to t, we have

$$v = -2t + A,$$

and since $v = 2$ when $t = 1$,

$$
\begin{aligned}
2 &= -2 + A, \\
\therefore A &= 4.
\end{aligned}
$$

The formula for v is thus

$$v = 4 - 2t.$$

Integrating again, we have

$$x = 4t - t^2 + B,$$

and since $x = 5$ when $t = 0$, it follows at once that $B = 5$. The formula for x is thus

$$x = 5 + 4t - t^2.$$

We now have formulae for x, v and a, and can use them to solve any numerical problems. To find the particle's velocity at the origin we first let $x = 0$ in the formula for distance and find the value of t:

$$
\begin{aligned}
0 &= 5 + 4t - t^2 \\
\therefore 0 &= (5 - t)(1 + t) \\
\therefore t &= 5 \text{ or } -1.
\end{aligned}
$$

Now we substitute the positive value $t = 5$ into the equation for v:

$$
\begin{aligned}
v &= 4 - 2(5) \\
&= -6.
\end{aligned}
$$

It follows that the velocity of the particle at the origin is -6 m s^{-1}.   ◁

EXERCISE 46b

All the motion is in a straight line and starts when $t = 0$. The units are metres and seconds throughout.

1 A body moves according to the equation $a = 2t$, and $v = 3$ when $t = 0$. Obtain an equation for v in terms of t.

2 A body starts at a point P and moves according to the equation $v = 6t + 2$. Obtain an equation for the body's distance from P in terms of t.

3 A body moves according to the equation $a = 4t$, and $v = 12$ when $t = 3$. Obtain an equation for v in terms of t.

4 A body moves according to the equation $v = 10t$, and when $t = 2$ its distance from a point P is 12 m. Obtain an equation for the distance from P in terms of t.

5 A body starts at a point P with a velocity of 3 m s^{-1}, and moves according to the equation $a = 12t$. Obtain equations for the velocity and distance from P, in terms of t.

6 A particle starts at the origin with a velocity of 3 m s^{-1}, and moves along the x-axis with a constant acceleration (in the positive direction) of 4 m s^{-2}. Obtain equations for v and x in terms of t.

7 A body moves according to the equation $a = -2t$, and $v = 5$ when $t = 1$. Find the value of v when $t = 2$.

8 A particle starts at the point (2,0), and moves along the x-axis according to the equation $v = 8t$. Find the value of x when $t = 2$.

9 A particle starts at the point (8,0), and moves along the x-axis according to the equation $v = -4t$. Find the time it takes to reach the origin.

10 A body starts with a velocity of 4 m s^{-1}, and moves such that $a = 1 - t$. Find the value of t at which its velocity is zero.

11 A body moves according to the equation $v = 2 - 4t$, and is 8 m from a point P after 2 s. Find its distance from P (a) at the start of the motion, (b) after $1\frac{1}{2}$ s, (c) when it is instantaneously stationary.

12 A particle starts at the point (4,0), and moves along the x-axis according to the equation $v = 3 - 2t$. Find the time at which the particle reaches the origin and its velocity at this time.

13 A particle starts at the point (2,0), and moves along the x-axis according to the equation $v = 4 - 2t$. Find the maximum value of x.

14 A body starts at a point P, and moves away from P with a constant acceleration of 2 m s^{-2}. If its velocity is 1 m s^{-1} after 2 s, find the time it takes to reach a point 10 m from P and its velocity at this point.

15 A stone is released with an initial speed of zero from a height of 45 m, and falls with a constant acceleration of 10 m s^{-2}. Find the time it takes to reach the ground and its speed on striking the ground.

16 A body starts with a velocity of 3 m s^{-1}, and moves such that its acceleration after t seconds is $(8 - 6t)$ m s^{-2}. Find the time it takes to come to instantaneous rest and the distance it has travelled at that time.

17 A body moves with a constant acceleration of 6 m s^{-2}. After 2 s its velocity is 9 m s^{-1} and its distance from a point P is 8 m. Find the body's initial distance from P, and its distance from P when it is instantaneously stationary.

18 A body starts with a velocity of 7 m s^{-1}, and moves with an acceleration given by $a = 6 - 2t$. Find (a) its maximum velocity, (b) its acceleration when instantaneously stationary.

19 A ball is thrown downwards with a speed of 11 m s^{-1}, and moves with a constant downward acceleration of 10 m s^{-2}. How long does it take to fall 12 m and what is its speed after falling this distance?

20 A ball is thrown upwards with an initial speed of 20 m s^{-1}, and it moves with a constant downward acceleration of 10 m s^{-2}. Find (a) its greatest height, (b) its speed on reaching a point 60 m below its starting point.

21 A particle starts at the point (18,0) with a velocity of 16 m s^{-1} (in the positive direction), and moves along the x-axis with a constant acceleration towards the origin of 4 m s^{-2}. Find (a) the time the particle takes to return to its starting point, (b) its speed on reaching the origin.

22 A particle starts at the point (10,0) with a velocity of 18 m s^{-1}, and moves along the x-axis with an acceleration given by $a = 6t - 12$. Find the particle's minimum velocity, and the position at which this velocity occurs.

Answers to Exercises

Exercise 1a (page 2)

1 −11 **2** −17 **3** −13 **4** 9 **5** 45 **6** −64 **7** −24 **8** 20
9 13 **10** −8 **11** −64 **12** 3 **13** 24 **14** −12 **15** 10
16 −18 **17** −2 **18** 11 **19** 17 **20** −25 **21** −16 **22** 3
23 −16 **24** −17 **25** −32 **26** 12 **27** $-\frac{3}{4}$ **28** 24

Exercise 1b (page 3)

1 $\frac{4}{5}$ **2** $\frac{3}{7}$ **3** $\frac{8}{9}$ **4** $\frac{8}{11}$ **5** $\frac{3}{11}$ **6** $\frac{5}{11}$ **7** $\frac{3}{4}$ **8** $\frac{1}{5}$ **9** $\frac{3}{7}$ **10** $\frac{17}{23}$
11 $3\frac{1}{3}$ **12** $15\frac{3}{5}$ **13** $13\frac{1}{2}$ **14** $12\frac{1}{4}$ **15** $7\frac{4}{13}$ **16** $12\frac{3}{4}$ **17** $9\frac{2}{3}$
18 $7\frac{5}{6}$ **19** $\frac{5}{7}$ **20** $\frac{7}{12}$ **21** $\frac{4}{9}$ **22** $4\frac{1}{2}$ **23** $\frac{1}{3}$ **24** 12 **25** 16
26 63 **27** 18 **28** 48 **29** 30 **30** 60 **31** 168 **32** $1\frac{1}{8}$
33 $\frac{13}{18}$ **34** $\frac{3}{8}$ **35** $\frac{1}{2}$ **36** $-\frac{1}{6}$ **37** $-\frac{17}{48}$ **38** $\frac{1}{18}$ **39** $-1\frac{13}{24}$
40 $-1\frac{1}{8}$ **41** $3\frac{1}{3}$ **42** $9\frac{2}{7}$ **43** $11\frac{7}{8}$ **44** $5\frac{1}{2}$ **45** $2\frac{5}{6}$ **46** $2\frac{5}{14}$
47 $-3\frac{1}{2}$ **48** $8\frac{4}{5}$ **49** $-6\frac{4}{9}$ **50** $\frac{11}{15}$

Exercise 1c (page 5)

1 $\frac{6}{7}$ **2** $2\frac{2}{9}$ **3** $2\frac{4}{5}$ **4** $\frac{2}{11}$ **5** $\frac{3}{17}$ **6** $\frac{3}{14}$ **7** $\frac{5}{48}$ **8** $\frac{1}{12}$ **9** $\frac{3}{11}$
10 $\frac{2}{13}$ **11** $\frac{4}{5}$ **12** $\frac{3}{7}$ **13** $\frac{5}{12}$ **14** $\frac{10}{21}$ **15** $\frac{1}{8}$ **16** 2 **17** $\frac{1}{6}$
18 $\frac{1}{8}$ **19** $2\frac{1}{4}$ **20** $\frac{20}{21}$ **21** $\frac{1}{6}$ **22** $3\frac{3}{4}$ **23** $15\frac{3}{4}$ **24** $1\frac{1}{3}$
25 $\frac{2}{3}$ **26** $3\frac{1}{3}$ **27** $2\frac{2}{5}$ **28** $\frac{1}{4}$ **29** $1\frac{13}{16}$ **30** $4\frac{1}{2}$ **31** $1\frac{1}{5}$
32 $2\frac{1}{10}$ **33** 2 **34** 7 **35** $2\frac{1}{2}$ **36** $\frac{3}{10}$ **37** $-4\frac{2}{5}$ **38** $\frac{1}{9}$
39 $-5\frac{1}{3}$ **40** $2\frac{2}{5}$

Exercise 1d (page 6)

1 £80 **2** 175 miles **3** 1 m² **4** 18 years **5** £900
6 (a) 120 (b) £320 **7** 40 **8** £2.50 **9** £400 **10** 1 hour
11 £1200 **12** £12 **13** £720 **14** 60 miles **15** 25 cm

Exercise 1e (page 9)

1 $\frac{2}{5}$ **2** $\frac{3}{50}$ **3** $\frac{1}{20}$ **4** $\frac{6}{25}$ **5** $\frac{1}{125}$ **6** $\frac{39}{50}$ **7** $\frac{2}{125}$
8 $\frac{201}{250}$ **9** $\frac{41}{400}$ **10** $\frac{117}{5000}$ **11** $\frac{1}{20\,000}$ **12** $\frac{241}{4000}$ **13** 0.8
14 0.625 **15** 0.167 **16** 0.714 **17** 0.55 **18** 0.84 **19** 0.364
20 0.538 **21** 0.066 **22** 0.133 **23** (a) 2.547 (b) 2.55
24 (a) 5.135 (b) 5.13 **25** (a) 0.050 (b) 0.05
26 (a) 0.910 (b) 0.91 **27** (a) 3.025 (b) 3.03
28 (a) 0.125 (b) 0.12 **29** (a) 0.295 (b) 0.30
30 (a) 0.008 (b) 0.01 **31** (a) 2460 (b) 2000
32 (a) 0.00393 (b) 0.004 **33** (a) 78.0 (b) 80
34 (a) 5.05 (b) 5 **35** (a) 2 500 000 (b) 3 000 000
36 (a) 0.750 (b) 0.7 **37** (a) 90 700 (b) 90 000
38 (a) 0.00804 (b) 0.008 **39** 2.47×10^2 **40** 5×10^3
41 8.264×10^1 **42** 5.384×10^8 **43** 8.3×10^7
44 7.64×10^8 **45** 2.9×10^{-3} **46** 4.38×10^{-5}
47 2.5×10^5 **48** 5×10^6 **49** 3.4×10^{-2}
50 2.78×10^{-6} **51** 8×10^5 **52** 6.2×10^{-8}

Exercise 1f (page 10)

1 2.455 **2** 0.09 **3** 3.373 **4** 0.032 **5** 0.0161 **6** 62.72
7 0.0016 **8** 0.25 **9** 0.0009 **10** 1.96 **11** 0.216
12 0.000004 **13** 0.02668 **14** 0.000096 **15** 1.37 **16** 1.6
17 9.1 **18** 8 **19** 0.13 **20** 150 **21** 0.3 **22** 0.29 **23** 28
24 0.0025 **25** 0.09 **26** 5 **27** 0.15 **28** 0.97 **29** 5.43
30 0.44 **31** 4.14 **32** 2.78 **33** 39.06

Exercise 2a (page 12)

1 2 : 3 **2** 6 : 7 **3** 3 : 4 **4** 2 : 1 **5** 1 : 2 : 3 **6** 10 :
7 3 : 7 : 11 **8** 7 : 9 : 10 **9** 7 : 5 **10** 2 : 3 : 6 **11** 2
12 3 : 5 : 9 **13** 2 : 5 : 7 **14** 3 : 5 **15** 4 : 3 : 4 : 6 **16**
17 2 : 3 **18** 4 : 9 **19** 2 : 3 **20** 3 : 5 **21** 4 : 1 **22**
23 7 : 9 : 12 **24** 8 : 12 : 15 **25** 6 : 15 : 20 **26** 15 :

Exercise 2b (page 14)

1 4, 8 **2** 4, 10 **3** 30, 20 **4** 9, 15 **5** 20, 100 **6** 4,
7 28, 7 **8** 18, 24 **9** 63 cm **10** 18, 15 **11** £400, £6
£1000 **12** 24, 40 **13** £350 **14** £119 **15** 21 cm
16 £1728 **17** 60, 114 **18** $8\frac{1}{2}$ **19** £2.10 **20** 108.5

Exercise 3a (page 16)

1 80% **2** 69% **3** $16\frac{2}{3}\%$ **4** 3.7% **5** 16% **6** 83.7%
7 $22\frac{2}{9}\%$ **8** 3.4% **9** $63\frac{7}{11}\%$ **10** $21\frac{1}{2}\%$ **11** 0.3%
12 $56\frac{1}{4}\%$ **13** 1.4% **14** $91\frac{2}{3}\%$ **15** $20\frac{5}{6}\%$ **16** $87\frac{1}{2}\%$
17 25% **18** 5.2% **19** 16% **20** $1\frac{1}{2}\%$ **21** 48%
22 $6\frac{1}{4}\%$ **23** 22% **24** 18%

Exercise 3b (page 17)

1 3.2 **2** 81 **3** $\frac{4}{5}$ **4** 148 **5** 12.6 **6** 38 **7** 32 **8** 1
9 15.4 **10** £4.20 **11** 26 p **12** 96 p **13** £381 **14**
15 345 g **16** 15 cm **17** 15 kg **18** 15 mm **19** 36
20 $12\frac{1}{2}$ cm³

Exercise 3c (page 18)

1 154 **2** 456 **3** $143\frac{3}{4}$ **4** 11.4 **5** £12.84 **6** £3.08
7 £375.30 **8** £422.82 **9** 84 p **10** £2989 **11** £2.5
12 8 p **13** 600 **14** 25 **15** 55 **16** 168 **17** 240
18 1400 **19** 115 **20** 75 **21** £4200 **22** £2890
23 £220 **24** £10 200 **25** (a) £152 (b) 30 m²
26 (a) £1.54 (b) £6.50 **27** £122.50 **28** £12 100
29 £750 **30** (a) 150 pounds (b) 162 pounds

Exercise 4a (page 21)

1 $37\frac{1}{2}\%$ **2** $6\frac{1}{4}\%$ **3** 10% **4** 100% **5** $41\frac{2}{3}\%$ **6** 16
7 0.8% **8** 0.5% **9** 0.1% **10** 0.1% **11** 0.3% **12**
13 £8.32 **14** £11.97 **15** 45 p **16** £12.40 **17** 66
18 £4.25 **19** £2090 **20** 65 p **21** 5% **22** £45
23 50% **24** £650 **25** £425 **26** (a) 15.7 cm² (b) 5
27 £4000 **28** (a) 1.2% (b) 2.4% **29** 28% **30** 3.5

Exercise 4b (page 23)

1 £30 **2** £210 **3** £6 **4** £1575 **5** £729.99 **6** £28
7 £3194.40 **8** £32.63 **9** £280 **10** £250 **11** $7\frac{1}{2}$ ye
12 £423.50 **13** 8% **14** £3812 **15** £2912 **16** £24
17 6 years **18** $7\frac{1}{2}\%$

Exercise 4c (page 25)

1 £1950 **2** £3136 **3** (a) £245 (b) £224 **4** 60 p
5 £11 525 **6** £10 310 **7** (a) £12 000 (b) £21 000
8 33 p **9** (a) 75 p (b) 80 p (c) 63 p **10** £948
11 £420 **12** £11 500 **13** 3 p **14** 7 p **15** (a) £24
(b) £512 (c) 19.6% **16** (a) £650 000 (b) 74 p **17** £
18 (a) £6 000 000 (b) £4 560 000 (c) 10.75% **19** £1
20 (a) 71 p (b) £2 000 000 (c) £100 000

rcise 4d (page 27)

% **2** 40% **3** $41\frac{2}{3}$% **4** 57% **5** 85% **6** 3.5%
8 87.5% **9** $56\frac{1}{4}$% **10** $66\frac{2}{3}$% **11** 7% **12** 44%
5% 14 $2\frac{2}{5}$% **15** 28 **16** $1\frac{1}{2}$ **17** 23 **18** $562\frac{1}{2}$
8 p **20** £15 **21** 90 p **22** £18.10 **23** 885 **24** 32.2
16 **26** 2425 **27** 17.2 **28** 3315 **29** 440 **30** 75
40 **32** 600 **33** 40

rcise 4e (page 27)

$\frac{2}{3}$% **2** $16\frac{2}{3}$% **3** 52% **4** £1125 **5** £64 **6** £3499
% **8** £2.40 **9** 5% **10** 50% **11** 1.9% **12** 7%
14 £420 **15** £20 **16** (a) 350 (b) 80 **17** £400
2% **19** (a) $6\frac{1}{2}$ (b) 32 **20** 64% **21** 78 p **22** 6%

rcise 4f (page 28)

00 **2** £3 **3** 20 **4** 27.1% **5** 16% **6** £2000
00 **8** $8\frac{1}{2}$ p **9** 75% **10** 1250 **11** $12\frac{1}{2}$% **12** 6
5% **14** $7\frac{1}{2}$% **15** £10 500

cise 5a (page 30)

0 m s^{-1} **2** 15 m s^{-1} **3** 500 cm s^{-1} **4** 9 km h^{-1}
0 m min^{-1} **6** (a) $62\frac{1}{2}$ m min^{-1} (b) $3\frac{3}{4}$ km h^{-1}
h **8** $17\frac{1}{2}$ km h **9** 6 min 40 s **10** 75 min
0 m s^{-1} **12** (a) 45m (b) 3 h 20 min **13** (a) 27 km
$3\frac{1}{2}$ km h^{-1} **14** (a) $4\frac{1}{2}$ h (b) $11\frac{1}{8}$ km h^{-1} **15** 153 km
km h^{-1} **17** 40 km h^{-1} **18** 3.8 m s^{-1}
5 h, 24 h, 32 h **20** 10 km h^{-1} **21** 1 h 56 min
$5\frac{2}{3}$ km h^{-1} **23** (a) 80 km, (b) 20 km h^{-1}
4.7 s **25** 10 s **26** 100 km h^{-1} **27** 5 m s^{-1}
) 2.4 m s^{-1} (b) 2.5 m s^{-1}

cise 5b (page 35)

km h^{-1}, 19 km h^{-1}, 47.5 km **2** 15.21 h, 5.8 km
11.28 h (b) 42 km (c) 11.19 h **4** (a) 17.5 km
.6 km h^{-1} **5** 150 km h^{-1}, 120 km h^{-1}, 18 min
14.48 h (b) 65 km (c) 66.7 km **7** (a) 4 km h^{-1},
h^{-1} (b) 10 min, 30 min **8** 80 min, 160 min,
nin, 39.2 km h^{-1} **9** (a) 117 km h^{-1} (b) 12.52 h
.6 km **10** 63 min, 140 km h^{-1}, 118 km h^{-1}

cise 6a (page 38)

2 2^6 **3** 2^{15} **4** 2^6 **5** 2^{12} **6** 2^{48} **7** 2^{28} **8** 2^2
10 2^4 **11** 2^{7x} **12** 2^{8x} **13** 2^{2p-3} **14** 2^{2b}
x **16** 2^3 **17** 2^{7x} **18** 2^{10w-1} **19** 2^{6x+1}
$a-10b$ **21** 5^9 **22** 5^2 **23** 5^7 **24** 5^2 **25** 5^{9x+6}
27 5^y **28** 5^{7a-b} **29** 5^{x-6} **30** 5^{3y} **31** x^6
$0w$ **33** y^x **34** m^{2x-2} **35** y^{5-a}

cise 6b (page 40)

2 1 **3** $\frac{1}{2}$ **4** 8 **5** 1 **6** $\frac{2}{3}$ **7** $2\frac{1}{4}$ **8** $\frac{16}{169}$ **9** 16
11 64 **12** 6 **13** 5 **14** 2 **15** 7 **16** -2
18 9 **19** 8 **20** 32 **21** 2401 **22** $2\frac{1}{4}$
$\frac{5}{8}$ **24** 3 **25** 4 **26** 2 **27** 1 **28** $\frac{1}{32}$ **29** 4
31 $\frac{3}{7}$ **32** $5\frac{1}{16}$ **33** -8 **34** 2 **35** $\frac{1}{27}$ **36** $\frac{8}{125}$
38 12 **39** 18 **40** 8

cise 7a (page 43)

2 65 **3** 195 **4** 198 **5** 11 **6** 128 **7** 80 **8** 22
10 78 **11** 103_6 **12** 30_6 **13** 523_6 **14** 532_6
252_6 **16** $20\,403_6$ **17** 1111_2 **18** $100\,000_2$
) 101_2 **20** $1\,110\,101_2$ **21** $11\,000\,100_2$ **22** 102_5
5 **24** 200_5 **25** 3122_5

Exercise 7b (page 45)

1 121_3 **2** 1514_7 **3** $100\,010_2$ **4** 422_5 **5** 1000_8
6 $101\,100_2$ **7** $11\,664_9$ **8** 2202_4 **9** 334_8 **10** $100\,111_2$
11 153_6 **12** 4356_7 **13** 2122_4 **14** $22\,356_8$ **15** $4\,050\,501_6$

Exercise 7c (page 45)

1 35_8 **2** 12_5 **3** 2 **4** 1001_2 **5** 34_6 **6** 22_3 **7** 22_3 **8** 34_5
9 2055_6 **10** 212_4 **11** 54_7 **12** 264_8

Exercise 8a (page 47)

1 (a) $\{P, E, R\}$ (b) $\{2, 0\}$ (c) $\{31, 37, 41, 43, 47\}$
(d) $\{42, 49, 56, 63\}$ (e) $\{49, 64, 81, 100, 121\}$
(f) $\{1, 2, 3, 5, 6, 10, 15, 30\}$ (g) $\{-5, 5\}$
2 (a) First four positive odd numbers (b) First four
consonants (c) First three square numbers, (d) Multiples of
9 from 45 to 72 inclusive (e) Black suits (f) Months with 30
days (g) Primes between 82 and 98 (h) Days beginning
with T
3 (a) Yes (b) No (c) Yes (d) Yes (e) No (f) No (g) Yes
(h) Yes (i) Yes (j) Yes (k) Yes
4 (a) No (b) Yes (c) Yes (d) No (e) Yes (f) No (g) No
(h) Yes (i) Yes
5 (a) 7 (b) 7 (c) 4 (d) 8 (e) 6 (f) 2 (g) 6 (h) 1 (i) 5 (j) 3
6 (a) $\in$ (b) $\subset$ (c) $\notin$ (d) $\notin$ (e) $\subset$ (f) $\not\subset$ (g) $\not\subset$ (h) $\in$ (i) $\in$
(j) $\not\subset$ (k) $\not\subset$
7 (f) F (b) T (c) F (d) F (e) F (f) F (g) T (h) F (i) T (j) T
8 $\{a\}, \{b\}, \{c\}, \{a, b\}, \{a, c\}, \{b, c\}$
9 (a) 6 (b) 5
10 81 **11** 83 **12** 58

Exercise 8b (page 52)

1 (a) $\{a, b, c, d, e, f, g, h\}$ (b) $\{b, g\}$
2 (a) $\{2, 3, 5, 7, 9, 11\}$ (b) $\{3, 5, 7\}$
3 (a) $\{a, b, c, d\}$ (b) $\{c\}$ (c) $\{d, e\}$ (d) $\{e\}$ (e) $\{a, b, d, e\}$ (f) $\{d\}$
4 (a) A (b) $\mathscr{E}$ (c) A (d) $\varnothing$ (e) A (f) $\varnothing$ (g) $\mathscr{E}$ (h) A
5 (a) B' (b) $(A \cup B)'$ or $A' \cap B$ (c) $A' \cap B$
6 (a) $\{1, 3, 4\}$ (b) $\{1, 3, 4, 5\}$ (c) $\{5\}$ (d) $\{4\}$
7 (a) $\{1, 4, 6, 8, 9, 10\}$ (b) $\{2, 11\}$ (c) $\{1, 3, 4, 5, 6, 7, 8, 9, 10\}$
(d) $\{4, 6, 8, 10\}$ (e) $\{1, 2, 4, 6, 8, 9, 10, 11\}$
8 (a) $\{-3, -2, -1, 0, 1, 2\}$ (b) $\{-2\}$ (c) $\{-2, -1, 0\}$
(d) $\{-2, -1, 0, 2\}$
9 (a) $A \cap B$ (b) $B' \cap C$ (c) $(A \cup B \cup C)'$ (d) z, w (e) x, y, p, s
(f) y, w
10 (a) $\{6\}$ (b) $\{2, 6, 8, 10, 12\}$ (c) $\{8, 12\}$
11 (a) $\varnothing$ (b) $\mathscr{E}$ (c) A (d) $\varnothing$ (e) $\mathscr{E}$ (f) $\varnothing$
12 (a) F (b) T (c) T (d) T (e) F (f) T
13 (a) 7 (b) 13 (c) 9 (d) 7
14 (a) T (b) T (c) F (d) F (e) T (f) T
15 (a) A (b) A (c) B (d) A
16 (a) $\{6\}$ (b) $\{1, 2, 4, 5\}$ (c) $\{6, 7, 8, 9\}$ (d) $\{4, 5, 7, 8\}$
17 (a) $B \cap C$ (b) $A \cap B' \cap C$ (c) $A \cap B' \cap C'$ (d) s, t, u, p
(e) r, q (f) q, t, u

Exercise 9a (page 57)

1 T **2** F **3** F **4** T **5** F **6** T **7** F **8** T **9** T **10** $A \cup B$
11 B **12** $A \cap B$ **15** T **16** T or F **17** F **18** T **19** T or F
20 T or F **21** F **22** T **23** F **24** T **25** T **26** T **27** T **28** F
29 T **30** T **31** A' **32** $A \cup B$ **33** B **36** T **37** T **38** F
39 F **40** T **41** T

Exercise 9b (page 60)

1 (a) $M \subset E$ (b) $E \cap P = \varnothing$ (c) $E \cap M \neq \varnothing$ (d) $E \cap P' \neq \varnothing$
2 (a) $T' \cap H = \varnothing$ (b) $F \cap T \cap H' \neq \varnothing$ (c) $F \subset T \cup H$
(d) $T \cap F' \neq \varnothing$
3 (a) $A \subset O \cup P$ (b) $D \subset A \cap P$ (c) $O \subset P'$ (d) $D \cap P = \varnothing$
(e) $P \cap O \cap A \neq \varnothing$ (f) $A \subset D$ (g) $O \cap D \cap P' \neq \varnothing$

4 (a) T or F (b) T (c) T or F
5 (a) T or F (b) T or F (c) F (d) T
6 (a) T (b) T (c) F
7 (a) T (b) T or F (c) T (d) T (e) T
8 (a) T (b) T (c) T (d) F

Exercise 10 (page 65)

1 28 **2** 8 **3** 30 **4** 6,7,8,9,10 **5** 10,2 **6** 5,6,7,8,9
7 3,4,5 **8** 6 **9** 3 **10** 8 **11** 10 **12** (a) 5 (b) 12 **13** 16
14 5 **15** 35% **16** 9 **17** 20 **18** (a) 16 (b) 12 **19** (a) 18
(b) 16 **20** (a) 2 (b) 4 **21** 11 **22** 42,13 **23** (a) 0 (b) 3 **24**
25 **25** (a) 4 (b) 25 **26** 16% **27** 4 **28** 8 **29** (a) 10 (b) 14
30 25% **31** 18 **32** (a) 10% (b) 62% **33** 34% **34** 3,7 **35**
(a) 24 (b) 140 **36** (a) 16 (b) 20

Exercise 11a (page 69)

1 6 **2** 5 **3** 24 **4** 36 **5** 36 **6** 8 **7** 3 **8** -1 **9** 1
10 Indeterminate **11** 0 **12** 4 **13** $-\frac{1}{2}$ **14** -1 **15** $1\frac{2}{3}$
16 Indeterminate **17** 2 **18** 0 **19** -8 **20** 32
21 Indeterminate **22** 3 **23** 48 **24** $\frac{1}{3}$ **25** 8 **26** $-\frac{1}{2}$ **27** 1
28 Indeterminate **29** 0 **30** Indeterminate

Exercise 11b (page 70)

1 $3b - 2a$ **2** $\frac{15x}{4}$ **3** $2p - 2$ **4** $\frac{7}{a}$ **5** $-\frac{a}{2} - 2b$ **6** $1 - \frac{7k}{6}$
7 $\frac{9}{x}$ **8** $x^3 - x^2 - x$ **9** $x + \frac{1}{x}$ **10** $7x^2$ **11** $12x^4$ **12** $\frac{2x^2}{3} + \frac{x}{2}$
13 $\frac{2}{x^2} + 1$ **14** $\frac{a^7}{2}$ **15** $-3xy - 3wx - wy$ **16** $\frac{a^3b}{2}$ **17** $-2x^2$
18 $2a^2b^2 - 2ab^2$ **19** $\frac{p^2}{32}$ **20** $\frac{13p^2}{9} - \frac{3}{4p^2}$

Exercise 11c (page 71)

1 $a^2 - ab$ **2** $2x^2 - 6xy$ **3** $-xy^2 + x^2y$ **4** $2x - 3x^2$
5 $-8a^3b - 4ab^3$ **6** $4p - 3r$ **7** $1 - x$ **8** $5pq - 10p^2q - 15pq^2$
9 $2x - \frac{1}{2y}$ **10** $12x^5y^4w^3 + 8x^2y^5w^4$ **11** $2y - \frac{x^2}{2}$
12 $-\frac{x}{2} + 1$ **13** $2p^2 + 3pq + q^2$ **14** $x^2 + 5x + 6$
15 $x^2 - 2x - 35$ **16** $a^2 - 9a + 18$ **17** $10 - 3k - k^2$
18 $12y^2 - 13y + 3$ **19** $7x^2 - 22x + 16$ **20** $2a^2 + 7ab - 4b^2$
21 $4p^2 - 9$ **22** $2x^3 - x^2 - 2x + 1$ **23** $r^4s^2 - t^2$
24 $4 - 3s^2 - s^3$ **25** $p^3 - 1$ **26** $8x^3 + 1$
27 $6a^2b + abc - bc^2$ **28** $a^2 + 2bc - b^2 - c^2$
29 $a^2 + 8a + 16$ **30** $p^2 - 6p + 9$ **31** $36 + 12y + y^2$
32 $9 - 6w + w^2$ **33** $4x^2 - 4x + 1$ **34** $9a^2 + 12ab + 4b^2$
35 $25x^2 + 40xy + 16y^2$ **36** $49p^2 - 56ps + 16s^2$
37 $1 - 6xy + 9x^2y^2$ **38** $4a^2b^2 - 4ab^2c + b^2c^2$
39 $y^2 - 2 + \frac{1}{y^2}$ **40** $\frac{4}{x^2} + 2 + \frac{x^2}{4}$ **41** $\frac{9}{a^2} - 1 + \frac{a^2}{36}$ **42** $-8x$
43 $8x^2 - 1$ **44** -1 **45** $4a^2b^2$

Exercise 12a (page 74)

1 4 **2** 2 **3** -4 **4** $-\frac{1}{3}$ **5** 2 **6** $1\frac{2}{3}$ **7** $\frac{2}{3}$ **8** $-\frac{3}{4}$ **9** $2\frac{3}{4}$
10 0 **11** $1\frac{5}{8}$ **12** 7 **13** -1 **14** 1 **15** $7\frac{2}{5}$ **16** $-\frac{4}{11}$
17 $1\frac{5}{7}$ **18** $2\frac{5}{8}$ **19** $-1\frac{1}{4}$ **20** 4

Exercise 12b (page 75)

1 $2\frac{2}{3}$ **2** -1 **3** ±2 **4** $1\frac{4}{5}$ **5** ±1 **6** $\frac{1}{2}$
7 $\pm2\sqrt{2}$ or ±2.83 to 3 s.f. **8** 2 **9** -8 **10** $+1\frac{1}{2}$ **11** ±2
12 $\frac{7}{16}$ **13** $\pm\sqrt{2}$ **14** $\pm\frac{\sqrt{14}}{2}$ or 1.87 to 3 s.f. **15** $\pm2\frac{1}{4}$

Exercise 12c (page 77)

1 $x > -3$ **2** $x \leq 4$ **3** $-1 < x < 2$ **4** $1 < x \leq 4$ **5** $x < 3$
6 $x < -\frac{1}{2}$ **7** $x < \frac{5}{7}$ **8** $x > -4$ **9** $x > 1\frac{1}{4}$ **10** $x < 6$
11 $x > \frac{3}{7}$ **12** $x > -\frac{8}{9}$ **13** $-2 < x < 3$ **14** $-3 < x < 4$
15 $x > 5$ **16** $0 < x < 3$ **17** $x < -2$ **18** $-3 < x < -2$

Exercise 12d (page 79)

1 (a) $\{1, 2\}$ (b) $\{-6, -3, 0\}$ **2** (a) $\{4, 6, 8\ldots\}$ (b) $\{5, 7\}$
3 (a) $\{1, 9, 25\}$ (b) $\{7, 14, 21\}$ **4** $\{121, 144, 169, 196\}$
5 $\{-1, 0, 1, 2\ldots\}$ **6** (a) $\{2, 4, 6, 8\}$ (b) $\{1, 4, 6, 8\}$
7 (a) $\{12, 24\}$ (b) $\{23, 29\}$ **8** $\{89, 97\}$ **9** $\{x:4 \leq x < 6\}$
10 $\{x:2 < x \leq 10\}$ **11** $\{3, 4, 5\}$ **12** $\{x:7 \leq x < 10\}$
13 $\{4, 5, 6\}$ **14** $\{-1, 0, 1, 2\}$ **15** $\varnothing$ **16** $\{11, 13, 17, 19\}$
17 $\{1, 2, 3\}$

Exercise 13a (page 82)

1 $2(x - 2y)$ **2** $x(y + x)$ **3** $2(1 - 2x + 3y)$ **4** $x(x - 1)$
5 $2p(1 + 2p^2)$ **6** $5a(1 - 2b + 3a^2)$ **7** $qr(p - s)$
8 $b(a - c - ac)$ **9** $a^6(a - 1)$ **10** $3x^2y^4(x - 2y)$
11 $2p^4r(2pr - 1)$ **12** $2abc(2ac^2 - 3b + 4a^2b^2c)$
13 $(x - y)(2 + x)$ **14** $(b - c)(a - b)$ **15** $(2x + 1)(2x - 3$
16 $(b - 2c)(a + 1)$ **17** $(x + 2y)(1 + x)$
18 $(1 - x)(x + y + 2)$ **19** $3p(q + r)$ **20** $(w - y)(3x - w$
21 $(x + 2)(3x + 2)$ **22** $(2 - x)(3 - x)$ **23** $(k + 3)(2k + 1$
24 $(r + 2)(p + 4)$ **25** $(a - 1)(2a + 3)$ **26** $(x - 1)(2 + x)$
27 $3p(r - s)$ **28** $(k - 1)(3 - k)$ **29** $(1 - 2ab)(1 + b)$
30 $3(2x - 5)(x - 2)$

Exercise 13b (page 83)

1 $(x + 3)(x - 3)$ **2** $(4 + a)(4 - a)$ **3** $(2y + 7)(2y - 7)$
4 $(p + 10q)(p - 10q)$ **5** $(1 + 3xy)(1 - 3xy)$
6 $(a^5 + 9)(a^5 - 9)$ **7** $(5r^3s^2 + 1)(5r^3s^2 - 1)$
8 $(x + 7)(x + 3)$ **9** $(y - 4)(y - 10)$ **10** $(7 - k)(1 + k)$
11 $(3x + 1)(x - 1)$ **12** $-3(2p - 1)(4p + 3)$
13 $3(1 + x)(1 - x)$ **14** $2(k + 4)(k - 4)$ **15** $y(y + 3)(y -$
16 $2a(a + 5)(a - 5)$ **17** $pq(p + 6)(p - 6)$
18 $y(y^2 + 1)(y + 1)(y - 1)$ **19** $2ab^2(2a + 3)(2a - 3)$
20 $(x - 3)(x - 1)(x - 5)$ **21** $(y + 1)(4 + y)(2 - y)$
22 $-b(2a - b)(a - b)^3$

Exercise 13c (page 84)

1 $(x - 2y)(3 + a)$ **2** $(p + 2)(p + s)$ **3** $(a - 4b)(2 + a)$
4 $(x + y)(x - 2)$ **5** $(2r + 1)(s - r)$ **6** $(a + 1)(1 + b)$
7 $(1 - r)(p + 1)$ **8** $(x - 2)(x - y)$ **9** $(3w - 2y)(2 - w)$
10 $(2a - b)(2 - b)$ **11** $(p - r)(1 - r)$
12 $(x - y)(x + y + 2)$ **13** $(k - 1)(k + 1 + t)$
14 $(a - 2b)(a + 2b - x)$ **15** $(y - x)(1 + y + x)$
16 $(a - b)(a + b - 2)$ **17** $(y + w)(y - w + 3)$
18 $(2x + 1)(2x - 1 + y)$ **19** $(x + y^2)(x - 9)$
20 $(3a - b)(3a + b - b^2)$ **21** $(2 + x)(2 - a^2x)$
22 $(2 - 3ax)(2 + 3ax - x)$ **23** $(p - 1)(p^2 + r)$
24 $(p - 1)(p^2 + p + r)$ **25** $(p - 1)(p + r)(p - r)$

Exercise 13d (page 87)

1 $(x + 6)(x + 2)$ **2** $(x + 8)(x + 3)$ **3** $2(x + 2)(x + 1)$
4 $(x - 4)(x + 2)$ **5** $(x + 5)(x - 4)$ **6** $(x - 9)(x - 4)$
7 $5(x - 4)(x - 1)$ **8** $(12x + 1)(x - 1)$ **9** $(3x - 1)^2$
10 $3(10 + x)(3 - x)$ **11** $(15 + x)(4 - x)$ **12** $(12 - x)(5$
13 $2(x - 6)(x + 1)$ **14** $3(3 + x)(2 - x)$ **15** $5(x + 1)^2$
16 $(2x + 1)(x + 3)$ **17** $(5x + 4)(x + 1)$ **18** $(3x + 1)(x -$
19 $(2x - 5)(2x - 1)$ **20** $(3x + 4)(3x - 2)$
21 $4(2x - 3)(x - 6)$ **22** $(5x + 4y)(x - 2y)$
23 $(5x - 3y)(2x - 3y)$ **24** $(2 - 3x)(4 + 5x)$
25 $(5 - 3x)(3 + 4x)$ **26** $(4x + 3)(2x + 1)$
27 $(7y + 8x)(4y - 3x)$ **28** $(5x - 2y)(3x - 4y)$

Exercise 13e (page 87)

1 $(3+ab)(3-ab)$ 2 $2ab^2(2a-3b)$ 3 $(1-9x)(1+2x)$
4 $(a-5b)(1+c)$ 5 $2(y-3)(y-2)$ 6 $(5a^2+1)(5a^2-1)$
7 $(5-y)(5+y+x)$ 8 $2y(4y+1)(4y-1)$
9 $(x-17)(x+3)$ 10 $(19+p)(4-p)$ 11 $(x-1)(x+2)$
12 $2a^3(a+2)(a-2)$ 13 $(a-3b)(2-b)$ 14 $3xy^2(2x^2-3y)$
15 $(5r+3)(2r-3)$ 16 $(2x+3y)(2+2x-3y)$
17 $(8a-3b)(2a-3b)$ 18 $-(x-5)(x+5)$
19 $(5+3p)(4-5p)$ 20 $(x+2y)(x-2y)(1+y)$

Exercise 13f (page 88)

1 $\frac{4}{x}$ 2 $\frac{x}{y+3}$ 3 $\frac{2}{1+5x}$ 4 $\frac{1}{1+2a}$ 5 $\frac{1+x}{2}$ 6 $\frac{y-3}{x}$
7 $-(3+x)$ 8 $-3xy$ 9 $\frac{2(p+5)}{p+1}$ 10 $\frac{x-y}{y}$ 11 $4a^2b$
12 $6x^2y^2$ 13 $24a^4b^2c^2$ 14 $3x(1-3x)$ 15 $3k^2(1+k)$
16 $(1-x)^2(1+x)$ 17 $2a(2a+1)(2a-1)$
18 $6x(x+2)(x-2)$ 19 $b(a+1)(a-1)$ 20 $2xy(2-x)$

Exercise 14a (page 90)

1 $-1,-3$ 2 $-2,-6$ 3 $2,-7$ 4 $-2,9$ 5 $3,-1$ 6 $4,5$
7 $-4,-6$ 8 $3,-2$ 9 6 10 $2,-8$ 11 $7,-6$ 12 $3,10$
13 $9,-4$ 14 5 15 $2,18$ 16 $3,-16$ 17 $\frac{1}{2},-\frac{1}{3}$ 18 $\frac{1}{3},\frac{1}{4}$
19 $\frac{1}{2}$ 20 $1\frac{1}{2},-1$ 21 $-1,-1\frac{2}{3}$ 22 $1,-\frac{4}{5}$ 23 $-\frac{1}{2},3\frac{1}{2}$
24 $\frac{2}{3},-1\frac{1}{2}$ 25 $1\frac{1}{2},-\frac{3}{4}$ 26 $\frac{2}{3}$ 27 $1\frac{1}{3},-1\frac{1}{2}$ 28 $-\frac{5}{9},-\frac{1}{2}$
29 $6,-5$ 30 $2,-6$ 31 $8,-5$ 32 $20,-10$ 33 $2,-3\frac{3}{4}$
34 $5,\frac{3}{8}$ 35 $2,10$ 36 $\frac{2}{3},1\frac{1}{4}$ 37 $50,80$ 38 $1\frac{1}{3},-\frac{5}{12}$
39 $2\frac{2}{9},1$ 40 $\frac{2}{3},1\frac{1}{8}$

Exercise 14b (page 92)

1 $0,3$ 2 $0,1\frac{2}{3}$ 3 ±4 4 ±2 5 $0,-\frac{1}{3}$ 6 $0,\frac{3}{4}$ 7 ±8 8 ±1
9 $0,1\frac{3}{4}$ 10 ±7 11 $0,\frac{3}{7}$ 12 $\pm\frac{2}{3}$ 13 $0,-\frac{2}{5}$ 14 ±6 15 $\pm2\frac{1}{2}$
16 $0,4$ 17 $\pm\frac{1}{5}$ 18 $0,-2$ 19 $0,\frac{5}{11}$ 20 $\pm2\frac{2}{5}$ 21 $0,-\frac{1}{4}$
22 ±3 23 $0,3\frac{2}{5}$ 24 $\pm3\frac{1}{3}$ 25 $0,-\frac{6}{7}$ 26 $0,1\frac{1}{5}$ 27 $\pm1\frac{1}{6}$
28 ±3 29 $0,\frac{1}{4}$ 30 ±9 31 ±16 32 $0,1\frac{6}{13}$

Exercise 14c (page 92)

1 $4,-1$ 2 $3,-4$ 3 $2,-1$ 4 $2,4$ 5 ±1 6 $2,12$ 7 $0,2$
8 $\frac{1}{2},-1$ 9 $0,\frac{1}{3}$ 10 $\frac{1}{9},-\frac{1}{4}$ 11 ±2 12 ±3 13 $-\frac{1}{2},-9$
14 $\pm3\frac{1}{2}$ 15 $5,-13$ 16 $-1,6$ 17 3 18 $\frac{2}{5},-2$ 19 $0,1\frac{1}{3}$
20 $8,-2$ 21 $\pm1\frac{1}{3}$ 22 $3,16$ 23 $3,-1$ 24 ±6 25 $6,-4$
26 $0,\frac{7}{9}$ 27 $\frac{2}{3},-1\frac{2}{7}$ 28 $\frac{8}{9},-\frac{1}{2}$ 29 $-\frac{1}{7},5$ 30 $\pm1\frac{1}{2}$ 31 $0,1$
32 $25,-20$ 33 $15,40$ 34 $\frac{3}{8},4$ 35 $\frac{5}{8},-1\frac{1}{3}$

Exercise 14d (page 95)

1 36 2 16 3 100 4 64 5 $6\frac{1}{4}$ 6 $\frac{1}{4}$ 7 $2\frac{1}{4}$ 8 $\frac{1}{16}$ 9 $\frac{1}{9}$
10 $\frac{9}{64}$ 11 $\frac{4}{25}$ 12 $\frac{49}{64}$ 13 $0.24,-4.24$ 14 $6.74,-0.74$
15 $-1.76,-6.24$ 16 $3.65,-1.65$ 17 $0.62,-1.62$
18 $-0.09,-2.91$ 19 $5.24,-1.24$ 20 $0.29,-2.29$
21 $0.44,-3.44$ 22 $-0.19,-1.31$ 23 $0.23,1.43$
24 $1.65,-0.85$ 25 $1.45,-3.45$ 26 $-1.45,3.45$
27 $1.84,8.16$ 28 $-0.29,-5.21$ 29 $0.36,-0.56$
30 $0.39,-1.72$ 31 $0.85,-2.35$ 32 $0.71,-4.71$
33 $2.45,-0.20$ 34 $0.29,5.21$ 35 $1.90,-0.40$ 36 $0.37,0.77$

Exercise 15a (page 99) (The pairs of values are those of x and y, respectively.)

1 $3,1$ 2 $2,1$ 3 $4,3$ 4 $2,1$ 5 $3,2$ 6 $2,-1$ 7 $2\frac{1}{2},1$
8 $4,-3$ 9 $3,5$ 10 $-2,-3$ 11 $1,-1$ 12 $2,4$ 13 $\frac{1}{3},\frac{2}{3}$
14 $4,-3$ 15 $-\frac{1}{6},-\frac{1}{3}$ 16 $5,3$ 17 $\frac{1}{3},\frac{1}{2}$ 18 $2,7$ 19 $1\frac{1}{2},-1\frac{1}{3}$
20 $-\frac{1}{10},-1\frac{2}{3}$ 21 $1\frac{1}{6},-7$ 22 $1\frac{3}{5},-1\frac{2}{3}$ 23 $3\frac{1}{5},\frac{1}{5}$ 24 $\frac{4}{13},1\frac{1}{3}$
25 $\frac{1}{6},\frac{1}{3}$ 26 $2,1$ 27 $-1,1$ 28 $\frac{2}{3},-1$ 29 $-8,9$ 30 $\frac{1}{2},-\frac{1}{4}$

Exercise 15b (page 100)

1 $3,-1$ and $-1,3$ 2 $5,2$ and $-5,-3$ 3 $2,3$ and $-3,8$
4 $1,-2$ and $4,-\frac{1}{2}$ 5 $3,2$ and $-2,-3$ 6 $2,-1$ and $1,-4$
7 $-1,-1$ and $2,\frac{1}{2}$ 8 $1,-1$ and $-3,-5$ 9 $-2,1$ and $1,4$
10 $1,1$ and $2,4$ 11 $5,2$ 12 $-1,3$ and $5,-9$
13 $2,-1$ and $-2,3$ 14 $4,1$ and $-3,-1\frac{1}{3}$
15 $2,1$ and $-1,-2$ 16 $1,1$ and $3,\frac{1}{3}$ 17 $3,4$ and $-2,-6$
18 $-2,6$ and $1\frac{1}{3},-\frac{2}{3}$ 19 $1,3$ and $-1\frac{1}{2},5\frac{1}{2}$
20 $-2,3$ and $-2\frac{1}{2},2$ 21 $1,2$ and $\frac{2}{3},3$ 22 $-2,3$ and $1\frac{2}{3},-4\frac{1}{3}$
23 $1,3$ and $1\frac{1}{4},4$ 24 $\frac{1}{2},4$ and $-1\frac{1}{3},-1\frac{1}{2}$
25 $2,3$ and $-12,17$ 26 $2,3$ and $-2,1$
27 $2,-1$ and $-\frac{2}{5},-2\frac{1}{3}$ 28 $3,-3$ and $-15,-9$ 29 $-1,-2$
30 $1,0$ and $3,4$ 31 $2,1$ and $-1,-5$ 32 $1,0$ and $2,-3$
33 $-1,-4$ and $1\frac{5}{6},4\frac{1}{2}$ 34 $\frac{1}{3},-2$ 35 $-2,5$ and $\frac{13}{20},-5\frac{3}{8}$

Exercise 15c (page 101)

1 $-5,\frac{1}{2}$ 2 $1,2$ and $-\frac{2}{5},-2\frac{2}{5}$ 3 $2,-9$ 4 $\frac{1}{2},1$
5 $2,-3$ and $-2\frac{2}{3},1\frac{2}{3}$ 6 $\frac{2}{3},-1$ 7 $-1,-1$ and $\frac{1}{2},2$
8 $2,1$ and $-\frac{2}{3},-1\frac{2}{3}$ 9 $\frac{5}{7},\frac{1}{2}$ 10 $-2,3$ 11 $0,-4$ and $-7,-7\frac{1}{2}$
12 $-4,-3$ 13 $1,-1$ and $4,5$ 14 $-4,3$
15 $-1,2$ and $-3,4$ 16 $3,1$ and $1\frac{2}{3},-1\frac{1}{3}$

Exercise 16a (page 105)

1 $6p,8p$ 2 8 cm 3 40 4 $5\frac{1}{2}$ cm 5 $3,2$ 6 $5,3$ 7 42
8 $\frac{2}{5}$ 9 $14p,8p$ 10 $3,5$ 11 $4,9$ 12 £80, £30 13 $5,-1$
14 72 15 $9,-3$ 16 16 km h^{-1}, 5 km h^{-1} 17 8 g, 20 g
18 $7,35$ 19 6 cm, 3 cm 20 12 21 $\frac{5}{11}$ 22 $4,-3$ or $-4,3$
23 $2,1$ 24 $35,13$ 25 5 cm, 2 cm
26 100 km h^{-1}, 120 km h^{-1} 27 12 cm 28 $4,1$

Exercise 16b (page 109)

1 7 2 3 s 3 12 4 2 5 $12,18$ 6 11 7 $9,13$ 8 6 cm
9 3 10 $2,5$ 11 £$\frac{20}{x}$, £$\frac{20}{x-3}$, 8 12 £$\frac{160}{x}$, £$\frac{160}{x-4}$, 20
13 3 or 8 14 4 cm 15 60 16 $\frac{200}{x}$, $\frac{200}{x+10}$, $40,25$ hours
17 17 cm 18 6 19 $\frac{288}{x}$, $\frac{288}{x+16}$, 64 km h^{-1} 20 10 p
21 $15,25$ 22 7 cm, 10 cm 23 $1\frac{1}{2}$ m s^{-1}
24 60 km h^{-1}, 80 km h^{-1} 25 7 26 30 m min^{-1} 27 60 p
28 $2\frac{1}{2}$ m s^{-1} 29 24 30 £100 31 80 km h^{-1} 32 4 or $\frac{2}{3}$

Exercise 16c (page 111)

1 4 or -6 2 $13,15$ 3 12 s 4 7 p, 10 p 5 $5,9$ 6 $2,4,6$
7 3 8 $\frac{80}{x}$ p, $\frac{80}{x-4}$ p, 20 9 15 10 $5,7$ 11 5 cm, 8 cm
12 4 cm, 8 cm 13 2 14 4 m s^{-1} 15 $1\frac{1}{2},\frac{1}{2}$ 16 12
17 20 cm, 21 cm, 29 cm 18 50 19 32 cm, 18 cm 20 500
21 $0.098, 0.1$ 22 50 23 40 p 24 $12,3$ 25 75 26 $40,48$
27 82 28 100

Exercise 17a (page 114)

1 $\frac{y}{3}$ 2 $\frac{b^2}{2}$ 3 $\frac{b}{3a}$ 4 $\frac{3y}{x}$ 5 $\frac{2}{xy}$ 6 $\frac{a}{bc}$ 7 $\frac{4s}{3}$ 8 $\frac{3y}{2xw}$
9 $\frac{1}{b}$ 10 $\frac{2x}{x+y}$ 11 $\frac{1}{2a}$ 12 $\frac{2s}{r}$ 13 $\frac{x(2+x)}{2}$ 14 $\frac{x(x+1)}{3}$
15 $-\frac{4}{a}$ 16 $-a$ 17 $-\frac{y}{(1+2y)^2}$ 18 $\frac{x+y}{2}$ 19 $\frac{1}{1+x}$ 20 xy
21 2 22 $-(ab+1)$ 23 $-\frac{1}{2p}$ 24 $\frac{2-3x}{x-1}$ 25 $\frac{1}{2b}$ 26 $\frac{a-2}{a-1}$

Exercise 17b (page 116)

1 $\frac{a-c}{b}$ 2 $\frac{y+1}{x^2}$ 3 $\frac{2x-1}{x}$ 4 $\frac{3s+r^2}{rs}$ 5 $\frac{1-2x}{2x}$

6 $\frac{a^2+b^2}{b}$ 7 $\frac{y}{x+y}$ 8 $-\frac{1}{x}$ 9 $-\frac{2b}{a+b}$ 10 $\frac{xy}{x-y}$ 11 $\frac{1}{a}$

12 $\frac{ac}{b(b-c)}$ 13 $\frac{2y-x}{2x^2}$ 14 $\frac{3}{ps}$ 15 $\frac{a}{2}$ 16 $\frac{1}{y}$ 17 $\frac{2}{5w}$ 18 $\frac{1}{y}$

19 $-\frac{a+b}{2ab}$ 20 $\frac{2-x}{2x^2}$ 21 $\frac{x+1}{2x^2}$ 22 $\frac{2-xy}{2xy}$ 23 $\frac{1+a^2}{1+a}$

24 $\frac{r^2}{s(r+s)}$ 25 $\frac{2}{(x-1)^2}$ 26 $\frac{8x}{(2-x)(2+x)}$

Exercise 17c (page 117)

1 $\frac{1}{x+1}$ 2 $\frac{5x-1}{x(x-5)}$ 3 $\frac{4}{a+1}$ 4 $\frac{13y-1}{2(1+y)(1-y)}$

5 $\frac{a+2}{2a(1-3a)}$ 6 $\frac{3}{2x}$ 7 $\frac{4}{x+1}$ 8 $\frac{1}{p+2}$ 9 $\frac{-1}{x(4x-1)}$

10 $\frac{11y-1}{2(2y-1)(3y+1)}$ 11 $\frac{2}{x(x+2)}$ 12 $\frac{3}{2(a+1)}$

Exercise 17d (page 118)

1 $-\frac{2}{3}$ 2 $1\frac{1}{4}$ 3 2 4 -5 5 $-1\frac{1}{2}$ 6 $\frac{3}{4}$ 7 $1\frac{1}{9}$ 8 $-3, -1$

9 $\frac{4}{13}$ 10 1,4 11 $\frac{2}{13}$ 12 $2, -\frac{1}{2}$

Exercise 18a (page 121)

1 $\frac{w+y}{a}$ 2 $ps+r$ 3 $\frac{cd}{2b}$ 4 $\frac{wy}{x}$ 5 $\pm\sqrt{\left(\frac{w-t}{s}\right)}$ 6 $\frac{ax^2+2}{3x}$

7 $\frac{y^2r}{9x^2}$ 8 $\pm\sqrt{\left(\frac{at}{by}\right)}$ 9 $\frac{x-2w}{2}$ 10 $\frac{a-b}{12a^2}$ 11 $\frac{yw-w}{2y}$ 12 $\frac{5c}{3a}$

13 $\frac{1+4a^2b^2}{4a^2b^2}$ 14 $\frac{3a^2-2}{2a}$ 15 $\frac{5xw+6}{4}$ 16 $\frac{9y^2w^2+4w}{4y}$

17 $\frac{\pm\sqrt{x^2y^2-4a^2}}{x}$ 18 $\frac{9-16w^2x}{9}$ 19 $\frac{\pm\sqrt{4-w^2x^2}}{w}$

20 $\frac{\pm\sqrt{p-r}}{2p}$

Exercise 18b (page 123)

1 $\frac{y}{y-a}$ 2 $\frac{r+s}{r-s}$ 3 $\frac{a-2b}{a-b}$ 4 $\frac{3x-5b}{x+2b}$ 5 $\frac{xw}{x-2w+6}$

6 $\frac{2}{2+y}$ 7 $\frac{3p}{3s+2}$ 8 $\frac{3y}{3x-4}$ 9 $\frac{bc}{b^2-c}$ 10 $\frac{y^2}{3y-6}$

11 $\frac{sw}{s-w}$ 12 $\frac{2wy}{w+y}$ 13 $\frac{sr}{2r-as}$ 14 $\frac{4y}{6ys+1}$ 15 $\frac{x}{x^2+1}$

16 $\frac{ac}{4a-6c+1}$ 17 $\frac{3a+12}{3y+4}$ 18 $\frac{\pm R}{\sqrt{a-1}}$ 19 $\frac{\pm 2R}{\sqrt{4-Q^2}}$

20 $\pm b\sqrt{2}$ 21 $\frac{4x}{4-y}$ 22 $\pm\sqrt{\left(\frac{P^2s-2rb^2}{2r}\right)}$ 23 $\sqrt[3]{\left(\frac{bc}{b^2-1}\right)}$

24 $\pm\sqrt{\left(\frac{3xy}{2y-3x}\right)}$ 25 $\frac{\pm xP}{\sqrt{a^2+x^2}}$ 26 $\frac{\pm wy}{\sqrt{y^2-1}}$

27 $\pm\sqrt{\left(\frac{2r+3x}{3r+2x}\right)}$ 28 $\frac{\pm a}{\sqrt{a^2-1}}$ 29 m^2 30 $\frac{r^2+t^2}{2pt}$

Exercise 19 (page 127)

1 (a) 36 (b) ± 5 2 (a) $\frac{1}{2}$ (b) 12 3 (a) 18 (b) $\frac{1}{8}$ (c) $\pm 1\frac{1}{2}$

4 (a) $-\frac{1}{2}$ (b) 4 5 (a) $\frac{1}{6}$ (b) $\frac{1}{4}$ 6 (a) 16 (b) $\frac{1}{6}$ 7 $y=\frac{k}{w^2}$ 8 8

9 $\frac{1}{4}$ 10 (a) 3 (b) ± 2 11 (a) 9 (b) $\frac{1}{4}$ 12 $\frac{1}{16}$

13 (a) 44% (b) 125% 14 (a) 1 (b) $\frac{1}{2}$ 15 (a) $\frac{1}{2}$ (b) 1

16 (a) 8 (b) $\pm\frac{1}{4}$ 17 (a) 12 (b) $\pm\frac{1}{2}$ 18 (a) 16 days (b) 105 m

19 (a) $\frac{2}{3}$ kg (b) 135 cm 20 (a) 2 (b) 2 21 20% 22 57

23 15 24 $16\frac{1}{2}$ 25 (a) £370 (b) 75 26 (a) $10\frac{1}{2}$ m (b) 5 s

Exercise 20a (page 131)

1 (a) -2 (b) 4 (c) -5 2 (a) -1 (b) -5 (c) 5 (d) 8

3 (a) 3 (b) 24 (c) 24 (d) $-\frac{3}{4}$ (e) $5\frac{1}{4}$

4 (a) 2 (b) -3 (c) -1 (d) $-4\frac{1}{4}$

5 (a) 3 (b) 0 (c) 10 (d) 6 (e) 36

6 (a) -2 (b) 5 (c) 24 (d) 0 (e) 49

7 (a) -4 (b) -2 (c) 0 (d) -32

8 (a) -6 (b) -8 (c) 0 (d) 0 (e) -18

9 (a) 17 (b) 2 (c) 58 (d) -38

10 (a) 0 (b) 27 (c) 59 11 (a) 1 (b) 2 (c) $\frac{1}{4}$ (d) 32 (e) $\frac{1}{8}$

12 (a) $\frac{1}{3}$ (b) 2 (c) 10 (d) $\frac{2}{3}$ 13 (a) 2 (b) 3 14 (a) 4 (b) 4 (c)

15 (a) 2 (b) -3 (c) $\frac{3}{5}$ 16 (a) -6 (b) 6 (c) 5

17 (a) $-1, 5$ (b) $-2, 6$ (c) 1, 3 18 (a) $\frac{1}{2}, -4$ (b) $-\frac{1}{2}, -3$

19 (a) 0 (b) $\frac{1}{2}$ (c) -2 (d) $1\frac{1}{2}$ 20 (a) 1 (b) -1 (c) 2 21 $-3,$

22 $\{x:0\leqslant x\leqslant 4\}$ 23 $\{x:3\leqslant x\leqslant 13\}$ 24 $\{x:2\leqslant x<\infty\}$

25 {odd numbers} 26 N 27 $\{2,3,4,5,6\}$ (b) 4 (c) 8

28 (a) $\{-2,0,4,10\}$ (b) 4 (c) 1, 3

29 (a) 1, 3, 9 (b) 4, 6, 8 (c) 3, 8

30 (a) 5, 2 (b) 83, 90, 97 (c) 3

31 (a) $\{x:-1\leqslant x<\infty\}$ (b) $-3, 6$ (c) 2

32 (a) $\{x:-3<x<\infty\}$ (b) $-3, 6$ (c) $-2, 0, \frac{3}{4}$

Exercise 20b (page 133)

1 (a) 13 (b) 33 (c) -7 (d) -19 2 (a) 16 (b) 0 (c) -4

3 (a) 10 (b) 22 (c) -25 (d) -13 (e) 75 (f) 5

4 (a) 16 (b) 34 (c) 36 (d) 14 (e) 81 (f) 7

5 (a) $\frac{1}{2}$ (b) $-\frac{2}{3}$ (c) -2 (d) 1 (e) 4 (f) -2

6 (a) -12 (b) -5 (c) -10 (d) -11

7 (a) 2 (b) 2 (c) 8 8 (a) -22 (b) -2 (c) 1 (d) -19

9 (a) $x\to 4x-5$ (b) $x\to 4x-20$ (c) $x\to x-10$ (d) $x\to 16x$
(e) $x\to 4x-25$ (f) $x\to 16x-20$

10 (a) $6x+1$ (b) $6x-2$ (c) $4x-3$ (d) $27x+13$

11 (a) x^2-1 (b) x^2+4x+1 (c) x^4-6x^2+6

12 (a) $x\to\frac{-x}{x+1}$ (b) $x\to\frac{1}{x}$ (c) $x\to\frac{x+1}{x+2}$ (d) $x\to x+1$

13 (a) $x\to -(6x+1)$ (b) $x\to 10-6x$ (c) $x\to 5-6x$

14 (a) $x+1$ (b) $x+1$ (c) $x+2$ 15 (a) -4 (b) -1 (c) 1

16 (a) $\frac{1}{2}$ (b) 1 (c) $\frac{1}{5}$ 17 (a) 0, 1 (b) $1\frac{1}{2}$ (c) 2

18 (a) $-1, -3$ (b) ± 1

19 (a) $\{x:-1\leqslant x\leqslant 9\}$ (b) $\{x:-2\leqslant x\leqslant 8\}$

20 (a) $\{x:9\leqslant x\leqslant 25\}$ (b) $\{x:3\leqslant x\leqslant 7\}$

21 (a) $\{x:0\leqslant x\leqslant 100\}$ (b) $\{x:0\leqslant x\leqslant 50\}$

22 (a) gf (b) ff (c) fg (d) ggg 23 (a) fff (b) fg (c) ggf (d) f

24 (a) fhg(x) (b) fgg(x) (c) fhh(x) (d) ffgh(x) (e) hgf(x)

25 $3x-1$ 26 $(x+1)^2$ 27 x^3 28 x^2-x+1 29 $3x-1$

30 $-4x+3$ 31 $4x^2$ 32 $\frac{1}{2x}$ 33 1 34 $1\frac{1}{3}$ 35 3

Exercise 20c (page 137)

1 (a) $x\to x-2$ (b) $x\to\frac{x}{3}$ (c) $x\to 5x$ (d) $x\to x^2$

2 (a) 6 (b) ± 2 (c) 4 (d) $\pm 1\frac{1}{2}$ 3 (a) 2 (b) -3 4 (a) -5 (b)

5 $\frac{x-1}{2}$ 6 $\frac{x}{2}-1$ 7 $2(x+3)$ 8 $2x+3$ 9 $\pm\sqrt{x-4}$

10 $\pm\sqrt{x}-4$ 11 $\frac{1}{x}+2$ 12 $\frac{3}{x+2}$ 13 $4-\frac{1}{x}$ 14 $\pm\sqrt{\left(\frac{1}{2-}\right)}$

15 $\frac{x^2-3}{2}$ 16 $(2-x)^2$ 17 $\frac{3-x^2}{4}$ 18 Numbers 9, 10, 14

19 $x\to\frac{1}{x-1}$ 20 $x\to\frac{1}{x+2}$ 21 $x\to\frac{x+1}{3-3x}$

22 $x\to\pm\sqrt{\left(\frac{x}{x+1}\right)}$ 23 $x\to\pm\sqrt{\left(\frac{y^2-1}{3x^2-2}\right)}$ 24 $\frac{x}{2}-1$

25 $2(x+3)$

26 (a) $x\to\pm\sqrt{\left(\frac{x+2}{3}\right)}$ (b) $x\to\frac{\pm\sqrt{x}}{3}+2$ (c) $x\to\frac{\pm\sqrt{x+2}}{3}$

27 f is its own inverse

29 (a) Yes (b) No (c) No (d) Yes (e) No (f) No
(g) Yes (h) Yes

30 -2 31 3 32 (a) 4 (b) 2, 4 (c) $\frac{1}{2}, 4$

Exercise 21a (page 140)

1 $x^3 + 5x^2 + 10x + 8$ **2** $x^3 - 3x^2 + 5x - 3$
3 $2x^3 - x^2 - 7x + 6$ **4** $x^4 + 6x^2 + 11x + 6$
5 $2x^3 - 3x^2 - 5x + 6$ **6** $6x^3 - 23x^2 + 16x - 3$ **7** $-5x^2$
8 $-x^2$ **9** 0 **10** $-x^2$ **11** $7x^2$ **12** $-12x^2$ **13** 25 **14** -20
15 47 **16** 12 **17** -1 **18** 108 **19** 3 **20** -2 **21** -3
22 -4 **23** -5 **24** $-\frac{3}{4}$ **25** 9 **26** ±14 **27** 16 **28** ±24
29 $x^2 - 5x + 6 = 0$ **30** $x^2 - 4x - 5 = 0$ **31** $x^2 + 7x + 12 = 0$
32 $2x^2 + 7x - 4 = 0$ **33** $6x^2 + 5x + 1 = 0$
34 $18x^2 - 9x - 2 = 0$ **35** $8x^2 + 30x + 27 = 0$ **36** 4 **37** 3
38 2, 3 **39** $-1, -5$ **40** $4, -2$

Exercise 21b (page 143)

1 $x + 6$ **2** $x - 6$ **3** $2x + 3$ **4** $3x - 4$ **5** $x^2 + 3x + 1$
6 $x^2 - x + 3$ **7** $x^2 - x - 5$ **8** $3x^2 + x - 2$ **9** $x^2 - 2x + 4$
10 $(x - 1)(x + 1)(x + 3)$ **11** $(x - 2)(x + 1)(x - 3)$·
12 $(x - 1)^2(x + 2)$ **13** $(x + 1)(x - 3)(x + 2)$
14 $(x + 1)(x - 3)(2x - 1)$ **15** $(x - 2)(x + 2)(2x - 1)$
16 $(x - 3)(3x - 1)(x + 4)$ **17** $(x + 3)^2(x - 6)$
18 $(x - 4)(2x - 1)(2x + 1)$ **19** $-3, (x - 1)(x - 4)(x + 2)$
20 $-5, (x + 2)(x - 1)(x - 3)$
21 $-18, (x - 3)(x + 3)(2x + 1)$
22 $9, (x + 1)(3x - 1)(3x - 2)$
23 $15, (x + 3)(x - 2)(2x - 3)$
24 $-13, (x + 2)(3x - 1)(2x + 1)$
25 $-1, -3$ **26** $4, -7$ **27** $0, -3$ **28** $2, -17$ **29** $-7, -6$
30 $3, -10$

Exercise 22a (page 147)

1 (a) 5 (b) -8 (c) -1 (d) 4 (e) 17 **2** (a) -2 (b) 2 (c) -2
(a) $\frac{1}{3}$ (b) 6 (c) 2 **4** (a) 4 (b) 3 (c) 2 (d) 4
(a) 4 (b) -3 (c) 7 (d) 11 **6** (a) 2 (b) 8 (c) 6 (d) 0
(a) -2 (b) -3 (c) 3, -2 **8** (a) 64 (b) 2 (c) 3 (d) -2 (e) $1\frac{1}{2}$
9 (a) p (b) r (c) r (d) q, r **10** (a) 4 (b) 2 (c) 1, 4 (d) 3
11 (a) 10 (b) 15 (c) 3 (d) 7 (e) 11, 12, 13, 14
12 (a) 4 (b) 6 (c) 1, 6 (d) 5 (e) 3 **13** (a) $y = x$ (b) $y = \frac{3x}{2}$
14 (a) 4, -2 (b) $-\frac{3}{4}$ (c) $1\frac{1}{2}, -1$ (d) $\frac{3}{5}, -1$

Exercise 22b (page 150)

1 (a) No (b) Yes (c) No (d) No (e) Yes
(f) Yes (g) Yes (h) No
2 (a) Yes (b) No (c) No (d) Yes (e) Yes
3 (a) 4 (b) 1, -2, 13 (c) 4 **4** (a) 3 (b) $1\frac{1}{2}$, -1
5 (a) Yes (b) No (c) Yes (d) Yes (e) Yes (f) No
6 (a) No (b) No (c) Yes **7** 4, 2 **8** 5, 2, 3
10 (b) s, q, t (c) r

Exercise 23a (page 155)

1 Right-angled **2** Isosceles **3** Right-angled isosceles
4 Rectangle **5** Parallelogram **6** Trapezium
7 (a) 10. (b) (4,3) **8** (a) 5 (b) $(3, 5\frac{1}{2})$ **9** (a) 8 (b) (1,2)
10 (a) 13 (b) $(6\frac{1}{2}, 8)$ **11** (a) $\sqrt{17}$ (b) $(3, \frac{3}{2})$ **12** (a) 16 (b) (2,3)
13 (a) $\sqrt{2}$ (b) $(3\frac{1}{2}, -\frac{1}{2})$ **14** (a) $2\sqrt{13}$ (b) (1,0) **15** (4,6)
16 (3,15) **17** (13,4) **18** (6,9) **19** (2,0) **20** (6,3) or (6,-3)

Exercise 23b (page 162)

1 4 **2** $2\frac{1}{3}$ **3** -2 **4** $-\frac{3}{4}$ **5** 2 **6** $\frac{2}{3}$ **7** 1 **8** $-1\frac{1}{4}$
9 $-2\frac{1}{7}$ **10** $\frac{4}{7}$ **11** 3, -2 **12** $-1, 4$. **13** $-1, -5$
14 $1\frac{1}{2}, -2$ **15** $-1\frac{3}{4}, \frac{1}{3}$ **16** $\frac{1}{6}, \frac{2}{3}$ **17** $(-2,0), (0,4), 2$
18 (4,0), (0,2), $-\frac{1}{2}$ **19** $(1\frac{1}{2},0), (0,3), -2$ **20** (5,0), (0,5), -1
21 Yes **22** Yes **23** No **24** Yes **25** No **26** No **27** (4,7)
28 (0,0) and (3,9) **29** (3,-1) **30** $(-4,-4)$ and (1,6)
31 (1,-1) **32** (3,4) and (-2,4) **33** $(\frac{1}{2},0)$ **34** (1,5)
35 T **36** F **37** F **38** F **39** T **40** T **41** F **42** T
43 F **44** F **45** T **46** F

Exercise 23c (page 168)

1 $(-2,0), (3,0)$ **2** $(-4,0), (1,0)$ **3** $(1,0), (3,0)$ **4** $(-2,0),$
$(1,0)$ **5** $(-2,0), (5,0)$ **6** $(0,0), (3,0)$ **7** $(2,0), (3,0)$ **8** $(0,0),$
$(\frac{1}{2},0)$ **9** $(-\frac{1}{2},0), (2,0)$ **10** $(\frac{1}{4},0), (1,0)$ **11** $(0,3)$ **12** $(0,5)$
13 $(0,0)$ **14** $(0,-1)$ **15** $(0,-4)$ **16** $x = 3$ **17** $x = 2$
18 $x = 1\frac{1}{2}$ **19** $x = 0$ **20** $x = \frac{3}{8}$ **21** No **22** No
23 Yes **24** Yes **25** $-3 < x < 5$ **26** $x < -5$ or $x > 1$
27 $x < 1$ or $x > 7$ **28** $0 < x < 5$ **29** $-2 < x < 2$
30 $x < -3$ or $x > 1$ **31** No values of x **32** $x < 0$ or
$x > \frac{2}{3}$ **33** $-3 < x < 2\frac{1}{2}$ **34** All values of x
35 $x < \frac{3}{4}$ or $x > 1\frac{1}{2}$ **36** T **37** T **38** F **39** F **40** T
41 F **42** F **43** F **44** T **45** F **46** T

Exercise 23d (page 172)

1 $x^2 - 2x + 3 = 0$ **2** $2x^2 - x - 4 = 0$
3 $x^3 + x^2 + 2 = 0$ **4** $x^3 - 3x^2 - 1 = 0$
5 $3x^2 - x - 2 = 0$ **6** $2x^2 - x - 3 = 0$
7 (a) 0 (b) 1 (c) 6 (d) 3 **8** (a) 0 (b) 2 (c) 5 (d) -4
9 $x^2 = 6$ **10** $x^2 = 3$ **11** $x^3 = 3$ **12** $x^3 = 10$ **13** $y = 2x$
14 $y = x + 5$ **15** $y = 2 - 2x$ **16** $2y + 5x = 4$

Exercise 23e (page 173)

1 4.32, 6.12, 5.52, 1.75 **2** (a) 1.72, -0.39 (b) 2.61,
-1.28 (c) -1.33 **3** (a) $1.59 < x < 4.41$ (b) $x < 0.55$ or
$x > 5.45$ **4** (a) -1.5 (b) 0.65, 5.35 **5** (a) 2 (b) -1.8
(c) $0.38 < x < 2.62$ **6** (a) 3.65, -1.65 (b) 3.24, -1.24
(c) 4.37, -1.37 **7** (a) $1.75 < x < 4.5$ (b) $1.86 < x < 4.27$
8 (a) 12.2 (b) 2.71 (c) 2.41 **9** (a) -12 (b) -32 (c) 4.78
10 (a) 2.83 (b) 0.59, 3,41 (c) 0.71 **11** (a) 1.73 (b) 1.39
12 (a) 1.25 (b) 3.17 **13** (a) 5.53, 2.24 (b) 1.22, -0.69
(c) 0.81, 6.19 **14** (a) $0.68 < x < 7.32$ (b) 1.53 (c) 0.65,
3.85.

Exercise 24a (page 181)

1 (a) No (b) Yes (c) No (d) No (e) No (f) No (g) Yes
2 (a) (1,2) (b) (3,6) (c) (2,1) (d) (1,5) (e) (2,3)
3 (a) (0,0), (2,0), (0,4) (b) (0,0), (4,2), (0,2) (c) $(-2, -4)$,
(6,8), (4,8) (d) $(-1,-3)$, (1,2), $(-1,5)$
4 (a) $x > 0$, $y < 1$, $2y > x$ (b) $x > 0$, $y > -1$,
$y + 2x < 3$ (c) $y > 0$, $x < 3$, $y < 4$, $3y + 4x > 0$
(d) $x > 0$, $3y > 2x$, $x < 3$, $y < x + 2$
(e) $x > -2$, $y < 6$, $x + y < 6$, $y > x - 6$
5 (a) (1,1), (2,1), (3,1), (1,2), (2,2) (b) 7 (c) 3 (d) 5
6 (a) $2\frac{1}{2}$ (b) 3 (c) 4 **7** (a) 16 (b) -3 (c) 5 **8** (a) 14
(b) -3 (c) 4 **9** (a) $7\frac{1}{2}$ (b) $7\frac{1}{2}$ (c) -6 **10** (a) 7 (b) 7 (c) -4

Exercise 24b (page 185)

1 25 **2** (a) 22 sweets and 11 chocolates or 21 sweets
and 12 chocolates, (b) 22 chocolates and no sweets
3 (a) 18 (b) 9 (c) 8, 7 (d) 20, 5 **4** (a) 1.9 kg of X,
3.4 kg of Y or 1.8 kg of X, 3.5 kg of Y (b) 5.8 kg of Y,
none of X **5** (a) 10, 5 (b) 9, 3 **6** (a) 12 (b) 15, 10 (c) 6, 16
7 (a) 13, (b) 10 (c) 17, 2 or 16, 3 (d) 8, 3 or 10, 2
8 (a) 302, (b) £4200 (c) £4400 (d) 25
9 (a) (i) 25, 18 or 24, 20, (ii) 20, 25 (b) 24, 8 or 25, 9
10 (a) 10 (b) 15 (c) 6, 15 or 7, 14 (d) 12, 7 (e) 4, 16

Exercise 25a (page 195)

1 $36°$ **2** $56°$ **3** $38°$ **4** $34°$ **5** $32°$ **6** $48°$ **7** $40°, 70°$
8 $70°, 112°$ **9** $75°, 45°$ **10** $110°, 45°$ **11** $48°, 92°$
12 $56°, 98°$ **13** $130°, 100°$ **14** $55°$ **15** $34°, 56°$
16 $30°$ **17** $144°$ **18** $24°$ **19** 12 **20** $67\frac{1}{2}°, 90°$ **21** $120°$
22 $15°, 45°$ **23** $18°, 72°$ **24** $67\frac{1}{2}$

Exercise 25b (page 198)

1 30 **2** $22\frac{1}{2}$ **3** 10 **4** 70° **5** 190° **6** 120° **8** $\frac{x}{2}$
9 (a) $90° - \frac{x}{2}, \frac{x}{2}$ (b) 60° **11** (a) $90° - x$ (b) $2x$
12 (a) $2x$, $180° - 4x$ (b) 36° **14** (a) $30° + x$ (b) $60° - x$

Exercise 26a (page 203)

1 No **2** SSS **3** No **4** SAS **5** AAS **6** No **7** RHS
8 SAS **9** ASA

Exercise 26b (page 212)

1 $13\frac{1}{2}$, 10 **2** 30, 32 **3** 35, 15 **4** 60, 55 **5** 5, 6 **6** 6, 3
7 20, 26 **8** 8, $7\frac{1}{2}$, **9** 5, $3\frac{1}{2}$, **10** $\frac{1}{3}, \frac{1}{2}, \frac{1}{2}$ **11** $\frac{3}{4}$, 3
12 $\frac{1}{3}$, 3, $\frac{1}{2}$ **13** $\frac{3}{5}, \frac{3}{2}, \frac{2}{5}, \frac{2}{3}$, **14** $\frac{3}{2}, \frac{16}{16}$ **15** *BDC* **16** *BDC*
17 *AED* **18** *DEC* **19** *ADE*

Exercise 26c (page 217)

1 (a) 1 : 2 (b) 1 : 4 **2** (a) 2 : 3 (b) 4 : 9 **3** (a) 4 : 5
(b) 4 : 5 **4** (a) 1 : 9 (b) 1 : 27 **5** (a) 2 : 3 (b) 8 : 27
6 27 : 125 **7** 27 **8** $62\frac{1}{2}$ litres **9** (a) 9 : 7 (b) 9 : 16
(c) 4 : 21 **10** 40 **11** 3 minutes **12** $5\frac{1}{3}$ **13** (a) 1
(b) $\frac{3}{4}$ **14** $10\frac{2}{3}$ litres **15** 4 : 9 **16** (a) 16 cm² (b) 5 : 2
17 £16.20 **18** 80 cm² **19** (a) $4\frac{1}{2}$ cm² (b) 18 cm
20 (a) 4 : 5 (b) 16 cm, 9 cm

Exercise 27a (page 220)

1 (a) (2,−1), (4,−1), (4,−2), (2,−2) (b) (−2,1), (−4,1),
(−4,2), (−2,2) (c) (2,5), (4,5), (4,4), (2,4)
2 (a) (−1,3), (2,3), (2,5) (b) (1,−3), (−2,−3), (−2,−5)
(c) (−3,−1), (−3,2), (−5,2)
3 (a) (4,0), (4,−1), (2,0) (b) (0,4), (1,4), (0,2) (c) (0,4),
(−1,4), (0,2) (d) (0,−4), (1,−4), (0,−2)
4 (a) (1,6), (2,6), (2,5) (b) (6,1), (6,2), (5,2) (c) (0,5),
(0,4), (1,4)
5 (a) (0,−4), (b) (0,3) (c) (2,0) (d) (2,−1) (e) (−1,−5)
(f) (−3,4) (g) $(a,−b)$
6 (a) (−3,0) (b) (1,0) (c) (−2,3) (d) (0,5) (e) (4,1)
(f) (5,−2) (g) $(−a,b)$
7 (a) (2,0), (0,0), (−6,0) (b) (0,−3), (0,−5), (0,0)
8 (a) (2,0) (b) (2,−2) (c) (−1,0) (d) (4,3) (e) (1,3)
(f) (7,−4)
9 (a) (0,−5) (b) (3,−4) (c) (3,−2) (d) (4,−3) (e) (5,3)
(f) (−5,−12)
10 (a) (1,0), (1,−2) (b) (3,−2), (1,−2), (0,−2)
11 (a) $y − 3 = 0$, $y + 2 = 0$ (b) $x = 4$,
$2x − 1 = 0$, $y + 2 = 0$
12 (a) (1,2) (b) (3,3) (c) (2,5) (d) (4,−2) (e) (−2,−1)
(f) (b,a)
13 (a) (−2,0) (b) (0,−3) (c) (−1, −2) (d) (−1,3) (e) (7,4)
(f) $(−b,−a)$
14 (a) $x = 3$ (b) $x = −2$ (c) $y = 6$ (d) $x = 5$
(e) $y = −1$ (f) $y = 1$
15 (a) (−2,−1) (b) (−2,−1) (c) (5,3) (d) (−5,−3)
(e) (0,−4) (f) (0,8) (g) (1,3) (h) (−4,1)
16 (a) $(−a,−b)$ (b) $(−a,−b)$ (c) $(−b,a)$ (d) $(b,−a)$
17 Y⁴, S², XYXY
18 (a) T (b) T (c) F (d) F (e) T (f) T (g) T

Exercise 27b (page 228)

1 (a) (0,1), (−2,0) (b) (−1,0), (0,−2) (c) (0,−1), (2,0)
2 (a) (−1,0), (−1,−3), (−2,−1) (b) (2,1), (5,1), (3,0)
3 (a) (−3,0) (b) (0,2) (c) (−3,−5) (d) (4,−1) (e) $(−a,−b)$
4 (a) (0,5) (b) (−3,0) (c) (2,0) (d) (−1,3) (e) (−5,−2)
(f) (1,−4) (g) $(−b,a)$
5 (a) (2,0) (b) (4,−1) (c) (−2,3) (d) (−5,−2) (e) $(b,−a)$

Exercise 27c (page 234)

1 (a) B, E, T (b) H, O (c) H, O, S
2 Rhombus, $x = 1$, $y = 2$ **3** Rectangle, running track
4 $y = 3$ **5** (1,0), (1,−2), (0,−1), (−2,−1), (−1,0), (−1,2)
6 $x = 2$, $y = 2$, $y = x$, $y = −x + 4$ **7** 9
8 (a) (0,5), (−2,2) (b) (1,5), (−3,0), (0,−2)
9 (a) Kite (b) Isosceles trapezium **10** $x = 3$, $y = 1$
11 (a) 4 (b) 1 **12** (3,1), (2,4), (−1,3) **13** $y = 2x$
14 (4,1), kite **15** (a) Mediator, (b) Bisectors of angles
16 (a) (−2,−5), (1,−3), (−4,2) (b) (5,7), (0,12)
17 (a) DID, OXO (b) OXO, AHA, MUM (c) OXO, SOS
18 (a) T (b) T (c) T (d) F (e) T
19 120°, 45° **20** (a) T (b) T (c) F (d) F

Exercise 28a (page 243)

1 52°, 128° **2** 47°, 53°, 53° **3** 124°, 62°, 118° **4** 64°
5 70°, 30° **6** 236°, 124° **7** 60° **8** 115° **9** 58° **10** 114°
11 100°, 100°, 80° **12** 50°, 40°, 70° **13** 54°, 126° **14** 80°
15 106° **16** 30° **17** 40°, 60°, 30° **18** 40°, 100° **19** 32°,
20 40° **21** 50° **22** 25 **23** 60°, 40° **24** 54°

Exercise 28b (page 246)

1 144°, 104° **2** 50° **3** 105°, 50° **4** 50°, 30° **5** 110°
6 70°, 110° **7** 18° **8** 16°, 46° **9** 43° **10** 110°, 140°
11 65°, 15° **12** 40°, 40° **13** 35°,75° **14** 60°, 25°
15 48°, 48° **16** 50° **17** 55°, 25° **18** 70°, 55° **19** 140°
20 56°

Exercise 28c (page 251)

1 80° **3** 70°

Exercise 28d (page 258)

1 $3\frac{3}{4}$ **2** 8 **3** 10 **4** $2\frac{1}{2}$ **5** 3, 6 **6** 3, $4\frac{2}{3}$ **7** 4, $4\frac{2}{3}$
8 12, 8 **9** $1\frac{1}{2}, 3\frac{1}{6}$ **10** 6, 4 **11** 24, 24, 16, 18 **12** 1, $\frac{4}{5}$,
$3\frac{1}{5}$ **13** $5\frac{1}{2}$, 4 **20** $6\frac{1}{2}$

Exercise 29a (page 269)

1 $2\frac{1}{2}$ **2** 6 **3** 4 **4** $4\frac{1}{2}$ **5** $1\frac{1}{2}$ **6** $4\frac{2}{3}$ **7** $3\frac{1}{2}$ **8** 2 : 1
9 13 : 6 **10** 90 **11** 12 **12** 75 **13** 10, 50 **14** 140
15 75 **16** 2 : 1, 2 : 3 **17** 1 : 4 **18** 1 : 3 **19** 3 : 2
20 1 : 2

Exercise 29b (page 271)

1 9 cm², $7\frac{1}{2}$ cm², 12 cm² **2** 4 : 5, 7 : 9 **3** 12 cm²,
6 cm² **4** 20 cm² **5** 24 cm², 8 cm² **6** 12, 10 **7** $5\frac{1}{3}$
8 3 : 2 **9** $13\frac{1}{3}$ cm², $21\frac{1}{3}$ cm² **10** 20, 32 **11** 6
12 (a) 1 : 3 (b) 1 : 2 (c) 3 : 1 (d) 1 : 8 **13** (a) 2 (b) 3

) 16 (d) $\dfrac{qr}{p-q}$ **14** 2, 3, $\frac{1}{6}$ **16** (a) 2 : 5 (b) 3

) $12\frac{1}{2}$ cm^2 **17** 2, 4 **19** 4 : 5, 2 : 3, 3 : 2 **20** 7 : 3

1 9 : 16 **22** $\frac{7}{18}$

xercise 30a (page 278)

The diameter perpendicular to the chords
A parallel plane
The two angular bisectors
A concentric circle
A horizontal square
The mediator of AB
(a) The circle, perpendicular to the line, of centre A and
dius AP (b) the plane through A perpendicular to the line
(a) Two half-lines (b) the surface of a cone
The mediator of AB
) (a) A cylindrical surface (b) a concentric sphere
A concentric circle
The line through the centre of the square perpendicular
its plane
(a) A circle parallel to the given plane (b) a plane parallel
the given plane
(a) A semicircle with diameter AC (b) a line parallel to
C

xercise 30b (page 287)

3.6 cm **3** 9.9 cm **4** 2.5 cm **5** 3.7 cm **6** 4 cm
4.6 cm **10** 2.9 cm **12** 2.7 cm **13** 6 cm **14** 5.9 cm
6.5 cm **17** 3.1 cm **18** 4.2 cm **19** 6.6 cm **20** 3.1 cm

xercise 30c (page 288)

7.8 cm **2** 11.2 cm **3** 7 cm **4** 5.75 cm **5** 6.9 cm
3.7 cm **7** 10.4 cm **8** 10.3 cm **9** 8.95 cm
10.95 cm **11** 7.9 cm **12** 10.6 cm **13** 10 cm
11.3 cm

xercise 31a (page 295)

12.7, 5.92 **2** 0.515, 0.266 **3** 14.0, 40.9 **4** 1440,
55 **5** 29.7°, 14 cm^2 **6** 4.02 cm, 5.63 cm^2 **7** 50.41°,
9 **8** 54.3° , 0.0975 **9** 1.52 m, 5300 cm^2 **10** 0.370,
1° **11** 3910, 50.2° **12** 2.54 km, 1.10 km^2 **13** 47.9°
10.4 **15** 17.5 **16** 0.566 **17** 28.3° **18** 20 **19** 28.4,
,8 **20** 42.2°, 46.6 **21** 144 **22** 108 cm^2 **23** 262 cm^2
9.72 cm **25** 8.58 cm^2 **26** 102°, 14.3 **27** 51.9°
36.9°

ercise 31b (page 298)

$\frac{12}{13}, \frac{5}{12}$ **2** $\frac{2}{\sqrt{5}}, \frac{1}{\sqrt{5}}$ **3** $\frac{4}{5}, 1\frac{1}{3}$
$\frac{2}{\sqrt{5}}, \frac{1}{2}$ **5** $\frac{15}{17}, \frac{8}{17}$ **6** $\frac{3}{4}, \frac{3}{\sqrt{7}}$
75 cm **8** 9 cm **9** 68 cm **10** 600 cm^2
18 cm, 24 cm **12** 10 cm **13** 12 cm
24 cm **15** 22 cm **16** 13 cm **17** 120 cm
30 cm **19** 18 cm **20** 20 cm **21** 35 cm
62.5 cm, 120 cm **23** 40 cm **24** 20 cm, 10 cm

ercise 31c (page 303)

9.43 km, 058° **2** 19.9 m **3** 33.7° **4** 320°
38.6 n.m. **6** 056° **7** 25 m **8** 276 km **9** 53.8°
210° **11** 4.54 m **12** (a) 24.1 n.m. (b) 17.9 n.m.
4.37 m **14** 56.9 n.m. **15** 56.1° **16** 88.2 km, 323°
18 s **18** 16.1° **19** 4 h 51 min **20** 2.89 m
17.8° **22** 9.81 m, 119° **23** (a) 28.2°, (b) 301 m

Exercise 32 (page 311)

1 $-\sin 20°$ **2** $\cos 60°$ **3** $-\tan 50°$ **4** $-\cos 25°$
5 $-\sin 75°$ **6** $\tan 38°$ **7** $\sin 76°$ **8** $-\cos 82°$
9 $-\tan 37°$ **10** $-\cos 67°$ **11** $-\sin 18°$ **12** $\cos 71°$
13 Second **14** Third **15** Fourth **16** Third **17** $-\dfrac{12}{13}$
18 0.8, $-1\frac{1}{3}$ **19** -0.87, -0.87 **20** -0.88, 0.88
21 0.84 **22** 0.64, -0.64 **23** 0.91 **24** $\dfrac{24}{25} - 3\frac{3}{7}$
25 $\dfrac{5}{13}, \dfrac{12}{13}$ **26** $-1\frac{7}{8}, \dfrac{15}{17}$ **27** -0.8 **28** 32 cm
29 24 cm **30** 210°, 330° **31** 90°, 270° **32** 71.6°, 252°
33 0°, 180°, 360° **34** 118°, 242° **35** 270° **36** 119°, 299°
37 0°, 360° **38** 20.5°, 160° **39** 43.1°, 317° **40** 45°, 225°

Exercise 33a (page 315)

1 4.57, 6.16 **2** 31.6, 30.0 **3** 0.578, 0.353 **4** 29.6°
5 27.0° **6** 41.3 cm, 38.7 cm **7** 6.43 cm, 5.13 cm
8 24.6° **9** 48.8° **10** 21.9°

Exercise 33b (page 319)

1 3.15 **2** 5.73 **3** 7.81 **4** 18.1 **5** 78.5° **6** 60° **7** 117°
8 112° **9** 5.18 cm, 8.55 cm^2 **10** 7.25 mm, 26.1 mm^2
11 1.92 m, 0.442 m^2 **12** 79.6°, 34.8° **13** 100° **14** 114°
15 73.0°, 47.3 cm^2 **16** 110°, 33.0 cm^2 **17** 46.8°,
99°, 34.2°, 35.1 mm^2 **18** 137°, 23°, 20°, 2730 cm^2

Exercise 33c (page 321)

1 (a) 27.9 m (b) 60.6° **2** (a) 109 m (b) 83.1 m **3** 2.30°
4 (a) 49.7 m (b) 40.7 m **5** 26.3 knots **6** (a) 93.7 m
(b) 47.8 m **7** 7 minutes **8** 26.7 n.m. **9** 242°
10 (a) 44 minutes (b) 44 n.m. **11** 12.1 n.m., 37 minutes
12 (a) 75.2 n.m. (b) 64.3 n.m. **13** 43.4 n.m., 217°
14 104 m **15** 11.1 n.m., 10.0 n.m. **16** 108 m
17 11.8 knots, 2.42 n.m. **18** (a) 11.9 km (b) 12.27 p.m.
19 (a) 5.39 km (b) 14.3 km (c) 025° **20** 46.5 n.m., 021°,
17.4 knots.

Exercise 34 (page 327)

1 (a) 6.71 cm (b) 3 cm (c) 8.19 cm (d) 13 cm
2 (a) 26.6° (b) 63.4° (c) 21.8° (d) 33.7° (e) 56.3° (f) 53.1°
3 24 cm **4** (a) 64.8° (b) 71.6° **5** (a) arc sin $\frac{3}{7}$
(b) arc tan 2 (c) arc sin $\frac{6}{7}$ **6** (a) 55.2° (b) 61.3°
7 (a) 56.3° (b) 50.2° (c) 63.4° **8** (a) 63.8° (b) 52.4°
(c) 35.5° **9** (a) 2 (b) 3.61 (c) 23.6° (d) 33.7°
10 (a) 36.9° (b) 40.9° (c) 60° **11** (a) 9.33 cm
(b) 9.98 cm (c) 69.2° **12** (a) 36.9° (b) 24.2° (c) 46.8°
(d) 33.2° **13** 28.3° **14** (a) 4.62 cm (b) 68.9° (c) 79.1°
15 (a) 5.20 m (b) 7.81 m (c) 41.7° (d) 87.8°
16 (a) 67.4° (b) 76.0° (c) 36.9° (d) $\frac{4}{5}$ **17** (a) 41.5°
(b) 51.3° (c) 77.3° **18** (a) 41.4° (b) 56.7° **19** 59.3°
20 17.5°

Exercise 35a (page 339)

1 (a) 1.25 cm^2 (b) 500 cm^2 (c) 28 mm^3 (d) 570 km^2
(e) 300 cm^3 **2** (a) 22 cm (b) 38.5 cm^2 **3** (a) 78.5 cm^2
(b) 11.5 cm^2 **4** $3\frac{2}{3}$g cm^{-3} **5** 12 cm^3 **6** 5.05 m
7 0.2 g cm^{-3} **8** $333\frac{1}{3}$ cm^3 **9** (a) 378 m (b) 8530 m^2
10 (a) 400 cm^3 (b) 360 cm^2 **11** 372 cm^3 **12** (a) $4\frac{1}{2}$ m^3
(b) 679 g **13** 1056 cm^2 **14** 63.6 m^2 **15** $\frac{19}{27}$
16 (a) 112 cm^3 (b) 84 g **17** (a) 1340 cm^3 (b) 541 cm^2
18 1560 cm^3 **19** (a) 276 cm^2 (b) 78.1 m^2 **20** 36.0 g
21 1640 cm^3 **22** 2.46 cm **23** 18 400 cm^3 **24** 3.76 cm
25 243 m^2 **26** 300 m^3 **27** 46.1 m **28** 750 m^3

29 62.8 kg **30** (a) 200 cm³ (b) 268 cm² **31** 7.56 cm
32 6 cm **33** 29 300 cm³ **34** 2 cm

Exercise 35b (page 342)

1 (a) 100 cm³ (b) 250 g **2** 2 cm **3** 20 cm **4** 5 cm
5 200 s **6** 5.83 cm, 4 cm **7** 40 **8** 4 cm² **9** 40.2 cm
10 3.76 cm **11** 125 cm s⁻¹ **12** 50 cm² **13** (a) 62.8 m
(b) 11 **14** (a) 18.8 m s⁻¹ (b) 13.3 **15** 53.1 cm

Exercise 36 (page 349)

1 (a) 5.24 cm (b) 13.1 cm² **2** (a) 33.6 cm (b) 420 cm²
3 (a) 18.8 cm (b) 37.7 cm² **4** (a) 33.1 cm (b) 199 cm²
5 49.1° **6** 30° **7** 229° **8** 65.3° **9** 72° **10** 252°
11 11.9 cm **12** 7.92 cm **13** 2.26 cm **14** 140 cm
15 6 cm **16** 32.4 cm² **17** 195 cm² **18** 96.3 cm²
19 22.7 cm² **20** 289 m **21** (a) 209 cm (b) 15.7 cm
22 1833 cm² **23** 68.5 cm² **24** 4 cm, 19.6 cm
25 (a) 29.3 (b) 48.3 **26** 138° **27** 1535 cm³
28 346 cm² **30** 15.3 **31** 34.4 cm² **32** 81.6 cm²

Exercise 37a (page 357)

1 11 100 km **2** 6670 km **3** 8890 km **4** 3340 km
5 10 000 km **6** 5000 km **7** 2780 km **8** 16 700 km
9 14 500 km **10** 21 100 km **11** 19 300 km
12 32 800 km **13** 27.0°N, 20°W **14** 0°N, 43.0°E
15 0°N, 22.5°W **16** 60°S, 51.0°W **17** 30°N, 114°W
18 17.9°N, 0°E **19** 40°S, 106°W **20** 20°N, 133°W
21 51.5 cm **22** 59.1° N or S **23** 70.1°N, 125°W
24 58.4°N or S **25** 35.0°N, 27.1°E **26** 19.4°S, 111°E
27 596 km **28** 1040 km h⁻¹

Exercise 37b (page 361)

1 2400 n.m. **2** 4080 n.m. **3** 10 800 n.m. **4** 3720 n.m.
5 5400 n.m. **6** 13 800 n.m. **7** 2630 n.m.
8 80°N, 40°W **9** 0°N, 55°E **10** 60°N, 105°W
11 25°N, 21.6°E **12** 16°S, 0°W **13** 48.2° N or S
14 75.5° N or S **15** 25°S, 35°W **16** 36°S, 120°W
17 700 knots **18** 15 knots **19** 1800 n.m.
20 36.9° N or S

Exercise 38a (page 364)

1 11 **2** 263 **3** 5 **4** 86.28 **5** 146.2 **6** 11 p **7** £5
8 65 **9** $\frac{5}{12}$ **10** 55% **11** 30 **12** $1\frac{1}{3}$ **13** £7 **14** £91.25
15 (a) £20 (b) 12 p **16** 56 p **17** 10 **18** 78 **19** £90
20 1.55 **21** 85% **22** 3, 11,13

Exercise 38b (page 365)

1 $\frac{10x + 12y}{x + y}$ **2** $\frac{5x + 7y}{12}$ **3** 5 **4** 71.2 **5** $\frac{15y - 10x}{y}$
6 30 **7** 30 p **8** $\frac{8x - 3y}{5}$ **9** 12 **10** 13

Exercise 38c (page 370)

1 (a) 1.8, 2, 3 (b) 7.2, 7, 7 (c) 40, 20, 0 (d) 0.5, 1, 5
(e) 0, -0.2, -0.3 **2** £4.75, £4, £2 **3** 4.6, 4.5, 4
4 $8\frac{2}{3}$ g, $8\frac{1}{2}$ g, 10 g **5** Median, 1 goal **6** 45%, 47%,
53%, 49% **7** Mean, 9 p; mode, 8 p **8** Median, 5;
mode, 5 **9** Mean, £112; mode, £120 **10** 18°, 180°,
126°, 36° **11** 144°, 126°, 90° **12** 30, 1$\frac{1}{6}$, 3, 3
13 (a) 11.4 p, 11.5 p, 12 p (b) 72°, 108°, 144°, 36°
14 150, 200, 250 **15** 35 **16** 30°, 60°, 120°, 150°
17 (a) 2.9, 3, 1 (b) 1$\frac{1}{3}$, 1.5, 1 (c) 21.6, 22.5, 25
18 48°, 120°, 96°, 96° **19** 45% **20** 40°, 80°, 100°, 140°
21 (a) 20, 2.35, 2, 1 (b) 90°, 72°, 54° **22** (a) 45%
(b) 30% **23** 4 cm, 4.5 cm, 6 cm

Exercise 38d (page 377)

1 (a) Discrete (b) Continuous (c) Continuous (d) Discrete
(e) Discrete (f) Discrete (g) Continuous **2** 4 cm,
176–179, 174.8 cm **3** 2, 9, 21, 31, 39 **4** (a) 3, 5 (b) 10
(c) 0 (d) 40 **5** (a) 5 (b) 3.4 **6** -0.075, 0, -1
7 (a) 74.85, 74.6 (b) 74–76, 74 **8** (a) 3.5, 9, 1.67
(b) 18.29 °C **9** 18.2 °C, 16.6 °C, 19.9 °C, 14.6 °C,
1.65 °C **10** 44, 30, 59, 71, 14.5 **11** (a) 52, 38, 61
(b) 132 (c) 51% **12** 49.9%

Exercise 39a (page 382)

1 (a) $\frac{1}{2}$ (b) $\frac{2}{3}$ (c) $\frac{1}{2}$ (d) $\frac{5}{6}$ **2** (a) $\frac{1}{5}$ (b) $\frac{7}{10}$ (c) 1
3 $\frac{12}{25}$ **4** (a) $\frac{1}{4}$ (b) $\frac{1}{2}$ **5** (a) $\frac{1}{2}$ (b) $\frac{2}{5}$ (c) $\frac{1}{5}$ (d) $\frac{3}{10}$ (e) $\frac{3}{10}$
(f) $\frac{3}{5}$ **6** (a) $\frac{1}{7}$ (b) $\frac{1}{76}$ (c) $\frac{15}{57}$ (d) $\frac{7}{13}$ (e) $\frac{15}{57}$ **7** 0.79
8 (a) $\frac{7}{25}$ (b) $\frac{13}{25}$ (c) $\frac{39}{50}$ (d) $\frac{12}{25}$ **9** (a) $\frac{1}{17}$ (b) $\frac{1}{24}$
10 (a) $\frac{1}{2}$ (b) $\frac{7}{10}$ (c) $\frac{3}{8}$ (d) $\frac{1}{10}$ (e) $\frac{2}{5}$ **11** (a) $\frac{1}{2}$ (b) $\frac{1}{10}$ (c) $\frac{9}{10}$
12 (a) $\frac{1}{12}$ (b) $\frac{1}{4}$ (c) $\frac{5}{12}$ (d) $\frac{2}{3}$ **13** (a) $\frac{5}{12}$ (b) $\frac{2}{3}$ (c) $\frac{1}{3}$ (d) $\frac{3}{4}$
14 36, (a) $\frac{1}{9}$ (b) $\frac{5}{36}$ (c) $\frac{1}{6}$ (d) $\frac{5}{36}$ (e) $\frac{5}{18}$
15 (a) $\frac{3}{5}$ (b) $\frac{1}{5}$ (c) $\frac{3}{10}$

Exercise 39b (page 387)

1 (a) $\frac{1}{12}$ (b) $\frac{1}{4}$ **2** (a) $\frac{1}{216}$ (b) $\frac{1}{27}$ (c) $\frac{1}{8}$ **3** (a) $\frac{1}{8}$ (b) $\frac{1}{8}$
(c) $\frac{7}{8}$ **4** (a) $\frac{2}{5}$ (b) $\frac{4}{15}$ (c) $\frac{2}{5}$ **5** (a) $\frac{1}{3}$ (b) $\frac{2}{3}$ **6** (a) $\frac{9}{25}$
(b) $\frac{4}{25}$ (c) $\frac{21}{25}$ **7** $\frac{1}{90}$ **8** (a) $\frac{1}{12}$ (b) $\frac{3}{4}$ (c) $\frac{1}{2}$ **9** (a) $\frac{4}{25}$
(b) $\frac{16}{25}$ (c) $\frac{3}{4}$ **10** (a) $\frac{27}{64}$ (b) $\frac{1}{64}$ (c) $\frac{63}{64}$ **11** (a) $\frac{3}{14}$ (b) $\frac{1}{7}$
(c) $\frac{15}{28}$ (d) $\frac{3}{28}$ **12** (a) 0.59 (b) 0.51 (c) 0.45 (d) 6
13 800 **14** (a) $\frac{1}{12}$ (b) $\frac{21}{55}$ (c) $\frac{41}{55}$ **15** (a) $\frac{1}{16}$ (b) $\frac{7}{8}$ (c) $\frac{37}{64}$
16 (a) $\frac{1}{11}$ (b) $\frac{14}{33}$ (c) $\frac{8}{33}$ (d) $\frac{19}{33}$ **17** (a) $\frac{7}{10}$ (b) 6
18 (a) $\frac{1}{16}$ (b) $\frac{5}{6}$ (c) $\frac{1}{24}$

Exercise 39c (page 391)

1 (a) $\frac{3}{8}$ (b) $\frac{3}{4}$ **2** $\frac{11}{12}$ **3** $\frac{1}{2}$ **4** $\frac{1}{2}$ **5** $\frac{1}{12}$, No **6** $\frac{3}{8}$
7 (a) $\frac{1}{4}$ (b) $\frac{1}{6}$ (c) $\frac{5}{12}$ **8** $\frac{5}{6}$ **9** (a) $\frac{16}{25}$ (b) $\frac{12}{25}$
10 $\frac{1}{3}$, Yes **11** (a) $\frac{4}{27}$ (b) $\frac{4}{9}$ **12** (a) $\frac{43}{50}$ (b) $\frac{14}{25}$ (c) $\frac{31}{50}$
13 $\frac{1}{12}$, Yes **14** (a) $\frac{3}{8}$ (b) $\frac{9}{64}$ **15** $\frac{5}{8}$, No

Exercise 39d (page 393)

1 (a) $\frac{2}{5}$ (b) $\frac{3}{5}$ **2** (a) $\frac{7}{18}$ (b) $\frac{1}{2}$ **3** (a) $\frac{8}{15}$ (b) $\frac{1}{5}$ (c) $\frac{2}{3}$
4 (a) $\frac{1}{2}$ (b) $\frac{3}{7}$ (c) $\frac{2}{7}$ **5** (a) $\frac{1}{5}$ (b) $\frac{2}{5}$ (c) $\frac{8}{15}$ (d) $\frac{1}{3}$
6 (a) $\frac{39}{125}$ (b) $\frac{32}{125}$ (c) $\frac{42}{125}$ **7** (a) $\frac{14}{27}$ (b) $\frac{11}{27}$ (c) $\frac{14}{27}$
8 (a) $\frac{11}{24}$ (b) $\frac{17}{24}$ (c) $\frac{1}{3}$ **9** (a) $\frac{7}{24}$ (b) $\frac{1}{6}$ (c) $\frac{35}{72}$
10 (a) $\frac{12}{25}$ (b) $\frac{6}{25}$

Exercise 39e (page 394)

1 (a) $\frac{3}{5}$ (b) $\frac{2}{5}$ (c) 0 (d) $\frac{3}{5}$ (e) $\frac{3}{2}$ **2** (a) xy (b) $y(1 - x)$
(c) $x + y - xy$ **3** (a) $\frac{7}{200}$ (b) $\frac{29}{200}$ (c) $\frac{12}{25}$ (d) $\frac{7}{25}$
4 (a) $\frac{1}{2}$ (b) $\frac{1}{4}$ (c) $\frac{3}{8}$ **5** $\frac{6}{9}$ **6** (a) $\frac{5}{9}$ (b) $\frac{4}{9}$ **7** $\frac{43}{20}$
8 $2p - p^2$, $\frac{2}{3}$ **9** (a) $\frac{1}{20}$ (b) $\frac{1}{5}$ (c) $\frac{1}{15}$ (d) $\frac{2}{15}$ (e) $\frac{9}{20}$
(f) $\frac{2}{5}$ **10** (a) $\frac{5}{12}$ (b) $\frac{7}{24}$ (c) $\frac{7}{24}$ **11** (a) 0.73 (b) 0.66
(c) 0.59 (d) 7 **12** (a) $\frac{1}{2}$ (b) $\frac{1}{6}$ (c) $\frac{1}{3}$ **13** (a) $\frac{9}{20}$ (b) $\frac{7}{10}$
14 (a) Yes (b) Yes (c) No (d) Yes **15** $\frac{1}{2}$, No **16** (a) $\frac{1}{2}$
(b) $\frac{1}{12}$ (c) $\frac{1}{6}$ (d) $\frac{1}{3}$ **17** (a) $\frac{3}{5}$ (b) $\frac{22}{35}$ (c) $\frac{12}{35}$ **18** (a) $\frac{4}{9}$
(b) $\frac{4}{9}$ (c) $\frac{1}{9}$ **19** $\frac{8}{27}$ **20** $\frac{7}{16}$ **21** 0.605 **22** (a) $\frac{15}{32}$
(b) $\frac{3}{8}$ (c) $\frac{5}{16}$

Exercise 40a (page 401)

1 (a) 2×1 (b) 2×2 (c) 1×3 (d) 3×2 **2** (a) -1
(b) 4 (c) -3 **3** (a) -2 (b) -1 (c) 3 **4** (a) Yes (b) No

(c) No (d) Yes (e) Yes **5** (a) No (b) $\begin{pmatrix} -4 \\ 6 \end{pmatrix}$ (c) $\begin{pmatrix} 2 & 2 \\ -1 & -8 \end{pmatrix}$

(d) No (e) $(-5 \quad -1)$ (f) $\begin{pmatrix} -2 & -1 \\ 6 & 15 \end{pmatrix}$ (g) No **6** (a) $\begin{pmatrix} 1 & -5 \\ 4 & -4 \end{pmatrix}$

(b) $(\frac{3}{4} \quad 2\frac{1}{3} \quad \frac{1}{2})$ (c) $\begin{pmatrix} \frac{5}{8} \\ 2 \end{pmatrix}$ (d) $\begin{pmatrix} 2 & -4 \\ -2 & 1 \end{pmatrix}$ **7** (a) $\begin{pmatrix} -6 & 9 \\ 0 & -3 \end{pmatrix}$

(b) $\begin{pmatrix} 2 & -4 \\ 8 & 0 \end{pmatrix}$ (c) $\begin{pmatrix} -3 & 4 \\ 4 & -2 \end{pmatrix}$ (d) $\begin{pmatrix} -8 & 13 \\ -8 & -3 \end{pmatrix}$ (e) $\begin{pmatrix} -2 & 5 \\ -16 & 1 \end{pmatrix}$

(f) $\begin{pmatrix} 12 & -21 \\ 24 & 3 \end{pmatrix}$ **8** (a) Yes (b) Yes **9** Yes

10 (a) $(3x \quad 2y + 1)$ (b) $\begin{pmatrix} m - 2 \\ 2 \end{pmatrix}$ (c) $\begin{pmatrix} 2a & -3 \\ b + 2 & -b \end{pmatrix}$

(d) $(0 \quad -a^2)$ (e) $\begin{pmatrix} -x^2 y \\ -3xy \end{pmatrix}$ (f) $\begin{pmatrix} -2 \\ x^2 \end{pmatrix}$ **11** (a) $\begin{pmatrix} 2x + 1 \\ 5x - 3 \end{pmatrix}$

(b) $\begin{pmatrix} -3 \\ x + 3 \end{pmatrix}$ (c) $\begin{pmatrix} 3x \\ 8x - 3 \end{pmatrix}$ (d) $\begin{pmatrix} x + 8 \\ -9 \end{pmatrix}$ **12** (a) $\begin{pmatrix} 8 \\ 14 \end{pmatrix}$

(b) $(-1 \quad 0 \quad -2 \quad 5)$ (c) $\begin{pmatrix} 1 & 4y \\ 2x^2 & 0 \end{pmatrix}$ (d) $\begin{pmatrix} a + b \\ a - b \\ 1 \end{pmatrix}$ (e) $\begin{pmatrix} 1 & x \\ 2x^2 & \frac{1}{x} \end{pmatrix}$

13 (a) $\begin{pmatrix} 2 \\ -3 \end{pmatrix}$ (b) $\begin{pmatrix} \frac{2}{3} \\ \frac{1}{8} \end{pmatrix}$ (c) $\begin{pmatrix} -2 \\ 3 \end{pmatrix}$ (d) $\begin{pmatrix} -\frac{1}{2}x^2 \end{pmatrix}$ (e) $\begin{pmatrix} 7 \\ 1 \end{pmatrix}$ (f) $\begin{pmatrix} 2 \\ -4 \end{pmatrix}$

14 (a) $4, \frac{2}{3}$ (b) $6, 4$, (c) $\frac{2}{3}, 2$ (d) $\frac{1}{4}, 4$ (e) $2, 1$ (f) $2, 3$ (g) $5, -4$

(h) $-3, \frac{1}{2}$ **15** (a) T (b) T (c) F (d) T (e) F (f) F (g) T (h) F

Exercise 40b (page 405)

1 (a) (23) (b) (110) (c) (1400) (d) (13) (e) (-33) (f) (20)
2 (a) $(3xy)$ (b) $(5x)$ (c) $(2y + 3x)$ (d) $(4x)$ (e)$(-5p)$

3 (a) $\begin{pmatrix} 11 \\ 19 \end{pmatrix}$ (b) $\begin{pmatrix} 8 \\ -10 \end{pmatrix}$ (c) $\begin{pmatrix} 8 \\ -9 \\ 12 \end{pmatrix}$ (d) $(70 \quad 60)$

(e) $(-2 \quad 4 \quad 12 \quad -28)$ (f) $\begin{pmatrix} 8 & 4 \\ 12 & 6 \\ 4 & 2 \end{pmatrix}$

4 (a) (25) (b) No (c) $\begin{pmatrix} 4 & -3 & 0 \\ 2 & 4 & -10 \end{pmatrix}$ (d) No

(e) $\begin{pmatrix} -4 & -10 & -2 \\ 2 & 5 & 1 \end{pmatrix}$ (f) No (g) No (h) $\begin{pmatrix} 1 & 0 \\ 0 & 4 \end{pmatrix}$

5 (a) $\begin{pmatrix} 5p \\ p^2 \end{pmatrix}$ (b) $(x - 3 \quad 1 - 2x)$ (c) $\begin{pmatrix} x & x^2 + 2 \\ 2x^2 - 3 & -3x \end{pmatrix}$

6 (a) $\begin{pmatrix} 9 & 25 \\ 5 & 14 \end{pmatrix}$ (b) $\begin{pmatrix} 13 & 12 \\ 9 & 16 \end{pmatrix}$ (c) $\begin{pmatrix} 17 & 18 \\ 10 & 10 \end{pmatrix}$ (d) $\begin{pmatrix} 11 & 1 \\ 2 & -11 \end{pmatrix}$

(e) $\begin{pmatrix} -21 & 14 \\ -17 & -20 \end{pmatrix}$ **7** (a) $\begin{pmatrix} 0 & -1 & 0 \\ 8 & 11 & -10 \\ 0 & -5 & 2 \end{pmatrix}$

(b) $x^2 \begin{pmatrix} 2 & 1 & 2 \\ 0 & 1 & 0 \\ 2 & 2 & 2 \end{pmatrix}$

8 (a) 2×4 (b) 3×4 (c) $p \times r$

9 (a) 3 (b) 4 (c) 2 (d) 3 or -1 (e) 2 or -5

10 (a) Yes (b) No (c) Yes (d) Yes (e) No

11 (a) $3, 1$ (b) $-2, 4$ (c) $1\frac{1}{2}, -\frac{1}{2}$ (d) $1, -2$

12 (a) $1, 3, 3, 2$ (b) $2, 1, -\frac{1}{2}, 1$

Exercise 40c (page 409)

1 (a) $\begin{pmatrix} 2 & 8 \\ 0 & 6 \end{pmatrix}, \begin{pmatrix} 6 & 0 \\ 10 & 2 \end{pmatrix}$, Yes (b) $\begin{pmatrix} 4 & 14 \\ 0 & 6 \end{pmatrix}$, No

$\begin{pmatrix} 4 & 13 \\ 6 & 15 \end{pmatrix}$, No **2** (a) F (b) T (c) F **4** (a) (-5) (b) No

$\begin{pmatrix} 4 \\ 0 \end{pmatrix}$ **6** (a) $\begin{pmatrix} 1 & 0 \\ 0 & 1 \end{pmatrix}$ (b) (1) **7** (a) 3×3 (b) 2×2

8 (a) **A** (b) **I** (c) **ABC** (d) 21_3 (e) $-3I_5$

9 $\begin{pmatrix} 4 & 0 \\ 0 & 4 \end{pmatrix}, \begin{pmatrix} 8 & 0 \\ 0 & 8 \end{pmatrix}, \begin{pmatrix} 16 & 0 \\ 0 & 16 \end{pmatrix}$ **10** I, S **11** 64I

12 $\begin{pmatrix} 73 & 56 \\ 84 & 73 \end{pmatrix}$, Yes **13** $x = 0$ or $y = z$, No

14 $p = 0$ or $q = 0$, No **16** (a) Yes (b) No (c) No (d) Yes
(e) Yes (f) No (g) Yes (h) No

Exercise 40d (page 412)

1 $\begin{pmatrix} 5 & -3 \\ -3 & 2 \end{pmatrix}$ **2** $\begin{pmatrix} 4 & -3 \\ -5 & 4 \end{pmatrix}$ **3** $\frac{1}{2} \begin{pmatrix} 9 & -8 \\ -2 & 2 \end{pmatrix}$ **4** Singular

5 $\frac{1}{4} \begin{pmatrix} 4 & -3 \\ -8 & 7 \end{pmatrix}$ **6** $\frac{1}{5} \begin{pmatrix} 1 & 1 \\ -3 & 2 \end{pmatrix}$ **7** Singular **8** $\frac{1}{2} \begin{pmatrix} -4 & -2 \\ 5 & 3 \end{pmatrix}$

9 $-2 \begin{pmatrix} 2 & -3 \\ -1 & 1\frac{1}{4} \end{pmatrix}$ **10** Singular **11** $-\frac{1}{4} \begin{pmatrix} 3 & 4 \\ 4 & 6 \end{pmatrix}$

12 $\frac{1}{4} \begin{pmatrix} 3 & -\frac{1}{2} \\ 4 & -\frac{2}{3} \end{pmatrix}$ **13** $\begin{pmatrix} \frac{4}{9} & \frac{1}{6} \\ -2 & 1\frac{1}{2} \end{pmatrix}$ **14** Singular **15** $2 \begin{pmatrix} 2 & \frac{3}{4} \\ 3\frac{1}{3} & 1\frac{1}{2} \end{pmatrix}$

16 Singular **17** $\frac{1}{x} \begin{pmatrix} 3 & -5 \\ -x & 2x \end{pmatrix}$ **18** $\frac{1}{ab} \begin{pmatrix} -b & 2b \\ -a & a \end{pmatrix}$

19 $\begin{pmatrix} -x - 3 & x + 4 \\ x + 4 & -x - 5 \end{pmatrix}$ **20** 6 **21** 3 **22** $2\frac{1}{2}$

23 ± 4 **24** 3 or -2 **25** $4\frac{1}{2}$ or -4 **26** All values of x

Exercise 40e (page 414)

1 $\begin{pmatrix} -7 & 2 \\ 5 & 0 \end{pmatrix}, \begin{pmatrix} -2 & 5 \\ 4 & -5 \end{pmatrix}$ **2** $\begin{pmatrix} -2 \\ 5 \end{pmatrix}$ **3** $(-4 \quad 3)$

4 $\frac{1}{4} \begin{pmatrix} 1 & 6 & 4 \\ -1 & 6 & 0 \end{pmatrix}$ **5** $\begin{pmatrix} 3 & 8 \\ -7 & -19 \end{pmatrix}, \begin{pmatrix} -8 & 13 \\ 5 & -8 \end{pmatrix}, \begin{pmatrix} 19 & 8 \\ -7 & -3 \end{pmatrix}$,

$\begin{pmatrix} 8 & 13 \\ 5 & 8 \end{pmatrix}$ **6** $2, 1$ **7** $3, 1$ **8** $4, -1$ **9** Parallel lines

10 $2, -1$ **11** $3, 4$ **12** $-1, 2$ **13** Coincident lines
14 $-2, 1\frac{1}{2}$ **15** $-2, -3$ **16** $2\frac{1}{2}, 2$ **17** Parallel lines
18 $\frac{1}{3}, \frac{2}{3}$ **19** $-3, -7$ **20** $4\frac{1}{2}, 4$ **21** $2, -5$ **22** $2\frac{1}{6}, \frac{2}{3}$

Exercise 41a (page 424)

1 (a) **p** (b) $-\mathbf{q}$ (c)$\frac{1}{2}\mathbf{p}$ (d) $\frac{1}{2}\mathbf{p} + \mathbf{q}$ (e) $-\mathbf{p} - \mathbf{q}$ (f) $\mathbf{q} - \frac{1}{2}\mathbf{p}$
2 (a) $\vec{AC}$ (b) $\vec{CB}$ (c) $\vec{AB}$ (d) $\vec{CB}$ (e) $\vec{AC}$ (f) $\vec{BA}$
3 (a) $\vec{AC}$ (b) $\vec{AD}$ (c) $\vec{AC}$ (d) $\vec{CE}$ (e) $\vec{BD}$ (f) $\vec{BA}$ (g) **O** (h) $\vec{AC}$
4 2.83 km, 090° **5** 20, 20 **6** 13 km, 023°
7 (a) $-\mathbf{g}$ (b) **O** (c) **d** (d) $-\mathbf{b}$ (e) $-\mathbf{c}$ (f) $-\mathbf{d}$
8 3.61 km h^{-1}, 56.3° **9** 13.9, 8 **10** (a) $1\frac{1}{2}\mathbf{q}$ (b) $\frac{1}{2}\mathbf{q} - \mathbf{p}$
11 67.1 cm s^{-1}, 63.4° **12** 10.3, 3.88 **13** 6.24 m s^{-1}, 129°
14 287° **15** (a) T (b) F (c) T (d) T

Exercise 41b (page 432)

1 $\begin{pmatrix} 1 \\ 3 \end{pmatrix}, \begin{pmatrix} 2 \\ 5 \end{pmatrix}, \begin{pmatrix} -3 \\ 1 \end{pmatrix}, \begin{pmatrix} 1 \\ 2 \end{pmatrix}, \begin{pmatrix} -2 \\ 4 \end{pmatrix}, \begin{pmatrix} 1 \\ -6 \end{pmatrix}$ **2** (a) $\begin{pmatrix} 1 \\ 1 \end{pmatrix}$

(b) $\begin{pmatrix} -6 \\ 9 \end{pmatrix}$ (c) $\begin{pmatrix} 1 \\ 6 \end{pmatrix}$ (d) $\begin{pmatrix} -10 \\ 20 \end{pmatrix}$ **3** $\begin{pmatrix} 0 \\ 1 \end{pmatrix}, \begin{pmatrix} 2 \\ 1 \end{pmatrix}, \begin{pmatrix} -1 \\ 4 \end{pmatrix}, \begin{pmatrix} 1 \\ 3 \end{pmatrix}$

4 (a) $\begin{pmatrix} 0 \\ 5 \end{pmatrix}$ (b) $\begin{pmatrix} -2 \\ 1 \end{pmatrix}$ (c) $\begin{pmatrix} 3 \\ 11 \end{pmatrix}$ **5** $\begin{pmatrix} 8 \\ 6 \end{pmatrix}, \begin{pmatrix} -5 \\ -2 \end{pmatrix}, \begin{pmatrix} 5\frac{1}{2} \\ 5 \end{pmatrix}$,

$\begin{pmatrix} -\frac{1}{2} \\ -3 \end{pmatrix}$ **6** (a) 5 (b) $\sqrt{13}$ (c) $\sqrt{74}$ (d) 26 (e) 20 (f) $4\sqrt{10}$

7 (a) $\sqrt{10}$ (b) $5\sqrt{2}$ (c) 11 **8** 5, 5, isosceles **9** (a) 27°

(b) 146° (c) 45° (d) 180° (e) 90° (f) 108° **10** $\begin{pmatrix} -3 \\ 1 \end{pmatrix}$, (2, 4),

parallelogram **11** (a) 9 (b) 2 (c) -6 (d) 20 (e) ± 2 (f) 5

(g) $4, -8$ **12** -2 **13** $\begin{pmatrix} 2 \\ -3 \end{pmatrix}$ **14** (a) $\begin{pmatrix} 0 \\ 5 \end{pmatrix}$ (b) $\begin{pmatrix} -8 \\ 0 \end{pmatrix}$

(c) $\begin{pmatrix} 12 \\ 16 \end{pmatrix}$ (d) $\begin{pmatrix} -28 \\ -96 \end{pmatrix}$ **15** (a) $\begin{pmatrix} 3 \\ -7 \end{pmatrix}$ (b) $\begin{pmatrix} -1 \\ 10 \end{pmatrix}$ (c) $\begin{pmatrix} 3 \\ 2 \end{pmatrix}$

(d) $\begin{pmatrix} 2 \\ 1 \end{pmatrix}$

Exercise 41c (page 436)

1 2 **4** $\frac{1}{2}$ **8** $\frac{2}{3}$ **9** Parallelogram **10** $1\frac{1}{2}$ **11** $\frac{2}{5}, \frac{4}{5}$

Exercise 42a (page 443)

1 (a) (−2,0), (−1,0), (−2,3) (b) (3,1), (4,1), (3,4) (c) (−1,−4), (0,−4), (−1,−1) **2** (a) (−2,0), (2,0), (0,1) (b) (−4,2), (0,2), (−2,3) **3** (a) $\begin{pmatrix} 3 \\ 4 \end{pmatrix}$ (b) $\begin{pmatrix} 1 \\ -3 \end{pmatrix}$ **4** (a) 2**u** (b) **u** + 2**v** (c) 2**u** − 2**v** (d) −2**u** − **v** **5** (a) JDF, **u** + **v** (b) BCD, **u** − **v** **6** (1,−1), (8,−4), (6,−3), (0,−1) **7** (a) $\begin{pmatrix} 2 \\ 3 \end{pmatrix}$ (b) $\begin{pmatrix} 1 \\ 2 \end{pmatrix}$ (c) $\begin{pmatrix} -8 \\ 0 \end{pmatrix}$ (d) $\begin{pmatrix} -4 \\ 1 \end{pmatrix}$ (e) $\begin{pmatrix} -3 \\ 5 \end{pmatrix}$ **8** (−3,5), (0,1), (−4,6) **9** (a) (2,4) (b) (7,−2) (c) (−8,−5) **10** (a) $\begin{pmatrix} 2 \\ -4 \end{pmatrix}$ (b) $\begin{pmatrix} 7 \\ 3 \end{pmatrix}$ (c) $\begin{pmatrix} 2 \\ 6 \end{pmatrix}$ (d) $\begin{pmatrix} -3 \\ -5 \end{pmatrix}$ **11** (a) (−1,−5) (b) (−1,1) (c)(−1,−3) (d) (−1,0) **12** JHB, JDF, EFD **13** JHF, **u** + **v**; CBD, 2**u** **14** (a) (0,5), (0,4), (2,5) (b) $\begin{pmatrix} 0 \\ 6 \end{pmatrix}$ **15** (a) (2,1), (2,0), (4,1) (b) $\begin{pmatrix} 2 \\ 2 \end{pmatrix}$ **16** (a) FEG, **u** + **v** (b) JHD, 2**u**; DEC,**u** − **v** (c) GHD, 2**u**; FEC, **u** − **v** **17** (a) Reflection in FE, (b) Translation of −**u** − **v**, (c) Half-turn about E **18** $\begin{pmatrix} -2 \\ -2 \end{pmatrix}$, $\begin{pmatrix} -1 \\ 1 \end{pmatrix}$, $\begin{pmatrix} -5 \\ -3 \end{pmatrix}$ **19** (a) (−2,−1), (0,−1), (−2,0) (b) $\begin{pmatrix} -3 \\ -1 \end{pmatrix}$ **20** (a) (2,1), (2,0), (1,0) (b) Half-turn about (1,1) (c) Reflection in y = x **21** (a) $\begin{pmatrix} 0 \\ -1 \end{pmatrix}$ followed by negative quarter-turn about A, (b) $\begin{pmatrix} 1 \\ 0 \end{pmatrix}$ followed by reflection in y = x, (c) Negative quarter-turn about O followed by $\begin{pmatrix} 0 \\ 1 \end{pmatrix}$, (d) Positive quarter-turn about ($\frac{1}{2}$, $1\frac{1}{2}$) **22** (a) $\begin{pmatrix} 0 \\ 6 \end{pmatrix}$ (b) $\begin{pmatrix} -6 \\ 0 \end{pmatrix}$ (c) Reflection in x = 1 (d) Reflection in y = 4

Exercise 42b (page 451)

1 (a) (2,2), (4,2), (2,6) (b) $(-\frac{1}{2}, -\frac{1}{2})$, $(-1, -\frac{1}{2})$, $(-\frac{1}{2}, -1\frac{1}{2})$ (c) (−2,2), (0,2), (−2,6) **2** (a) (−3,0), (−1$\frac{1}{2}$,3), (−3,6) (b) (5,0), (4,−2), (5,−4) (c) (−1,4), (−1$\frac{1}{2}$,3), (−1,2) **3** (a) (6,3) (b) (−12,15) (c) (3a,3b) **4** (a) (−2,−1) (b) (−3,5) **5** (a) (2,3) (b) (−1,0) (c) (5,6) (d) (−4,−6) (e) (−13,−12) **6** (a) (2,5) (b) (6,3) (c) (4,7) (d) (−2,−6) (e) (−6,−5) **7** (a) (1,1) (b) (2,3) (c) (4,2) (d) (−2,9) **8** (2,1), (2,3), (1,2) **9** (a) (2,6) (b) (−4,−2) (c) (8,−3) **10** (a) (3,3) (b) (−1,2) **11** 5, 12 **12** 4, 11 **13** 6, 3 **14** (a) (2,1), 2 (b) (1,1), 3 (c) (4,3), $\frac{1}{2}$ (d) (−2,2), −2 **15** 4, $\frac{1}{4}$ **16** 4, 16, 36, 1 **17** (a) (3,1), (4,1), (3,3) (b) Translation of $\begin{pmatrix} 2 \\ 0 \end{pmatrix}$ **18** (a) (2,0), (4,0), (4,1) (b) (1,−4), (3,−4), (2,−7) (c) (−1,0), (0,0), (−$\frac{1}{2}$,1) **19** Enlargement of centre (−2,1) and scale factor 3 **20** 18 **21** x = −4 **22** (a) (2,1), (3,1), (4,2) (b) (0,−2), (1,1), (0,−1) **23** (a) (4,3) (b) (12,5) (c) (−1,0) (d) (−2,−2) **24** (a) y = −2 (b) x + y = 2 **25** (a) 2y = x (b) 3y = x (c) 5y = 2x (d) y = −2x **26** 2 cm from A on AB **27** 16 cm from A on CA produced

Exercise 43a (page 459)

1 (2,3), (7,21), (1,19), (−10,−29) **2** (0,−2), (8,−2), (12,−4),

(−4,4) **3** $\begin{pmatrix} 1 & -1 \\ -1 & 2 \end{pmatrix}$, $\begin{pmatrix} 2 & -5 \\ -3 & 8 \end{pmatrix}$, $\frac{1}{2}\begin{pmatrix} 3 & -2 \\ -5 & 4 \end{pmatrix}$, −$\frac{1}{3}\begin{pmatrix} 6 & 3 \\ 7 & 4 \end{pmatrix}$, $\frac{1}{10}\begin{pmatrix} 4 & -2 \\ 3 & -4 \end{pmatrix}$ **4** X, $\begin{pmatrix} 1 & 0 \\ 0 & -1 \end{pmatrix}$ **5** Q⁻¹, H, Q **6** (a) H (b) Reflection in y = −x (c) Enlargement, scale factor $\frac{1}{2}$, (d) Enlargement, scale factor −$\frac{1}{2}$ **7** $\begin{pmatrix} 2 & 5 \\ 1 & 3 \end{pmatrix}$ $\begin{pmatrix} 3 & -5 \\ -1 & 2 \end{pmatrix}$ **8** $\begin{pmatrix} 2 & -1 \\ 3 & 1 \end{pmatrix}$, $\begin{pmatrix} 1 & -3 \\ 9 & -2 \end{pmatrix}$ **9** Enlargements, scale factors 2, 4, $\frac{1}{2}$ **10** I **11** $\begin{pmatrix} 0 & 1 \\ 1 & 0 \end{pmatrix}$, reflection in y = x; $\begin{pmatrix} 0 & -1 \\ -1 & 0 \end{pmatrix}$, reflection in y = −x **12** 90°, 2 **13** y-axis, 3 **14** √2, rotation of 45° **15** √10, 3 **16** T, I; reflection **17** y = 2x **18** One-way stretch, y-axis invariant, scale factor 2 **19** Shear with x-axis invariant **20** $\begin{pmatrix} \frac{1}{2} & 0 \\ 0 & 1 \end{pmatrix}$ $\begin{pmatrix} 4 & 0 \\ 0 & 1 \end{pmatrix}$, $\begin{pmatrix} 8 & 0 \\ 0 & 1 \end{pmatrix}$; one-way stretches, scale factors $\frac{1}{2}$, 4, **21** $\begin{pmatrix} 1 & 0 \\ 0 & -1 \end{pmatrix}$ **22** (a) $\begin{pmatrix} 0 & -1 \\ 1 & 0 \end{pmatrix}$ (b) $\begin{pmatrix} 0 & -1 \\ -1 & 0 \end{pmatrix}$

Exercise 43b (page 465)

1 (a) $\begin{pmatrix} 2 & 1 \\ 3 & 5 \end{pmatrix}$ (b) $\begin{pmatrix} -5 & 3 \\ 2 & -4 \end{pmatrix}$ (c) $\begin{pmatrix} 4 & 3 \\ 1 & 0 \end{pmatrix}$ (d) $\begin{pmatrix} -2 & -4 \\ 0 & 2 \end{pmatrix}$ **2** X, H, Y; Yes **3** (a) $\begin{pmatrix} 3 & 2 \\ 2 & 1 \end{pmatrix}$ (b) $\begin{pmatrix} 5 & 4 \\ 3 & 2 \end{pmatrix}$ (c) $\begin{pmatrix} -1 & 2 \\ 3 & -5 \end{pmatrix}$ (d) $\begin{pmatrix} -1\frac{1}{2} & 0 \\ -5 & 2 \end{pmatrix}$ **4** Q, reflection in y = x, Y, X **5** Q⁻¹, H, Q **6** One-way stretches and enlargement, all of scale factor 3. Yes **7** $\begin{pmatrix} 0 & -1 \\ -1 & 0 \end{pmatrix}$, I, reflection in y = −x, reflection in y = −x **8** (a) $\begin{pmatrix} 0 & -1 \\ 1 & 0 \end{pmatrix}$, (b) $\begin{pmatrix} 0 & 1 \\ -1 & 0 \end{pmatrix}$ **9** (a) Reflection in y = x (b) reflection in y = −x (c) I (d) Y (e) Q⁻¹ (f) reflection in y = x **10** (a) 2, Y (b) 4, reflection in y = x (c) $\frac{1}{2}$, Q **11** (a) $\begin{pmatrix} 0 & 3 \\ -3 & 0 \end{pmatrix}$ (b) $\begin{pmatrix} -\frac{1}{3} & 0 \\ 0 & -\frac{1}{3} \end{pmatrix}$ (c) Q **12** √2, −45° **13** (a) 9 (b) 1 (c) 2 (d) 4 (e) 50 **14** (a) 6 (b) 15 (c) 1$\frac{1}{2}$ (d) 60 **15** (a) 2, 1 (b) −3, −5 (c) 1, 2 **16** Singular **17** (a) I (b) $\begin{pmatrix} -1 & 0 \\ 0 & -1 \end{pmatrix}$ (c) $\begin{pmatrix} 0 & 1 \\ -1 & 0 \end{pmatrix}$ **18** $\begin{pmatrix} 64 & 0 \\ 0 & 1 \end{pmatrix}$ **19** (a) I (b) T **20** (a) $\begin{pmatrix} 1 & 0 \\ 21 & 1 \end{pmatrix}$ (b) $\begin{pmatrix} 1 & 0 \\ 36 & 1 \end{pmatrix}$ **21** (a) 16I (b) 128$\begin{pmatrix} 0 & 1 \\ 1 & 0 \end{pmatrix}$ **22** (a) 128$\begin{pmatrix} 0 & 1 \\ -1 & 0 \end{pmatrix}$ (b) 128$\begin{pmatrix} 1 & 0 \\ 14 & 1 \end{pmatrix}$ **23** H **24** 53° **25** Q, Q⁻¹, 45° **26** (a) Yes (b) Yes (c) R (d) M (e) N (f) R (g) Yes **27** (a) Y (b) Yes (c) P (d) N (e) M (f) P (g) Yes **28** (a) M (b) I (c) M

Exercise 43c (page 469)

1 (a) (i) y + 2x = 0 (ii) y = 2x (b) (i) 3y =x (ii) y = 2x (c) (i) 5y = 2x (ii) y + x = 0 **3** (a) 2y= x (b) 3y + x = 0 (c) 2y + 5x = 0 **5** 3y = x **6** Shear with invariant line y = x **7** 2y = x **8** 13, 2y = 3x **9** One-way stretch with invariant line y + 2x = 0 **10** 15, −0.75

Exercise 44a (page 473)

1 $9x^8$ **2** $12x^{11}$ **3** $10x^4$ **4** $42x^6$ **5** $9kx^8$ **6** 4 **7** 0 **8** 2x + 1 **9** 3 **10** a **11** 0 **12** $2x^3$ **13** $\frac{x^2}{2}$ **14** 3x **15** $\frac{3}{2}$ **16** $\frac{15x^5}{2}$ **17** $\frac{kx^3}{2}$ **18** x^{k-1} **19** $12x^2 - 10x + 7$ **20** $2 - 6x - 3x^2$ **21** $-6 - 15x^2 + 40x^4$ **22** $2ax + b$ **23** $\frac{2x^2}{3} + \frac{x}{2} - \frac{1}{3}$ **24** 2x − 1 **25** 12x − 5 **26** 2 − 16x **27** $18x^2 - 34x + 5$ **28** $12x^2 - 32x + 21$ **29** $2apx + aq +$

0 1 31 $2x - 3$ **32** $6x^2 - \frac{x}{2}$ **33** $6x^3 + \frac{8x}{3}$ **34** $\frac{1}{2} - \frac{3x}{5} + \frac{x^4}{4}$

5 $-\frac{1}{x^2}$ **36** $-\frac{1}{x^3}$ **37** $-\frac{6}{x^3}$ **38** $\frac{1}{3x^4}$ **39** $\frac{10}{x^6}$ **40** $-\frac{10}{3x^5}$

1 $2 - \frac{1}{2x^3}$ **42** $3x^2 + \frac{8}{x^3}$ **43** $-\frac{1}{2x^2} + 6x$ **44** $\frac{4}{x^4}$ **45** $2x - \frac{2}{x^3}$

6 $2 + \frac{2}{x^2} + \frac{1}{2x^3}$

15 $y = \frac{4}{x^2} + 2$ **16** $y = 2x - \frac{1}{3x}$

Exercise 45c (page 490)

1 6 **2** 9 **3** 6 **4** 4 **5** 10 **6** 8 **7** 0 **8** $31\frac{1}{2}$ **9** 0 **10** 12
11 4 **12** $-13\frac{1}{2}$ **13** 64 **14** $2\frac{5}{8}$ **15** $11\frac{5}{6}$ **16** -4 **17** $-\frac{5}{6}$
18 $-5\frac{1}{4}$ **19** $\frac{3}{8}$ **20** $3\frac{1}{2}$ **21** $3\frac{1}{4}$ **22** $-6\frac{2}{3}$

Exercise 44b (page 476)

1, 5, -5, -6 **2** -3, -1, 9, 11 **3** 8, $4\frac{1}{2}$, $\frac{1}{8}$ **4** 4, -2, 10, -8
20, 8, $\frac{1}{2}$ **6** -1, 2, 3 **7** -7, -5, 1, -11 **8** ± 4 **9** ± 6
0 ± 2 **11** ± 3 **12** ± 3 **13** ± 5 **14** $\pm 1\frac{1}{3}$ **15** 6 **16** 27
7 $-\frac{1}{2}$, -8 **18** -4 **19** $1\frac{1}{3}$, 4 **20** $-2\frac{1}{2}$, -10 **21** ± 2
2 ± 4 **23** 0, ± 6 **24** 5, ± 7 **25** -11, ± 5 **26** (3,9)
7 (2,2) **28** $(-2,8)$ **29** (4,16) **30** $(-2,-4)$ **31** (2,8),
$-2, -8)$ **32** $(-1,0)$, $(\frac{1}{3}, \frac{4}{27})$ **33** (1,8), $(-3,-36)$ **34** $(4,1\frac{1}{3})$,
$-2, -1\frac{2}{3})$ **35** $(2,\frac{1}{2})$, $(-2,-\frac{1}{2})$ **36** $(-1,2)$ **37** (3,4) **38** $(\frac{1}{2}, -1)$

Exercise 45d (page 493)

1 8 **2** 14 **3** 4 **4** 22 **5** 5 **6** 12 **7** $10\frac{2}{3}$ **8** $4\frac{1}{2}$ **9** $6\frac{1}{6}$
10 $27\frac{3}{4}$ **11** 9 **12** $4\frac{1}{2}$ **13** 36 **14** $1\frac{1}{3}$ **15** $5\frac{1}{3}$ **16** $2\frac{2}{3}$ **17** $3\frac{5}{6}$
18 $2\frac{2}{3}$ **19** $6\frac{3}{4}$ **20** $42\frac{2}{3}$ **21** 44 **22** $1\frac{1}{3}$ **23** $20\frac{5}{6}$ **24** $10\frac{2}{3}$
25 6 **26** 8 **27** $11\frac{1}{3}$ **28** 30 **29** 36 **30** $10\frac{5}{6}$

Exercise 44c (page 480)

1 $(1,-1)$ min **2** (2,4) max **3** $(-\frac{1}{2}, -\frac{1}{4})$ min **4** (0,4) max
$(-1,9)$ max **6** $(\frac{1}{2},0)$ min **7** $(-2,25)$ max **8** (0,2) max,
$-2)$ min **9** (1,6) max, $(-1,2)$ min **10** (0,10) max,
$-4, -22)$ min **11** $(-1,17)$ max, $(3,-15)$ min
7 $(-2,16)$ max, $(1,-11)$ min **13** $(\frac{1}{2}, 3\frac{3}{4})$ max, $(-1,-3)$ min
5 $(\frac{1}{2},2)$ max, $(-\frac{1}{2},0)$ min **15** (2,8) max, (3,7) min
5 (3,6) min, $(-3,-6)$ max **17** (2,1) min, $(-2,-1)$ max
8 $(-1,-3)$ max **19** $(2,1\frac{1}{2})$ min **20** $(2,\frac{1}{4})$ max

Exercise 45e (page 496)

1 21π **2** 6π **3** $6\frac{2}{5}\pi$ **4** 16π **5** 28π **6** 38π **7** 7π **8** 24π
9 8π **10** $5\frac{1}{4}\pi$ **11** $\frac{\pi}{30}$ **12** 8.1π **13** $1\frac{1}{3}\pi$ **14** $32\frac{2}{5}\pi$ **15** 8π
16 $25\frac{3}{5}\pi$ **17** 144π **18** 4π **19** $\frac{7\pi}{15}$ **20** $18\frac{2}{3}\pi$ **21** $\frac{7\pi}{10}$
22 $48\frac{3}{5}\pi$ **23** $\frac{\pi}{2}$ **24** 21π

Exercise 44d (page 482)

1 9 m **2** $2\frac{1}{2}$ **3** 100 **4** 450 **5** 18 m² **6** -64 m s⁻¹
7 8 cm² **8** 200 **9** 450 cm² **10** 4000 cm³ **11** 16 cm³
2 20 cm² **15** 432 m³

Exercise 45f (page 499)

1 28 **2** 14 **3** (a) $5\frac{1}{3}$ (b) 5 (c) $5\frac{1}{4}$ **4** 25.5, more **5** 1.58
6 17.9, less **7** (a) 9.63 (b) 14.4 **8** 0.256 **9** 36.4 m
10 2.10

Exercise 44e (page 485)

1 (a) 5 m year⁻¹, 3 m year⁻¹(b) 10 years, 25 m **2** (a) -4,
4 (b) $-7\frac{1}{2}$ **3** 7 cm s⁻¹, 45 **4** (a) $2\frac{1}{4}$ cm s⁻¹, 3 cm s⁻¹,
cm s⁻¹(b) 20 s, (c) 40 cm **5** (a) 102 m (b) 40 s, 200 m
8 5 m s⁻¹ **6** (a) 12 500, 2000 per year (b) 10 years, 22 500
1000 per year (d) 22 100 **7** (a) 2 m, 3 m s⁻¹(b) $\frac{3}{4}$ s
8 $\frac{7}{8}$ m (d) 1 m **8** (a) 2 cm², 4 cm² s⁻¹(b) $5\frac{2}{3}$ cm² (c) $7\frac{1}{3}$ cm²
9 (a) 6 s (b) 8 cm s⁻¹ (c) 12 cm s⁻¹ (d) 39 cm **10** (a) 15 500
9 200 per week (c) 17 750

Exercise 45a (page 487)

1 $\frac{x^8}{8} + c$ **2** $\frac{x^{12}}{12} + c$ **3** $\frac{x^2}{2} + c$ **4** $5x + c$ **5** $3x^3 + c$ **6** c
7 $\frac{x^4}{8} + c$ **8** $\frac{2x^3}{5} + c$ **9** $\frac{x^4}{3} + c$ **10** $\frac{x^6}{4} + c$ **11** $x^2 - x + c$
12 $x^3 - 2x^2 + 7x + c$ **13** $\frac{8x^3}{3} - x^2 + c$ **14** $\frac{3x^3}{2} - \frac{3x^2}{4} + c$
15 $2x - \frac{x^2}{10} - \frac{x^3}{4} + c$ **16** $2x^2 - x + c$ **17** $x^3 - \frac{2x}{3} + c$
18 $\frac{x^3}{2} - x^2 + \frac{x}{2} + c$ **19** $-\frac{1}{x} + c$ **20** $\frac{2}{x^2} + c$ **21** $-\frac{1}{6x^3} + c$
22 $\frac{1}{5x^2} + c$ **23** $x^2 + \frac{2}{x^3} + c$ **24** $\frac{x^5}{5} - 6x - \frac{3}{x^3} + c$

Exercise 45b (page 489)

1 $y = 2x + 3$ **2** $y = 3x + 7$ **3** $y = 3 - x$ **4** $2y = x + 12$
5 $3y = 2x + 7$ **6** $2y + 3x = 0$ **7** $y = x + 2$
8 $y = 2x^2 + 3x$ **9** $2y = 2 + 4x - x^2$ **10** $6y = 6 + 2x - x^2$
11 $y = 2x^3 - x^2 - 3$ **12** $y = x^3 + x^2 - x + 1$
13 $2y = 3x^3 - 2x^2 - x + 2$ **14** $y = 3x^3 + 3x^2 - 8x + 5$

Exercise 46a (page 507)

1 3 m, 4 m, 3 m; 2 m s⁻¹, 0 m s⁻¹, -2 m s⁻¹ **2** 1 m, 4 m,
9 m; 4 m s⁻¹, 8 m s⁻¹, 12 m s⁻¹ **3** 1 m s⁻¹, 5 m s⁻¹, 11 m s⁻¹,
3 m s⁻², 5 m s⁻², 7 m s⁻² **4** (a) 4 s (b) 5 s **5** 2 s, -2 m s⁻¹
6 (a) 6 m s⁻¹ (b) 3 m s⁻² × 3 (c) ± 1 m s⁻² **7** (a) 5 m s⁻¹
(b) -4 m s⁻² (c) 1 s (d) -6 m s⁻² **8** 2 s, 20 m s⁻¹
9 (a) 27 m (b) 3 m s⁻¹ (c) 15 m s⁻¹ (d) 4 m s⁻² (e) 14 m
(f) 5 m s⁻¹ **10** (a) 0 m s⁻¹ (b) 15 m s⁻² **11** 16 m s⁻¹
12 (a) 15 m, 10 m s⁻¹ (b) -10 m s⁻² (c) 20 m (d) 4 s
13 -8 m, 18 m s⁻² **14** (a) (5,0) (b) 4 m s⁻¹ (c) (9,0) (d) (8,0)
(e) 5 s (f) -6 m s⁻¹ **15** $37\frac{1}{2}$ m s⁻¹ **16** (a) 10 m s⁻¹ (b) 2 s
(c) 20 m s⁻¹ (d) $6\frac{1}{4}$ m **17** $2\frac{7}{8}$ m, $6\frac{1}{4}$ m s⁻¹ **18** (a) 6 s (b) 5
(c) -16 (d) -8 m s⁻¹ **19** (a) $3\frac{1}{5}$ m (b) -18 m s⁻¹ **20** (a) 4
(b) 2 s (c) 3 s (d) -4 m s⁻¹ **21** (a) 80 m s⁻¹ (b) 27 m s⁻²
22 (a) $\frac{4}{5}$ s (b) 2 s (c) 24 m s⁻¹ **23** (a) 25 m, 20 m s⁻¹ (b) 45 m
(c) 4 s (d) 5 s **24** 28 m s⁻¹

Exercise 46b (page 511)

1 $v = t^2 + 3$ **2** $s = 3t^2 + 2t$ **3** $v = 2t^2 - 6$ **4** $s = 5t^2 - 8$
5 $v = 6t^2 + 3, s = 2t^3 + 3t$ **6** $v = 4t + 3, x = 2t^2 + 3t$ **7** 2
8 18 **9** 2 s **10** 4 **11** (a) 12 m (b) $10\frac{1}{2}$ m (c) $12\frac{1}{2}$ m **12** 4 s,
-5 m s⁻¹ **13** 6 **14** 5 s, 7 m s⁻¹ **15** 3 s, 30 m s⁻¹ **16** 3 s,
18 m **17** 2 m, $1\frac{1}{4}$ m **18** 16 m s⁻¹, -8 m s⁻² **19** $\frac{4}{5}$ s,
19 m s⁻¹ **20** (a) 20 m (b) 40 m s⁻¹ **21** (a) 8 s (b) 20 m s⁻¹
22 6 m s⁻¹, (30,0)